Alan McSeveny
Rob Conway
Steve Wilkes
Michael Smith

International
Mathematics
for the Middle Years

2

PEARSON
Education

Pearson Education Australia
A division of Pearson Australia Group Pty Ltd
20 Thackray Road
Port Melbourne 3207 Victoria Australia
www.pearsoned.com.au/schools

Offices in Sydney, Brisbane and Perth, and associated companies
throughout the world.

Text designed by Pierluigi Vido
Cover designed by Anita Adams
Cover image by Getty Images
Cartoons by Michael Barter and Bruce Rankin
Technical illustrations by Wendy Gorton
Edited by Fiona Brodribb
Typeset by Sunset Digital Pty Ltd, Brisbane
Set in Berkeley and Scala Sans
Produced by Pearson Education Australia
Prepress work by The Type Factory
Printed in China (SWTC/02)

National Library of Australia
Cataloguing-in-Publication data

McSeveny, A. (Alan).
International mathematics 2 : for middle years

Includes index.
For secondary school students.
ISBN 9780733983887 (pbk).

1. Mathematics – Textbooks. I. Smith, Michael, 1957- . II. Title.

510

Contents

Interactive Student CD

You can access this material by clicking on the links provided on the Interactive Student CD. Go to the Home Page for information about these links.

Challenge Worksheets

Worksheet Answers

Technology Applications

The material below is found in the Companion Website which is included on the Interactive Student CD as both an archived version and a fully featured live version.

Activities and Investigations

Drag and Drops

Chapter Review Questions

These can be used as a diagnostic tool or for revision. They include multiple-choice, pattern-matching and fill-in-the-gaps style questions.

Destinations

Links to useful websites which relate directly to the chapter content.

Features of International Mathematics for the Middle Years

International Mathematics for the Middle Years is organised with the international student in mind. Examples and exercises are not restricted to a particular syllabus and so provide students with a global perspective.

Each edition has a review section for students who may have gaps in the Mathematics they have studied previously. Sections on the language of Mathematics and terminology will help students for whom English is a second language.

Areas of Interaction are given for each chapter and Assessment Grids for Investigations provide teachers with aids to assessing Analysis and Reasoning, Communication, and Reflection and Evaluation as part of the International Baccalaureate Middle Years Program (IBMYP). The Assessment Grids will also assist students in addressing these criteria and will enhance their understanding of the subject content.

How is International Mathematics for the Middle Years organised?

As well as the student coursebook, additional support for both students and teachers is provided:
- Interactive Student CD — **free** with each coursebook
- Companion Website
- Teacher's Resource — printout and CD.

Coursebook

Chapter-opening pages summarise the key content and present the learning outcomes addressed in each chapter.

Areas of Interaction References are included in the chapter-opening pages. For example, Human Ingenuity.

Prep Quizzes review skills needed to complete a topic. These anticipate problems and save time in the long run. These quizzes offer an excellent way to start a lesson.

Well-graded exercises — Within each exercise, **levels of difficulty** are indicated by the colour of the question number.

1 green ... foundation   **4** blue ... core   **9** red ... extension

---

2 Write each as a power.
  a 7×7 b $8 \times 8 \times 8$

7 A farmer has chickens and cows. If there are 18 heads and 52 feet on these altogether, how many cows are there?

16 Place the following numbers into two groups of four, so that the sum of one group is as close as possible to the sum of the other group. {9, 10, 18, 21, 25, 42, 49, 51}

Worked examples are used extensively and are easy for students to identify.

worked examples

1   392 = CCCXCII   **2**   1987 = MCMLXXXVII   **3**   56 049 = $\overline{\text{LVM}}$XLIX

Important rules and concepts are clearly highlighted at regular intervals throughout the text.

Cartoons are used to give students friendly advice or tips.

The table of values looks like this!

Foundation Worksheets provide alternative exercises for students who need to consolidate earlier work or who need additional work at an easier level. Students can access these on the CD by clicking on the Foundation Worksheet icons. These can be copied from the Teacher's Resource CD or from the Teacher's Resource Centre on the Companion Website.

> **Foundation Worksheet 6:09**
> Factorising
> **1 a** Expand $2(x + 4)$.
>   **b** Factorise $2x + 8$.
> **2** Complete:
>   **a** $3x - 3 = 3(\ldots - \ldots)$
> **3** Factorise $8x + 16$.

Challenge activities and worksheets provide more difficult investigations and exercises. They can be used to extend more able students.

Fun Spots provide amusement and interest, while often reinforcing course work. They encourage creativity and divergent thinking, and show that Mathematics is enjoyable.

Investigations and **Practical Activities** encourage students to seek knowledge and develop research skills. They are an essential part of any Mathematics course. Each Investigation is accompanied by a sample Assessment Grid which can be modified or used as it stands to assist teachers in assessing criteria B, C and D as prescribed by the Middle Years Program (MYP).

Students should be made aware of the criteria *before* beginning the Investigation so that they know what is required of them.

Diagnostic Tests at the end of each chapter test students' achievement of learning outcomes. More importantly, they indicate the weaknesses that need to be addressed by going back to the section in the text or on the CD listed beside the test question.

Assignments are provided at the end of each chapter. Where there are two assignments, the first revises the content of previous chapters, while the second concentrates on developing the student's ability to work mathematically.

The **See** cross-references direct students to other sections of the coursebook relevant to a particular section.

Arithmetic/Algebra Cards (see pp xx–xxi) are used to practise basic arithmetic and algebra skills. Corresponding terms in columns can be added, subtracted, multiplied or divided by each other or by other numbers. This is a great way to start a lesson.

The Language of Mathematics

Within the coursebook, Mathematics literacy is addressed in three specific ways:

ID Cards (see pp xiv–xix) review the language of Mathematics by asking students to identify common terms, shapes and symbols. They should be used as often as possible, either at the beginning of a lesson or as part of a test or examination.

Mathematical Terms met during the chapter are defined at the end of each chapter. These terms are also tested in a **Drag and Drop** interactive that follows this section.

Reading Mathematics help students to develop mathematical literacy skills and provide opportunities for students to communicate mathematical ideas. They present Mathematics in the context of everyday experiences.

An **Answers** section provides answers to all the exercises in the coursebook, including the ID Cards.

Interactive Student CD

This is provided at the back of the coursebook and is an important part of the total learning package.

Bookmarks and links allow easy navigation within and between the different electronic components of the CD that contains:
- A copy of the student coursebook.
- Appendixes A–I for enrichment and review work, linked from the coursebook.
- Printable copies of the Foundation Worksheets and Challenge Worksheets, linked from the coursebook.
- An archived, offline version of the Companion Website, including:
  - Chapter Review Questions and Quick Quizzes
  - All the Technology Applications: activities and investigations, drag-and-drops and animations
  - Destinations (links to useful websites).

All these items are clearly linked from the coursebook via the Companion Website.
- A link to the live Companion Website.

Companion Website

The Companion Website contains a wealth of support material for students and teachers:
- **Chapter Review Questions** which can be used as a diagnostic tool or for revision. These are self-correcting and include multiple-choice, pattern-matching and fill-in the-gaps style questions. Results can be emailed directly to the teacher or parents.
- **Quick Quizzes** for each chapter.
- **Destinations** — links to useful websites which relate directly to the chapter content.

- **Technology Applications** — activities that apply concepts covered in each chapter and are designed for students to work independently:

 Activities and investigations using technology such as Excel spreadsheets and The Geometer's Sketchpad.

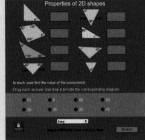

 Drag and Drop interactives to improve mastery of basic skills.

Sample Drag and Drop

 Animations to develop key skills by manipulating visually stimulating and interactive demonstrations of key mathematical concepts.

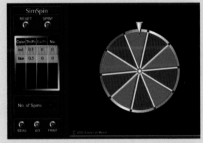

Sample Animation

- **Teacher's Resource Centre** — provides a wealth of teacher support material and is password protected:
  — Coursebook corrections
  — Topic Review Tests and answers
  — Foundation and Challenge worksheets and answers
  — Answers to the exercises in the Homework Book.

Teacher's resource

 This material is provided as both a printout and as an electronic copy on CD:
- Electronic copy of the complete Student Coursebook in PDF format
- Unit Plans in editable MS Word format with ideas for linking to Areas of Interaction
- Practice Tests and Answers in editable MS Word format
- Foundation and Challenge worksheets and answers
- Sample projects
- Sample guiding questions.

Most of this material is also available in the Teacher's Resource Centre of the Companion Website.

Using this Book for Teaching MYP for the IB

- Holistic Learning
- Intercultural Awareness
- Communication

These elements of the MYP Mathematics course are integrated throughout the text. Links are made possible between subjects, and different methods of communicating solutions to problems through investigations allow students to explore their own ideas.

The Areas of Interaction
- Approaches to Learning
- Community and Service
- Health and Social Education
- Environments
- Human Ingenuity

Areas of Interaction covered are outlined at the start of each chapter, allowing teachers to develop links between subjects and formulate their own Interdisciplinary Units with additional assistance in the Teacher's Resource.

Addressing the Objectives

Assessment grids are provided for Investigations throughout the text to not only help teachers assess criteria B, C and D of the MYP, but also to assist students in addressing the criteria. The assessment grids should be modified to suit the student where necessary.

A **Knowledge and Understanding**
   This criterion is addressed in the Diagnostic Tests and Revision Assignments that accompany each chapter. Teachers can also use the worksheets from the CD to add to material for this criterion.

B **Application and Reasoning**
   It is possible to address this criterion using the Working Mathematically sections accompanying each chapter, and also using the Investigations throughout the text.

C **Communication**
   This can be assessed using the Investigations throughout the book.

D **Reflection and Evaluation**
   This can be assessed using the Investigations throughout the book.

Fulfilling the Framework for Mathematics

The content of the text covers the five broad areas required to fulfil the Framework:
- Number
- Algebra
- Geometry
- Statistics
- Discrete Mathematics

Although the material in the text is not exhaustive, it covers the required areas in sufficient depth. Teachers can use the text as a resource to build on as they develop their own scheme of work within their school.

Metric Equivalents

Length
1 m = 1000 mm
= 100 cm
= 10 dm
1 cm = 10 mm
1 km = 1000 m

Area
$1 \text{ m}^2 = 10\,000 \text{ cm}^2$
$1 \text{ ha} = 10\,000 \text{ m}^2$
$1 \text{ km}^2 = 100 \text{ ha}$

Mass
1 kg = 1000 g
1 t = 1000 kg
1 g = 1000 mg

Volume
$1 \text{ m}^3 = 1\,000\,000 \text{ cm}^3$
$= 1000 \text{ dm}^3$
1 L = 1000 mL
1 kL = 1000 L
$1 \text{ m}^3 = 1 \text{ kL}$
$1 \text{ cm}^3 = 1 \text{ mL}$
$1000 \text{ cm}^3 = 1 \text{ L}$

Time
1 min = 60 s
1 h = 60 min
1 day = 24 h
1 year = 365 days
1 leap year = 366 days

Months of the year
30 days each has September,
April, June and November.
All the rest have 31, except February alone,
Which has 28 days clear and 29 each leap year.

Seasons
Northern Hemisphere
Summer: June, July, August
Autumn/Fall: September, October, November
Winter: December, January, February
Spring: March, April, May

Southern Hemisphere
Summer: December, January, February
Autumn/Fall: March, April, May
Winter: June, July, August
Spring: September, October, November

It is important that you learn these facts off by heart.

The Language of Mathematics

You should regularly test your knowledge by identifying the items on each card.

ID Card 1 (Metric Units)			
1 m	**2** dm	**3** cm	**4** mm
5 km	**6** m^2	**7** cm^2	**8** km^2
9 ha	**10** m^3	**11** cm^3	**12** s
13 min	**14** h	**15** m/s	**16** km/h
17 g	**18** mg	**19** kg	**20** t
21 L	**22** mL	**23** kL	**24** °C

See page 497 for answers.

ID Card 2 (Symbols)			
1 +	**2** −	**3** ×	**4** ÷
5 =	**6** ÷ or ≈	**7** ≠	**8** <
9 ⩽	**10** ≮	**11** >	**12** ⩾
13 ≯	**14** ≱	**15** 4^2	**16** 4^3
17 $\sqrt{25}$	**18** $\sqrt[3]{27}$	**19** %	**20** ∴
21 eg	**22** ie	**23** $n\overset{\frac{3}{4}}{\curvearrowright}$.........	**24** $d\overset{\frac{3}{4}}{\longrightarrow}$.........

See page 497 for answers.

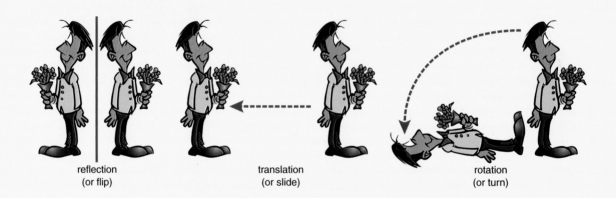

reflection (or flip)   translation (or slide)   rotation (or turn)

ID Card 3 (Language)			
1 6 minus 2	**2** the sum of 6 and 2	**3** divide 6 by 2	**4** subtract 2 from 6
5 the quotient of 6 and 2	**6** $\frac{3}{2\overline{)6}}$ the divisor is	**7** $\frac{3}{2\overline{)6}}$ the dividend is	**8** 6 lots of 2
9 decrease 6 by 2	**10** the product of 6 and 2	**11** 6 more than 2	**12** 2 less than 6
13 6 squared	**14** the square root of 36	**15** 6 take away 2	**16** multiply 6 by 2
17 average of 6 and 2	**18** add 6 and 2	**19** 6 to the power of 2	**20** 6 less 2
21 the difference between 6 and 2	**22** increase 6 by 2	**23** share 6 between 2	**24** the total of 6 and 2

See page 497 for answers

.

You won't have to hide if you learn the language.

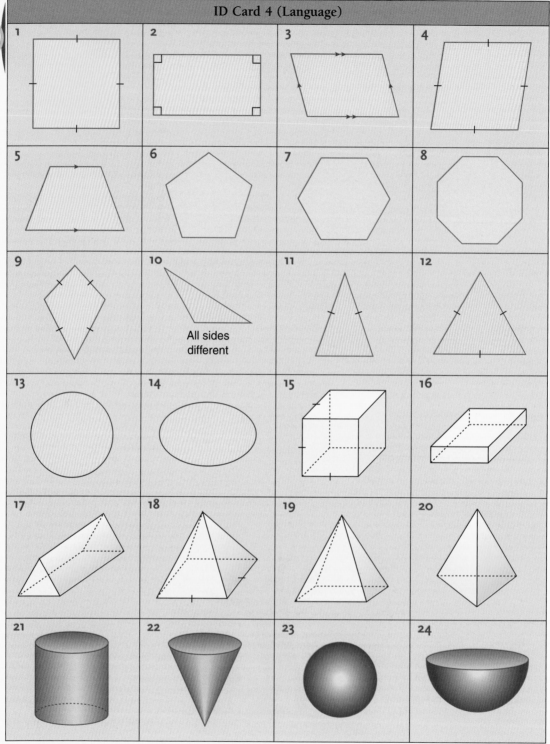

1	**2**	**3**	**4**
5	**6**	**7**	**8**
9	**10** All sides different	**11**	**12**
13	**14**	**15**	**16**
17	**18**	**19**	**20**
21	**22**	**23**	**24**

See page 497 for answers.

ID Card 5 (Language)

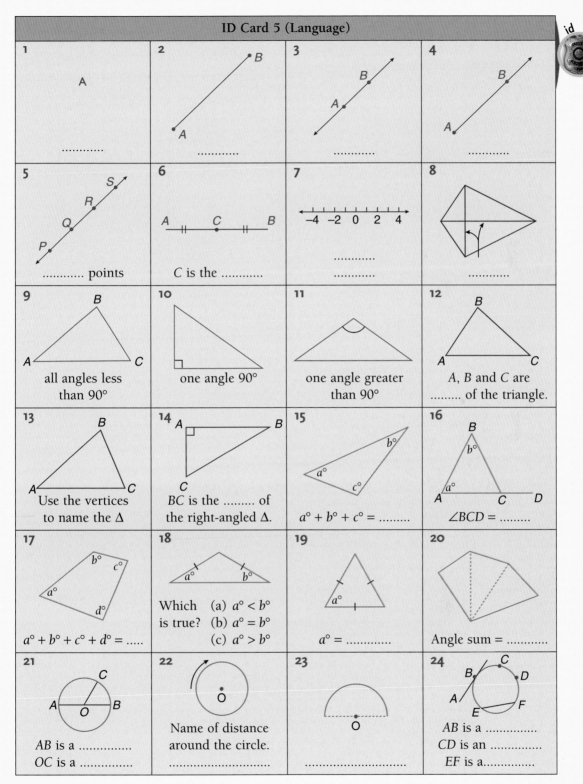

1

A

....

2

B

A

....

3

B

A

....

4

B

A

....

5

S

R

Q

P

.... points

6

A   C   B

C is the ....

7

−4 −2   0   2   4

....

8

....

9

B

A   C

all angles less
than 90°

10

one angle 90°

11

one angle greater
than 90°

12

B

A   C

A, B and C are
.... of the triangle.

13

B

A   C

Use the vertices
to name the Δ

14

A   B

C

BC is the .... of
the right-angled Δ.

15

b°

a°

c°

a° + b° + c° = ...

16

B

b°

a°

A   C   D

∠BCD = ...

17

b°   c°

a°

d°

a° + b° + c° + d° = ...

18

a°   b°

Which   (a) a° < b°
is true?   (b) a° = b°
           (c) a° > b°

19

a°

a° = ...

20

Angle sum = ...

21

C

A   O   B

AB is a ....
OC is a ....

22

O

Name of distance
around the circle.

....

23

O

....

24

C

B   D

A

E   F

AB is a ....
CD is an ....
EF is a...............

See page 497 for answers.

xvii

ID Card 6 (Language)

1 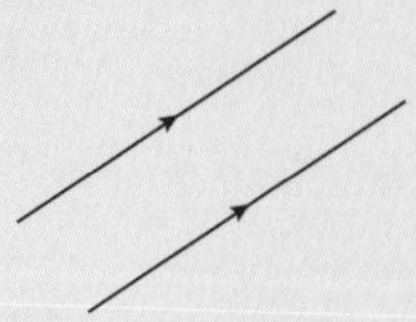
.... lines

2 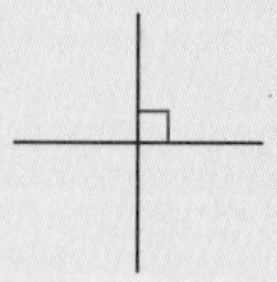
.... lines

3 
v ....
h ....

4 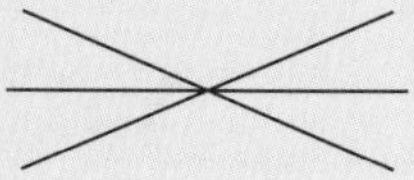
.... lines

5 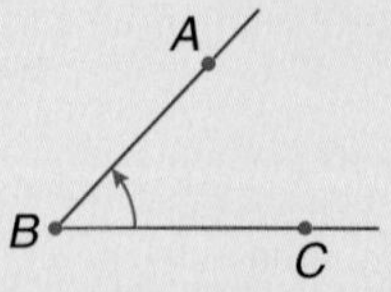
A
B
C
angle ....

6 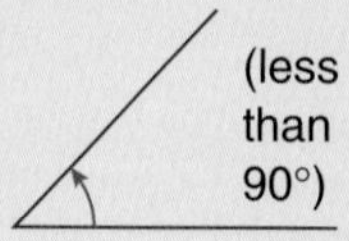
(less than 90°)
.... angle

7 
(90°)
.... angle

8 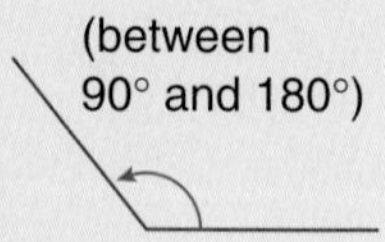
(between 90° and 180°)
.... angle

9 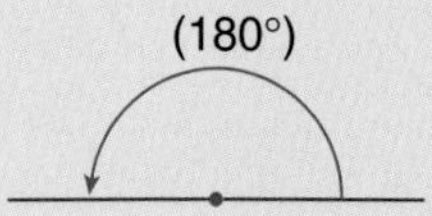
(180°)
.... angle

10 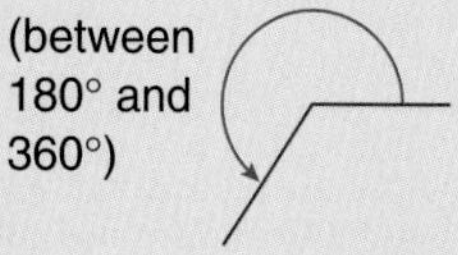
(between 180° and 360°)
.... angle

11
(360°)
....

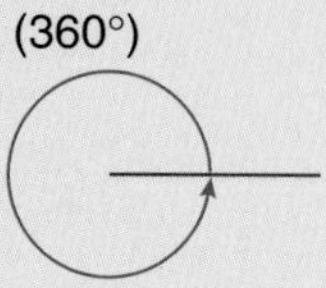

12
.... angles 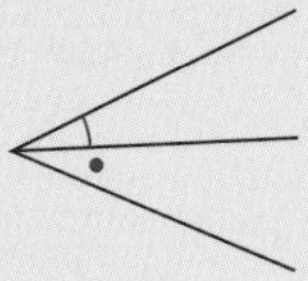

13 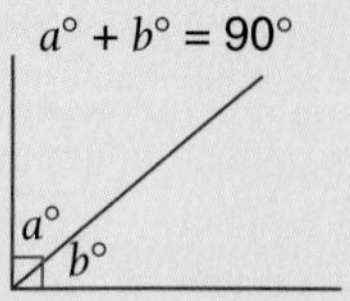
$a° + b° = 90°$
$a°$
$b°$
.... angles

14 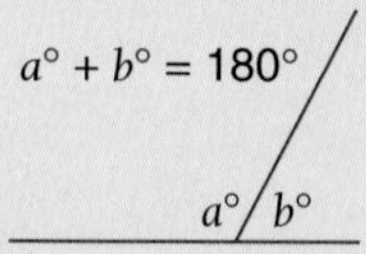
$a° + b° = 180°$
$a°$ $b°$
.... angles

15 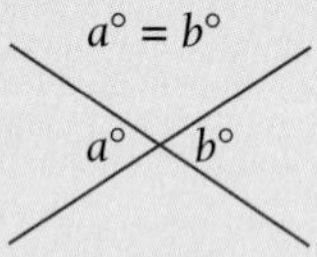
$a° = b°$
$a°$ $b°$
.... angles

16 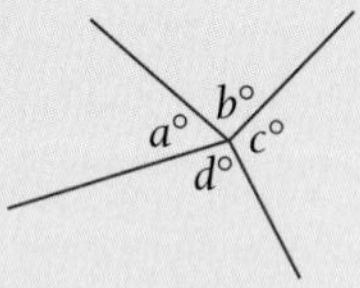
$a°$ $b°$
$d°$ $c°$
$a° + b° + c° + d° =$ .....

17
....

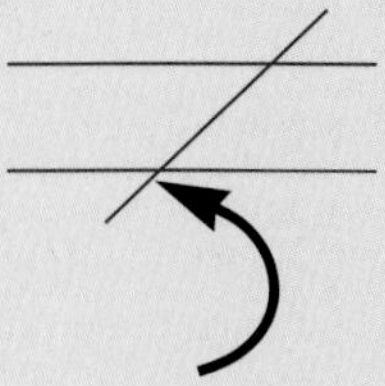

18 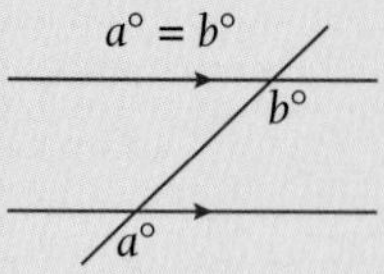
$a° = b°$
$b°$
$a°$
.... angles

19 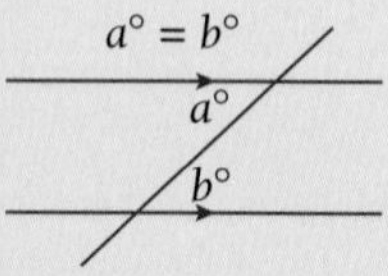
$a° = b°$
$a°$
$b°$
.... angles

20 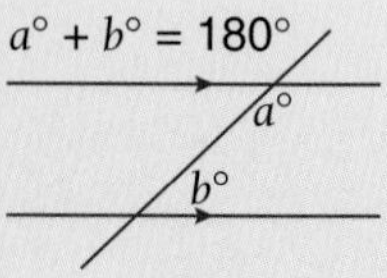
$a° + b° = 180°$
$a°$
$b°$
.... angles

21 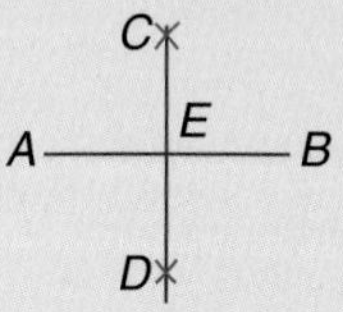
C
A — E — B
D
b............ an interval

22 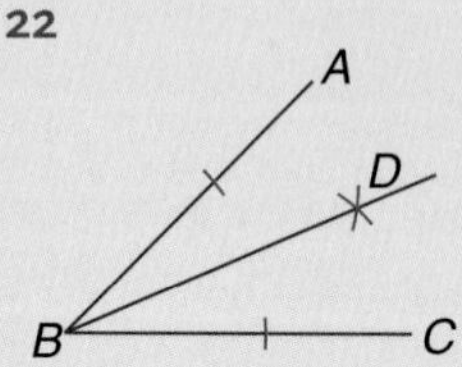
A
D
B — C
b............ an angle

23 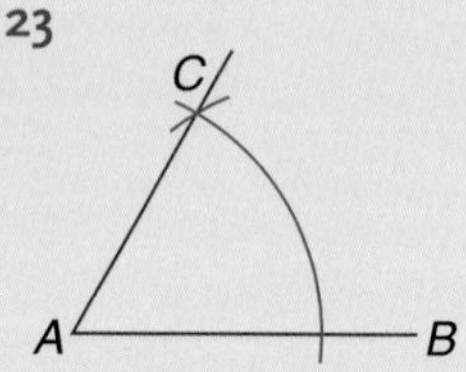
C
A — B
$\angle CAB =$ ....

24 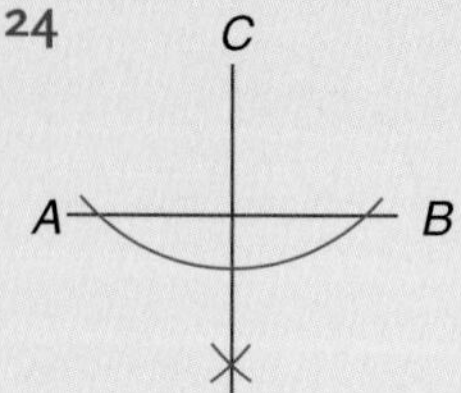
C
A — B
CD is p.......... to AB.

See page 497 for answers.

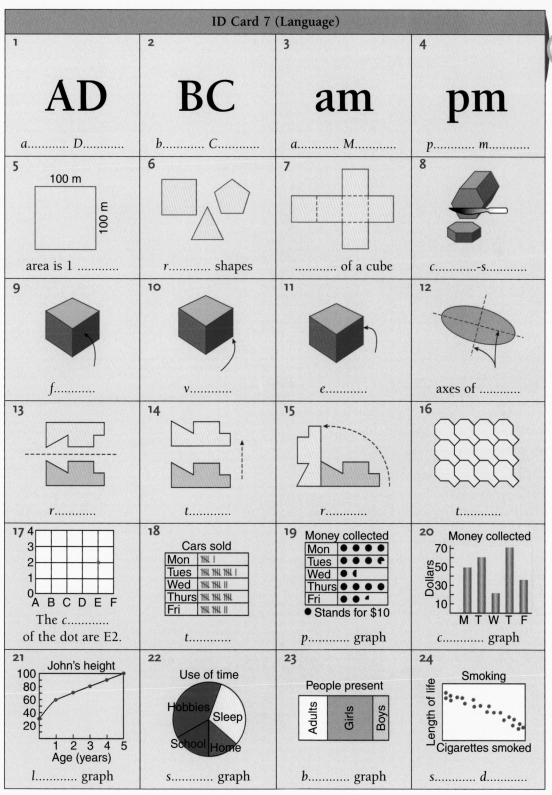

ID Card 7 (Language)

1 AD

a.......... D..........

2 BC

b.......... C..........

3 am

a.......... M..........

4 pm

p.......... m..........

5

100 m

100 m

area is 1 ....

6

r.......... shapes

7

.... of a cube

8

c..........-s..........

9

f..........

10

v..........

11

e..........

12

axes of ....

13

r..........

14

t..........

15

r..........

16

t..........

17

4
3
2
1
0
A B C D E F

The c..........
of the dot are E2.

18

Cars sold

Mon	ЖЦ I
Tues	ЖЦ ЖЦ ЖЦ I
Wed	ЖЦ ЖЦ II
Thurs	ЖЦ ЖЦ ЖЦ
Fri	ЖЦ ЖЦ II

t..........

19

Money collected

Mon	● ● ● ●
Tues	● ● ● ●
Wed	● ◖
Thurs	● ● ● ●
Fri	● ● ◢

● Stands for $10

p.......... graph

20

Money collected

70
50
30
10

Dollars

M T W T F

c.......... graph

21

John's height

100
80
60
40
20

1 2 3 4 5
Age (years)

l.......... graph

22

Use of time

Hobbies
Sleep
School
Home

s.......... graph

23

People present

Adults
Girls
Boys

b.......... graph

24

Smoking

Length of life

Cigarettes smoked

s.......... d..........

See page 497 for answers.

Arithmetic and Algebra Cards

Arithmetic card

	A	B	C	D	E	F	G	H	I	J	K	L
1	2	5	$\frac{1}{2}$	100	0·2	5%	$\frac{2}{3}$	90	0·9	15%	13	56
2	3	8	$\frac{1}{3}$	90	0·1	40%	$\frac{1}{7}$	30	0·5	35%	18	36
3	9	7	$\frac{3}{4}$	80	0·7	20%	$\frac{1}{5}$	20	0·3	1%	15	21
4	5	12	$\frac{1}{5}$	20	0	60%	$\frac{1}{6}$	80	0·1	44%	10	96
5	4	15	$\frac{3}{5}$	80	0·5	25%	$\frac{1}{8}$	100	0·6	95%	19	88
6	1	18	$\frac{2}{3}$	30	0·4	10%	$\frac{1}{4}$	60	0·2	65%	12	24
7	0	4	$\frac{4}{5}$	60	0·8	50%	$\frac{1}{2}$	10	0·4	90%	20	43
8	11	3	$\frac{1}{4}$	40	0·3	80%	$\frac{4}{5}$	60	0·2	100%	14	62
9	10	10	$\frac{3}{10}$	70	0·6	30%	$\frac{2}{5}$	30	0·8	$33\frac{1}{3}\%$	18	75
10	7	9	$\frac{2}{5}$	50	0·9	75%	$\frac{1}{3}$	70	0·7	85%	16	45

How to use these cards

As an example, if the instruction given for the Arithmetic Card is 'column B + column K', then you write down answers for the following problems:

1 5 + 13   **2** 8 + 18   **3** 7 + 15   **4** 12 + 10   **5** 15 + 19

6 18 + 12   **7** 4 + 20   **8** 3 + 14   **9** 10 + 18   **10** 9 + 16

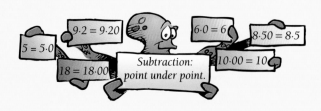

5 = 5·0   9·2 = 9·20   6·0 = 6   8·50 = 8·5

18 = 18·00   Subtraction: point under point.   10·00 = 10

Algebra card

	A	B	C	D	E	F	G	H	I	J	K	L
1	4	−7	−11	x	2y	−3x	−6y	x^2	2m	x^7	−5y	−4
2	3	−6	7	5x	7y	−x	−5y	x^5	3d	x^2	8y	−3
3	5	−8	−9	2x	10y	4x	4y	x^3	−2c	x^8	−12y	−2
4	8	−2	−7	3x	4y	−9x	−9y	x^6	−8h	x^4	0y	−1
5	7	−10	−8	10x	5y	−5x	−2y	x	9w	x^3	−7y	0
6	2	−12	6	7x	15y	−7x	−3y	x^8	−4d	x^5	0y	1
7	0	−15	−5	4x	6y	5x	−8y	x^4	−9n	x	−17y	2
8	1	−5	9	11x	3y	8x	−y	x^7	3x	x^9	−9y	3
9	9	−3	8	6x	y	−4x	−12y	x^3	−2w	x^6	5y	4
10	10	−4	−3	8x	9y	−8x	−7y	x^4	−7m	x^{10}	−8y	5

For convenience, stick copies of these pages in your book.

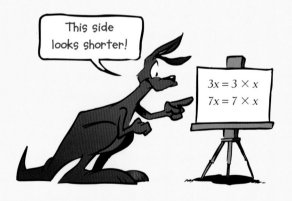

xxi

Review of last year's work

Chapter Contents

Learning Outcomes

In this chapter students will revise all areas of work covered last year. As a result, outcomes addressed are from Number, Problem Solving, Mathematical Analysis and Geometry.

Areas of Interaction

Approaches to Learning (Knowledge Acquisition, Thinking Skills, Reflection Skills)

Note: A complete review of the previous year's content is found in Appendix A located on the Interactive Student CD.

This is a summary of the work covered in *International Mathematics 1*. For an explanation of the work, refer to the cross-reference on the right-hand side of the page which will direct you to the Appendixes on the Interactive Student CD.

1:01 | Beginnings in Number

Exercise 1:01

CD Appendix

1 Write these Roman numerals as basic numerals in our number system.
   a LX   b XL   c XXXIV   d CXVIII
   e MDCCLXXXVIII   f MCMLXXXVIII   g $\overline{\text{V}}$CCCXXI   h MDCXV

A:01A

2 Write these numerals as Roman numerals.
   a 630   b 847   c 1308   d 3240
   e 390   f 199   g 10 000   h 1773

A:01A

3 Write the basic numeral for:
   a six million, ninety thousand
   b one hundred and forty thousand, six hundred
   c $(8 \times 10\,000) + (4 \times 1000) + (7 \times 100) + (0 \times 10) + (5 \times 1)$
   d $(7 \times 10^4) + (4 \times 10^3) + (3 \times 10^2) + (9 \times 10) + (8 \times 1)$

   ▨ 'Basic' means 'simple'.

A:01B

4 Write each of these in expanded form and write the basic numeral.
   a 5^2 b 10^4 c 2^3 d 2^5

A:01D

5 Write $6 \times 6 \times 6 \times 6$ as a power of 6.

A:01D

6 Write the basic numeral for:
   a 8×10^4 b 6×10^3 c 9×10^5 d 2×10^2

A:01E

7 Use leading digit estimation to find an estimate for:
   a $618 + 337 + 159$ b $38\,346 - 16\,097$ c $3250 \times 11 \cdot 4$
   d $1987 \div 4$ e $38 \cdot 6 \times 19 \cdot 5$ f $84\,963 \div 3 \cdot 8$

A:01F

1:02 | Number: Its Order and Structure

Exercise 1:02

CD Appendix

1 Simplify:
   a $6 \times 2 + 4 \times 5$ b $12 - 6 \times 2$ c $4 + 20 \div (4 + 1)$
   d $(6 + 7 + 2) \times 4$ e $50 - (25 - 5)$ f $50 - (25 - [3 + 19])$

A:02A

2 Simplify:
   a 347×1 b 84×0 c $36 + 0$
   d $3842 + 0$ e $1 \times 30\,406$ f $864 \times 17 \times 0$

A:02B

3 Write true or false for:
   a $879 + 463 = 463 + 879$ b $76 \times 9 = 9 \times 76$
   c $4 + 169 + 96 = (4 + 96) + 169$ d $4 \times 83 \times 25 = (4 \times 25) \times 83$
   e $8 \times (17 + 3) = 8 \times 17 + 8 \times 3$ f $4 \times (100 - 3) = 4 \times 100 - 4 \times 3$
   g $7 \times 99 = 7 \times 100 - 7 \times 1$ h $17 \times 102 = 17 \times 100 + 17 \times 2$

A:02B

4 List the set of numbers graphed on each of the number lines below.   A:02C

a

-1 0 1 2 3 4 5 6 7

b

-1 0 1 2 3 4 5 6 7

c

15 16 17 18 19 20 21 22 23

d

6 6·5 7 7·5 8 8·5 9 9·5 10

e

0 0·1 0·2 0·3 0·4 0·5 0·6 0·7 0·8

f

$0 \quad \frac{1}{4} \quad \frac{1}{2} \quad \frac{3}{4} \quad 1 \quad 1\frac{1}{4} \quad 1\frac{1}{2} \quad 1\frac{3}{4} \quad 2$

5 Use the number lines in Question **4** to decide true or false for: A:02C

a $3 < 5$ **b** $-1 < 0$ **c** $7 > 4$ **d** $0 > -1$

e $7·5 < 9$ **f** $0 > 0·7$ **g** $\frac{1}{4} < \frac{1}{2}$ **h** $1\frac{1}{4} > \frac{3}{4}$

6 Which of the numbers in the set {0, 3, 4, 6, 11, 16, 19, 20} are: A:02D

a cardinal numbers? **b** counting numbers? **c** even numbers?

d odd numbers? **e** square numbers? **f** triangular numbers?

7 List all factors of: A:02E

a 12 **b** 102 **c** 64 **d** 140

8 List the first four multiples of: A:02E

a 7 **b** 5 **c** 12 **d** 13

9 Find the highest common factor (HCF) of: A:02E

a 10 and 15 **b** 102 and 153 **c** 64 and 144 **d** 294 and 210

10 Find the lowest common multiple (LCM) of: A:02E

a 6 and 8 **b** 15 and 9 **c** 25 and 20 **d** 36 and 24

11 a List all of the prime numbers that are less than 30.   A:02F

b List all of the composite numbers that are between 30 and 40.

12 a Use a factor tree to write 252 as a product of prime factors.   A:02G

b Write 400 as a product of prime factors.

c Write 1080 as a product of prime factors.

d Find the HCF of 400 and 1080.

e Find the LCM of 400 and 1080.

13 Find the smallest number that is greater than 2000 and: A:02H

a is divisible by 2 **b** is divisible by 3 **c** is divisible by 4

d is divisible by 5 **e** is divisible by 6 **f** is divisible by 8

g is divisible by 9 **h** is divisible by 10 **i** is divisible by 11

j is divisible by 25 **k** is divisible by 100 **l** is divisible by 12

14 Complete the following: A:02I

a If $15^2 = 225$, then $\sqrt{225} = \ldots$ **b** If $8^3 = 512$, then $\sqrt[3]{512} = \ldots$

c If $13^2 = 169$, then $\sqrt{169} = \ldots$ **d** If $4^3 = 64$, then $\sqrt[3]{64} = \ldots$

1:03 | Fractions

CD Appendix

Exercise 1:03

1 Change each fraction to a whole or mixed numeral.

  a $\frac{10}{2}$ **b** $\frac{9}{4}$ **c** $\frac{87}{10}$ **d** $\frac{11}{8}$

A:03B

2 Change each mixed numeral to an improper fraction.

  a $3\frac{1}{2}$ **b** $5\frac{3}{10}$ **c** $1\frac{3}{4}$ **d** $3\frac{1}{7}$

A:03C

3 Simplify each fraction.

  a $\frac{8}{10}$ **b** $\frac{20}{50}$ **c** $\frac{15}{100}$ **d** $\frac{18}{24}$

A:03D

4 Complete the following equivalent fractions.

  a $\frac{2}{5} = \frac{\square}{10}$ **b** $\frac{3}{4} = \frac{\square}{100}$ **c** $\frac{4}{1} = \frac{\square}{10}$ **d** $\frac{1}{3} = \frac{\square}{120}$

A:03E

5 **a** $\frac{3}{10} + \frac{4}{10}$ **b** $\frac{19}{100} - \frac{6}{100}$ **c** $\frac{3}{8} + \frac{7}{8}$ **d** $\frac{5}{12} - \frac{1}{12}$

A:03F

6 **a** $\frac{3}{5} + \frac{3}{10}$ **b** $\frac{9}{10} - \frac{3}{4}$ **c** $\frac{3}{4} + \frac{2}{5}$ **d** $\frac{31}{100} - \frac{1}{5}$

A:03G

7 **a** Which fraction is the smaller: $\frac{3}{4}$ or $\frac{6}{10}$?

  b Which fraction is the larger: $\frac{2}{5}$ or $\frac{1}{3}$?

  c Arrange in order, from smallest to largest: $\{\frac{8}{10}, \frac{17}{20}, \frac{3}{4}\}$.

  d Arrange in order, from largest to smallest: $\{\frac{1}{2}, \frac{3}{5}, \frac{1}{4}, \frac{2}{3}\}$.

A:03H

8 **a** $3\frac{2}{5} + 1\frac{3}{4}$ **b** $10\frac{7}{8} - 3\frac{1}{2}$ **c** $5 - 2\frac{3}{5}$ **d** $10\frac{1}{5} - 1\frac{1}{2}$

A:03I

9 **a** $\frac{2}{5} \times \frac{3}{4}$ **b** $\frac{3}{10} \times \frac{7}{10}$ **c** $\frac{3}{5} \times \frac{2}{3}$ **d** $\frac{9}{10} \times \frac{15}{16}$

A:03J

10 **a** $4 \times \frac{3}{5}$ **b** $1\frac{7}{8} \times 3$ **c** $3\frac{3}{4} \times 1\frac{1}{3}$ **d** $2\frac{1}{2} \times 1\frac{4}{5}$

A:03K

11 **a** $\frac{9}{10} \div \frac{1}{2}$ **b** $\frac{3}{8} \div \frac{3}{5}$ **c** $4 \div \frac{3}{5}$ **d** $1\frac{1}{2} \div 3\frac{3}{4}$

A:03L

12 **a** Find $\frac{3}{5}$ of 2 km.   **b** What fraction of 2 m is 40 cm?

A:03M

1:04 | Decimals

CD Appendix

Exercise 1:04

1 **a** Write $(1 \times 10) + (7 \times 1) + (5 \times \frac{1}{10}) + (3 \times \frac{1}{100}) + (7 \times \frac{1}{1000})$ as a decimal.

A:04A

  b Write $(6 \times 100) + (8 \times 10) + (4 \times 1) + (0 \times \frac{1}{10}) + (2 \times \frac{1}{100})$ as a decimal.

2 Change each decimal to a fraction or mixed numeral in simplest form.   A:04B

    a   0·7   **b**   2·13   **c**   0·009   **d**   5·3

    e   0·85   **f**   0·025   **g**   1·8   **h**   9·04

3 Change each fraction or mixed numeral to a decimal.   A:04B

    a $\frac{9}{10}$ **b** $\frac{13}{100}$ **c** $1\frac{1}{2}$ **d** $2\frac{99}{100}$

    e $\frac{3}{5}$ **f** $\frac{33}{200}$ **g** $\frac{5}{8}$ **h** $\frac{3}{11}$

4 Write in ascending order (smallest to largest):   A:04C

    a   {0·3, 0·33, 0·303}   **b**   {2, 0·5, 3·1}   **c**   {0·505, 0·055, 5·5}

Do not use a calculator to do these.

5   **a**   3·7 + 1·52   **b**   63·85 − 2·5   **c**   8 + 1·625   **d**   8 − 1·625   A:04D

6   **a**   0·006 × 0·5   **b**   38·2 × 0·11   **c** $(0·05)^2$ **d**   1·3 × 19·1   A:04E

7   **a**   0·6 × 100   **b**   0·075 × 10   **c**   81·6 ÷ 100   **d**   0·045 ÷ 10   A:04F

8   **a**   48·9 ÷ 3   **b**   1·5 ÷ 5   **c**   8·304 ÷ 8   **d**   0·123 ÷ 4   A:04G

    e   3·8 ÷ 0·2   **f**   0·8136 ÷ 0·04   **g**   875 ÷ 0·05   **h**   3·612 ÷ 1·2

9   **a** $362 + $3·42   **b** $100 − $41·63   **c** $8·37 × 8   **d** $90 ÷ 8   A:04I

10   **a**   Round off 96 700 000 to the nearest million.   A:04J

    b   Round off 0·085 to the nearest hundredth.

    c   Round off 86·149 correct to one decimal place.

    d   Write 0·6̇, rounded off to two decimal places.

> ▨ When you round off, you are making an approximation.

1:05 | Percentages

Exercise 1:05   CD Appendix

1 Write each percentage as a fraction or mixed numeral in simplest form.   A:05A

    a   9%   **b**   64%   **c**   125%   **d** $14\frac{1}{2}$%

2 Write each fraction or mixed numeral as a percentage.   A:05B

    a $\frac{3}{4}$ **b** $1\frac{3}{8}$ **c** $\frac{37}{300}$ **d** $4\frac{3}{5}$

3 Write each percentage as a decimal.   A:05C

    a   47%   **b**   4%   **c**   325%   **d**   300%

    e   50%   **f**   104%   **g**   12·7%   **h**   0·3%

4 Change each decimal to a percentage.   A:05D

    a   0·87   **b**   1·3   **c**   5   **d**   0·825

5   **a**   8% of 560 L   **b**   70% of 680 g   **c**   5% of $800   **d**   10% of 17·9 m   A:05F

    e   Joan scored 24 marks out of 32. What is this as a percentage?

    f   250 g of sugar is mixed with 750 g of salt. What percentage of the mixture is sugar.

1:06 | Angles

1 Name each angle marked with a dot, using the letters on the figures.

A:06A

a   b 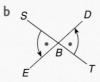 c 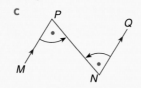 d

2 Use a protractor to measure ∠ABC.

A:06B

a 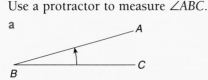 b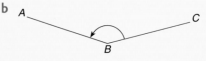

3 Classify each angle using one of these terms: acute, right, obtuse, straight, reflex, revolution.

A:06C

a 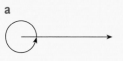 b  c  d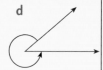

e   f  g 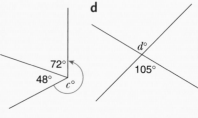 h

4 Draw a pair of:

A:06D

   a adjacent complementary angles   **b** vertically opposite angles
   c alternate angles   **d** adjacent supplementary angles.

5 Find the value of the pronumeral in each.

A:06D

a  b c 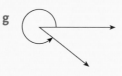 d

e  f 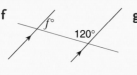 g   h

1:07 | Plane Shapes

1   a   What is the name of the shape on the right.   A:07A
    b   How many vertices has this shape?
    c   How many sides has this shape?
    d   How many angles has this shape?
    e   How many diagonals has this shape?

2   Choose two of these names for each triangle and find the vale of the pronumeral: A:07D
    equilateral, isosceles, scalene, acute-angled, right-angled, obtuse-angled

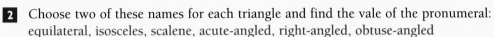

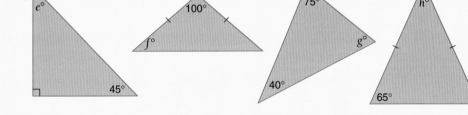

3   Calculate the value of the pronumeral in each quadrilateral.   A:07G

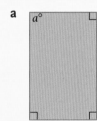 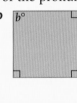 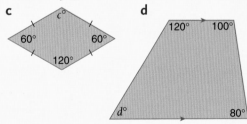

4   a   Give the special name of each figure in Question **3**.   A:07F
    b   Which of the shapes in Question **3** have:
      i opposite sides equal?   **ii** all sides equal?   **iii** two pairs of parallel sides?
      iv only one pair of parallel sides?   **v** diagonals meeting at right angles?

5   Use a ruler, a pair of compasses and a protractor to construct each of these figures.   A:07B
                                                          A:07E

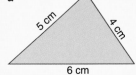 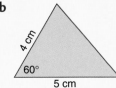 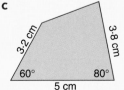

1:08 | Solid Shapes

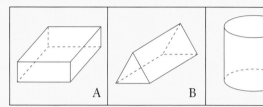

A   B   C   D

E

1 **a** Give the name of each solid above.

A:08A

  b Which of these solids have curved surfaces?

A:08B

  c For solid B, find:

A:08C

  i the number of faces (F) **ii** the number of vertices (V)

  iii the number of edges (E) **iv** number of edges + 2 (ie $E + 2$)

  v number of faces + number of vertices (ie $F + V$)

2 Name the solid corresponding to each net.

A:08D

  a   **b**   **c**

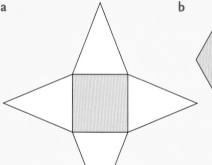

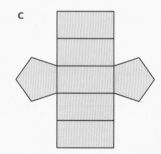

3

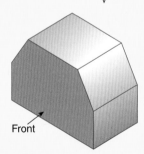

Front

  a Draw the front view of this prism.

A:08E

  b Draw the side view of this prism.

  c Draw the top view of this prism.

1:09 | Measurement

CD Appendix

Exercise 1:09

1 Write down each measurement in centimetres, giving answers correct to 1 decimal place.   A:09B

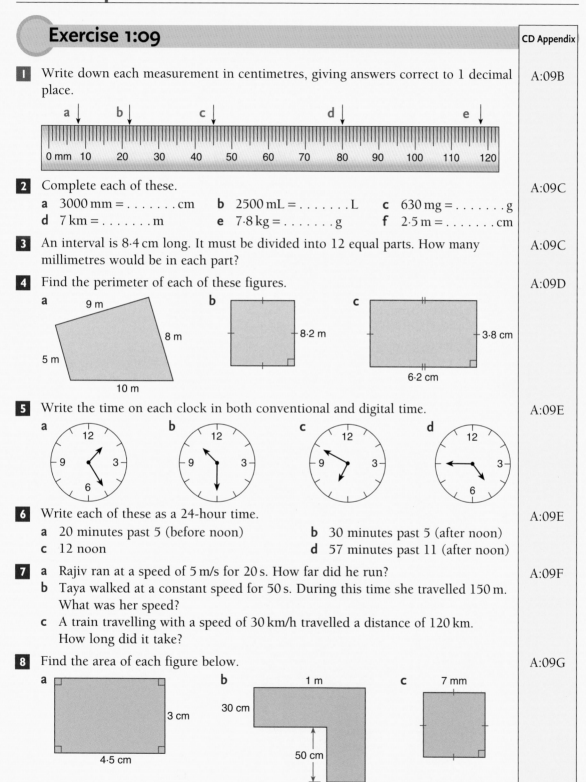

2 Complete each of these.   A:09C
  a 3000 mm = ... cm   **b** 2500 mL = ... L   **c** 630 mg = ... g
  d 7 km = ... m   **e** 7·8 kg = ... g   **f** 2·5 m = ... cm

3 An interval is 8·4 cm long. It must be divided into 12 equal parts. How many   A:09C
  millimetres would be in each part?

4 Find the perimeter of each of these figures.   A:09D
  a 9 m 8 m 5 m 10 m
  b 8·2 m
  c 3·8 cm 6·2 cm

5 Write the time on each clock in both conventional and digital time.   A:09E
  a   **b**   **c**   **d**

6 Write each of these as a 24-hour time.   A:09E
  a 20 minutes past 5 (before noon)   **b** 30 minutes past 5 (after noon)
  c 12 noon   **d** 57 minutes past 11 (after noon)

7 **a** Rajiv ran at a speed of 5 m/s for 20 s. How far did he run?   A:09F
  b Taya walked at a constant speed for 50 s. During this time she travelled 150 m.
     What was her speed?
  c A train travelling with a speed of 30 km/h travelled a distance of 120 km.
     How long did it take?

8 Find the area of each figure below.   A:09G
  a 3 cm 4·5 cm
  b 1 m 30 cm 50 cm 30 cm
  c 7 mm

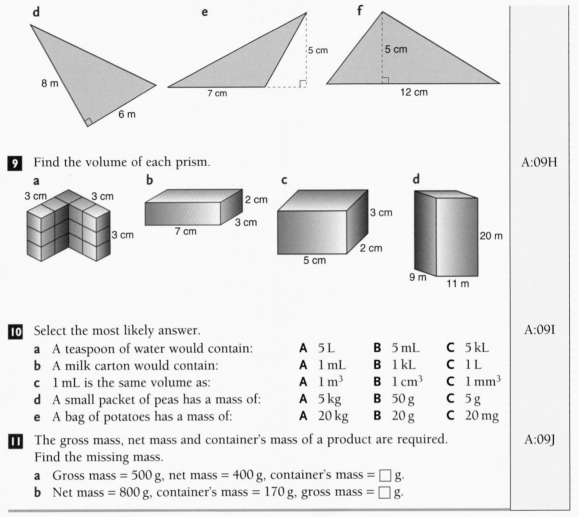

d 8 m, 6 m

e 5 cm, 7 cm

f 5 cm, 12 cm

9 Find the volume of each prism.

A:09H

a 3 cm, 3 cm, 3 cm, 3 cm

b 2 cm, 3 cm, 7 cm

c 3 cm, 2 cm, 5 cm

d 20 m, 9 m, 11 m

10 Select the most likely answer.

A:09I

a A teaspoon of water would contain: **A** 5 L   **B** 5 mL   **C** 5 kL
b A milk carton would contain: **A** 1 mL   **B** 1 kL   **C** 1 L
c 1 mL is the same volume as: **A** 1 m³   **B** 1 cm³   **C** 1 mm³
d A small packet of peas has a mass of: **A** 5 kg   **B** 50 g   **C** 5 g
e A bag of potatoes has a mass of: **A** 20 kg   **B** 20 g   **C** 20 mg

11 The gross mass, net mass and container's mass of a product are required. Find the missing mass.

A:09J

a Gross mass = 500 g, net mass = 400 g, container's mass = ☐ g.
b Net mass = 800 g, container's mass = 170 g, gross mass = ☐ g.

- List the 3D shapes that you can find in this picture.

1:10 | Directed Numbers

Exercise 1:10

CD Appendix

A:10A
A:10B
A:10C

1 Which members of the following set are integers: $\{-3, \frac{1}{2}, -1.5, 4, 0, -10\}$?

2 Give the basic numeral for each of the following.

a $-7+11$	**b** $-3+15$	**c** $-9+2$	**d** $-25+5$
e $2-13$	**f** $7-10$	**g** $-7-5$	**h** $-10-3$
i $6-(-10)$	**j** $14-(-1)$	**k** $3+(+7)$	**l** $15+(+1)$
m $10-(3-9)$	**n** $15-(2-5)$	**o** $3+(-7+11)$	**p** $11+(-5+18)$

3 Simplify:

A:10D

a -4×-3	**b** -8×-2	**c** -0.2×-3	**d** -0.1×-15
e -4×14	**f** -5×8	**g** $7\times(-1.1)$	**h** $6\times(-12)$
i $-35\div(-5)$	**j** $(-40)\div(-10)$	**k** $60\div-6$	**l** $14\div-7$
m $\dfrac{-21}{-3}$	**n** $\dfrac{-24}{-4}$	**o** $\dfrac{-48}{6}$	**p** $\dfrac{-1.8}{2}$

4 Write down the basic numeral for:

A:10

a $-3+6\times2$	**b** $-4-8\times2$	**c** $6-4\times4$	**d** $-30+2\times10$
e $-8+6\times-3$	**f** $10+5\times-2$	**g** $(2-20)\div3$	**h** $(8-38)\div-3$
i $8\times\$1.15-18\times\$1.15$		**j** $35°+2\times15°-4\times20°$	

1:11 | The Number Plane

Exercise 1:11

CD Appendix

A:11B

1 Find the coordinates of each of the points A to J.

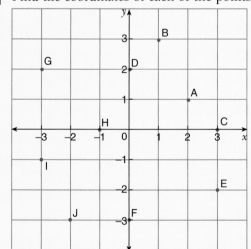

(0, 0) is the origin

The negatives are on the left on the *x*-axis. The negatives are at the bottom on the *y*-axis.

2 On a number plane like the one in Question **1**, plot the following points. Join them in the order in which they are given, to draw a picture.

A:11C

$(2, 0)$ $(3, 0)$ $(3, -1)$ $(1, -1)$ $(1, -1.5)$ $(2, -1.5)$ $(2, -1)$ $(-2, -1)$ $(-2, -1.5)$
$(-1, -1.5)$ $(-1, -1)$ $(-3, -1)$ $(-3, 0)$ $(-2, 0)$ $(-1, 1)$ $(1, 1)$ $(2, 0)$ $(-2, 0)$

1:12 | Algebra

Exercise 1:12

CD Appendix

1 If s represents the number of squares formed and m is the number of matches used, find a rule to describe each pattern and use it to complete the table given.

A:12A

a

 ,  , 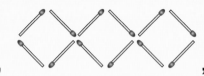 , ...

$m = \ldots\ldots\ldots\ldots$

s	1	2	3	4	10	20	30	100
m								

b

 , 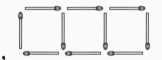 , ...

$m = \ldots\ldots\ldots\ldots$

s	1	2	3	4	10	20	30	100
m								

2 Rewrite each of these without the use of $\times$ or $\div$ signs.

A:12B

  a $5 \times h + 2$ **b** $a + 3 \times y$ **c** $6 \times (a + 7)$ **d** $5 \times a \div 7$

3 Rewrite each of these, showing all multiplication and division signs.

A:12B

  a $3a + 8$ **b** $5p - 6q$ **c** $4(x + 2)$ **d** $\dfrac{a + 7}{3}$

4 Given that $x = 3$, find the value of:

A:12C

  a $6x$ **b** $2(x + 5)$ **c** $5x^2$ **d** $10 - 3x$

5 If $a = 2$ and $b = 5$, find the value of:

A:12C

  a $3a + 7b$ **b** $\dfrac{10a}{b}$ **c** $4a(b - a)$ **d** $a^2 + b^2$

6 If $m = 2t + 1$, find the value of m when $t = 100$.

A:12C

7 Discover the rule connecting x and y in each table.

A:12D

a

x	1	2	3	4	5
y	7	10	13	16	19

b

x	1	2	3	4	5
y	11	15	19	23	27

8 Simplify:

A:12E

  a $1m$ **b** $1 \times a$ **c** $4 \times y$ **d** $y + y + y + y$

  e $f \times 5$ **f** $a \times b$ **g** $5 \times k$ **h** $5 \times a \times b$

  i $8x \times 0$ **j** $4y \times 0$ **k** $6m + 0$ **l** $3a \times 1$

m $7a + 5a$	**n** $10a + a$	**o** $7b - b$	**p** $114a - 64a$
q $m - 3m$	**r** $4b - 6b$	**s** $4x^2 + 3x^2$	**t** $6ab - 5ab$

9 Simplify:

a $3 \times 5a$	**b** $6 \times 10b$	**c** $7m \times 3p$	**d** $8x \times 4y$
e $a \times 4b$	**f** $6m \times 5$	**g** $-3k \times -5$	**h** $-6y \times 3$
i $12t \div 3$	**j** $30t \div 3$	**k** $6m \div 2a$	**l** $10a \div 5b$
m $15r \div 10$	**n** $8m \div 6$	**o** $3ab \times 7a$	**p** $5ab \times 4b$

A:12E

10 Simplify:

a $5m + 7m - 10m$	**b** $8x - 6x - x$	**c** $5x + 2y + 7y$
d $12a + 3b - 2a$	**e** $7p + 2q + 3p + q$	**f** $3r + 2A + 3A + 5r$
g $6a + 7b - 2a + 5b$	**h** $4m + 3 - 2m + 1$	**i** $8m + 2a - 2m - 8a$
j $7a^2 - 4a + 2a^2$	**k** $2x^2 + 3x + 2x$	**l** $2x^2 + 3x + 2x + 3$

A:12E

11 Expand, by removing grouping symbols:

a $3(a + 9)$	**b** $5(x + 2)$	**c** $10(m - 4)$
d $9(2a - 3)$	**e** $6(4t + 3)$	**f** $5(2 + 4x)$
g $m(m + 7)$	**h** $a(a - 3)$	**i** $a(6 + a)$

A:12F

12 Solve these equations.

a $x + 5 = 9$	**b** $x + 4 = 28$	**c** $12 - a = 5$	**d** $6 - a = -1$
e $6m = 42$	**f** $5m = 100$	**g** $m + 7 = 2$	**h** $m - 1 = -5$

A:12H

13 The sum of two consecutive numbers is 91. What are the numbers?

A:12I

14

, , , ...

A:11A
A:11B

This pattern of triangles formed from matches gives the following table.

Number of triangles (t)	1	2	3	4
Number of matches (m)	3	5	7	9

Plot these ordered pairs on a number plane like the one to the right.

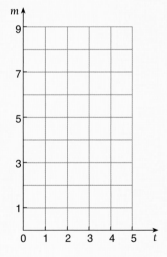

Chapter 1 | Working Mathematically

1 Use ID Card 7 on page xix to identify:
  a 5   b 7   c 8   d 17
  e 18   f 19   g 20   h 21
  i 22   j 23

Consecutive numbers follow one after the other.

2 Use a calculator to find:
  a three consecutive numbers that have a sum of 822.
  b three consecutive numbers that have a sum of 1998.
  c three consecutive numbers that have a sum of 24 852.
  d three consecutive numbers that have a product of 336.
  e three consecutive numbers that have a product of 2184.
  f three consecutive numbers that have a product of 15 600.

3 Which counting number, when squared, is closest to:
  a 210?   b 3187?   c 2·6?

4 After the twin towers of the World Trade Centre fell in New York on 11 September 2001, it took 3.1 million hours of labour to remove 1 590 227 tons of debris. If this was completed on 10 May 2002, find:

  a the number of days that passed until all debris was removed.
  b the average mass of debris that was removed in each hour of labour.
  c the number of tonnes of debris removed if 1 ton = 907 kilograms. (Remember: 1 tonne = 1000 kg.)

5 A recent survey carried out by a Singaporean bank suggested that Singaporeans are not saving enough of their income.

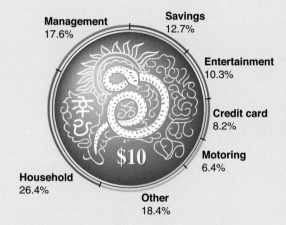

Management 17.6%
Savings 12.7%
Entertainment 10.3%
Credit card 8.2%
Motoring 6.4%
Other 18.4%
Household 26.4%
$10

  a If the wage represented in the above graph is $960 per week, how much is allocated to:
    i savings?   ii mortgage/rent?
    iii credit card?   iv motoring?
  b What do you think was the most popular reason for saving?
  c The three top reasons for saving were given in the article. Try to guess these three reasons in just five guesses.

Technology Applications

Drag and Drops

1 Order of operations

Chapter Review

Questions

Working Mathematically

Learning Outcomes

Students will:

- Ask questions that could be explored using mathematics.
- Apply strategies to real-life situations.
- Communicate ideas using mathematical terminology, notation, symbols, diagrams, text and tables.
- Identify relationships and the strengths and weaknesses of different strategies.
- Link mathematical ideas and make connections with and generalisations about existing knowledge and understanding.

Areas of Interaction

Approaches to Learning (Knowledge Acquisition, Problem Solving, Thinking Skills), Environments, Health and Social Education

2:01 | Working Mathematically

Working mathematically in a real-life situation may require us to ask questions, apply problem solving strategies, communicate mathematical ideas, apply reasoning and think about the mathematical ideas that apply.

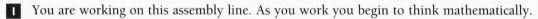

Exercise 2:01

1 You are working on this assembly line. As you work you begin to think mathematically.

a Communication
Explain how this assembly line works.

b Reasoning
Make up three questions to do with this assembly line that you could explore.

c Application
  i Each chocolate carton contains 8 boxes of chocolates. Each person on the assembly line places 5 chocolates into each box. 32 cartons are filled every hour in a 10-hour working day. How many chocolates are packed in one working day?
  ii There is a red marker on the conveyor belt. Estimate how far the marker travels in one working day if the width of a box of chocolates is 20 cm. (If you need help, read the hints at the bottom of this page.)

d Reasoning
  i Which are the most important parts of the process?
  ii What are the problems that would need to be addressed to keep the assembly line going?

e Reflection and Evaluation
  i If the engine running the assembly line broke down, how would you organise the workers so that the packing could continue in an efficient way?
  ii What would you do to improve this assembly line?

Hints for Question **c** ii:
  1 It appears that there is a gap after each five boxes, so the belt moves about 8·5 cm in the picture to allow 5 boxes to be filled.
  2 Each box has a width of about 6 mm on the picture. This is equal to 20 cm in real life.
  3 2560 boxes are filled each day.

---

2 Alan drenched 800 sheep. This involved squirting between 8 and 10 mL of a mineral supplement into the mouth of each sheep to keep them healthy. Using men and dogs, David, the farmer, herded the sheep along the chute to a conveyor belt that Alan operated by foot.

a Communication

How has David organised the drenching to reduce the time taken to finish the task? Explain how he has planned to complete the whole task of drenching the sheep.

b Reasoning

What questions would you ask the farmer so that you understand all of the preparations he has made for the sheep drenching? Write at least three questions.

c Application

   i How many sheep can be drenched in 3 hours if one sheep is drenched every 30 seconds?

   ii If one sheep in 60 misses treatment, how many of the 800 sheep would miss treatment? Of the 800 sheep, how many would have been treated?

   iii During the drought, a bale of hay cost $380. In a normal year the cost was $120. What was the increase in price? What percentage is this increase of the original price?

   iv Because of the drought it was decided to sell these 800 sheep. The farmer estimates that by the time of the sale, 18 sheep will have died. Each truck has 12 pens and 23 sheep fit into each pen. How many truckloads will be needed to take the sheep to market? If each sheep was sold for $57, how much money was received for the sale?

d Reasoning

If you had twice as many dogs and three times as many people to help drench the 800 sheep, how much time is likely to be saved?

e Reflection and Evaluation

The sheep are harder to handle when they can see shadows as this makes them more fearful. How would you use this information in the planning of the drenching of sheep? Could you improve the process shown in the picture? How could it be done in a different way? The farmer receives money from the sale of his sheep. List as many costs as you can, that the farmer would have, in order to earn this money.

Leaning Tower of Pisa

- The lean of the tower was:
  - 1.43 m in 1372
  - 3.77 m in 1550
  - 4.75 m in 1817
  - 4.8 m in 1935
  - 5.2 m in 1997
- What do you think could be done to save the building?
- Search the Internet to discover what has been done.

Last year you were introduced to a variety of problem-solving strategies. These, along with strategies you have been using all your life, are the skills you bring to a problem. The problem may be as simple as finding your way from home to school or as complex as trying to balance your budget.

Steps for solving problems

Step 1 Read the question carefully.
Step 2 Decide what you are asked to find.
Step 3 Look for information that might be helpful.
Step 4 Decide on the method you will use.
Step 5 Set out your solution clearly.
Step 6 Make sure that your answer makes sense.

To estimate, ask:
- Will the answer be big or small?
- How big? How small?
- Will the answer be a whole number?
- Does my estimate make sense?
- Is it reasonable?

Useful strategies include:
- Making a list, chart, table or tally
- Eliminating possibilities
- Working backwards
- Acting it out
- Looking for patterns
- Solving a simpler problem
- Guess, check and refine
- Making a drawing, diagram or model.

Make an estimate of the answer before you begin calculating.

worked examples

Example 1
Make a drawing, diagram or model
A firefighter stood on the middle rung of a ladder, spraying water on a burning house. He then climbed up 6 rungs before the heat of the flames caused him to come down 10 rungs. After some minutes he was able to climb 18 rungs to the very top rung of the ladder. How many rungs did the ladder have?

Solution 1
First draw a picture of the ladder.
Let the middle rung be the zero position.
To get to the top rung the firefighter has gone up 6, then down 10, then up 18.
$$6 - 10 + 18 = 14$$
∴ there are 14 rungs above the middle rung.

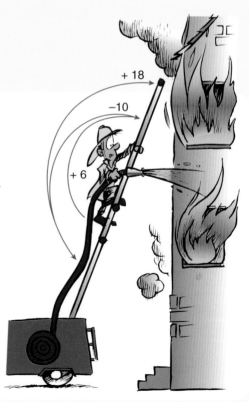

+ 18
−10
+ 6

There are also 14 rungs below the middle rung.
∴ the total number of rungs is 14 + 1 + 14.
There are 29 rungs on the ladder.

Example 2

Guess, check and refine

Heather is told to build 22 stools. Each stool must have either 3 or 4 legs and all 81 legs supplied must be used. How many of each type will she build?

Solution 2

The total number of stools is 22.

Guess 1:   10 three-legged stools and 12 four-legged stools.

Check 1:   Number of legs = $(10 \times 3) + (12 \times 4)$
$$= 30 + 48$$
$$= 78$$

This is 3 legs too few. (We need to use 3 more legs.)

Guess 2:   7 three-legged stools and 15 four-legged stools.

Check 2:   Number of legs = $(7 \times 3) + (15 \times 4)$
$$= 21 + 60$$
$$= 81$$

This is the correct number of legs.

∴ Heather will build 7 three-legged stools and 15 four-legged stools.

Exercise 2:02

Foundation Worksheet 2:02

Solving problems
1 In how many different orders can you write the words 'red', 'white' and 'blue'?
2 Three coins are tossed. In how many different ways could they fall? (One way is 3 heads.)

1 Use the suggested strategy to solve each problem.

a Making a list. Three girls, Naomi, Elizabeth and Anna, were being considered for girl's captain and vice-captain, and two boys, Luke and Kuan, were being considered for boy's captain and vice-captain. In how many different ways could the captains and vice-captains be chosen? One choice would be: Naomi (c), Elizabeth (v-c), Luke (c), Kuan (v-c).

b Eliminating possibilities. Each group in our class selected 6 bricks and found their total mass. Each brick selected by my group had a mass between 1·3 kg and 1·8 kg. The results from the groups were:

Group A	Group B	Group C	Group D
6·3 kg	7·8 kg	8·6 kg	11·1 kg

Which was my group?

c **Working backwards**. A scientist attached a radio transmitter to a dolphin to record its movements.

She recorded the starting and finishing points on this grid. The length of each small square represents 3 km.

After travelling 6 km east, 3 km south, 9 km west, 6 km north and then 12 km west, the dolphin finished up at A2. What was the dolphin's starting point?

d **Acting it out**. Tia and Rajiv decided to play noughts and crosses using a larger grid.

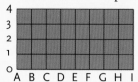

To win, there must be four noughts or crosses in a line, either across, down or diagonally.

   i How many ways are there to get four in a row?

   ii How many ways are there to get three in a row with no empty squares between them?

e **Looking for patterns**. A bus which has no passengers stops at five bus stops. At the first bus stop eight people get on, and at each stop afterwards two fewer people get on each time than at the stop before. Whenever possible two passengers get off at each stop. How many people were on the bus when it left the fifth stop?

f **Solving a simpler problem**. How many faces would be showing if 102 cubes were placed on a table end to end, in a straight line. (Consider the case of 3 cubes first to help find a solution.)

g **Guess, check and refine**. For our school play, tickets cost $18 for adults and $15 for children. I was handed $297 as the payment for 17 tickets. How many of these tickets were for children?

h **Making a drawing, diagram or model**. Eight tennis players are to play in a *round robin*, where each player must play all other players in one set of singles. How many sets must be played?

2 Use any strategy you like to solve these problems.

a A coin bought for $36 doubled its value each year for five years. What was its value after the five years?

b A plant which was bought for $9.50 had a height of 27 cm. In the first month it grew 2 cm in height. The growth for the next four months was double the growth of the previous month. How high was the plant after five months?

c Milo kept a cube made of heavy wire in his room. Its side lengths were 15 cm. A fly walked along the edges of the cube, from one vertex (or corner) to the opposite vertex of the cube. How far did the fly walk?

d The Bills family, the Collison family and the Foster family live in three houses side by side. The family in the middle house have no children and the family on the left do not own a fox terrier. Jennifer is proud of her whippet. Jennifer Collison and Damien Bills go to the same school. The whippet and the fox terrier are not neighbours. Who lives in each house.

e The City Zoo spent $250 000 on lions and tigers. They bought at least four lions and two tigers. If a lion costs $20 000 and a tiger costs $30 000, what possible purchases could they have made?

f In how many ways can 50 cents change be given if only 5 cent, 10 cent and 50 cent coins can be used?

g Mr French, Mr English, Mr Kraft and Mr Musik are four teachers who teach French, English, Craft and Music, however, none of them teaches a subject that sounds like his name. Mr French does not teach Music. When Mr French and Mr Kraft beat the other two at tennis, the English teacher is a bad loser but the music teacher is a gracious winner. What subject does each teacher teach?

h As the horses raced away, we noticed that there were 15 more legs than tails. How many horses were there?

i Sailors from a shipwreck were lost at sea. Search parties were sent out to find them. On the first day $\frac{1}{6}$ of the sailors were found. On the second day $\frac{1}{5}$ of those still lost were found. On the third day $\frac{1}{4}$ of those then lost were found. $\frac{1}{3}$ of those still lost were found on the fourth day. On the fifth day $\frac{1}{2}$ of those still lost were found and on the sixth day the last three sailors were found. How many sailors were lost originally?

nnology
lications

2:02 **A beautiful mind**

tivities

Challenge worksheet 2:02 **This puzzle is good 'training'.**

Investigation 2:02 | The left-hand rule for mazes

Please use the Assessment Grid on the following page to help you understand what is required for this Investigation.

Use a pointer to travel through each of the following mazes in order to investigate these questions.

- Can you find your way through these mazes *by putting your hand on the left wall and walking forward?*
- Using this method, in which cases do you visit every part of the maze? For what kind of mazes would you visit every part?

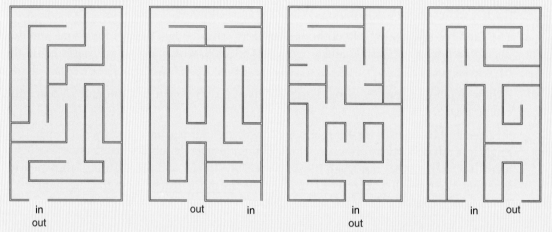

in
out

out in

in
out

in out

By changing these mazes slightly and by drawing others, test your conclusions and ideas.

2:03 | Problem Solving Using Venn Diagrams

Sets and Venn diagrams

A set may have many numbers, like the set of even numbers less than 70. On the other hand, a set may have no members at all, like the set of people who can run 100 m in 5 seconds.

Sets of things are frequently referred to in problem solving, and the most popular method of showing the relationship between sets is to use **Venn diagrams**. Here each set is represented by a region (eg a circle).

- **A *set* is a collection of things.**
- **We can describe or list the members of a set using braces, eg {students who have dogs}, {0, 1, 2}.**
- **A Venn diagram is used to represent sets simply, so that we may solve problems more easily. Each set is represented by a *region* (eg a circle).**

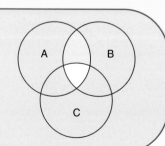

Assessment Grid for Investigation 2:02 | **The left-hand rule for mazes**

The following is a sample assessment grid for this investigation. You should carefully read the criteria *before* beginning the investigation so that you know what is required.

			Assessment Criteria (B, C, D)		Achieved ✓
Criterion B Investigating Patterns	a		The way through some of the mazes has been found.	1	
				2	
	b		The way through all of the mazes has been found in an organised way.	3	
				4	
	c		The mazes in which every part is visited have been identified and a reason for this has been given.	5	
				6	
	d		A description has been given in words or symbols of the sort of mazes in which every part is visited and why this method works.	7	
				8	
Criterion C Communication	a		The way through the maze has been found using trial and error with no written explanation.	1	
				2	
	b		Some explanation of how the student solved the mazes has been given and a result for all mazes has been found.	3	
				4	
	c		The mazes drawn illustrate the result for all mazes and show that the method works.	5	
				6	
Criterion D Reflection in Mathematics	a		An attempt has been made to explain the result for all mazes and an attempt has been made to check the result.	1	
				2	
	b		The result is well explained; one or two extra mazes have been used to illustrate the explanation.	3	
				4	
	c		The result is well explained and other possibilities have been explored for all mazes with a comparison of alternative methods.	5	
				6	

These students are standing in the shapes on the playground.

- The set of students inside the oval   = {A, B, C, D, E}.
- The set of students inside the triangle = {D, E, F, G}.
- The set of students inside both shapes = {D, E}. (This is known as the **intersection** of the two larger sets.) {A, B, C} is the set of students in the oval but not in the triangle. {F, G} is the set of students in the triangle but not in the oval.

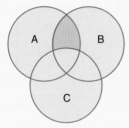

The orange part is in A and B but not C.

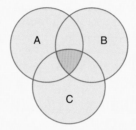

The orange part is in A, B and C.

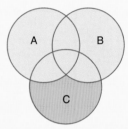

The orange part is in C but not in A or B.

worked examples

Example 1

Of 30 table tennis players, 12 can play with the left hand but two can play with both the left hand and the right hand.

a   How many can only play left-handed?
b   How many can play only with the right hand?
c   How many can play right-handed?

Solution 1

Use a Venn diagram to illustrate the problem.

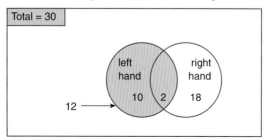

- The left circle represents those who can play with the left hand.
- The part where the circles overlap represents those who can play with either hand.

a Those who can only play left-handed
= 12 − 2, as two of the twelve can play with the right as well.
∴ 10 can only play left-handed.

b The part of the right circle not coloured represents whose who can play only with the right hand.
Only right-handed = 30 − 12
∴ 18 can only play right-handed.

c We add the 2 who can play with both hands to the 18 who can only use their right hand.
∴ 20 can play right-handed.

Example 2

42 copies of the *Telegraph* and 62 copies of the *Herald* were delivered to 80 homes.

a How many homes received two papers?
b How many homes received only the *Telegraph*?
c How many homes received only the *Herald*?

Solution 2

Use a Venn diagram to illustrate the problem.

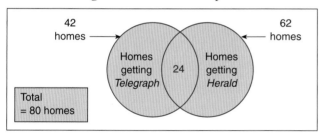

- We can assume that each home received at least one paper.
- We also assume that no home received more than two papers.

a Total number of papers sold = 42 + 62
= 104
If one paper were delivered to each of the 80 homes, 24 (ie 104 − 80) papers would remain.
∴ 24 homes received two papers.

b 42 homes received the *Telegraph* but 24 of these also got the *Herald*.
∴ 18 homes (ie 42 − 24) received only the *Telegraph*.

c 62 homes received the *Herald* but 24 of these also got the *Telegraph*.
∴ 38 homes (ie 62 − 24) received only the *Herald*.

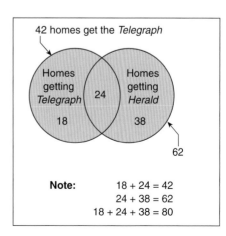

Note: 18 + 24 = 42
24 + 38 = 62
18 + 24 + 38 = 80

1 The diagram shows the number of students in 7W who have dogs or cats as pets.
A = {students who have dogs}
B = {students who have cats}
  a How many students have both dogs and cats?
  b How many students have dogs but not cats?
  c How many students have dogs?

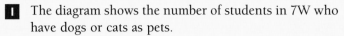

2 Of 65 table tennis players, 8 can play with the left hand but three of those can play with both the left and the right hand.
  a How many can only play left-handed?
  b How many can play only with the right hand?
  c How many can play right-handed?

3 65 copies of the *Telegraph* and 37 copies of the *Herald* were delivered to 85 homes.
  a How many homes received two papers?
  b How many homes received only the *Telegraph*?
  c How many homes received only the *Herald*?

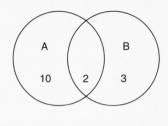

I belong to both!

4 The tennis club and the football club joined to form one club. There were 40 people in the tennis club and 75 people in the football club but only 97 people in the combined club.
  a Explain why there were not 115 people in the combined club.
  b How many people belonged to both the tennis and the football club?
  c How many people in the football club did not belong to the tennis club?

5 Sandy's cake shop sells white bread and brown bread. During the morning 65 people bought bread. 51 people bought white bread and 37 people bought brown bread. How many people bought both white bread and brown bread?

6 The Venn diagram on the right shows three intersecting sets: those who play cricket (C), those who play hockey (H) and those who play tennis (T). A number in one part shows the number of people in that part.
  • Our class has 28 students and every student plays at least one of these sports.
  • 2 students play all three sports, 4 play only cricket and hockey, 5 play hockey and tennis but not cricket, a total of 5 play cricket and tennis, a total of 12 play hockey, and altogether 15 play cricket.

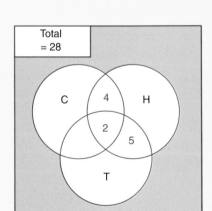

How many play:

a only hockey?
b only cricket and tennis?
c only cricket?
d only tennis?
e tennis?
f both cricket and hockey?
g cricket or hockey?
h tennis or hockey?

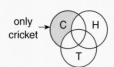

7 Each of 20 students put their first initial in the part of the Venn diagram which described their test results. How many students passed in:

a Music?
b English?
c Maths?
d all three subjects?
e both Music and English?
f only Music?
g only Music and English?
h English and Maths but not Music?

How many students did not pass in:

i Music?
j English?
k Maths?
l any subject?

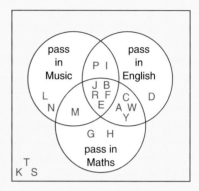

8 In our baseball team 5 players like to field, 8 players like to bat and one player does not like batting or fielding.
If there are 11 players in the team, how many:

a like both batting and fielding?
b like batting but not fielding?
c like fielding but not batting?

9 One hundred people were asked what type of TV programs they like out of news (N), movies (M) and documentaries (D). 64 like news, 80 like movies, 2 like only documentaries, 23 like movies and documentaries, 51 like movies and news, 34 like only movies and news, and 10 like only news and documentaries.
How many of these people like:

a all three types?
b only news?
c news and documentaries?
d only movies and documentaries?
e only movies?
f none of these types?

How many of these people do not like?

g news?
h movies?
i documentaries?

10 In order to make money for the World Vision children's fund, Year 7 were asked to buy cakes, drinks and sandwiches. 58 students bought cakes, 70 bought drinks, 46 bought sandwiches, 10 bought all three, 23 bought both cakes and drinks, 35 bought both drinks and sandwiches, 24 bought only cakes and 14 students bought nothing.

How many students:

a bought cakes and drinks but not sandwiches?
b bought drinks and sandwiches but not cakes?
c bought cakes and sandwiches but not drinks?
d bought cakes and sandwiches?
e bought only sandwiches?
f bought only drinks?
g were in Year 7?

All profit goes to charity!

Cake Day

fun spot

2:03

Fun Spot 2:03 | Counting the rings

Mr McSeveny took his students to a cove frequently visited by sharks. He grouped the students in teams of 12 and asked each team to work out a way of getting the best possible estimate of the number of metal rings which can be seen in the shark net below. Some rings are visible under the water which, at the centre of this 40-m wide net, is 2 m deep. The teams of students have only 20 minutes to find the number of rings as accurately as possible.

• You are the captain of a team and must direct your team members in the task. Write down your plan and the directions you would have to give to the other 11 students.

Chapter 2 | Revision Assignment

1 Change these Roman numerals into our own numerals.
   a XXXIV   b MDCXL
   c MMCDXIII   d MCMXCII

2 Write 3^4 in expanded form and write its basic numeral.

3 What is the basic numeral for 9×10^5?

4 Simplify:
   a $15 - 4 \times 3$
   b $(6 + 4) \div (15 - 11)$
   c $50 - (16 - 10)$

5 Graph $\{0, 3, 4\}$ on the number line.

6 Answer true or false:
   a $0 < -4$ b $(-3)^2 > 2^2$
   c $\frac{1}{5} < \frac{1}{4}$

7 List all of the factors of 24.

8 Simplify:
   a $\frac{20}{50}$ b $\frac{40}{5}$ c $\frac{9}{4}$
   d $\frac{3}{5} - \frac{2}{10}$ e $\frac{3}{10} \times \frac{7}{10}$ f $\frac{4}{5} \div \frac{1}{5}$

9 Answer true or false:
   a $0 \cdot 7 > 0 \cdot 65$
   b $(0 \cdot 05)^2 = 0 \cdot 0025$
   c $(\frac{1}{2})^2 = \frac{1}{4}$

10 a Change 9% into a decimal.
   b Write 60% as a fraction in its simplest form.
   c Change $\frac{3}{4}$ to a percentage.
   d Find 8% of 560 km.

Chapter 2 | Working Mathematically

1 A machine was used to measure the heartbeats of various animals. It was found that the horse's heart was beating 30 times each minute, the rabbit's heart was beating 125 times each minute and the dog's heart was beating 92 times each minute. If the machine recorded the horse's heart for 10 minutes, the rabbit's heart for 5 minutes and the dog's for 4 minutes, what was the total number of heartbeats recorded?

2 Heather is told to build 24 stools. Each stool must have either 3 or 4 legs and all 87 legs supplied must be used. How many of each type will she build?

Here we go again!

3 A firefighter stood on the middle rung of a ladder, spraying water on a burning house. He then climbed up 9 rungs before the heat of the flames caused him to come down 14 rungs. After some minutes he was able to climb 20 rungs to the very top of the ladder. How many rungs did the ladder have?

4 How many different groups of four people could be chosen to play tennis from the six people who have come to play?

5 Sandy bought two beautiful Australian finches, a gouldian finch and a diamond firetail finch. If the gouldian cost $16 more than the diamond firetail, find the cost of each bird if Sandy paid $72 altogether.

6 Use ID Card 3 on page xv to identify numbers (1) to (24).

Technology Applications

Drag and Drops

1 Powers of numbers

2 Percentages

3 Money

The Round Tower: Clonmacnoise, County Offaly, Ireland.

- When Vikings attacked, the local people would use a ladder to enter the door and then pull the ladder up after them.
- Estimate the height of the tower and the height of the door above the ground.

3

Percentages

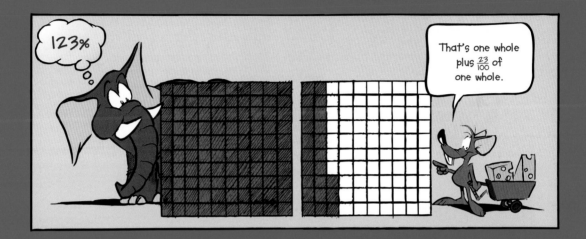

Chapter Contents

Learning Outcomes

Students will operate with fractions, decimals, percentages, ratios and rates.

Areas of Interaction

Approaches to Learning (Knowledge Acquisition, Problem Solving, Communication Skills, Thinking Skills), Environments, Human Ingenuity

3:01 | Review of Percentages

Percentages are used in all walks of life. We all therefore need to understand percentages and to be able to perform calculations involving them.

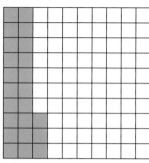
Exercise 3:01

1 Change these percentages to fractions.
   a 1%   b 9%   c 3%   d 57%

2 Change each percentage to its equivalent basic fraction.
   a 20%   b 50%   c 60%   d 5%

3 Change each percentage to a whole or mixed number.
   a 100%   b 115%   c 350%   d 400%

4 Change each fraction to a percentage.
   a $\frac{1}{100}$ b $\frac{3}{100}$ c $\frac{7}{100}$ d $\frac{10}{100}$

5 Write each as a percentage. Change to 100ths first.
   a $\frac{3}{10}$ b $\frac{7}{50}$ c $\frac{11}{20}$ d $\frac{2}{5}$ e $\frac{9}{25}$
   f $3\frac{7}{100}$ g $1\frac{1}{2}$ h $2\frac{1}{10}$ i $3\frac{4}{5}$ j 2

> To change a fraction to a percentage 'multiply by $\frac{100}{1}$%'.

6 Write each fraction as a percentage by multiplying by $\frac{100}{1}$%.
   a $\frac{7}{40}$ b $\frac{3}{8}$ c $\frac{4}{5}$ d $\frac{1}{3}$ e $\frac{5}{6}$

7 Change each to an improper fraction, then write each as a percentage.
   a $1\frac{1}{8}$ b $3\frac{1}{7}$ c $4\frac{1}{12}$ d $2\frac{1}{4}$ e $10\frac{3}{5}$

$\frac{115}{100}$

115 for every 100

1·15

115%

115 per 100

See Appendix A:05A to A:05E for explanations of each type.

3 = 300%

worked examples

$91\% = \frac{91}{100} = 0.91$ $400\% = \frac{400}{100} = 4$ $0.22 = \frac{22}{100} = 22\%$

$4\% = \frac{4}{100} = 0.04$ $106\% = \frac{106}{100} = 1.06$ $0.9 = 0.90$

$40\% = \frac{40}{100} = 0.4$ $350\% = \frac{350}{100} = 3.5$ $\quad = \frac{90}{100} = 90\%$

8 Write each percentage as a decimal.
- **a** 14%   **b** 63%   **c** 85%   **d** 32%   **e** 11%
- **f** 3%   **g** 9%   **h** 1%   **i** 2%   **j** 6%
- **k** 10%   **l** 30%   **m** 50%   **n** 90%   **o** 70%

9 Write each decimal numeral as a percentage.
- **a** 0.05   **b** 0.01   **c** 0.08   **d** 0.66   **e** 0.17
- **f** 0.5   **g** 0.4   **h** 0.1   **i** 0.3   **j** 0.8

> ■ To change a decimal to a percentage, multiply by 100%.
> eg $3.7 = 3.70 \times 100\%$
> $\qquad = 370\%$

10 Write each set of numbers in order, smallest to largest.
- **a** $\frac{1}{4}$, 100%, 0.5
- **b** $\frac{1}{10}$, 1%, $\frac{1}{2}$
- **c** $\frac{13}{100}$, 9%, $\frac{3}{4}$
- **d** 1, 5%, $\frac{99}{100}$

11 Express each as a whole number or decimal.
- **a** 200%   **b** 600%   **c** 100%   **d** 300%   **e** 500%
- **f** 120%   **g** 209%   **h** 197%   **i** 250%   **j** 390%

> ■ $147\% = 147 \div 100$

12 Change each decimal to a percentage.
- **a** 1.45   **b** 3.65   **c** 1.25   **d** 2.35   **e** 1.85
- **f** 2.9   **g** 1.1   **h** 3.6   **i** 0.34   **j** 0.7

13 Use a calculator (or divide by 100 mentally) to change each percentage to a decimal.
- **a** 146%   **b** 113%   **c** 124%
- **d** 68%   **e** 35%   **f** 43%
- **g** 9%   **h** 6%   **i** 4%
- **j** 248%   **k** 2%   **l** 18%
- **m** 13.6%   **n** 9.2%   **o** 16.3%
- **p** 12.25%   **q** 10.75%   **r** 83.625%

On a calculator 147% is 147 ÷ 100 =.

14 Write each set of numbers in order, smallest to largest.
- **a** $\frac{3}{5}$, 15%, 0.51
- **b** 1.8, 18%, $1\frac{1}{8}$
- **c** 152%, 15.2, $1\frac{1}{2}$
- **d** $\frac{2}{3}$, 60%, 0.65

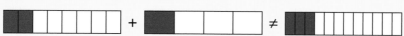

- Explain why $\frac{2}{8} + \frac{1}{4}$ is not equal to $\frac{3}{12}$.

3:02 | Estimating Percentages

When estimating percentages mentally, divide one whole into 100 parts.

Remember: $\frac{1}{2} = 50\%$, $\frac{1}{4} = 25\%$, $\frac{1}{10} = 10\%$, $\frac{1}{5} = 20\%$.

worked examples

Estimate the percentage coloured to the nearest 10%.

1
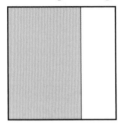

2
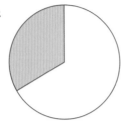

3
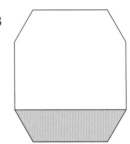

4 If one square is 100%, what percentage is coloured?

This is more than 100%.

Solutions

1 Almost $\frac{3}{4}$ is coloured.
∴ estimate = 70%.

2 About $\frac{1}{3}$ is coloured.
∴ estimate = 30%.

3 Less than $\frac{1}{4}$ is coloured.
∴ estimate = 20%.

4 All of the first square and about $\frac{2}{10}$ of the second is coloured.
∴ estimate = 100% + 20% = 120%

Exercise 3:02

1 Estimate the percentage coloured in each, to the nearest 10%.

a

b

c

d

e

f
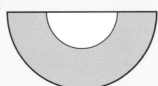

g
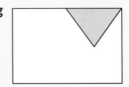

h  **i** 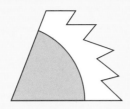 **j**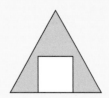

k Percentage covered = …

l What percentage is the smaller of the larger?

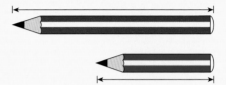

What percentage of each container is filled? Answer to the nearest 10%.

m  **n**   **o**  **p**

2 If one square is 100%, estimate the percentage coloured, in each part, correct to the nearest 10%.

a   **b**

These are more than 100%.

c   **d**

3 For each picture, estimate to the nearest 10% the percentage of the wall still not painted.

4

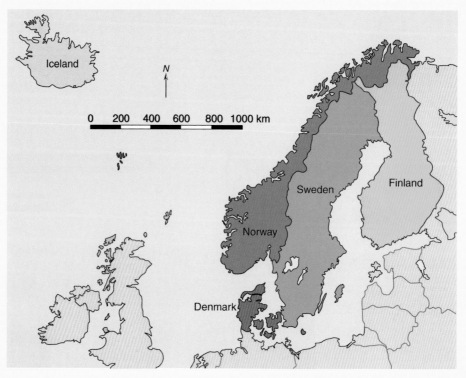

Use the map above to estimate the percentage of Scandinavia's land area that is in:
a Norway   **b** Sweden   **c** Denmark   **d** Finland   **e** Iceland
Add your answers for **a** to **e**. Do they come to about 100%?

• What percentage of the jig saw puzzle is not in place?

• Estimate what percentage of the time a 12 would be thrown.

3:03 | Harder Conversions

Write as decimals: **1** $12\frac{1}{2}$ **2** $6\frac{1}{4}$ **3** $11\frac{3}{4}$ **4** $109\frac{1}{2}$

Simplify: **5** 0.625×100 **6** 0.333×100 **7** $0.\dot{3} \times 100$ **8** $0.1\dot{6} \times 100$

Which two are equivalent? **9** $1\%, \frac{1}{100}, 0.1$ **10** $10\%, \frac{1}{10}, 0.01$

worked examples

1 Change 0·125 to a percentage.

2 Write $\frac{1}{6}$ as a percentage, correct to 2 decimal places.

3 Convert 13·8% to a decimal.

4 Convert $6\frac{1}{4}\%$ to a decimal.

Solutions

1 $0.125 = 0.125 \times 100\%$
    $= 12.5\%$

2 $\frac{1}{6} = (1 \div 6) \times 100\%$
    $= 0.1666\ldots \times 100\%$
    $\doteqdot 16.67\%$

3 $13.8\% = 13.8 \div 100$
    $= 0.138$

4 $6\frac{1}{4}\% = 6.25\%$
    $= 6.25 \div 100$
    $= 0.0625$

> ■ *Using a Calculator*
>
> 1 0.125 ⊗ 100 ⊜
>   12.5
>
> 2 1 ÷ 6 ⊗ 100 ⊜
>   16.666667
>
> 3 13.8 ⊘ 100 ⊜
>   0.138
>
> 4 6.25 ⊘ 100 ⊜
>   0.0625

Exercise 3:03

Foundation Worksheet 3:03
Percentage conversions
1 Change to percentages:
  a 0·23 **b** 0·07 **c** 0·3
2 Change to a decimal:
  a 12% **b** 25% **c** 60%
3 Change to a percentage:
  a $\frac{13}{100}$ **b** $\frac{1}{2}$ **c** $\frac{1}{10}$

1 Change these decimals to percentages.

   a 0·375   **b** 0·086   **c** 0·174

   d 1·245   **e** 6·125   **f** 2·375

   g 2·3   **h** 0·015   **i** 0·005

2 Convert each percentage to a decimal.

   a 14·5%   **b** 27·9%   **c** 95·4%

   d 2·1%   **e** 9·6%   **f** 23·85%

   g 87·35%   **h** 112·5%   **i** 287·5%

3 Convert each to a decimal. (Change the fraction part to a decimal first.)

   a $12\frac{1}{2}\%$ **b** $87\frac{1}{2}\%$ **c** $13\frac{1}{2}\%$

   d $7\frac{1}{4}\%$ **e** $10\frac{3}{4}\%$ **f** $15\frac{1}{4}\%$

   g $106\frac{3}{4}\%$ **h** $254\frac{1}{2}\%$ **i** $131\frac{1}{4}\%$

> You may need me for these.

4 Convert each to a percentage, rounding off correct to 2 decimal places.

   a $\frac{2}{7}$ **b** $\frac{5}{6}$ **c** $\frac{7}{8}$

   d $\frac{15}{16}$ **e** $\frac{2}{3}$ **f** $\frac{3}{40}$ **g** $1\frac{1}{6}$ **h** $2\frac{5}{6}$

3:04 | Finding a Percentage of a Quantity

1 25% of a square is shaded red, 13% is shaded blue. What percentage of the square is neither red nor blue?

2 $\frac{1}{3} = 33\frac{1}{3}\%$ $\therefore \frac{2}{3} = \ldots\%$ **3** $\frac{2}{4} = 50\%$ $\therefore \frac{1}{4} = \ldots\%$

4 $\frac{2}{8} = 25\%$ $\therefore \frac{1}{8} = \ldots\%$ **5** $\frac{2}{16} = 12\frac{1}{2}\%$ $\therefore \frac{1}{16} = \ldots\%$

Change to a fraction in its simplest form: **6** 25%   **7** 20%

Change to a decimal: **8** 24%   **9** 6%   **10** $14\frac{1}{2}\%$

> To find a percentage of a quantity, write the percentage as a decimal (or fraction) and multiply by the quantity.

worked examples

1 9% of 1600 g
(by fractions)

$= {}_{1}\frac{9}{100} \times \frac{1600^{16}}{1}$

$= \frac{144}{1}$

$= 144$ g

2 8% of 1600 g
(by decimals)

$= (8. \div 100) \times 1600$

$= (0.08 \times 1600)$

$= 128.0$

$= 128$ g

3 47% of 185 m

$= (47. \div 100) \times 185$

$= 0.47 \times 185$

$= 86.95$ m

OR   47 ÷ 100 × 185 =

Calculators use decimals.

4 3% of 7 km

$= 3\%$ of 7000 m

$= (3. \div 100) \times 7000$

$= 0.03 \times 7000$

$= 210.0$

$= 210$ m

5 120% of 12 L

$= (120. \div 100) \times 12$

$= 1.2 \times 12$

$= 14.4$ L

6 6.8% of $185
(correct to the nearest cent)

$= (6.8 \div 100) \times 185$

$= 0.068 \times 185$

$= \$12.58$

Exercise 3:04

1 Replace the percentage with a fraction to evaluate these.
(See Worked Example 1.)

   a 5% of 1600 g   **b** 9% of 2500 m

   c 6% of $850   **d** 8% of 2000 L

   e 83% of 40 cm   **f** 70% of 410 mL

   g 40% of 85 min   **h** 67% of 20 000 t

   i 17% of $300   **j** 24% of $36.50

Foundation Worksheet 3:04

Finding a percentage of a quantity

1 Complete:
   6% means . . . out of . . .

2 **a** 15% of $100
   b 15% of $200

3 Write as a decimal:
   a 18%   **b** 10%   **c** 3%

2 Replace the percentage with a decimal to evaluate these (see Worked Examples **2–6**).

- **a** 15% of $8
- **b** 30% of 150 L
- **c** 12% of $40
- **d** 8% of 1800 g
- **e** 2% of 3000 t
- **f** 5% of 180 min
- **g** 3% of 800 km
- **h** 4% of 100 min
- **i** 7% of 5000 L
- **j** 105% of 800 m
- **k** 115% of $2000
- **l** 102% of 10 000 km
- **m** 120% of 140 kL
- **n** 379% of 162 km
- **o** 280% of 365 days

$$■ \; 0.48 \times 600 \text{ g}$$
$$= (0.48 \times 100) \times 6$$
$$= 48 \times 6$$
$$= 288 \text{ g}$$

3 Either replace the percentage with a decimal or use a calculator to evaluate these.

- **a** 3% of 945 L
- **b** 6% of 2425 m
- **c** 84% of 10 t
- **d** 76% of 8 km
- **e** 35% of 9·6 m
- **f** 120% of 2·8 g
- **g** 245% of 0·9 t
- **h** 1·2% of 840 mm
- **i** 13·6% of 50 s
- **j** 0·6% of 350 mL
- **k** 0·7% of 150 000
- **l** 0·08% of 8000 g
- **m** 1·5% of 10 km
- **n** 8·4% of 5 L
- **o** $7\frac{1}{2}$% of $60
- **p** $12\frac{1}{2}$% of 320 g
- **q** $8\frac{1}{4}$% of 8900 kg
- **r** $8\frac{3}{4}$% of $1000

$■$ 1 3% of 794·8 t
$$= (3 \div 100) \times 794 \cdot 8 \text{ t}$$
3 ÷ 100 × 794·8 = 23·844

2 $106\frac{1}{4}$% of 1·35 km
$$= (106 + \tfrac{1}{4}) \div 100 \times 1 \cdot 35 \text{ km}$$
106 + 1 ÷ 4 = ÷ 100 × 1·35 =

1·434

Reading mathematics 3:04 | Conversions

Fraction to decimal
$\frac{3}{8} = 3 \div 8$ $= 8\overline{)3 \cdot 000}$ $0 \cdot 375$

Fraction to percentage
$\frac{3}{8} = \frac{3}{8_2} \times \frac{\overset{25}{100}}{1} \%$ $= 37\frac{1}{2}\%$

Decimal to percentage
$0 \cdot 375 = 0 \cdot 375 \times 100\%$ $= 37 \cdot 5\%$

Decimal to fraction
$0 \cdot 375 = \frac{375}{1000}$ $= \frac{3}{8}$

Percentage to fraction
$37\frac{1}{2}\% = \frac{37 \cdot 5}{100}$ $= \frac{375}{1000}$ $= \frac{3}{8}$

Percentage to decimal
$37 \cdot 5\% = 37 \cdot 5 \div 100$ $= 0 \cdot 375$

Explain using words how you would convert:

1 a fraction to a decimal
2 a decimal to a fraction
3 a fraction to a percentage
4 a percentage to a fraction
5 a decimal to a percentage
6 a percentage to a decimal.

- Can you see connections?

3:05 | Applications of Percentages

Write these percentages as decimals:

1 50%   2 3%   3 72%   4 3·5%   5 125%

Find:

6 3% of $100   7 87% of $100   8 6·7% of $100

How many:

9 grams in a kilogram?   10 milligrams in a gram?

worked example

Boris, the teenage tennis star, was delighted to hear that he had received a total of $288 000 during the year from prize money and advertising. However, during this year he had paid $55 000 for expenses and $86 000 in tax. He banked 86% of what was left. How much did he bank?

Solution

Amount left $= \$288\,000 - (\$55\,000 + \$86\,000)$

               $= \$147\,000$

Amount banked $= 86\%$ of $\$147\,000$

               $= 0·86 \times 147\,000$

               $= \$126\,420$

Exercise 3:05

Foundation Worksheet 3:05

Applications of percentages
1 I earned $100. I wish to give 15% of this to my mother. How much should I give her?
2 3% of the computers are not working. How many are not working if there are 200 computers?

1 The Hollier family decided to donate 5% of their earnings for December to famine relief through World Vision. How much will the family donate if the parents together earned £6100 and the four children together earned £950?

2 It has been said that 38% of the world's population would be needed to do the work of the world's automatic telephone exchanges. How many people is this if the world's population is 6 000 000 000?

3 Advertising for the show *Nicholas Nickleby* accounted for 7% of the production costs of €1 500 000. How much was spent on advertising?

4 Random breath tests are used to discover whether a driver has drunk too much alcohol to drive safely. On New Year's Eve 2% of all drivers tested were above the legal limit. If 8000 were tested, how many were above the legal limit?

5 In 1980 there were 4.8 million computers in use worldwide; 65% of these were in the USA. How many computers were being used by the rest of the world?

6 In order to borrow enough money to buy the home she chose, Skye needed to have 28% of the cost of the home. If the home cost $425 000, how much did she need to have?

7 It is estimated that in the UK 6.8% of adults and 1.8% of children suffer from asthma. If the population of the UK is 59.8 million people and approximately 20% are children, how many of its children suffer from asthma?

8 Jay gained 93% of a possible 600 marks. How many more marks would he need to have scored to gain 96% of the marks?

9 George can run 400 m in 50 s. He needs to reduce his time by 4% to equal the Olympic record. What is the Olympic record for 400 m?

10 Following a survey of 2500 men of age 40 years and 2500 men of age 50 years, it was found that 43% of the 40-year-old men were substantially bald, while 58% of the 50-year-old men were substantially bald. How many more of the 50-year-old men were bald than of the 40-year-old men?

11 Her Majesty's Theatre has a capacity of 1000 people. On the opening night the theatre was 90% full. On the second night it was 85% full. How many people attended the theatre on the first two nights?

12 Find the new price of each of the items advertised below.

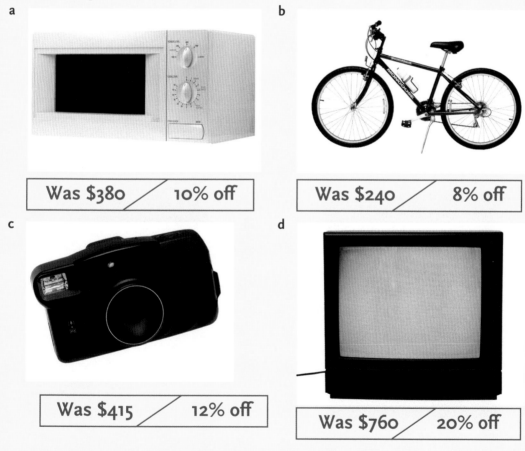

a Was $380 / 10% off

b Was $240 / 8% off

c Was $415 / 12% off

d Was $760 / 20% off

3:06 | Percentage Composition

What is the first quantity as a fraction of the second quantity?

1 50 g, 100 g **2** $2, $8 **3** 15 t, 20 t **4** 8c, 80c

Change the following fractions to percentages.

5 $\frac{1}{2}$ **6** $\frac{1}{4}$ **7** $\frac{3}{4}$ **8** $\frac{1}{10}$

9 Change $\frac{7}{8}$ to a percentage. **10** What fraction is 200 g of 2 kg?

 To express one quantity as a percentage of another, write the first quantity as a fraction of the second and then convert to a percentage by multiplying by $\frac{100}{1}$ %.

---

worked examples

1 Express 4 g as a percentage of 25 g. **2** What percentage of 2 min is 51 s?

3 A tin of fishcake mix contains 204 g of Australian salmon, 156 g of potato, 24 g of seasoning and 16 g of cornflour. Find the percentages by weight of salmon and of potato.

Solutions

1 4 g as a fraction of 25 g

$= \dfrac{4}{25}$

$= \dfrac{4}{25_1} \times \dfrac{100^4}{1}$ % (changing to a percentage)

$= 16\%$

∴ 4 g is 16% of 25 g.

2 51 s as a fraction of 2 min

$= \dfrac{51}{120}$ (since 2 min = 120 s)

$= \dfrac{51^{17}}{120_{6_2}} \times \dfrac{100^5}{1}$ % (changing to a percentage)

$= \dfrac{85}{2}\%$ or $42\frac{1}{2}\%$

∴ 51 s is $42\frac{1}{2}\%$ of 2 min.

3 Weight of contents is 400 g
(ie 204 + 156 + 24 + 16)
204 g of salmon as a fraction of 400 g.

$= \dfrac{204}{400}$

$= \dfrac{204^{51}}{400_{1}} \times \dfrac{100^1}{1}$ % (changing the fraction to a percentage)

$= \dfrac{51}{1}\%$

∴ 51% of the ingredients is salmon.
156 g of potato as a percentage of 400 g

$= \dfrac{156^{39}}{400_{1}} \times \dfrac{100^1}{1}$ %

$= 39\%$

∴ 39% of the ingredients is potato.

> If the question is given as a sentence, give the answer as a sentence.

$\frac{4}{6}$ is shaded.

∴ percentage shaded

$= \dfrac{4^2}{6_3} \times \dfrac{100}{1}$ %

$= \dfrac{200}{3}$ %

$= 66\frac{2}{3}\%$ or $66 \cdot \dot{6}\%$

By calculator: $\frac{4}{6} \times 100\%$

4 ÷ 6 × 100 = 66·666667

Percentage shaded is $66 \cdot \dot{6}$ %.

Exercise 3:06

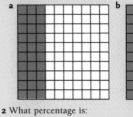

Foundation Worksheet 3:06

Percentages

1 What percentage is shaded?

1 What percentage of each figure has been shaded?

a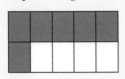

b

c

d

2 What percentage is:
   a 3 of 100?   **b** 6 of 10?

2 In each case express the first quantity as a percentage of the second.
   a 2 g, 20 g   **b** 5 m, 20 m   **c** 2 L, 200 L
   d 15 mL, 60 mL   **e** 24 s, 120 s   **f** 372 ha, 600 ha
   g 3 m, 40 m   **h** 14 kg, 80 kg   **i** 930 cm², 1200 cm²
   j 150 g, 450 g   **k** 27 m, 500 m   **l** 70 min, 105 min
   m 6 L, 2 L   **n** 80 m, 64 m   **o** 440 g, 400 g

▪ If the first is bigger, the percentage is greater than 100%.

3 What percentage is the first quantity of the second?
   a 42 s, 1 min   **b** 3 min, 1 h   **c** 18 h, 1 day
   d 27 h, 1 day   **e** 14 cm, 2 m   **f** 650 mm, 80 cm
   g 2 m, 800 cm   **h** $3, 40c   **i** 20 men, 10 men
   j $1.80, $6   **k** 7000 g, 2 kg   **l** 35 m, 400 cm
   m 7·2 m, 800 cm **n** 26 kg, 1·3 t   **o** 40 g, 32 kg

▪ In each case the units must be made the same.

4 **a** A tin of fishcake mix contains 204 g of salmon, 156 g of potato, 24 g of seasoning and 16 g of cornflour. Find the percentage by weight of seasoning and of cornflour.
   b My Doggie dog food contains a minimum of 8·0% crude protein, a maximum of 0·5% crude fibre and 0·3% salt. If the tin contains 380 g (the net mass):
      i what is the mass of salt in the tin?
      ii what is the least amount of crude protein that might be in the tin?
      iii what is the greatest amount of crude fibre that might be in the tin?
   c A 420 g (net) tin of corn kernels contains sweet corn, water, salt, and 4·2 g of added sugar. What percentage of the contents of the tin is added sugar?
   d In an 800 g tin of Cream of Mushroom soup, there is 6·2 g of protein, 20·7 g of fat, 34 g of carbohydrate, 0·4 g of sugars, 3·43 g of sodium and 150 mg of potassium.
   Find the percentage in the tin (correct to 2 decimal places of a per cent) of:
      i carbohydrate   **ii** fat   **iii** sugars

e Because of safety regulations only 600 people were permitted into the basketball stadium for the final between Midlands Secondary College and Sebastapol Secondary College. Team members (including coaches and umpires) accounted for 24 of these people, while there were 321 female spectators. The rest of the crowd were male spectators. Find the percentage composition of those present.

The percentage composition is the percentage of each group present.

f Mrs Morris, the school principal, interviewed 40 of the students who left last year. Only 7 did not have a job. Find:
   i the percentage who did not have a job
   ii the percentage who did have a job

g Interest of €840 was charged on a loan of €6000. What percentage of the loan is the interest?

h Mr and Mrs Taylor decided to sell their home for $750 000. They paid the estate agent $26 250 to sell the home. What percentage is this of the selling price?

i A time-and-motion study was carried out to determine how a secretary spent 8 hours at work in one day. The results were: typing 3 h, filing $1\frac{1}{2}$ h, sorting mail 30 min, telephone 15 min, meetings 45 min, other activities 2 h. Find the percentage composition for the activities of this 8-hour period.

j Use the information below to find the total number of people employed in each industry. Find the percentage of the total number employed in each industry. (Give percentages correct to 1 decimal place.)

(000) means 'thousands'.

EMPLOYED PERSONS BY INDUSTRY				
	Number (000)			
Industry	Males	Females	Persons	% of total
Agriculture, forestry, fishing and hunting	284·7	109·0	393·7	5·9
Mining	86·5	7·2		
Manufacturing	841·5	295·5		
Food beverages and tobacco	123·6	51·7		
Metal products	175·2	28·0		
Other manufacturing	542·7	215·7		
Electricity, gas and water	121·9	11·1		
Construction	422·8	62·2		
Wholesale and retail trade	738·8	579·7		
Transport and storage	308·7	57·1		
Communication	107·0	39·8		
Finance, property and business services	351·2	301·0		
Public administration and defence	202·9	121·0		
Community services	425·3	715·6		
Recreation, personal and other services	192·4	249·4		
Total	4083·8	2548·5	6632·3	100%

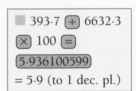

393·7 ÷ 6632·3
× 100 =
5·936100599
= 5·9 (to 1 dec. pl.)

3:07 | Percentage Change

1 What percentage do you have if you decrease 100% by 40%?
2 What percentage do you have if you decrease 100% by 13%?
3 What percentage do you have if you increase 100% by 18%?
4 What percentage do you have if you increase 100% by 300%?
5 100% − 20%   6 100% + 125%
7 100% + 6%   8 100% − 4%
9 85% of 200   10 115% of 200

- 'Decrease' means make smaller.
- 'Increase' means make bigger.

My Dad says he'll change my allowance by 25%....

INCREASE?   DECREASE?

$5 + 25% of $5
= (100% + 25%) of $5
= 125% of $5
= 1·25 × $5
= $6.25

1·25 ⊗ 5 ＝ 6·25

$5 − 25% of $5
= (100% − 25%) of $5
= 75% of $5
= 0·75 × $5
= $3.75

0·75 ⊗ 5 ＝ 3·75

To increase an amount by 15%, find 115% of the amount (ie 100% + 15% = 115%).
To decrease an amount by 15%, find 85% of the amount (ie 100% − 15% = 85%).

Exercise 3:07

Foundation Worksheet 3:07

Percentage change
1 Change to a decimal:
  a 13%   b 103%
2 Use a calculator to find:
  a 0·13 × $400   b 1·03 × $400
3 Use the method in Question 2
  to find:
  a 13% of $400 b 103% of $400

1 What percentage of an amount must I find
if I wish to increase the amount by:
a 25%?   b 15%?   c 10%?   d 9%?
e 100%?   f 300%?   g 155%?   h 132%?

2 What percentage of an amount must I find,
if I wish to decrease the amount by:
a 25%?   b 15%?   c 10%?   d 9%?
e 1%?   f 95%?   g 37%?   h 30%?

3
a Increase $800 by 10%. b Increase $300 by 20%.
c Increase 5 m by 16%. d Increase 4 L by 12%.
e Increase 60 g by 85%. f Increase 70 t by 42%.
g Increase 10 kg by 4%. h Increase 30 ha by 6%.
i Increase 56 h by 100%. j Increase 81 s by 200%.

4
a Decrease $60 by 20%. b Decrease $360 by 80%.
c Decrease 8 m by 14%. d Decrease 3 m by 37%.
e Decrease 3·25 m by 40%. f Decrease 9·5 L by 30%.
g Decrease 20 kg by 5%. h Decrease 800 mm by 4%.
i Decrease 4 t by 23%. j Decrease 588 L by 90%.

5 To determine the selling price (retail price) of anything to be sold in her shop, June increased (marked up) the cost price (wholesale price) by 45%. Find the selling price for each of the following articles.
a jacket: cost price $90 b scarf: cost price $8
c hat: cost price £30 d belt: cost price $12
e dress: cost price $200 f blouse: cost price €57

6 After a long hearing in a wage case, the court awarded an increase of 4% in all wages. Find to the nearest cent the new wage paid to a person who was earning:
a $400 b $360 c $2111
d $304.21 e $856.22 f $1041.80

7 In a sale all marked prices were reduced by 30%. Find the sale price for each of these items.

a

Was $475

b

Was $860

c

Was $595

8 Last year a new Geomobile cost $24 800 but because of inflation its price has risen by 11%. What is the new price?

9 Margaret and Peter purchased timber to build the frame of their house. They purchased 342 metres of timber. If wastage was 8%, what length of timber was actually used in the frame?

10 To relieve famine in Africa, 53 000 tonnes of food was sent by ship. If 35% of the food was spoilt at sea, how much food could be used for famine relief?

11 The population of Carbi in 2003 was 149 600. It was expected then that by the year 2009 the population would have increased by 19%. What was the expected population of Carbi for the year 2009?

12 Jacky is in the school swim squad and needs to increase his training to stay in the team. At the start of the semester he could swim 4000 metres in a session. He has increased this by 64%. How far can he now swim in a session?

13 The value of my car depreciated 18% this year. If its value was $8640, what is its value now?

'Depreciation' means 'a loss in value'.

14 Emma wished to buy books to the value of $87.50. Because she is a regular customer, she was given a discount (reduction) of 16%. How much did she pay?

15 Lorraine purchased $1200 worth of shares. Within a month their value had dropped by 20%. During the following month there was an increase in the value of the shares by 20%. What was the value of the shares at the end of the second month? Why was this not $1200?

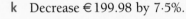

Use a calculator for these, giving answers accurate to two decimal places.

16 a Increase $248.60 by 84%. b Increase €946.85 by 74%.
 c Increase ¥99.85 by 29%. d Increase $465.35 by 147%.
 e Increase €88.95 by 12.5%. f Increase £475.64 by $135\frac{1}{2}$%.
 g Decrease $6.75 by 18%. h Decrease ¥73.45 by 81%.
 i Decrease £0.94 by 35%. j Decrease $138.97 by 68%.
 k Decrease €199.98 by 7·5%. l Decrease ¥384.66 by $18\frac{1}{2}$%.

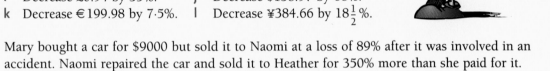

17 Mary bought a car for $9000 but sold it to Naomi at a loss of 89% after it was involved in an accident. Naomi repaired the car and sold it to Heather for 350% more than she paid for it. What price did Heather pay for the car?

18 Since the Betting Agent takes 15% of all bets made on a race, a person placing the same amount of money on every horse in a race could expect to lose 15% of his investment. Mixed-up Maurice wanted to boast that he backed the winner of each of the 7 races on the program. For the first race he invested $1000, dividing this up so that he placed the same amount on each horse. He invested his return on the second in the same way and continued doing this until all 7 races were over. Calculate how much money he had left at the end of 7 races if he lost 15% of his investment on each race? (Use a calculator and answer to the nearest dollar.)

3:08 | Further Applications of Percentages

1 52% of students are boys. What percentage are girls?

2 0·7 = 70%. True or false?   **3** 82% of $1

4 $\frac{a}{50} = 14\%$ ∴ $a = \ldots$ **5** $\frac{x}{10} = 40\%$ ∴ $x = \ldots$

6 Write 32% as a decimal.

7 Increase $30 by 100%.   **8** Reduce $30 by 100%.

9 What fraction of 8 m is 8 cm?   **10** What percentage of 8 m is 8 cm?

People who use mathematics are not always honest. Percentages are often misused to create an impression or to sell a product.

Exercise 3:08

1 One store advertises golf clubs for '20% off'. Another advertises the same clubs for '30% off'. Do we know which shop is cheaper? Why or why not?

2 At a football match 80% of people interviewed said that they were in favour of capital punishment. If only 5 people were interviewed, how many of these were in favour of capital punishment? Had enough people been asked to find out what Australians think about this?

3 Shifty Discounts had trouble selling their watches for $6, so they increased the price to $10 and advertised the watches at '30% off their marked price'. What was the new selling price of the watches?

4 Two stores advertised the same range of books. Honest Anne offered '20% off the publisher's recommended price'. Fair Freddie offered 'up to 50% off the publisher's recommended price'.

 A *discount* is a reduction from the normal selling price.

   a At Honest Anne's I bought books with a total marked price of £120. What price did I pay after getting the 20% discount?

   b At Fair Freddie's I bought the same books and was given 10% off on £100, and 50% off on £20. How much did I pay for the books altogether?

   c Which shop was the cheapest and by how much?

5 Screen doors marked at $98.50 were discounted by 40% if five or more doors were purchased. Shirley needed one screen door but couldn't resist this bargain. She bought five doors. How much did they cost? Did she really save money?

6 The book *Maths is Wonderful* was advertised at '$15.80 with a 10% discount' or '$20.40 with a 35% discount'. Which of these is the cheaper, and by how much?

■ When percentages are used, ask:
- 'Have I been told the full story?'
- 'How did they get their percentages?'

7 A TV commercial claimed that 'Only 4% of people disliked our drink Fizz'. It did not give the information in the table below.

Reaction to Fizz	Number
disliked	24
not impressed	540
liked	36

a What percentage liked Fizz?
b What percentage were not impressed with Fizz?
c Why didn't the advertiser use the percentages in **a** and **b**?

8 A discount of $84 was given on a CD player with a marked price of $280. Find:
a the price paid
b the discount as a percentage of the marked price.

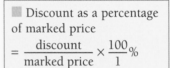

■ Discount as a percentage of marked price

$$= \frac{discount}{marked\ price} \times \frac{100}{1}\%$$

Profit and Loss

When buying and selling: **Selling price = cost price + profit**

OR

Selling price = cost price − loss

9 Complete the table below.

	Cost price	Profit or loss	Selling price
a	$176	$8.80 profit	
b	$460	$92 loss	
c	$1.80	$0.63 profit	
d		$5000 loss	$25 000
e		$4.20 profit	$42
f		$2560 loss	$8000
g	$1680		$4800

10 For Parts **a** to **d** of Question **9**, find the profit or loss as a percentage of the cost price.

11 For Parts **d** to **g** of Question **9**, find the profit or loss as a percentage of the selling price.

12 James bought an old coin for $5 and later sold it for $10. Find:
a his profit from the sale
b the profit as a percentage of the cost price
c the profit as a percentage of the selling price.

worked example

John bought a painting for $600 and sold it for $648. Find the profit as a percentage of the cost.

Solution

Profit = selling price − cost
$\quad\quad$ = $648 − $600
$\quad\quad$ = $48

Profit as a % of cost

$= \dfrac{profit}{cost\ price} \times \dfrac{100}{1}\%$

$= \dfrac{48^8}{600_6} \times \dfrac{100^1}{1}\%$

$= 8\%$

∴ profit is 8% of cost.

13 Heather paid $640 for her wedding dress. After the wedding, she sold the dress to her friend Sarah for $400. Find:
   a Heather's loss from the sale
   b the loss as a percentage of the cost price
   c the loss as a percentage of the selling price.

14 Alan bought some land for ¥4 million and later sold it, making a profit of 20% on his cost. Find:
   a the profit   **b** the selling price
   c the profit as a percentage of the selling price.

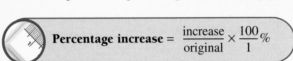

$$\textbf{Percentage increase} = \frac{\text{increase}}{\text{original}} \times \frac{100}{1}\%$$

15 John began the year with 6 rabbits and ended the year with 18 rabbits.
   a What was the increase?
   b What percentage is this increase of the original amount?
   c What percentage is this increase of the final amount?

16 The number of books in Rhonda's library 5 years ago was 3800. Today it is 11 600.
   a What is the increase in the number of books?
   b What is the percentage increase over the 5 years?
   c What percentage is the increase of the present number of books?

---

investigation

3:08

Investigation 3:08 | Are percentages ever misused?

Please use the Assessment Grid on the following page to help you understand what is required for this Investigation.

1 Collect three examples of media reports or advertising claims that use percentages.
   a State how reliable you think each percentage is.
   b State whether the truth of the figure can be tested or assessed and, if so, explain how this could be done.
   c Judge whether useful information may not have been given. List things you could have been told but were not.
2 Make a collection of examples where it is possible that percentages have been misused. Share your results with others.
3 Find the interest earned for different investments in banks, building societies and elsewhere. Find the interest charged by banks, building societies, finance companies and elsewhere. How do these compare?

Assessment Grid for Investigation 3:08 | **Are percentages ever misused?**

The following is a sample assessment grid for this investigation. You should carefully read the criteria *before* beginning the investigation so that you know what is required.

Assessment Criteria (B, C, D)				Achieved ✓
Criterion B Investigating Patterns	a	Appropriate examples have been collected.	1	
			2	
	b	Appropriate examples have been collected and comments made on the reliability of the percentages.	3	
			4	
	c	Examples have been described where percentages have been misused.	5	
			6	
	d	Reasons why the percentages gathered are either unreliable or have been misused are given and a description of how they could be tested is given.	7	
			8	
Criterion C Communication	a	Some explanation of the reliability of the percentages is given.	1	
			2	
	b	A full explanation of the reliability of the percentages is given and a judgment has been made on whether information was missing.	3	
			4	
	c	Judgments are fully explained and a list of information which could have been added to the percentages is included.	5	
			6	
Criterion D Reflection in Mathematics	a	An attempt has been made to explain why/how the percentages are misused.	1	
			2	
	b	A justified explanation of how the percentages are misused is given and some discussion of the missing information is made.	3	
			4	
	c	Reasonable examples of information that could help make the percentages in the student's examples more reliable are given, and the reason for choosing the missing information is justified.	5	
			6	

3:09 | Commission and Simple Interest

A salesperson is often given a *commission* (which is usually a percentage of the value of goods sold) as payment for selling the goods.

The harder I work, the more I am paid.

worked example

Csaba was given a commission of 6% on the first $20 000 of sales made and 4% on sales in excess of $20 000. How much commission would he make on sales of:

a $18 500? **b** $365 000?

Solution

a $18 500 is less than $20 000.
∴ Commission = 6% of $18 500
   = $1110

b Csaba will earn 6% of the first $20 000 and 4% of the rest.
∴ Commission = 6% of $20 000 + 4% of ($365 000 − $20 000)
   = $1200 + $13 800
   = $15 000

...that's only if you sell something people want to buy...

Interest can be a charge for money borrowed or a payment for money invested.
For *simple interest*, equal payments are made for equal time periods. (*Note:* p.a. means per year.)
Simple interest = number of years × interest for one year.

worked example

I was able to borrow $36 400 at 8·5% simple interest for 4 years. How much interest did I pay altogether?

Solution

Interest for one year = 8·5% × $36 400
∴ interest for 4 years = 4 × (8·5% × $36 400)
   = $12 376

WAGES UP BY 5%

BANK WITH US! 8% p.a.

Exercise 3:09

1 Calculate the commission given to each salesperson below if 8% commission was given on sales made.

a Jan: $360 sales **b** Ron: $3400 sales
c Irene: $4200 sales **d** Chad: $1160 sales

2 An estate agent charged a commission of 6% on the first $15 000 of a sale and 2% on the balance of money received. He sold a house for $135 000. Find:

  a his commission on the first $15 000 of the sale

  b his commission on the remaining $120 000

  c his total commission for the sale.

3 Elizabeth is offered a sales position with a retainer (which is a guaranteed wage) of $200 plus commission of 3% on sales. How much would she receive in one week if she had total sales for the week of:

  a $1200?   **b** $4850?   **c** $11 465?

4 Find the simple interest earned on:

  a ¥800 at 11% p.a. for 1 year

  b €800 at 11% p.a. for 3 years

  c $450 at 9% p.a. for 1 year

  d £450 at 9% p.a. for 5 years

  e €25 000 at 15% p.a. for 1 year

  f $25 000 at 15% p.a. for 8 years

  g $7000 at 13·5% p.a. for 1 year

  h ¥7000 at 13·5% p.a. for 4 years

  i $1850 at 8% p.a. for 1 year

  j £1850 at 8% p.a. for 18 years

worked example

Find the simple interest on $600 at 11% p.a. for:

  a 1 year   **b** 3 years

Solution

a Interest for 1 year
= 11% of $600
= 0·11 × $600
= $66

b Interest for 3 years
= 3 × (interest for 1 year)
= 3 × $66
= $198

5 Scrooge agreed to lend Donald $80 000 if he paid him 14% p.a. simple interest. How much interest would Donald pay in:

  a 1 year?   **b** 3 years?   **c** 8 years?

p.a. means 'per annum'.

6 Minnie invested her savings of $2800 with the bank for 5 years at a rate of 13% p.a. simple interest, with the interest to be paid at the end of each year. How much interest would she have received after:

  a 1 year?   **b** 3 years?   **c** 8 years?

7 Find the percentage rate of simple interest if:

  a an investment of $1200 earns $96 interest in 1 year

  b an investment of $1500 earns $360 interest in 2 years

  c an investment of $28 000 earns $22 400 interest in 5 years.

SALE! UP TO 60% OFF ALL STOCK!

POPULATION UP by 5%

REDUCED BY 20%

3:10 | Finding a Quantity if a Percentage is Known (Extension)

Discussion

The same kind of coin has been placed on 12 of the 100 squares on this percentage chart. If the value of these coins is 60 cents, how much money would be needed to cover every square with the same kind of coin?
- What is the value of 12 coins?
- What is the value of 1 coin?
- What is the value of 100 coins?

> If a percentage of a quantity is known, to find the quantity we first find 1% (or 10%), then multiply to find 100% (the whole quantity).

worked examples

1. I spent 8% of my money on a new graphite tennis racquet which cost $108. How much money did I have before the purchase?

2. In a basketball game Tien scored 38 of his team's points. If this was 35% of their points, what was his team's final score?

Solutions

1.
$$8\% \text{ of my money} = \$108$$
$$\therefore 1\% \text{ of my money} = \$108 \div 8$$
$$= \$13.50$$
$$\therefore 100\% \text{ of my money} = \$13.50 \times 100$$
$$= \$1350$$
$$\therefore \text{ I had } \$1350 \text{ before the purchase.}$$

2.
$$35\% \text{ of the score} = 38$$
$$\therefore 1\% \text{ of the score} = 38 \div 5$$
$$\therefore 100\% \text{ of the score} = 38 \div 35 \times 100$$

Exercise 3:10

Foundation Worksheet 3:10

Finding the quantity if a percentage is known
1 50% of my mass is 35 kg. What is my mass?
2 10% of my money is $5. How much do I have?

1. Determine the size of a quantity if:
   a 4% of it is 20 m   b 3% of it is 813 ha   c 30% of it is 27 kg
   d 80% of it is 2800 t   e 28% of it is $29.12   f 94% of it is $564
   g 120% of it is 840 mm   h 112% of it is $115.36

2. I spent 12% of my money on a surfboard which cost $468. How much money did I have?

3. If I. Beltem scored 32 runs in a one-day cricket match and this was 16% of his team's runs, how many runs did his team score?

4. The 132 injuries occurring on sports fields in December represented 11% of the year's total injuries on sports fields. How many injuries occurred in the year?

5. Emma raised $238.55 for the Girls' Friendly Society at Springvale. If this represented 13% of all money raised in the Bicentennial year, how much was raised that year?

Fun Spot 3:10 | Why did the hen feed her chickens concrete?

Work out the answer to each question and put the letter for that part in any box that is the correct answer.

A Write 1% as a decimal.

B Write 10% as a fraction.

C Write $\frac{4}{5}$ as a percentage.

D Write $1\frac{1}{4}$ as a percentage.

E Write 1 as a percentage.

H Write 205% as a decimal.

I 1% of 100

K 200% of 1

L If $16\frac{2}{3}\% = \frac{1}{6}$, what fraction is $8\frac{1}{3}\%$?

M How many metres is 5% of 2 km?

N 5 men, 3 women and 2 children are in a bus. What is the percentage of women?

O What percentage has been coloured?

R The cost price is $100. The profit is 10% of the cost price. What is the selling price?

S The cost price is $100. The loss is 10% of the cost price. What is the selling price?

T $200 was invested at 10% p.a. simple interest for 3 years. How much interest was earned?

W 5% + 8%

Y 100% − 17%

$90	2·05	100%	13%	0·01	30%	$60	100%	125%	$60	2·05	100%	100	$60	75%

$\frac{1}{10}$	100%	80%	75%	100	100%	$\frac{1}{10}$	$110	1	80%	2	$\frac{1}{12}$	0·01	83%	100%	$110	$90

Mathematical terms 3

commission
- A sum or percentage paid to a salesperson for making the sale.

cost price
- The money paid for an item before reselling.

depreciation
- The loss of value as time passes.

discount
- A deduction from the normal selling price.

interest
- A payment or charge for borrowing or investing money.
- *Simple interest*: The same interest is paid in each time period.

loss
- Occurs when the selling price is less than the cost price.

marked price
- The price shown on the tag or advertising.
- The original selling price.

per annum (or p.a.)
- Each year.
  eg 25% p.a. means 25% each year.

percentage
- Out of 100.
  eg 17% means 17 out of 100.

percentage increase
- The percentage by which an amount has increased.

percentage decrease
- The percentage by which an amount has decreased.

percentage composition
- The percentages of parts that make up the whole.

profit (or gain)
- Occurs when the selling price is more than the cost price.

selling price
- The price paid when an item is purchased.

Mathematical terms 3

- Estimate the percentage of the earth's surface that is habitable.
- Estimate the percentage of the earth's surface that is able to be cultivated.
(The answers are at the end of this chapter.)

Diagnostic Test 3: | Percentages

- Each section of the test has similar items that test a certain type of example.
- Failure in more than one item will identify an area of weakness.
- Each weakness should be treated by going back to the section listed.

	Section
1 Change to fractions or mixed numerals in simplest form: a 9% b 48% c 350%	3:01
2 Change to percentages: a $\frac{173}{100}$ b $\frac{11}{25}$ c $3\frac{1}{7}$	3:01
3 Change to decimals: a 17% b 4% c 106%	3:01
4 Change to percentages: a 0·22 b 0·9 c 3·7	3:01
5 Estimate the percentage coloured to the nearest 10% if each whole is 100%. a b 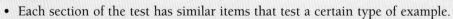	3:02
6 Change to decimals: a 13·8% b $6\frac{1}{4}\%$ c $87\frac{1}{2}\%$	3:03
7 Change to percentages: a 0·125 b 1·625 c $\frac{1}{6}$	3:03
8 Find: a 8% of 1600 g b 3% of 7 km c 120% of 12 L	3:04
9 a Express 4 g as a percentage of 25 g. b What percentage is 51 s of 2 min? c A tin of fishcake mix contains 204 g of Australian salmon, 156 g of potato, 24 g of seasoning and 16 g of cornflour. Find the percentage by weight of salmon.	3:06
10 a Increase $5 by 15%. b Decrease $5 by 15%. c Increase $70 by 42%.	3:07
11 a 15% discount is given on a pen that has a marked price of $8. How much must be paid for the pen? b A car is bought for $8000 and sold for $8500. What is the profit as a percentage of the cost price?	3:08
12 a Sue was given a commission of 6% when she sold goods to the value of $650. How much did she receive? b Find the simple interest earned on $800 invested at 12% p.a. for 3 years.	3:09

Chapter 3 | Revision Assignment

1 Perform the following conversions.
   a 7·5 L to mL   b 400 L to mL
   c 14 000 mL to L   d 2100 L to kL

2 Simplify:
   a $4 - 10$ b $-2 + 3$ c $-4 - 6$
   d $-4 \div -2$ e 10×-2

3 Draw a number lattice with scales from −5 to 5 on both axes. Plot the points (0, 5); (2, −3); (−2, −3); (−4, 1); (1, 4).

4 Write the following, showing all multiplication and division signs.
   a $3a$ b $4m + 2n$ c $5(x + y)$
   d $\dfrac{a}{5}$ e $\dfrac{3m}{2}$

5 If $a = 5$ and $b = 3$, evaluate:
   a $4a$ b $5b + 3$
   c $\dfrac{(a + b)}{2}$ d $a^2 + b^2$

6 If $21 \times 72 = 1512$, write down the answers to:
   a $2·1 \times 7·2$ b $21 \times 7·2$
   c $0·21 \times 7·2$

7 Write each of the following in index notation.
   a $a \times a \times a \times a \times a$ b $10 \times 10 \times 10$
   c $a \times a \times a \times b \times b$ d $4 \times p \times p \times 3 \times p$

8 Expand each of the following.
   a $5(a + 4)$ b $2(2a + 3)$
   c $4(m - 5)$ d $a(2b - 3)$

9 a Write down the factors of 36.
   b Write down the factors of 54.
   c What is the highest common factor of 36 and 54?
   d Write down the first four multiples of 36 and 54, and then write down the lowest common multiple of 36 and 54.

Chapter 3 | Working Mathematically

1 Tom, Jim and Ed have a race. In how many different orders could they finish the race, assuming that no dead heats are possible?

2 Tom, Jim, Ed and Jan have a race. In how many different orders could they finish the race, assuming that no dead heats are possible?

3 Heather had one pair of cats. These had six kittens, three of which were female. Within the following year each young female had 5 kittens, while the old female had two more litters of 6. If no cats died, how many would Heather have at the end of that year period?

4 It took Dad 7 minutes to join two pieces of pipe to make one length of pipe. How long would it take him to join 10 pieces of pipe to make one length of pipe?

5 Thirty students were waiting in line while Mrs Foster selected some to assist visiting parents. She chose the second student and every fourth after that. How many students were selected?

6 A seven-digit number is formed from the digits 1, 2, 3, 4, 5, 6 and 7. What are the third-largest and third-smallest numbers that can be formed?

1 **Writing fractions as decimals**
2 **Percentages to fractions and decimals**
3 **Fractions and decimals to percentages**

Technology
Applications

Drag and Drops

Chapter Review

Questions

Answers to questions on page 58:
• 15% of the earth's surface is habitable.
• 10% of the earth's surface is able to be cultivated.

4

Ratio, Rates and Scale Drawing

Chapter Contents

Learning Outcomes

Students will be able to operate with fractions, decimals, percentages, ratios and rates.

Areas of Interaction

Approaches to Learning (Knowledge Acquisition, Problem Solving, Thinking Skills), Health and Social Education, Environments, Community and Service, Human Ingenuity

4:01 | Ratio

Examples of ratio are found in many real-life situations. One such situation occurs when you have to add water to a juice concentrate to make up a fruit drink.

So that's what 'watering it down' means.

The instructions on this juice packet say: 'Mix 1 part juice with 3 parts water'.

This example illustrates many of the important aspects of ratio.

- First, a ratio is a comparison of two like quantities. In this example we are comparing the **volume** of juice that needs to be mixed with the **volume** of water.

  The relative sizes of the numbers give the correct sweetness to the drink. Varying the numbers in the ratio will give either a sweeter drink or a watered-down drink.

- Second, the order of the numbers in the comparison is important. If the instructions read '3 parts juice with 1 part water', this would not be the same as '1 part juice with 3 parts water'.

- Notice that there is no mention of units. The word 'parts' is used to indicate that whatever units are used to measure the juice must also be used to measure the water. The size of the unit or measure is not important.

So:
- 1 litre of juice would need 3 litres of water, *or*
- 500 millilitres of juice would need 3 × 500 millilitres of water, *or*
- 100 millilitres of juice would need 3 × 100 millilitres of water, and so on.

I get it! The size of the container is not important as long as you use the same container to measure the juice and the water.

To write this ratio down we could write:
- ratio of juice to water = 1 : 3, *or*
- ratio of water to juice = 3 : 1.

Alternatively we could write it in fraction form:
- ratio of juice to water = $\frac{1}{3}$, *or*
- ratio of water to juice = $\frac{3}{1}$

1 bucket of juice would need 3 × 1 buckets of water.

A *ratio* is a comparison of numbers in a definite order. The numbers are expressed in the same units and are called the *terms* of the ratio. The ratio can be written in the form *a : b* or $\frac{a}{b}$ or *a to b*.

1 Jill says to Jack: 'My fish is six times as long as your fish'. Jill is comparing the length of her fish to the length of Jack's fish.
  a Write down the ratio of:
     i the length of Jill's fish to the length of Jack's fish
     ii the length of Jack's fish to the length of Jill's fish.
  b Does Jill's statement tell us the actual length of either fish?

6 : 1 is read as '6 to 1'

Solution
  a If Jack's fish is 1 unit long, then Jill's fish is 6 units long. So the ratio of:
     i the length of Jill's fish to the length of Jack's fish = 6 : 1
     ii the length of Jack's fish to the length of Jill's fish = 1 : 6.
  b Jill's statement does not tell us anything about the actual lengths of the two fish. All it says is that whatever the length of Jack's fish, her fish is six times longer. If we know the length of either fish we could work out the length of the other.

2 Bronte buys a guinea pig for \$2 and later sells it for \$3. Find the ratio of her:
  a selling price to cost price
  b selling price to profit
  c cost price to profit
  d cost price to profit to selling price

Solution
Now, selling price = cost price + profit.
$$\therefore \text{ cost price} = \$2$$
$$\text{profit} = \$1$$
$$\text{selling price} = \$3$$
  a selling price : cost price = $3 : 2$ or $\frac{3}{2}$
  b selling price : profit = $3 : 1$ or $\frac{3}{1}$
  c cost price : profit = $2 : 1$ or $\frac{2}{1}$
  d cost price : profit : selling price = $2 : 1 : 3$

If there are only 2 terms in the ratio, it can be written as a fraction.

We can use ratios to compare more than 2 numbers.
eg I earned \$A in week 1, \$B in week 2 and \$C in week 3.
Ratio of earnings of week 1 : week 2 : week 3 = A : B : C

1 Liam says that he has four times as much money as Bronwyn.
  a What is the ratio of:
   i Liam's amount of money to Bronwyn's amount of money?
   ii Bronwyn's amount of money to Liam's amount of money?
  b Do we know the amount of money that Liam or Bronwyn actually has?

2 'I can lift twice as much as you', says Milla to Dominic.
  a Do we actually know how much either person can lift?
  b What is the ratio of:
   i the amount that Milla can lift to the amount that Dominic can lift?
   ii the amount that Dominic can lift to the amount that Milla can lift?

3 The ratio of cement to sand in a mortar mix is $1:4$ (1 part cement to 4 parts sand).
  a What fraction of the mortar is cement?
  b What fraction of the mortar is sand?

4 A particular paint colour, 'Sunset', is made by mixing red and yellow paints.
  a If $\frac{3}{5}$ of 'Sunset' is red, what fraction of 'Sunset' is yellow?
  b What is the ratio of red paint to yellow paint in 'Sunset'?

5 Kylie buys chickens for $3 and sells them for $5. Find the ratio of:
  a selling price to cost price   **b** selling price to profit
  c cost price to profit   **d** profit to selling price
  e cost price to profit to selling price.

6 A class contains 14 boys and 16 girls.
  a What is the ratio of boys to girls?
  b What is the ratio of girls to boys?
  c What is the ratio of boys to the total number of students in the class?
  d What fraction of the class is boys?
  e What is the ratio of girls to the total number of students in the class?
  f What fraction of the class is girls?

7 A breeder of parrots notes that the colours of birds born are in the ratio
   yellow : blue : other colours $= 5:3:2$.
  a What colour is the most common?
  b What colour is the least common?
  c What fraction of the birds is yellow?
  d What fraction of the birds is blue?
  e What is the ratio of blue birds to the total number of birds?

8 Concrete is made by mixing cement, sand and gravel in the ratio $1:2:4$.
  a What fraction of concrete is cement?
  b What fraction of concrete is gravel?
  c What is the ratio of cement to gravel?
  d What is the ratio of sand to gravel?
  e If we use 1 kg of cement, how much gravel should we use?

Ratios can
have more than
two terms.

9 What is the ratio of:
   a a centimetre to a millimetre?   **b** a metre to a centimetre?
   c a kilogram to a gram?   **d** a litre to a millilitre?
   e a minute to a second?

10 The line below is divided into ten equal parts.

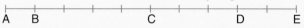

A   B   C   D   E

Find the ratios:

   a $\dfrac{AB}{AE}$ **b** $\dfrac{AB}{BC}$ **c** $\dfrac{AE}{AB}$ **d** $\dfrac{CD}{CB}$ **e** $\dfrac{CD}{AE}$

11 One-third of a class is girls.
   a What fraction of the class is boys?
   b What is the ratio of boys to girls?
   c What is the ratio of girls to boys?

12 What is the ratio of:
   a length of rectangle A to length of rectangle B?
   b width of rectangle A to width of rectangle B?
   c area of rectangle A to area of rectangle B?

13 The correct sweetness for a drink is obtained by mixing cordial and water in the ratio of $1:3$.
   a If the ratio of cordial to water were $1:4$, would the drink be sweeter than if it were mixed properly?
   b Bill mixes water and cordial in the ratio $2:1$. Would his drink be sweeter or watered down compared to the proper mixture?

I hope I get the ratios right next time...

14 **a** A pink-coloured paint is made by mixing red and white in the ratio of $1:5$. If the red and white paints were mixed in the ratio $1:8$, would the paint be lighter or darker than the original?
   b Cement mortar is made by mixing sand and cement in the ratio $5:2$. Stronger mortar is made by increasing the fraction of cement in the mixture. If the ratio of sand to cement in a mix were $7:2$, would this be stronger or weaker than the mix mentioned above?

You can increase the ratio by using more cement.

4:02 | Equivalent Ratios

In comparing two quantities we often do not know the actual size of either. For example, the statement 'My fish is twice as long as yours' only gives us the **relative** sizes of the two fish. There are an infinite number of actual ratios that could describe this situation, such as:

a 16 cm : 8 cm   **b** 10 cm : 5 cm   **c** 1 m : $\frac{1}{2}$ m

In all of these, the first term is twice the second term, and the simplest ratio to express this relationship is 2 : 1. In this way the set of ratios behaves like the set of equivalent fractions, $\frac{16}{8}$, $\frac{10}{5}$, etc, so we can simplify ratios in the same way that we simplify fractions.

> **If the terms of a ratio are multiplied or divided by any number (except zero), an *equivalent ratio* is formed.**

worked examples

1 Are the ratios 3 : 1 and 12 : 10 equivalent?

2 Simplify these ratios:
    a 15 : 12   **b** 3·5 : 1·5   **c** 3 : $\frac{1}{2}$
    d $2\frac{1}{3}$: 1   **e** 1 m : 20 cm

3 A school has 650 girls and 500 boys. What is the ratio of boys to girls?

Simplifying ratios is just like simplifying fractions.

Solutions

1 $3 : 1 = \frac{3}{1}$ and $12 : 10 = \frac{12}{10}$

$\frac{3}{1} = \frac{3 \times 4}{1 \times 4} = \frac{12}{4}$ not $\frac{12}{10}$

∴ 3 : 1 and 12 : 10 are not equivalent.

2 a 15 : 12   or   15 : 12

$= \frac{15}{3} : \frac{12}{3}$ $= \frac{15}{12}$

$= 5 : 4$ $= \frac{5}{4}$

               $= 5 : 4$

b 3·5 : 1·5

$= \frac{3\cdot5 \, (\times 10)}{1\cdot5 \, (\times 10)}$

$= \frac{35 \, (\div 5)}{15 \, (\div 5)}$

$= \frac{7}{3}$

$= 7 : 3$

c 3 : $\frac{1}{2}$

$= 3 \times 2 : \frac{1}{2} \times 2$

$= 6 : 1$

d $2\frac{1}{3}$: 1

$= \frac{7}{3} : \frac{3}{3}$

$= 7 : 3$

e 1 m : 20 cm
(Change to the same units.)

$= 100 \, cm : 20 \, cm$

$= \frac{100}{20} : \frac{20}{20}$

$= 5 : 1$

3 boys : girls $= 500 : 650$

$= \frac{500}{50} : \frac{650}{50}$

$= 10 : 13$

1 Copy and complete the following.

a $2:1 = 6:\square$ b $15:1 = 30:\square$ c $1:4 = 20:\square$ d $2:3 = 6:\square$

e $9:5 = \square:15$ f $3:13 = \square:52$ g $3:4 = \square:12$ h $6:5 = \square:20$

i $6:4 = 3:\square$ j $9:3 = 3:\square$ k $12:8 = 3:\square$ l $20:6 = 10:\square$

m $10:15 = \square:3$ n $24:36 = \square:3$ o $48:100 = \square:20$ p $35:120 = \square:24$

2 Simplify the following ratios.

a $15:5$ b $10:30$ c $24:16$ d $16:30$

e $25:75$ f $120:8$ g $100:10$ h $100:1000$

i $66:11$ j $12:72$ k $8:20$ l $320:48$

m $8:96$ n $14:49$ o $30:42$ p $15:200$

q $27:18$ r $40:72$ s $\frac{5}{15}$ t $\frac{20}{5}$

u $\frac{16}{40}$ v $\frac{100}{45}$ w $\frac{24}{36}$ x $\frac{42}{12}$

3 Simplify the following ratios after first changing to the same units.

a $3\,\text{cm}:1\,\text{mm}$ b $5\,\text{cm}:20\,\text{mm}$ c $1\,\text{m}:50\,\text{cm}$

d $25\,\text{m}:1\,\text{km}$ e $1\cdot5\,\text{km}:200\,\text{m}$ f $3\cdot5\,\text{L}:500\,\text{mL}$

g $1\frac{1}{2}\,\text{h}:30\,\text{min}$ h $200\,\text{kg}:1\,\text{t}$ i $1\frac{1}{4}\,\text{min}:15\,\text{s}$

j $2\,\text{days}:6\,\text{h}$ k $\$5:50\text{c}:\$5.50$

Don't let decimals or fractions become a spanner in the works!

4 Simplify the following ratios.

a $1\cdot2:1$ b $3\cdot6:1\cdot2$ c $4\cdot5:6$

d $6\cdot25:1$ e $1\cdot2:6$ f $\frac{1}{2}:\frac{1}{10}$

g $\frac{1}{10}:\frac{1}{5}$ h $\frac{2}{3}:1$ i $1:\frac{3}{4}$

j $20:70:50$ k $8:4:12$

l $33:9:12$ m $100:65:35$

5 a In 7M there are 16 boys and 14 girls. What is the ratio of:
   i boys to girls?   ii girls to boys?
   iii boys to the total number in the class?
   iv boys to girls to the total number in the class?

b If a woman sells a pot for $60, thereby making a profit of $20, find the ratio of:
   i profit : cost price   ii selling price : cost price
   iii profit : selling price   iv cost : profit : selling price

c On a scale drawing 1 cm represents 1 m. Write this as a ratio.

d A store has a discount sale. A suit marked at €250 is sold for €200.
   i What is the ratio of the discount to the marked price?
   ii What is the ratio of the marked price to the discount to the selling price?

■ A discount is a reduction in price.

e Two business partners, Carol and Sharon, invest $4500 and $2500 each in a business.
   What is the ratio of Carol's share to Sharon's share?

f In an election, Bagnell scored 225 votes, Farrant 175 votes and McGregor 125 votes.
   Find the ratio of: Bagnell's votes : Farrant's votes : McGregor's votes.
   (Express this ratio in its simplest form.)

g An alloy is made by combining 2·5 kg of metal A with 1·5 kg of metal B and 2 kg of metal C. Find the ratio of the weights of:

   i metal A to metal B   **ii** metal B to metal C

   iii metal A to metal C   **iv** metal A to the alloy

   v metal A to metal B to metal C.

> **Note:**
> $2·5 : 1·5 : 2$
> (Multiply by 10)
> $= 25 : 15 : 20$

h On a map, a distance of 1·5 cm represents 5 km. What is the ratio of the distance on the map to the real distance?

6 Express each of the following ratios in the form of $a : 1$ by dividing both terms by the second term, eg $7 : 5 = \frac{7}{5} : \frac{5}{5} = 1·4 : 1$.

   a $16 : 5$ **b** $12 : 8$ **c** $9 : 12$ **d** $1·6 : 1·2$ **e** $0·2 : 0·8$

7 Express each of the following ratios in the form $1 : b$ by dividing both terms by the first term, eg $6 : 8 = \frac{6}{6} : \frac{8}{6} = 1 : 1\frac{1}{3}$.

   a $20 : 12$ **b** $16 : 8$ **c** $8 : 15$ **d** $1·5 : 6$ **e** $2·4 : 8·4$

Challenge 4:02 | How are you at mixing paint?

When green paint is mixed with white paint you get a light green colour. The more white you use, the lighter green you get.

4:02

            A   **B**

- If the paints in each picture were mixed, which mixture would give the darker green? Give a reason for your choice.

- Which of the reasons below are correct?

   a Batch **B** is a darker green because more green paint is used.

   b They are the same because you get **B** if you add one tin of green paint and one tin of white to batch **A**.

   c In **A**, for every green tin there are $1\frac{1}{2}$ white tins. In **B**, for every green tin there are $1\frac{1}{3}$ white tins. There is less white in **B** so it's a darker green.

   d $\frac{2}{5}$ of batch **A** is green. $\frac{3}{7}$ of batch **B** is green. $\frac{3}{7}$ is greater than $\frac{2}{5}$ so **B** is the darker green.

   e To batch **A** add half as much paint again. We then have 3 green and $4\frac{1}{2}$ white. In batch **B** we have 3 green and 4 white so **B** gives a darker green.

   f There are 4 white tins in Batch **B** and only 3 in batch **A** so batch **A** gives the darker green.

   g If I took 3 lots of batch **A** and 2 lots of batch **B** both lots would have 6 tins of green paint. The 3 lots of batch **A** would have 9 tins of white paint while the 2 lots of batch **B** would have only 8, so batch **B** would give a darker green.

4:03 | Using Ratio to Solve Problems

'My fish is three times longer than yours.'
Find the length of the bigger fish if the smaller fish is:

1 10 cm long   **2** 30 cm long   **3** 1 m long.

Find the length of the smaller fish if the bigger fish is:

4 30 cm long   **5** 1·2 m long.

Complete the following: **6** $\dfrac{3}{4} = \dfrac{\square}{20}$ **7** $\dfrac{15}{8} = \dfrac{\square}{24}$ **8** $\dfrac{9}{16} = \dfrac{27}{\square}$

Solve the equations: **9** $\dfrac{x}{8} = \dfrac{5}{4}$ **10** $\dfrac{x}{5} = \dfrac{4}{3}$

- We have seen that statements such as 'My fish is three times longer than yours' do not give the actual size of either fish. However, once the length of either fish is known, the length of the other can be calculated.
- In many problems we are told the ratio of two quantities. We are then given one quantity and asked to calculate the other.

worked example 1

A woman mixes sand and cement in the ratio 5 : 2 by volume. If she uses 5 buckets of cement, how much sand should she use?

Solution

Method 1 (the unitary method)

2 buckets of cement to 5 buckets of sand

1 bucket of cement to $\dfrac{5}{2}$ buckets of sand

5 buckets of cement to $\dfrac{5}{2} \times 5$ buckets of sand

∴ 5 buckets of cement needs 12·5 buckets of sand.

Method 2 (the ratio method)

Let the number of buckets of sand be x.

$$\therefore \frac{\text{buckets of sand}}{\text{buckets of cement}} = \frac{5}{2}$$

$$\therefore \frac{x}{5} = \frac{5}{2}$$

$$x = \frac{5}{2} \times 5$$

$$= 12\cdot 5$$

∴ She needs 12·5 buckets of sand.

These ratios are equivalent.

	2 : 5
=	2 parts : 5 parts
=	1 part : $\dfrac{5}{2}$ parts
=	5 parts : $\dfrac{25}{2}$ parts

worked example 2

Two business partners, Jim and Larry, decide to divide the profits from a business venture in the same ratio as their investments. If Jim invests $9000 and Larry invests $5000, how much should Larry receive if Jim receives $3600?

Solution

Method 1

Jim's share : Larry's share = 9 : 5

9 shares earn $3600

1 share earns $3600 ÷ 9 = $400

5 shares earn $400 × 5 = $2000

∴ Larry's share = $2000.

Method 2

Let Larry's share be $x.

$$\therefore \quad \frac{\text{Larry's share}}{\text{Jim's share}} = \frac{5}{9}$$

$$\therefore \quad \frac{x}{3600} = \frac{5}{9}$$

$$x = \frac{5}{9} \times 3600$$

$$= \$2000$$

∴ Larry receives $2000.

Use Method 2 whenever you can. Write the ratios as fractions.

Exercise 4:03

Foundation Worksheet 4:03

Ratio problems

1 Simplify each ratio.
  a 4 : 2   b 20 : 30
2 A map has a scale of 1 : 1000. Two places are 1 cm apart on the map. What is the distance between these places?

1 Solve the following equations.

a $\dfrac{x}{5} = \dfrac{7}{4}$ b $\dfrac{x}{3} = \dfrac{7}{2}$

c $\dfrac{x}{5} = \dfrac{5}{8}$ d $\dfrac{x}{4} = \dfrac{5 \cdot 6}{3}$

e $y : 4 = 7 : 2$ f $m : 10 = 4 : 12$

g $3 : 2 = 7 : a$ h $3 : b = 4 : 5$

2 a The ratio of boys to girls in the room is 2 : 1. If there are 8 girls, how many boys are there?

$$\frac{\text{no. of boys}}{\text{no. of girls}} = \frac{2}{1}$$

b Alan and Rachel share some money in the ratio 5 : 3. If Rachel receives $204, how much does Alan receive?

$$\frac{\text{Alan's share}}{\text{Rachel's share}} = \frac{5}{3}$$

c The ratio of children to adults on a trek is 10 : 3. If there are 12 adults, how many children are there?

d Liam and Bronte divided some money in the ratio 2 : 3. If Liam has $5.40, how much does Bronte have? How much money was divided?

e A mortar mix is made up of sand and cement in the ratio 4 : 1. If 12 parts of sand are used, how many parts of cement are needed?

f A two-stroke petrol mixture is made by mixing petrol and oil in the ratio of 25 : 1. How many litres of petrol need to be added to 200 mL of oil to make this mixture?

3 a The ratio of a boy's mass to that of his father is $\frac{3}{8}$. If the boy weighs 27 kg, what does his father weigh?

b A type of solder is made by mixing lead and tin in the ratio of $2:3$.
  i How much lead would need to be mixed with 5·4 kg of tin to make the solder?
  ii How much tin would need to be mixed with 285 g of lead to make the solder?

c A model aeroplane is built to a scale of $1:80$. If the wingspan of the model is 85 cm, what is the wingspan of the aeroplane?

d A kindergarten works on the basis of two teachers for every 19 children. How many teachers would be needed for 38 children?

e The ratio of the selling price of an item to the cost price is $11:10$. Find the cost price if the selling price is $59.51.

4 a The scale on a map is $1:25\,000$. What actual distance would be represented by a length of 3·5 cm on the map?

b A concrete is made by mixing gravel, sand and cement in the ratio of $5:4:2$. How much gravel and sand would be added to 5 parts of cement?

c An alloy is made by mixing copper, tin and zinc in the ratio of $10:12:9$. If only 28 kg of copper is used, how much tin and zinc is needed to make the alloy?

d A sum of money was divided among three people in the ratio $8:3:5$. If the smallest share was $720, what were the other shares and how much money was there to be divided?

5 9-carat gold is a mixture of three parts gold to five parts other metals (to add hardness).
a What is the ratio of gold to other metals?
b If 24 g of gold is used to make 9-carat gold, how much of the other metal is used?
c If 60 g of other metals was used, how much gold would be needed?

investigation

4:03

Investigation 4:03 | Using ratio

Please use the Assessment Grid on the following page to help you understand what is required for this Investigation.

1 Square tiles of length 20 cm are arranged in the pattern on the right. This square of nine tiles, some black and some white, is repeated to cover a rectangular floor 6 metres long and 3 metres wide.
  a How many tiles are needed to cover the floor?
  b How many black tiles are needed?
  c How many of each tile needs to be ordered, allowing for 10% breakages?
  d What would be the total cost if each black tile costs $1.85 and each white tile costs $2.40?

2 Investigate which measurements for rectangular floors would allow this pattern to fit nicely on the floor (with only complete patterns used).

3 Investigate the various gears of a 10-speed racing bicycle.

Assessment Grid for Investigation 4:03 | Using ratio

The following is a sample assessment grid for this investigation. You should carefully read the criteria *before* beginning the investigation so that you know what is required.

		Assessment Criteria (B, C, D)		Achieved ✓
Criterion B Investigating Patterns	a	The student had some difficulty calculating the number of tiles.	1	
			2	
	b	The number of tiles has been found, but not in an organised way.	3	
			4	
	c	A systematic method has been used to calculate the total number of tiles and also how many black and white tiles are needed (ratio).	5	
			6	
	d	The method used is explained and ratio has been used to help solve the problem.	7	
			8	
Criterion C Communication	a	Working out is not clear and there has been little use of diagrams.	1	
			2	
	b	Good explanations are given and the working out is clear and logical.	3	
			4	
	c	Complete solutions are given and diagrams have been used to help explain the steps.	5	
			6	
Criterion D Reflection in Mathematics	a	The method used is explained and there has been an attempt to show that the solution is correct.	1	
			2	
	b	The reason for adopting the method used is given and there has been a reasonable attempt to show that the solution is correct.	3	
			4	
	c	The method is fully justified, the reasonableness of the solution is considered and the advantages/disadvantages of alternatives have been noted.	5	
			6	

4:04 | Dividing a Quantity in a Given Ratio

A second type of ratio problem involves dividing or sharing a quantity between a number of people in a given ratio. These types of problems and their solutions are given below.

5 : 4, eh?
5 for me, 4 for you.
5 for me...

---

worked examples

1 A school consists of boys and girls in the ratio 4 : 3. If there are 560 students in the school, find how many boys and girls are in the school.

2 Two brothers, Cliff and Richard, are to divide $1890 between them in the ratio 5 : 4. How much does each receive?

Solutions

1 Method 1

There are 560 students.
Ratio of boys : girls = 4 : 3
The total number of parts is 7.
∴ Each part = $\frac{560}{7}$ = 80
∴ Number of boys = 4 × 80
= 320
∴ Number of girls = 3 × 80
= 240

Method 2

There are 560 students.
Ratio of boys : girls = 4 : 3
∴ Boys are $\frac{4}{7}$ of total population.
∴ Girls are $\frac{3}{7}$ of total population.
∴ Number of boys = $\frac{4}{7}$ of 560
= 320
∴ Number of girls = $\frac{3}{7}$ of 560
= 240

2 Method 1

$1890 is to be divided into 9 shares.
Cliff will take 5 shares.
Richard will take 4 shares.
9 shares = $1890
∴ 1 share = $210 (ie $\frac{\$1890}{9}$)
∴ 4 shares = $840 (ie $210 × 4)
5 shares = $1050 (ie $210 × 5)
∴ Cliff receives $1050 and Richard receives $840.

Method 2

$1890 is to be shared.
Cliff will take $\frac{5}{9}$ of the money.
Richard will take $\frac{4}{9}$ of the money.
Cliff's share = $\frac{5}{9}$ of $1890
= $1050
Richard's share = $\frac{4}{9}$ of $1890
= $840
∴ Cliff receives $1050 and Richard receives $840.

Discussion

Ravi and Jane put their money together to buy a car. Ravi puts in $3000 and Jane puts in $5000. Two years later they sell the car for $5600.

• If only the money invested is considered, how much should each receive from the sale?

• What other information do you think could influence the size of the shares in the car when it is sold? Discuss with others in your class.

Exercise 4:04

1
a Divide 16 in the ratio $5:3$.
b Divide 200 in the ratio $1:4$.
c Divide 420 in the ratio $7:5$.
d Divide 1510 in the ratio $3:2$.
e Divide 585 in the ratio $1:3:5$.
f Divide 41 400 in the ratio $6:4:5$.

2
a Pewter is made by mixing tin and lead in the ratio $4:1$. How much of each metal would there be in 20 kg of pewter?
b In a town the ratio of adults to children is $2:5$. How many children are there in the town if the population is 8400?
c A tin of two-stroke petrol mixture holds 3·9 L. If the mixture is made from petrol and oil in the ratio $25:1$, find the amount of oil in the mixture.
d A fruit drink is made by mixing juice and water in the ratio $3:1$. How much juice would be needed to make 1200 mL of drink?
e A brand of fertiliser is made by mixing nitrates, potash and phosphates in the ratio $2:3:3$. How many kilograms of each are in a 50 kg bag of fertiliser?
f A certain range of bricks is made by mixing three different types of bricks in the ratio $4:1:3$. If 28 000 bricks are needed to build a house, how many of each type will be needed?
g A dry concrete mix is made by mixing gravel, sand and cement in the ratio $6:4:1$ by mass. Find the mass of each required to make 66 kg of the dry cement mix.
h The lengths of the sides of a triangle are in the ratio $1:2:3$. Find the lengths of the sides if the triangle has a perimeter of 42·6 cm.

3
a
A   B   C   D   E   F   G   H   I   J   K

Which point divides the line AK in the ratio:
i $9:1$?   **ii** $7:3$?   **iii** $3:7$?
iv $4:1$?   **v** $1:4$?

b Draw a line *AB*, 12 cm long, and divide it into 6 equal parts. Then find the point that divides the line in the ratio $5:1$.
c Draw a line 8 cm long and divide it in the ratio $5:3$.
d Draw a line 6 cm long and divide it in the ratio $1:4$.

Use the letter X to divide each interval.

4
a A rectangle has a perimeter of 64 cm. If the ratio of its length to its breadth is $5:3$, find the length of the rectangle.
b The ratio of the populations of town A and town B is $3:8$, while the ratio of the populations of towns B and C is $5:2$. If the total population of the three towns is 85 342, find the population of each town.
c A chemical solution is made by mixing an acid with water in the ratio $1:24$. This solution is then taken and mixed with water in the ratio $1:3$. How much acid would there be in 200 mL of this final solution?

Fun Spot 4:04 | Multiplication can be fun

Long multiplication sums can be a pain. But have you tried doing them like this?
For a sum like 58 × 25, follow the steps given below.

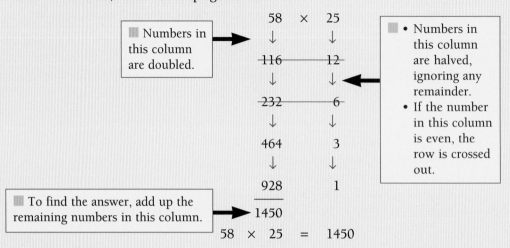

Numbers in this column are doubled.

58   ×   25
↓   ↓
~~116~~   ~~12~~
↓   ↓
~~232~~   ~~6~~
↓   ↓
464   3
↓   ↓
928   1
―――
1450

58   ×   25   =   1450

- Numbers in this column are halved, ignoring any remainder.
- If the number in this column is even, the row is crossed out.

To find the answer, add up the remaining numbers in this column.

Here's another example for you to follow:

35   ×   21
↓   ↓
~~70~~   ~~10~~
↓   ↓
140   5
↓   ↓
~~280~~   ~~2~~
↓   ↓
560   1
―――
735

∴ 35 × 21 = 735

How about that! It works!

Now try some examples of your own.

Now try some questions of your own. Check your answers with a calculator.

Practical Activities 4:04 | Ratio research

1 Collect information from containers of products that need to be mixed. In each case write the instructions as a ratio.
2 Make a list of cases you discovered where different units are used in the same ratio, eg three teabags to one teapot of boiling water.
3 Make a list of appliances and machines used for mixing ingredients in a given ratio, eg a cement mixer.
4 Discuss your findings with others in the class.

4:05 | Rates

You need to be able to compare quantities that have different units.
- 4 teaspoons of coffee : 2 mugs of water
- 1 cap of detergent : 5 litres of water
- 6 small buttons : 8 large buttons
- 90 kilometres : 2 hours

- **As seen above, a *rate* is a comparison of unlike quantities.**
- **The most commonly used rate is speed which compares *distance travelled* to *time taken*.**
  eg 20 km : 2 hours = 10 km : 1 hour = 10 km/h

- To make rates easier to work with, we usually change the rate to an equivalent rate where we write down how many of the first quantity correspond to one of the second quantity. Rates can be changed (as with ratios) by multiplying or dividing both quantities by the same number.

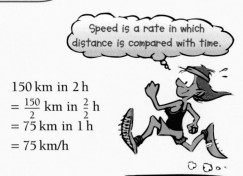

Speed is a rate in which distance is compared with time.

150 km in 2 h
$= \frac{150}{2}$ km in $\frac{2}{2}$ h
$= 75$ km in 1 h
$= 75$ km/h

- **To simplify rates we can multiply or divide both terms by the same number, just as we do for ratios.**
- **When using a rate we must show the units.**
- **Rates are usually expressed by writing down how many of the first quantity correspond to one of the second.**
  eg 6000 mL for 10 bottles = 600 mL per 1 bottle
  = 600 mL/bottle

600 mL per BOTTLE

- The solution of rate problems is also similar to the solution of ratio problems. The two basic problems are shown in Worked Examples **2** and **3** on the next page.

worked examples

1 Express each of the following as a rate in its simplest form.
   a A woman travels 210 km in 3 hours.   **b** 500 sheep are grazed on 200 hectares.

Solution

70 km/h

a 210 km in 3 hours
    Divide each term by 3.
    = 70 km in 1 hour
    = 70 km/h

b 500 sheep on 200 hectares
    Divide by 200.
    $= \frac{500}{200}$ sheep on 1 hectare
    = 2·5 sheep/hectare

2 A mine supplies ore at the rate of 1500 tonnes per day.
  a How many tonnes can the mine supply in 4 weeks?
  b How long will it take to supply 60 000 tonnes?

In worked examples (2) and (3), both types of rate problems are given.

Solution

a 1500 t/day

$$= \frac{1500 \times 28 \text{ t}}{1 \times 28 \text{ days}}$$

(since 4 weeks = 28 days)

$$= \frac{42\ 000 \text{ t}}{4 \text{ weeks}}$$

∴ 42 000 t can be supplied in 4 weeks.

OR

1500 t in 1 day
= 1500 × 28 t in 28 days
= 42 000 t in 4 weeks

b 1500 t/day

$$= \frac{1500 \text{ t} \times 40}{1 \text{ day} \times 40}$$

(since 60 000 ÷ 1500 = 40)

$$= \frac{60\ 000 \text{ t}}{40 \text{ days}}$$

60 000 t/40 days

∴ 60 000 t can be supplied in 40 days.

OR

1500 t in 1 day
$= 1 \text{ t in } \dfrac{1}{1500} \text{ days}$
$= 60\ 000 \text{ t in } 60\ 000 \times \dfrac{1}{1500} \text{ days}$
= 60 000 t in 40 days

3 A shearer sheared 70 sheep in 2 hours. If he could continue at this rate, find:
  a how long it would take to shear 200 sheep, to the nearest hour
  b how many sheep could be sheared in 8 hours.

Solution

a 70 sheep in 2 hours
= 35 sheep in 1 hour
= 35 sheep/h

Now 35 sheep in 1 h
$= 1 \text{ sheep in } \dfrac{1}{35} \text{ h}$
$= 200 \text{ sheep in } 200 \times \dfrac{1}{35} \text{ h}$
$= 200 \text{ sheep in } 5\dfrac{5}{7} \text{ h}$

∴ 200 sheep would take 6 h to shear, to the nearest hour.

b 35 sheep in 1 hour
= 35 × 8 sheep in 8 hours
= 260 sheep in 8 hours

∴ 260 sheep could be sheared in 8 hours.

■ *Notice:*
One type of rate problem is solved using multiplication. The other uses division.

Exercise 4:05

Foundation Worksheet 4:05

Rates
1 Simplify each rate.
  a $80 for 8   b 20 km/2 h
2 a I can buy 10 apples for $2.
    How many apples can I buy
    for $5?

1 Write each of the following as a rate in simplest form.

a 8 km in 2 h   b 10 kg for $5

c 5 km in 20 min   d 120 L in 4 h

e 500c for 20 g   f $315 for 7 days

g 120 children for 4 teachers   h 20 degrees in 5 min

i 60 sheep in 3 hours j 40 kg over 8 m^2 k 70 g for 10 cm^3

l 60 km in $1\frac{1}{2}$ h   m 150 L in $1\frac{1}{2}$ h   n 18 min for 4·5 km

2 Complete the equivalent rates.

a 2 km/min = ... km/h   b 4 kg/min = ... kg/h   c 0·02 kg/m^2 = ... kg/ha

d 5 L/h = ... L/day   e $5/g = $.../kg   f 5 mL/min = ... mL/h

g 4 km/h = ... m/h   h 2 L/h = ... mL/h   i 1·2 t/d = ... kg/d

j 20c/min = $... /min   k $2.45/kg = ... c/kg   l 15 mL/min = ... L/min

m 3 m/s = ... km/h   n 25 mL/s = ... L/h   o 15 t/h = ... t/day

p 20 g/m^2 = ... kg/ha   q 10 km/L = ... m/mL   r 7 g/cm^3 = ... t/m^3

3 a I walk at 5 km/h. How far can I walk in 3 hours?

b How far will a car travelling at 80 km/h travel in $2\frac{1}{2}$ hours?

c A jet plane is travelling at 600 km/h. How far will it travel in 25 minutes?

d A girl cycled at 18 km/h for $4\frac{1}{2}$ h. How far did she cycle?

e How long will it take to travel 200 km at 80 km/h?

f How long should it take to run 14 km at an average speed of 4 min/km?

g A train travels 960 km at an average speed of 80 km/h. How long will the trip take?

h How long will it take a spacecraft travelling at 1700 km/h to travel 238 000 km?

i A train left town A at 9 am and arrived at town B at 4 pm. What was its average speed if it travelled 665 km?

j A rocketship takes $1\frac{1}{2}$ hours to make an orbit of the Earth. If one orbit is 30 000 km, what is its speed? How far would it travel in 10 minutes at this speed?

k A woman runs the marathon in 2 hours 25 minutes. If she covers 42·2 km, calculate her average speed.

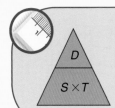

D = distance, S = speed, T = time

If you cover the quantity you are trying to calculate, this triangle will tell you what to do. So:

$$D = S \times T \qquad S = \frac{D}{T} \qquad T = \frac{D}{S}$$

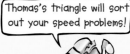

Thomas's triangle will sort out your speed problems!

4 a Nails cost $4.60 per kg. What is the cost of 20 kg?

b A rugby team kicks an average of 5 goals/game. How many goals did they score in 17 games?

c A shearer could shear 15 sheep/hour. How many sheep could he shear in 8 hours?

d The density of iron is 7·5 g/cm^3. What is the mass of 500 cm^3?

e A heart is beating at 90 beats/min. How many beats will it make in 1 hour?

f Perfume costs $12 for 100 mL. How much would 1 L cost?

g A mine supplies 1200 t of ore per hour. How much would it supply in 1 week?

h If Euro €1 = pounds sterling £0.671, what is the value in pounds sterling (£) of €500?

i Fertiliser is spread at a rate of 1 kg/40 m². What area can be covered by 25 kg?

j Water is dripping from a tap at a rate of 5 L/h. How much water will leak in 1 day?

5 **a** Nails cost $4.60/kg. How many kilograms can be bought for $20?

    b If I can save $40/week, how long should it take to save $1000?

    c A bulldozer is moving soil at the rate of 15 t/h. How long will it take to move 400 t?

    d A tank that holds 1000 L is leaking at a rate of 2·5 L/min. How long will it take to lose 400 L at this rate?

    e Blue metal is moved at a rate of 22 t/truck. How many trucks would be needed to move 480 t of metal?

    f A car uses petrol at the rate of 9·5 L/100 km. How many litres would be used in travelling 350 km?

    g A machine fills bottles at the rate of 120 bottles/min. How long would it take to fill 1000 bottles at this rate?

    h Fertiliser is to be spread at a rate of 20 kg/ha. How many hectares can be covered by 50 kg?

    i If it takes 25 tiles to cover 1 m², how many square metres will be covered by 175 tiles?

    j Singapore airport has an aircraft movement rate of 18 aircraft/hour. How many hours would it take to record 270 aircraft movements?

6 **a** Light travels at 300 000 km/s.

      i How far does it travel in 1 minute?

      ii How long would it take light to travel from the sun, which is 148 800 000 km away?

    b The density of iron is 7·5 g/cm³. Find the mass in kilograms of a rectangular block of iron 100 cm long, 100 cm wide and 2 cm thick.

    c The fastest man in the world can run 100 m in 10 s. If he could continue at this rate, what would his speed be in kilometres per hour?

    d A racing car travels at a speed of 180 km/h. How long would it take to travel 100 m?

    e Land rates are paid at 4·95 cents per dollar of the land's value.

      i How much will the rates be for land with a value of $15 000?

      ii What would be the value of land for which the rates are $544.50?

7 **a** Pump A can fill a tank in 5 minutes while pump B can fill a tank in 10 minutes. How long will it take to fill the tank if both are working together?

    b In making one revolution, a car wheel travels 200 cm. How fast are the wheels spinning, in revolutions per minute, when the car is travelling at 60 km/h? (Answer to the nearest revolution per minute.)

Some algebra would be handy in these equations

    c A girl paddles her kayak upstream from her home to her friends home, taking $2\frac{1}{2}$ hours for the journey. She returns that afternoon in $1\frac{1}{2}$ hours. If the river is flowing at $2\frac{1}{2}$ km/h, find:

      i her paddling speed in still water

      ii the distance to her friend's place.

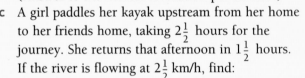

4:06 | Scale Drawing

Complete the following:

1 1 m = ... cm   **2** 1 cm = ... mm   **3** 1 m = ... mm

Convert: **4** 2000 cm to m

    5 250 000 mm to m

Simplify the ratios: **6** 1 cm : 1 m

    7 1 mm : 1 m

Complete the following:

8 $1 : 100 = 5 : \square$ **9** $1 : 1000 = 6.8 : \square$

10 $1 \text{ cm} : 1 \text{ m} = 5 \text{ cm} : \square$

Scale drawings are used often in everyday life. People such as architects and engineers make scale drawings of buildings and bridges, and people such as builders must be able to read them so that these things can be built.

- Scale drawings have the same shapes as the objects that they represent but they are of different sizes.
- The scale of a drawing = length on drawing : real length.
  So a scale of 1 : 100 means that the real length is 100 times the length on the drawing.
- The scale determines the size of the drawing. The closer the size of terms in the scale ratio, the closer the drawing is to real size. So a 1 : 10 scale drawing would be bigger than a 1 : 100 scale drawing of the same object.

1 : 10 gives a bigger drawing than 1 : 100.

In scale drawing work there are only two types of problems.

- The first type involves making a scale drawing of an object.
- The second type involves calculating the real sizes of objects from the drawing.

A scale drawing of an object is the same shape as the object but a different size.

Scale = length on drawing : real length

A scale can be written in two ways, as 1 cm : 1 m   OR   1 : 100.

- **If the scale drawing is larger than the real length, then the scale drawing is called an *enlargement* and the first term of the scale would be the larger, eg 5 : 1.**

---

1 Simplify these scales: **a** 1 mm : 1 m   **b** 1 cm : 2 m   **c** 5 mm : 1 km

2 **a** The scale on a drawing is 1 : 100. What is the real distance between two points that are 5 cm apart on the drawing?

b Two trees are 50 m apart. How far apart would they be on a drawing with a scale of 1 : 500?

3

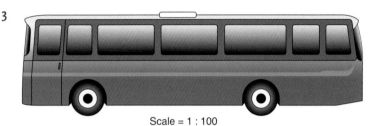

Scale = 1 : 100

From the drawing, by measurement and calculation, find:

a the maximum length of the bus

b the maximum height of the bus.

Solutions

1 **a** 1 mm : 1 m
= 1 mm : 1000 mm
= 1 : 1000

b 1 cm : 2 m
= 1 cm : 200 cm
= 1 : 200

c 5 mm : 1 km
= 5 mm : 1000 m
= 5 mm : 1 000 000 mm
= 1 : 200 : 000

2 **a** Scale = 1 : 100

$$\therefore \frac{1}{100} = \frac{5 \text{ cm}}{\text{real distance}}$$

$\therefore$ real distance = 5 × 100 cm
= 500 cm
= 5 m

b Scale = 1 : 500

$$\therefore \frac{1}{500} = \frac{\text{dist. on drawing}}{50 \text{ m}}$$

$\therefore$ 500 × dist. on drawing = 50 m

$$\text{distance on drawing} = \frac{50 \text{ m}}{500}$$

$$= \frac{1}{10} \text{ m}$$

$$= 10 \text{ cm}$$

3 **a** Length of drawing = 93 mm
$\therefore$ Real length = 100 × 9·3 cm
= 930 cm
= 9·3 m

b Height on drawing = 27 mm
$\therefore$ Real height = 100 × 2·7 cm
= 270 cm
= 2·7 m

You can generally only measure to the nearest millimetre.

■ The accuracy of answers in scale drawing work is determined by the scale and the limitations of our measuring instruments.

Exercise 4:06

1 Copy and complete each of the following.

a $1:100 = 1\,\text{cm}: \ldots$ b $1:1000 = 1\,\text{cm}: \ldots$ c $1:1000 = 1\,\text{m}: \ldots$

2 Write each of the following scales in ratio form.

a $1\,\text{cm}$ to $1\,\text{m}$ b $1\,\text{cm}$ to $10\,\text{m}$ c $1\,\text{mm}$ to $10\,\text{m}$ d $1\,\text{mm}$ to $5\,\text{m}$

e $2\,\text{cm}$ to $1\,\text{m}$ f $5\,\text{mm}$ to $1\,\text{m}$ g $5\,\text{cm}$ to $1\,\text{m}$ h $5\,\text{cm}:1\,\text{km}$

3 Calculate the real distance between points which are the following distances apart on a map if the scale on the map is $1:1000$.

a $5\,\text{cm}$ b $3.5\,\text{cm}$ c $10.6\,\text{cm}$ d $8.1\,\text{cm}$

e $1\,\text{mm}$ f $8\,\text{mm}$ g $26\,\text{mm}$ h $0.5\,\text{mm}$

4

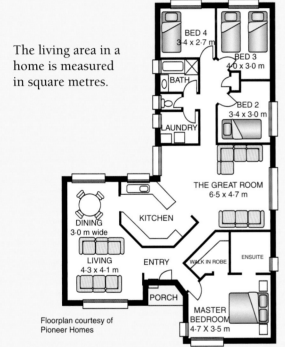

The living area in a home is measured in square metres.

BED 4 3.4 x 2.7 m
BED 3 4.0 x 3.0 m
BATH
BED 2 3.4 x 3.0 m
LAUNDRY
THE GREAT ROOM 6.5 x 4.7 m
DINING 3.0 m wide
KITCHEN
LIVING 4.3 x 4.1 m
ENTRY
WALK IN ROBE
ENSUITE
PORCH
MASTER BEDROOM 4.7 X 3.5 m

Floorplan courtesy of Pioneer Homes

The scale used in this house plan is $1:200$.

a What real distance is represented by $1\,\text{cm}$?

b Find the real length of:

   i the bathroom

   ii bedroom 3

   iii the house

   iv the inner kitchen wall

c Find the real area of bedroom 3.

d Find the inside area of the house to the nearest square metre.

e Find the area of the great room.

f How much would it cost to tile the floor of the great room at $38.50 per square metre.

5 The scale on a drawing is $1\,\text{cm}$ to $5\,\text{m}$. Calculate the real distance between two points if they are the following distances apart on the drawing:

a $2\,\text{cm}$ b $5\,\text{cm}$ c $6.4\,\text{cm}$ d $4.2\,\text{cm}$

e $1\,\text{mm}$ f $42\,\text{mm}$ g $27\,\text{mm}$ h $59\,\text{mm}$

6 A scale drawing is to be made using a scale of $1:100$. What lengths would the following real distances be represented by on the drawing?

a $100\,\text{cm}$ b $300\,\text{cm}$

c $750\,\text{cm}$ d $4.3\,\text{m}$

e $63\,\text{m}$ f $42\,\text{m}$

g $15.6\,\text{m}$ h $2.4\,\text{m}$

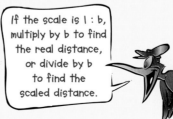

If the scale is $1:b$, multiply by b to find the real distance, or divide by b to find the scaled distance.

7 The distances between pairs of points in real life are measured. How far apart will each of these be on a scale drawing with a scale of 1 cm : 20 m?

a 40 m   **b** 60 m   **c** 200 m   **d** 30 m

e 8 m   **f** 25 m   **g** 11 m   **h** 315 m

8 **a** The plan of a house is drawn to a scale of 1 : 100. If a room measures 36 mm by 42 mm on the plan, how big is the room in real life?

b A model aeroplane is built to a scale of 1 : 72. What would the real wingspan be if the wingspan of the model is 30 cm?

c A map has a scale of 1 : 250 000. What real distance would be represented by a scaled distance of:

i 1 mm?   **ii** 35 mm?   **iii** 1 cm?   **iv** 5·2 cm?

d A girl made this scale drawing to calculate the height, *AB*, of a triangular wall.

   i Measure the distance *CB* on the scale drawing and calculate the scale of the drawing.

   ii By measurement and calculation, find the height *AB*.

   iii Find the area of this triangular wall.

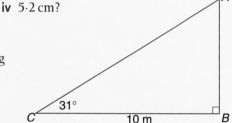

9 **a** An oval is 85 m long and 58 m wide. What would these lengths be on a scale drawing if the scale was:

i 1 cm : 10 m?   **ii** 1 cm : 5 m?   **iii** 1 : 200?

b A house fits inside a rectangle 23 300 mm long and 12 200 mm wide. What is the smallest size of paper on which a scale drawing could be made if the scale is 1 : 100?

c A 1 : 50 scale model of a yacht is to be built. If the yacht is 25 m long, how long will the model yacht be?

d A scale drawing is to be made of a car. If the car is 6·25 m long and the model is to be 25 cm long, what should the scale be?

e A kitchen design company is asked to design a kitchen for a new house. The dimensions of the kitchen are 5200 mm by 3800 mm. What would the scaled size of the kitchen be if the scale is 1 : 100? Calculate the scaled size of the refrigerator (real size 600 mm by 600 mm) and the sink (real size 1200 mm by 500 mm).

10 Use the scale on the map to find the distance by road from:

a Riga to Cesis

b Valmiera to Aluksne

c Stende to Valga

d Mersrags to Ogre

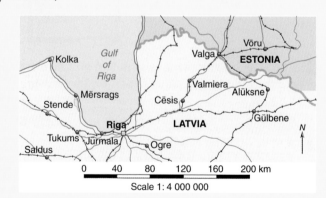

Investigation 4:06 |
Scale my room!

Please use the Assessment Grid on the following page to help you understand what is required for this Investigation.

- Make a scale drawing of a room in your house.
- Calculate the scaled sizes of the furniture in the room and mark the position of each piece on the drawing.
- Make paper cut-outs to represent the furniture.
- Use paper cut-outs to rearrange the furniture in the room. Can you find a better arrangement?

Challenge 4:06 | Cutting rectangles

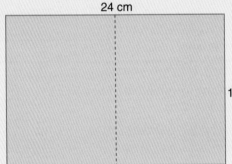

24 cm

16 cm

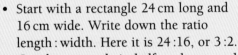

- Start with a rectangle 24 cm long and 16 cm wide. Write down the ratio length : width. Here it is 24 : 16, or 3 : 2.
- Cut the rectangle in half as shown and continue to do this again and again, each time recording the ratio length : width in its simplest form.
- What pattern did you discover? (Explain this in full sentences.)
- Investigate what happens when you start with a rectangle that has:
  a length 16 cm, width 16 cm
  b length 24 cm, width 8 cm.

Assessment Grid for Investigation 4:06 | **Scale my room!**

The following is a sample assessment grid for this investigation. You should carefully read the criteria *before* beginning the investigation so that you know what is required.

			Assessment Criteria (B, C, D)		Achieved ✓
Criterion B Investigating Patterns	a		The scale used and the drawing of the room is not realistic.	1	
				2	
	b		The scale used is a realistic one and the steps used to convert the dimensions are reasonably organised.	3	
				4	
	c		Different layouts of the room are shown including the positions of the furniture, with some conclusions made.	5	
				6	
	d		The best of the choices is given and the reason for this layout have been discussed, with relative advantages of each layout.	7	
				8	
Criterion C Communication	a		Only basic diagrams are given with one or two options.	1	
				2	
	b		Many options are shown; diagrams are clear with a written explanation.	3	
				4	
	c		A clear explanation is given for the best choice of layout and this progresses logically from the working.	5	
				6	
Criterion D Reflection in Mathematics	a		Some attempt has been made to explain the working out.	1	
				2	
	b		A good explanation is given for the work done and the reasonableness of each layout has been discussed to some extent.	3	
				4	
	c		Layouts are explored in detail and the relative advantages discussed. The reason for the final choice is justified in full.	5	
				6	

Fun Spot 4:06 | What do you call a deer with no eyes?

Work out the answer to each part and put the letter for that part in the box above the correct answer.

E Simplify the ratio $12:8$.

I Find x if $12:8 = x:40$.

A Find m if $\dfrac{m}{3} = \dfrac{20}{6}$.

O Simplify the rate $18\,\text{L}$ in $6\,\text{m}^2$.

Find the value of y if:

N $12\,\text{L/s} = y\,\text{L/min}$

D $0{\cdot}6\,\text{kg/h} = y\,\text{g/h}$

720	$3\,\text{L/m}^2$	60	600	$3:2$	10

What do you call a deer with no eyes and no legs?

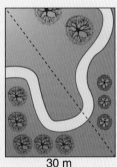

30 m

This rectangle is a scale drawing of a garden. Find the ratio of:

L length : breadth

A length : diagonal

D diagonal : breadth

O How many metres long is the garden?

L What is the scale used in this drawing?

I What is the area of the scale drawing?

T What is the area of the garden?

I What is the ratio of the area of the scale drawing to the area of the garden?

150 newspapers are divided in the ratio $7:3$.

S How many newspapers are in the smaller share?

N How many newspapers are in the larger share?

E What fraction of the newspapers is the smaller share?

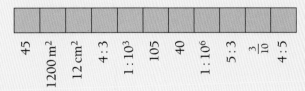

45	$1200\,\text{m}^2$	$12\,\text{cm}^2$	$4:3$	$1:10^3$	105	40	$1:10^6$	$5:3$	$\dfrac{3}{10}$	$4:5$

- Estimate the ratio of:
  a red lollies : green lollies
  b red lollies : green lollies : black lollies

Mathematical terms 4

rate
- A comparison of unlike quantities written in a definite order.
  eg 20 km in 5 h or 20 km/h
- Units are used in this comparison.
  eg 8 *people* per *car*

ratio
- A comparison of like quantities or numbers written in a definite order.
- Equivalent ratio (an equal ratio). This is formed when the terms of a ratio are multiplied or divided by the same number.

scale
- The ratio of the length that a drawing has to the original length.
- If a map has a scale of 1 : 10 000, then 1 cm on the map represents 10 000 cm (ie 100 m) in real terms.

scale drawing
- A scale drawing has the same shape as the object it represents but a different size.
- The scale of a drawing
  = length on drawing : real length.

Mathematical terms 4

Diagnostic Test 4: | Ratio, Rates and Scale Drawing
- Each section of the test has similar items that test a certain type of question.
- Errors made will indicate areas of weakness.
- Each weakness should be treated by going back to the section listed.

		Section

1 Concrete is made by mixing 1 part cement with 2 parts sand and 4 parts gravel. Write down the ratio of:
  a cement to sand   **b** cement to gravel
  c cement to sand to gravel   **d** gravel to cement to sand
		4:01

2 Simplify the ratios: **a** $10:4$ **b** $16:4$ **c** $1{\cdot}5:6$ **d** $1\frac{1}{2}:2\frac{1}{4}$		4:02

3 Complete the following:
  a $5:2=10:\square$ **b** $1:3=6:\square$
  c $4:3=\square:18$ **d** $2:5=\square:20$
		4:03

4 Solve the following:

a $\dfrac{x}{3} = \dfrac{5}{8}$ b $\dfrac{x}{5} = \dfrac{10}{3}$ c $\dfrac{x}{4} = \dfrac{1\cdot8}{5}$ d $\dfrac{2\cdot5}{6} = \dfrac{x}{4}$

4:03

5 a The ratio of boys to girls is $6:5$. If there are 15 girls, how many boys are there?

b Sand and cement are mixed in the ratio $7:2$. If 3 kg of cement are used, how much sand is used?

c Liam and Bronte share money in the ratio $2:3$. If Liam's share is $1.80, what is Bronte's share?

d An alloy is made by mixing metals A, B and C in the ratio $2:5:3$. If 9 kg of C are used, how much of B is used?

4:03

6 a Divide 15 in the ratio $3:2$. b Divide 45 in the ratio $2:7$.

c Divide 420 in the ratio $11:10$. d Divide 120 in the ratio $1:2:7$.

4:04

7 Simplify the rates:

a 50 km in 2 hours b 600 t in 4 hours

c 100 g for 8 cm^3 d 4 kg over 10 m^2

4:05

8 Complete the following:

a 1 m/s = ... m/h b 200 kg/h = ... t/day

c $15/g = $... /kg d 6 L/h = ... mL/min

4:05

9 a Ore is supplied at a rate of 200 t/day. How much is supplied in 2 weeks?

b A car travels at a speed of 100 km/h. How far will it travel in $3\frac{1}{2}$ h?

c Water is pumped at a rate of 100 L/h. How long will it take to pump 550 L?

d A car uses petrol at a rate of 9·6 km/L. How many litres will it use to travel 200 km?

4:05

10 A drawing has a scale $1:100$. Convert the following scaled distances to real distances.

a 3 cm b 5·2 cm c 1 mm d 42 mm

4:06

11 Repeat Question **10** using a scale of 1 cm : 5 m.

4:06

12 A drawing has a scale of $1:100$. Convert the following real distances to scaled distances.

a 5 m b 43 m c 75 cm d 4·8 m

4:06

13 Repeat Question **12** using a scale of 1 cm : 2 m.

4:06

Chapter 4 | Revision Assignment

1 Use a scale drawing to find the value of each pronumeral.

a
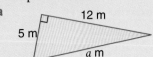
12 m
5 m
a m

b
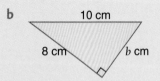
10 cm
8 cm
b cm

2 Simplify:
  a $6m + 3n + 8 + 2n$
  b $4(3a + 1) + 6(3 - a)$
  c $\dfrac{6a + 6b}{6}$

3 Which of each set has the smallest value?
  a $\{0.75,\ 1.125\%,\ \frac{1}{4}\}$
  b $\{99.1\%,\ \frac{5}{2},\ 1\frac{1}{4}\}$

4 a How much will I pay for a coat costing $120 at a 10% discount sale?
  b I invest $1000 at an interest rate of $12\frac{1}{2}\%$ p.a. How much interest will I earn in 18 months?

5 If $M = \dfrac{A}{A - 5}$, evaluate M when:
  a $A = 25$ **b** $A = 7.5$

6 The formula for the area of a trapezium is $A = \frac{1}{2}h(a + b)$. Find A when $h = 3.6$, $a = 2.4$ and $b = 6.8$.

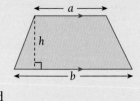

7 a Find the area of the rectangle *ABCD*.
  b Find the area of the rectangle *GBEF*.
  c Use your answers from parts **a** and **b** to find the area of the coloured figure.

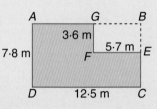

8 Use the method in Question **7**, or another method, to find the area of the coloured figure.

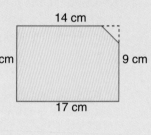

9 Solve the equations:
  a $5a = 16$ **b** $\dfrac{3m}{4} = 5$
  c $p - 6 = 2p + 4$

Chapter 4 | Working Mathematically

4B

4

1 Use ID Card 5 on page xvii to identify figure:
   a 2   b 3   c 4   d 5
   e 8   f 16   g 17

2 Find two numbers that have a sum of 12 and a product of 35.

3 All 10 girls in 7B3 play tennis or hockey. Some play both sports. If 8 of the girls play tennis and 8 of the girls play hockey, how many play both sports?

4 If it's true that 'all dogs bark', and that 'Nero is a dog', which of the following must be true?
   a Nero does not bark.
   b Nero is not a dog.
   c Nero barks.
   d All dogs are called Nero.

5

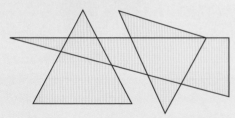

How many triangles are there in this figure? (Be careful, some may be hidden.)

6 Find a number less than 100 which is a perfect square and has as the sum of its two digits an even number.

7 List the decisions a school might make about the use of textbooks in class if the following conditions are true.
   • Parents are expected to pay for their child's textbook.
   • 5 parents out of 30 can't or won't pay.
   • The school has not been given money to pay for textbooks.
   • Most parents want their children to receive the best education possible.
   • The government says that all students must have access to the same resources and education is 'free'.

1 Simplifying ratios
2 Equivalent ratios
3 Rates

Technology Applications
Drag and Drops

Chapter Review
Questions

• Each domino can use numbers from zero to six on each part and no two dominoes are alike. How many dominoes are in a set?

5

Using Calculators and Spreadsheets

Estimate, then **Calculate!**

IMPORTANT NOTICE.
Not all calculators are the same. Your calculator may not have all of the keys mentioned in this book, or your calculator may expect you to use a key in a different way. Check your instruction booklet to be sure.

Chapter Contents

Learning Outcomes

Students will be able to:
- Recognise the properties of special groups of whole numbers and apply a range of strategies to aid computation.
- Compare, order and calculate with integers.
- Operate with fractions, decimals, percentages, ratios and rates.

Areas of Interaction

Approaches to Learning (Knowledge Acquisition, Problem Solving, Information and Communication Technology Skills), Health and Social Education, Environments, Community and Service, Human Ingenuity

5:01 | Using a Calculator

Calculators usually have 'order of operations' built in. Check the operation of your calculator by pushing the keys shown and comparing your answer with the one given.

Question	Calculator sentence	Answer
$100 + 4 \times 7$	100 [+] 4 [×] 7 [=] (If your calculator does not have order of operations built in, your answer would be 728.)	128
$935 \cdot 6 - 9 \cdot 817 + 37 \cdot 85$	935·6 [−] 9·817 [+] 37·85 [=]	963·633
$80 \cdot 94 \div 3 \cdot 8 \times 45$	80·94 [÷] 3·8 [×] 45 [=]	958·5
$81 \cdot 75 \times (2 \cdot 47 + 6 \cdot 53)$	81·75 [×] [(] 2·47 [+] 6·53 [)] [=] (OR) 2·47 [+] 6·53 [=] [×] 81·75 [=]	735·75
$4862 \div (4 \cdot 81 + 8 \cdot 19)$ (OR) $\dfrac{4862}{4 \cdot 81 + 8 \cdot 19}$	4862 [÷] [(] 4·81 [+] 8·19 [)] [=] (OR) 4·81 [+] 8·19 [=] [Min] 4862 [÷] [MR] [=] Here the [Min] key puts what is on the screen into the calculator's memory and [MR] brings it back when needed. Some calculators use [STO] and [RCL].	374
$1 \cdot 9 + 24 \div 0 \cdot 8 - 7$	1·9 [+] 24 [÷] 0·8 [−] 7 [=], if it has order of operations, or, if not: 24 [÷] 0·8 [=] [Min] 1·9 [+] [MR] [−] 7 [=]	24·9
Add the answers to 9×8, 6×9, $81 \div 0 \cdot 3$	9 [×] 8 [=] [Min] 6 [×] 9 [=] [M+] 81 [÷] 0·3 [=] [M+] [MR] Here [M+] adds what is on the screen to what is in the memory.	465

On some calculators
Min = STO,
MR = RCL.

1 First do these in your head, then check your answers using a calculator.

- **a** $800 + 500 + 80 + 6$
- **b** $2000 + 800 + 90 + 1$
- **c** $30\,000 + 2000 + 700 + 40 + 5$
- **d** $30 - 10 - 5 - 2$
- **e** $64 - 32 - 16 - 8 - 4$
- **f** $4000 - 2000 - 1000 - 500$
- **g** $9 + 6 + 4 + 8 + 1$
- **h** $30 + 80 + 40 + 60 + 10$
- **i** $500 + 300 + 600 + 900$
- **j** $60 \div 10 \times 7$
- **k** $1{\cdot}2 \times 8 \div 8$
- **l** $50 \times 2 \div 5$
- **m** $27 - (10 + 7)$
- **n** $9 \times (11 + 9)$
- **o** $15 - (15 - 10)$
- **p** $6 + 4 \times 6$
- **q** $10 + 15 \times 10$
- **r** $20 - (9 + 7)$
- **s** $4 \times 3 + 4 \times 2$
- **t** $5 \times 8 - 5 \times 4$
- **u** $100 \times 4 - 2 \times 4$

2 Use a calculator to find the answers.

- **a** $841{\cdot}675 + 94{\cdot}325$
- **b** $8\,764\,832 + 7\,399\,407$
- **c** $0{\cdot}0843 + 0{\cdot}009\,86$
- **d** $555{\cdot}56 - 183{\cdot}945$
- **e** $6\,009\,000 - 8\,714\,814$
- **f** $924 - 89{\cdot}574$
- **g** 685×934
- **h** 5814×87
- **i** $4{\cdot}8906 \times 8400$
- **j** $17\,350\,000 \div 16$
- **k** $441{\cdot}114\,66 \div 378$
- **l** $7{\cdot}469\,55 \div 503$
- **m** $8{\cdot}45 \times 3{\cdot}14 \times 9{\cdot}18$
- **n** $2 \times 85{\cdot}7 + 2 \times 91{\cdot}4$
- **o** $8{\cdot}625 \times 0{\cdot}816 \div 25$
- **p** $17\,391\,000 \div 17 + 895$
- **q** $19{\cdot}86 \times 467 - 9174{\cdot}62$
- **r** $84{\cdot}56 + 8{\cdot}45 \times 7$
- **s** $8{\cdot}7 \times 3{\cdot}8 + 1{\cdot}8 \times 4{\cdot}5$
- **t** $0{\cdot}6 \times 3{\cdot}8 - 1{\cdot}4 \times 1{\cdot}61$
- **u** $88{\cdot}8 - 4{\cdot}44 \times 3{\cdot}33$

3 Find the value of each of the following.

- **a** $\dfrac{4{\cdot}32}{3{\cdot}2 - 1{\cdot}4}$
- **b** $\dfrac{20{\cdot}46}{17{\cdot}5 - 10{\cdot}9}$
- **c** $\dfrac{3{\cdot}8 + 4{\cdot}2}{3{\cdot}8 - 4{\cdot}2}$

4
- **a** If 1 ton is equal to $1{\cdot}016$ tonnes, how many tonnes are there in 85 tons?
- **b** If 1 km is equal to $0{\cdot}621$ miles, how many miles are in 870 km?
- **c** Light travels at a speed of $299\,800$ km each second. How far would light travel in 57 seconds?
- **d** If Marion's pulse rate is 72 beats per minute while she is resting, how many times would her heart beat in 3 hours of rest?
- **e** In the South Pacific in 1998, $25\,800$ Australians visited Papua New Guinea, 3100 visited Vanuatu, $82\,100$ visited Fiji and 5100 visited New Caledonia. How many visits is this altogether?
- **f** After treating Prospect Park with ammonium sulphate, it was estimated that the number of bindi-eye plants had been reduced from $84\,600$ to $39\,700$. By how many had these plants been reduced?
- **g** If 36 people are to share an inheritance of $\$1\,971\,000$ equally, how much would each receive?
- **h** In the stock market slump of 1987, Rhonda's 1547 shares, which had been valued at $\$4.75$ per share, dropped to a value of $\$3.60$ per share. By how much altogether had the value of the 1547 shares fallen?

5:02 | Estimation

Round off each number as instructed:

1 769 (to the nearest hundred)   **2** 72·39 (to the nearest ten)

3 7·8305 (to the nearest whole)   **4** 17 452 (to the nearest thousand)

Round off correct to 2 decimal places:

5 0·6852   **6** 0·349   **7** 0·3333   **8** 0·096

Round off each number as instructed:

9 7·4 million (to the nearest million)   **10** 0·1874 (to the nearest tenth)

 When making an estimate, round off each number to the place holding the first non-zero digit and then perform the operations. This is called *leading digit estimation*.
eg $8174 \times 3·814 \div 8000 \times 4$ or $32\,000$

If your estimate is close to the calculator answer, you should accept that answer. If not, you should do the question again.

worked examples

	Question	Rounding off	Estimate	Calculator display
1	$432·8 \div 16·95$	$400 \div 20$	20	25·533923
2	$41·85 \times 19·3$	40×20	800	807·705
3	$684·15 + 34·9$	$700 + 30$	730	719·05
4	$604 - 3·42$	$600 - 3$	597	600·58

In each case, the estimate and answer are close.

5 John gets an answer of 403·6669 on his calculator when he does the calculation $63·37 \times 63·37$. However, his estimate is 3600. What should he do next?

As his estimate of 3600 is very different from his answer, he should carefully enter the question into the calculator again.

If the answer is still unchanged, he should check the estimate.

63·37 × 63·37 = gives 4015·7569

The last answer is close enough to the estimate but John should do it once again in order to be sure of his answer.

Estimate:
60 × 60
= 3600

1 Complete the table below. Do it again if the estimate and calculator display are not close.

	Question	Rounding off	Estimate	Calculator display
a	747·6 + 156·8 + 85·47			
b	193 600 − 87 500 − 43 400			
c	38·16 × 9·814 × 34·2			
d	$3121.10 ÷ 46 − $41.70			
e	$6·9 million × 7·2 × 9·8			

2 Estimate the answer to each question and then use your calculator to find the answers. If these are not close, do the question again. (Round off correct to 2 dec. pl.)

a 8180·91 + 6532·47   b 95·345 − 38·608   c 567·85 + 356·9 − 196·3

d 5481·96 × 53·8   e 19·125 × 8·142 × 33   f 3·142 × 38·4 × 38·4

g 8000 − 146·35 × 8·85   h 46·87 + 3·82 × 6·004   i 63·045 × 85·67 × 14

j 77 400 ÷ 36·7 ÷ 1·85   k 97·814 ÷ 18·3 + 3·89   l 93·6 × 8·75 + 3·9 × 2·85

investigation

5:02

Investigation 5:02 | Weighing cornflakes

Please use the Assessment Grid on the following page to help you understand what is required for this Investigation.

- Weigh some cornflakes.
- Count them and work out the average (mean) mass of one cornflake.
- Use the net mass shown on the box to calculate how many cornflakes would be in the box.
- Repeat the investigation several times using different amounts of flakes.

How many?

Assessment Grid for Investigation 5:02 | **Weighing cornflakes**

The following is a sample assessment grid for this investigation. You should carefully read the criteria *before* beginning the investigation so that you know what is required.

		Assessment Criteria (B, C, D)		Achieved ✓
Criterion B Investigating Patterns	a	The results indicate that the student had difficulty understanding what was required.	1	
			2	
	b	An attempt has been made at an organised approach with some success.	3	
			4	
	c	The approach is well organised and explained, and the steps involved are easy to follow.	5	
			6	
	d	An explanation is given for the patterns and variations in the answers and a conclusion has been explained about how many cornflakes could be in the box.	7	
			8	
Criterion C Communication	a	The working out is hard to follow and the steps are not communicated clearly.	1	
			2	
	b	The working out is clear and the results are set out in an organised way; for example, in a table.	3	
			4	
	c	A well-structured solution is given showing all the required steps and results with a clear conclusion.	5	
			6	
Criterion D Reflection in Mathematics	a	An attempt has been made to explain the variations in the results.	1	
			2	
	b	Variations in results are explained and the reasonableness of the results has been discussed.	3	
			4	
	c	Variations in the results have been considered when developing a conclusion and possible alternatives or improvements have been investigated.	5	
			6	

5:03 | +/−, x^y, INV, FIX, C, AC, Constant Operator

Check the keys on your calculator by entering each calculator sentence and comparing your answer with the one given.

Key or question	Explanation or calculator sentence	Answer
[+/−] or [(−)] Find 6 × (−3)	We use this sign change key to obtain negative numbers. 6 [×] 3 [+/−] [=] (OR) 6 [×] [(−)] 3 [=]	−18
[x^y] Find 3^4	The power key: $3^4 = 3 \times 3 \times 3 \times 3$ 3 [x^y] 4 [=]	81
[INV], [2nd F] or [SHIFT]	On some keys there is a second function (shown in a different colour). To use this function press [2nd F] or [SHIFT] before the function key.	
[FIX]	A calculator can round off answers to a given number of decimal places. Different calculators do this in different ways. The simplest method uses a [FIX] key.	
Round off 53·1427 correct to 2 dec. pl.	53·1427 [INV] [FIX] 2 The [MODE] key may have to be used on some calculators.	53·14
Find 84·79 × 3·1856 correct to 4 dec. pl.	[INV] [FIX] [4] 84·79 [×] 3·1856 [=] (OR) [MODE] [FIX] [4] 84·79 [×] 3·1856 [=]	270·1070
[C] (or [AC] or [CE]) or [DEL]	These keys may be used to clear the last number only. Keys pressed beforehand are remembered.	
[AC] (or [CA] or [C])	These keys may wipe out everything in the calculator except what is stored in the memory.	
Constant Operator	The constant operator is used when the same operation is performed on many different numbers. Again the keys used vary from calculator to calculator.	

■ Note that [C] is in both groups, so check your calculator by pushing:

5 [×] 6 [C] 2 [=] .

You will get either 10 or 2.

worked examples

1 $\dfrac{5 - 15\cdot08}{-2\cdot8}$ Steps: 5 $\boxed{-}$ 15·08 $\boxed{=}$ $\boxed{\div}$ 2·8 $\boxed{+/-}$ $\boxed{=}$ Answer: 3·6

or $\boxed{[(}$ 5 $\boxed{-}$ 15·08 $\boxed{)]}$ $\boxed{\div}$ 2·8 $\boxed{+/-}$ $\boxed{=}$

2 $(-1\cdot8)^5$ Steps: 1·8 $\boxed{+/-}$ $\boxed{x^y}$ 5 $\boxed{=}$ Answer: $-18\cdot89568$

Exercise 5:03

1 Use your calculator to evaluate these correct to 3 decimal places.

a 3·141 592 7
b 0·142 857 14
c 5 ÷ 6
d 1 ÷ 11
e 63·5 − 147 ÷ 18·7
f 13·86 × 1·443 001 4

Use $\boxed{+/-}$ to make a negative.

−3 − 4   3 $\boxed{+/-}$ $\boxed{-}$ 4 $\boxed{=}$
−3 + 4   3 $\boxed{+/-}$ $\boxed{+}$ 4 $\boxed{=}$
−3 − (−4)   3 $\boxed{+/-}$ $\boxed{-}$ 4 $\boxed{+/-}$ $\boxed{=}$

2 Use your calculator to evaluate these correct to 3 decimal places.

a −8·16 − 3·14
b −3·046 + 7·814
c −4·6 − 1·8 − 1·2
d −9·6 + 3·8 + 4·9
e 8·57 − (−9·6)
f 4·667 − −2·048
g −3·142 × 4·8
h 7·923 481 ÷ (−3·578)
i $(-13\cdot4)^2$
j 96·3 ÷ (−3·84) + 10·4
k −20·65 ÷ −8 + 31·5
l Add −4·1, −3·6 and −5·8
m Add 9·3, −4·6 and −8·6
n Subtract −6·911 from −3·6
o $\dfrac{-3\cdot85 + 17\cdot972}{2\cdot3}$
p $\dfrac{3\cdot6764 + 5\cdot546}{-8\cdot8}$
q $\dfrac{-16\cdot8 - 17\cdot364}{-3\cdot65}$

3 Use the $\boxed{x^y}$ key to find the simplest answer for:

a 3^4
b 10^5
c 2^6
d 3^3
e $(-2)^{10}$
f $(-7)^5$
g $(-5)^4$
h $(-8)^3$

4 Give answers correct to 2 decimal places for:

a $2\cdot04^4$
b $(-3\cdot1)^5$
c $0\cdot3^2 + 0\cdot3^3$
d $1\cdot1^6$
e $0\cdot9^6 + 1\cdot1^6$
f $6^3 + 7 \div 3$
g $3\cdot81 \times 1\cdot08^2$
h $1\cdot9^2 + 3\cdot6^2$
i $1 + 0\cdot3^2$
j $1 + 0\cdot3^2 + 0\cdot3^3$
k $(2\cdot7 - 8\cdot6)^4$
l $(2\cdot7 - 8\cdot6)^3$

5 One extension cord costs $3.89. Use your constant operator to find the cost of:

a 8 cords
b 19 cords
c 73 cords
d 586 cords
e 8167 cords

5:04 | Speed and Accuracy

Exercise 5:04

Time how quickly you can do each set of questions. Add 10 seconds for each mistake.

1
a $0.87 - 9.6$ b 1.9^3
c $8874 \div 29$ d $-5.9 + 3.8$
e How many 18 cent pencils can you buy for $11.45?
f One litre of petrol costs 78·5 cents. What is the cost of 28 L?
g Find the value of $\frac{1}{3} \times 3.14 \times 9^2$.
h Change $\frac{11}{32}$ to a decimal.
i Find $\frac{7}{8}$ of 6·8 m.
j What is 13% of $876?

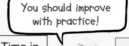
You should improve with practice!

Time in seconds	
1	
2	
3	
4	
5	

■ $\frac{7}{8}$ of 12·2 m:

7 ÷ 8 × 12·2 =

Answer = 10·675 m

■ 23% of $156:

23 ÷ 100 × 156 =

Answer = $35.88

2
a $3.42 - 6.7$ b 1.5^3
c $8604 \div 18$ d $-9.1 + 7.3$
e How many 27 cent pencils can you buy for $15.85?
f One litre of petrol costs 81·5 cents. What is the cost of 24 L?
g Find the value (correct to 3 dec. pl.) of $\frac{1}{3} \times 3.14 \times 7^2$.
h Change $\frac{19}{32}$ to a decimal.
i Find $\frac{3}{8}$ of 7·4 m.
j What is 17% of $687?

3
a $1.86 - 5.4$ b 1.7^3
c $7326 \div 37$ d $-6.2 + 3.8$
e How many 19 cent pencils can you buy for $16.85?
f One litre of petrol costs 79·6 cents. What is the cost of 45 L?
g Find the value (correct to 3 dec. pl.) of $\frac{1}{3} \times 3.14 \times 8^2$.
h Change $\frac{21}{32}$ to a decimal.
i Find $\frac{5}{8}$ of 5·6 m.
j What is 19% of $753?

4
a $7.86 - 8.3$ b 1.6^3
c $8970 \div 26$ d $-8.8 + 1.9$
e How many 36 cent pencils can you buy for $22.55?
f One litre of petrol costs 83·4 cents. What is the cost of 35 L?
g Find the value of $\frac{1}{3} \times 3.14 \times 6^2$.
h Change $\frac{13}{32}$ to a decimal.
i Find $\frac{5}{6}$ of 4·5 m.
j What is 21% of $496?

5
a $4.72 - 6.1$ b 2.1^3
c $7475 \div 25$ d $-7.4 + 2.7$
e How many 39 cent pencils can you buy for $27.65?
f One litre of petrol costs 82·5 cents. What is the cost of 38 L?
g Find the value (correct to 3 dec. pl.) of $\frac{1}{3} \times 3.14 \times 5^2$.
h Change $\frac{27}{32}$ to a decimal.
i Find $\frac{3}{4}$ of 3·9 m.
j What is 27% of $388?

5:05 | $\sqrt{}$, $\sqrt[3]{}$, $a\dfrac{b}{c}$, $\dfrac{1}{x}$

Give the basic numeral for:

1 5^2 **2** 4^2 **3** 14^2 **4** 2^3 **5** 3^3 **6** 4^3

7 Find the number that has a square of 36.

8 Find the number that has a square of 100.

9 If $1764 = (2 \times 3 \times 7) \times (2 \times 3 \times 7)$, what is the number that has a square of 1764?

10 What number has a square of 10 000?

If the square of 15 is 225, then the square root of 225 is 15.

If $15^2 = 225$, then $\sqrt{225} = 15$.

If the cube of 8 is 512, then the cube root of 512 is 8.

If $8^3 = 512$, then $\sqrt[3]{512} = 8$.

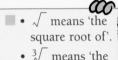

- $\sqrt{}$ means 'the square root of'.
- $\sqrt[3]{}$ means 'the cube root of'.

The number which, when squared, gives 225 is called the **square root** of 225.
The number which, when cubed, gives 512 is called the **cube root** of 512.

Enter each calculator sentence and compare your answer with the one given.

Key or question	Explanation or calculator sentence	Answer
$\boxed{\sqrt{}}$ $\sqrt{9} + \sqrt{100}$	The square root key 9 $\boxed{\sqrt{}}$ $\boxed{+}$ 100 $\boxed{\sqrt{}}$ $\boxed{=}$ $\big(OR\big)$ $\boxed{\sqrt{}}$ 9 $\boxed{+}$ $\boxed{\sqrt{}}$ 100 $\boxed{=}$	13
$\boxed{\sqrt[3]{}}$ $6 \times \sqrt[3]{27}$	The cube root key 6 $\boxed{\times}$ 27 $\boxed{\sqrt[3]{}}$ $\boxed{=}$ $\big(OR\big)$ 6 $\boxed{\times}$ $\boxed{\sqrt[3]{}}$ 27 $\boxed{=}$ You may need to use $\boxed{INV}$ $\boxed{\sqrt[3]{}}$	18
$\boxed{a\frac{b}{c}}$ **a** $\frac{3}{4} \times \frac{5}{8}$ **b** $3\frac{1}{2} + 4\frac{7}{8}$	The fraction key 3 $\boxed{a\frac{b}{c}}$ 4 $\boxed{\times}$ 5 $\boxed{a\frac{b}{c}}$ 8 $\boxed{=}$ 3 $\boxed{a\frac{b}{c}}$ 1 $\boxed{a\frac{b}{c}}$ 2 $\boxed{+}$ 4 $\boxed{a\frac{b}{c}}$ 7 $\boxed{a\frac{b}{c}}$ 8 $\boxed{=}$	**a** $\frac{15}{32}$ **b** $8\frac{3}{8}$
$\boxed{1/x}$ or $\boxed{x^{-1}}$ $\dfrac{1}{1 \cdot 4 + 1 \cdot 8}$	The reciprocal key turns your answer 'upside down'. 1·4 $\boxed{+}$ 1·8 $\boxed{=}$ $\boxed{1/x}$ $\boxed{=}$ You may need to use $\boxed{INV}$ $\boxed{1/x}$	0·3125

Exercise 5:05

1 Evaluate:

a $\sqrt{676}$ b $\sqrt{15\,625}$ c $\sqrt{11\cdot56}$ d $\sqrt{0\cdot0361}$

e $\sqrt[3]{125}$ f $\sqrt[3]{2744}$ g $\sqrt[3]{1\cdot728}$ h $\sqrt[3]{0\cdot343}$

2 Evaluate, correct to 1 decimal place:

a $\sqrt{3} + \sqrt{2}$ b $5 \times \sqrt{7}$ c $\sqrt{115} \div 4$ d $2 - \sqrt{87}$

e $\sqrt[3]{814\,806}$ f $7\cdot1 \times \sqrt[3]{64}$ g $\sqrt[3]{4} + \sqrt[3]{3}$ h $\sqrt[3]{8} \div 3$

3 Use the fraction key to do these.

a $\frac{3}{5} + \frac{3}{4}$ b $\frac{7}{8} - \frac{2}{3}$ c $4\frac{1}{2} - 1\frac{2}{3}$ d $3\frac{5}{8} + 2\frac{11}{20}$

e $\frac{7}{8} \times \frac{5}{6}$ f $\frac{6}{25} \div \frac{7}{10}$ g $1\frac{3}{4} \div \frac{5}{8}$ h $5\frac{1}{2} \times 6\frac{3}{4}$

i $6 \times \frac{3}{8}$ j $4\frac{3}{5} \div 5$ k $8 \div 2\frac{3}{4}$ l $2\frac{1}{8} + 5 \times \frac{3}{4}$

4 Use the $\boxed{1/x}$ key to evaluate these, giving answers correct to 3 decimal places.

a $\dfrac{1}{1\cdot8 + 3\cdot6}$ b $\dfrac{1}{4\cdot7 - 1\cdot8}$ c $\dfrac{1}{4\cdot1 - 9\cdot2}$ d $\dfrac{1}{4\cdot3 + 7\cdot6}$

e $\dfrac{1}{4\cdot1 \times 1\cdot7}$ f $\dfrac{1}{6 + 3 \times 1\cdot5}$ g $\dfrac{1}{3\cdot14 \times 3\cdot85}$ h $\dfrac{1}{-3\cdot8 \div -1\cdot6}$

---

investigation

5:05

Investigation 5:05 | The calculator and the fraction bar

Please use the Assessment Grid on the following page to help you understand what is required for this Investigation.

- What happens when $\dfrac{1}{4\cdot1 \times 2\cdot9}$ is done as

  1 $4\cdot1$ $2\cdot9$ on the calculator?

> ■ The fraction bar acts as a grouping symbol above and below the bar.

- Consider the question $\dfrac{1}{5 \times 20}$.

  What answer would you expect?

  What is the answer to 1 5 20 ?

  Why is this answer incorrect?

- Discuss your findings including a possible way to get the correct answer.

- Write your findings in a few full sentences.

- Try similar questions of your own and investigate the answers.

Assessment Grid for Investigation 5:05 |

The calculator and the fraction bar

The following is a sample assessment grid for this investigation. You should carefully read the criteria *before* beginning the investigation so that you know what is required.

		Assessment Criteria (B, C, D)		Achieved ✓
Criterion B Investigating Patterns	a	The answers to the calculations have been found but the student cannot explain why the answers are incorrect.	1	
			2	
	b	An attempt has been made to explain why the answers are incorrect.	3	
			4	
	c	Few further examples have been given leading to a conclusion is described.	5	
			6	
	d	Further examples have been explored successfully and a correct conclusion has been drawn together with a possible solution.	7	
			8	
Criterion C Communication	a	Working out is difficult to follow and findings have not been given.	1	
			2	
	b	Working out is clear and findings are communicated clearly.	3	
			4	
	c	Working out follows a logical progression and findings are discussed in full.	5	
			6	
Criterion D Reflection in Mathematics	a	An attempt has been made to explain the results, but a lack of investigation has made this difficult.	1	
			2	
	b	The reliability of the results has been checked with some success but the explanations are insufficient.	3	
			4	
	c	Results have been thoroughly checked and explanations are given. Possible solutions to the problem have been explored.	5	
			6	

5:06 | Calculator Applications

Use a calculator to find answers correct to 2 decimal places where necessary.

1 $659 + 13 \times 27$ **2** $4.48 + (2.6 \times 3.7)$ **3** $81 \div 0.2$

4 $\dfrac{7.184}{1.38 \times 0.95}$ **5** $\sqrt{186} - 5$ **6** $\sqrt[3]{93.6} \times 5$

7 $\dfrac{3}{8} \div \dfrac{5}{6}$ **8** $\dfrac{1}{2.853}$ **9** $(-13.86) \div (-8.4) - 5$ **10** 1.8^4

A *multiple* of a counting number is obtained when you multiply it by another counting number.

A *factor* of a counting number is a counting number that divides the first one exactly. eg $15 \times 7 = 105$. Here 15 and 7 are factors of 105, and 105 is a multiple of both 15 and 7.

Exercise 5:06

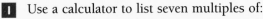

1 Use a calculator to list seven multiples of:

     a 15   **b** 27   **c** 153   **d** 617   **e** 333

2 Which of the prime numbers 2, 3, 5, 7, 11, 13, 17, 19, 23, 29 and 31 are factors of:

     a 119?   **b** 561?   **c** 27 094?   **d** 96 577?   **e** 10 015 005?

3 Use the rule given to write the next five numbers in the pattern.

	Rule	Pattern
a	Multiply the last term by 57 and subtract 403·1.	7·2, 7·3, . . ., . . ., . . ., . . ., . . .
b	Divide the last term by 100 and add 0·27.	0·27, 0·2727, . . ., . . ., . . ., . . ., . . .
c	Multiply the last term by 0·7 and add 686.	5020, 4200, . . ., . . ., . . ., . . ., . . .
d	Divide the last term by 8 and subtract 4096.	32 768, 0, . . ., . . ., . . ., . . ., . . .

4 By adding each row, column and diagonal, discover whether each is a magic square or not.

     a

365	775	201	→ ☐
283	447	661	→ ☐
693	119	529	→ ☐

↓ ↓ ↓ ↓ ↓
☐ ☐ ☐ ☐ ☐

     b

537	−233	845	→ ☐
691	383	75	→ ☐
−79	999	229	→ ☐

↓ ↓ ↓ ↓ ↓
☐ ☐ ☐ ☐ ☐

☐ In a magic square the numbers in each row, column and diagonal have the same sum.

5 Change each fraction into a decimal. (*Note:* $0.833333\ldots = 0.8\dot{3}$)

  a $\frac{15}{16}$ **b** $\frac{5}{8}$ **c** $\frac{1}{6}$ **d** $\frac{2}{3}$

6 Change each fraction into a decimal, approximating correct to 2 decimal places.

  a $\frac{1}{3}$ **b** $\frac{5}{7}$ **c** $\frac{5}{6}$ **d** $\frac{6}{11}$

7 If $a = 173\,155$, $b = 2308.2$, $c = 384.7$ and $d = 4$, find the value of:

  a $a + b$ **b** $b \times c$ **c** $c \div d$ **d** $b - c$

  e $500 - c$ **f** $14c$ **g** ad **h** $b \div 15$

  i c^2 **j** $10c - b$ **k** $a - 45^2$ **l** $\sqrt{1024d}$

■ *Note:*
$10c = 10 \times c$
$ad = a \times d$

8 a Below is an invoice (or bill). Calculate how much Mr Wilkes had to pay for each item (net amount) and then calculate the amount he had to pay altogether (net total).

■ The 'Net Amount', which is the amount to be paid, can be calculated by subtracting 'Discount' from the 'Gross Amount'.

MLM Building Materials Centre   INVOICE 142696

Name	Mr S. Wilkes	
Street		Lot II Stonebridge
Suburb		Rd Glenbrook

C O D

MLM REFERENCE No.	SALESMAN'S INITIALS	DATE
45888	RY	27/10/04

Item	Size	Specification	Qty	Rate	Gross Amount		Discount		Net Amount	
1		Bags of Cement	6	14.90	89	40	8	94		
2		Black Oxide	3 kg	12.00	36	00	3	60		
3	$6' \times 3' \times \frac{1}{2}''$	Particle Board	1 sheet	28.65	28	65	2	86		
4	$6' \times 3' \times \frac{3}{4}''$	Particle Board	2 sheets	33.15	66	30	6	63		
5	$3'' \times 2''$	Timber	15 metres	13.65	204	75	–	–		
6		Nails	2 kg	14.40	28	80	–	–		
7										

CUSTOMER COPY   **NET TOTAL $**

(Goods left at unattended sites are at customer's risk.)   GST is included in price.

b The invoice in Part **a** uses the old Imperial measurements in the Size column. If $1'' = 25.4\,\text{mm}$ and $1' = 304.8\,\text{mm}$, write the following in millimetres.

  i $2''$ **ii** $3''$ **iii** $\frac{1}{2}''$ **iv** $\frac{3}{4}''$ **v** $3'$ **vi** $6'$

5:07 | Problem Solving with the Calculator

Exercise 5:07

1
a How many different coloured towers (2 blocks high) is it possible to make using a red block and a blue block?
b How many different coloured towers (3 blocks high) is it possible to make using three blocks of different colours?
c When Wilma did Parts **a** and **b** she discovered that there were (2 × 1) ways for 2 blocks, (3 × 2 × 1) ways for 3 blocks and she guessed that there would be (4 × 3 × 2 × 1) different coloured towers (4 blocks high) that could be made using four blocks of different colours. Is she correct?
d Assume that the pattern she has discovered is correct and find the number of different coloured towers she could build using:
  i 5 blocks of different colours (towers being 5 high)
  ii 8 blocks of different colours (towers being 8 high)
  iii 11 blocks of different colours (towers being 11 high)

11! That's 11 × 10 × 9 × 8 × 7 × 6 × 5 × 4 × 3 × 2 × 1.

■ *Polygons*
5 sides: pentagon
6 sides: hexagon
7 sides: heptagon
8 sides: octagon
9 sides: nonagon
10 sides: decagon

2 How many times must 123 914 be added to 214 615 so that the total is greater than one million?

3 A huge regular polygon is to be made from 18 m of ribbon as part of a Christmas display. What is the greatest number of sides the polygon can have if each side must have a length of 1·75 m? What kind of polygon is this?

4
a Use a calculator to discover which numbers between 0 and 20 are factors of 4389.
b Use your answer to Part **a** to list as many factors of 4389 as you can.
(*Note:* If 3 is a factor, then 4389 ÷ 3 is also a factor and if 3 and 11 are both factors, then 3 × 11 must also be a factor.)

5 Use your calculator to list the five numbers along the path that have a sum of 1000.

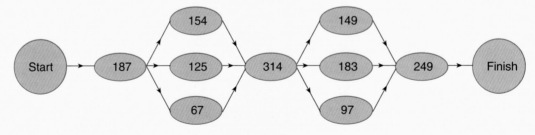

6　**a**　Which two numbers have a sum of 79 and a product of 1288?
　　b　Which two numbers have a difference of 11 and a product of 5226?
　　c　Which two numbers have a sum of 1200 and a difference of 68?

7　Calculate how much has been paid for each item if:
　　a　1200 items were bought for a total cost of 1620 cents
　　b　1200 items were bought for a total cost of $1620
　　c　84 100 items were bought for a total of 769 515 cents
　　d　84 100 items were bought for a total cost of $769 515

8　If one Australian dollar is worth 71·9 American cents, find the value of American currency (to the nearest cent) that could be exchanged for Australian currency to the value of:
　　a　$95 000　　　　　**b**　$8460　　　　　**c**　$3416
　　d　$9.86　　　　　　**e**　$21.80　　　　　**f**　$0.37

9　If one American dollar is worth 137·45 Japanese yen or 1·43 Australian dollars, give to the nearest cent the value in American currency of:
　　a　32 400 yen　　　　　　**b**　895 yen　　　　　　**c**　8460 yen
　　d　$1 000 000 Australian　　**e**　$814.50 Australian　　**f**　87 cents Australian

10

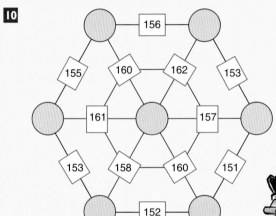

The numbers 74, 75, 77, 77, 78, 79 and 83 must be placed in the coloured circles so that the number in each square is the sum of the numbers in the circles on either side of it.

Which of these numbers must be placed in the centre circle?

Guess and check.

Guess a number for the centre circle. To check, work out the numbers which then have to go in the other circles.

Fun Spot 5:07 | Make words with your calculator

Use the calculations and the clues to complete the crossword.
To do this, you will need to read the reflection of the calculator display in a mirror.
(Ignore any decimal points in the answers.)

When you look in a mirror, '26' becomes 'as'.

Across

1 Hard to get over.
($2705^2 + 743$)

6 A bunch of tiny eggs.
($116 \cdot 66 \div 0 \cdot 38$)

7 Responsible for a close shave.
(261 232 less than 1 000 000.)

8 Enemy of fish.
($13 \cdot 7 \times 438 \cdot 4 + 1 \cdot 26 \times 2192$)

9 With one only, you go round in circles. ($2^{10} - 264$)

10 Not the stinging kind.
(How many 47 cent stamps could I buy for $17.86?)

11 A pattern of related numbers.
($11 586 600 \div [11 \cdot 84 + 38 \cdot 16]$)

13 'Yes . . .!' said the students.
(Round off $7 \cdot 115$ correct to 2 decimal places.)

Down

1 They say 'everyone has his price'.
($196^2 - 238$)

2 Robin Hood and Ned Kelly.
($107 + 3 \times 912 900$)

3 Animal madness.
($98 410 + 174 386 - 40 929$)

16 No long ears here!
($\frac{23}{9}$ as a decimal, correct to 1 decimal place.)

18 This one has long ears.
($\frac{4}{5}$ of $28 \cdot 25$)

19 Got up.
($179^2 + 35$)

22 I am, they . . . .
($556 \cdot 48 \div 148$)

23 What's anger?
(25 calculators at $14.84 each.)

24 This is human, to forgive is divine.
($\sqrt{597 529}$)

25 A horse sometimes does it.
(Six people share $1658.22. How much does each get?)

26 Weep.
($[14\frac{3}{4} + 35\frac{3}{8}] \times 16$)

4 These are hard to avoid.
($23^4 - 9068$)

5 The cause of much unhappiness.
($73 \cdot 375$, correct to 2 decimal places)

10 Goldie broke his chair.
($\frac{2}{3}$ of 11 457)

12	Not quite as hard. (1 000 000 minus 268 737)	17	'As' for 16 across. $(3 + \sqrt{529})$
14	My wife's favourite flower. $\left(\dfrac{48\,105}{6} - \dfrac{9621}{2}\right)$	19	Extent of surface. $(7970 \times [\frac{17}{40} + \frac{3}{8}])$
		20	Mineral aggregates. (1500 pencils at $1.58 each)
15	Fertile spot in the desert. (-1063×-20)	21	A great help in learning. $(307 \times 3{\cdot}8 + 307 \times 5{\cdot}2)$

5:08 | Spreadsheets on a Computer

Working through the following spreadsheet exercises will make you familiar with the Microsoft Excel program and you will learn how to use spreadsheets. You will find an Excel spreadsheet on the Companion Website or on the Interactive Student CD.

Spreadsheet 1: Australian Swimmers

Skills: Opening the Excel program, naming cells, using the tool bars, producing a table and saving your work.
- A spreadsheet allows you to make a table and use that table to calculate and graph interesting information.
- **Below is a picture of the Excel screen.** It shows a title, toolbars, cell content bar, column and row bars, and a sheet tab at the bottom. A table called Australian Swimmers is on the spreadsheet.

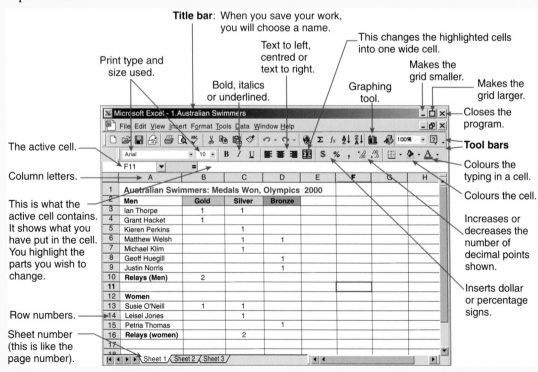

Naming cells

- Each cell is named using the letter at the top of the column followed by the row number on the far left, eg A4 or G11.
- The cell that is highlighted by the rectangle (in this case F11) is called the **active cell**.

Saving and storing work

Press (**Control + S**), *or* press **File** at the top left of the screen. (This will cause a menu to drop.) From the file select **Save**.

You will then have to decide where you want to save your work. You will need a file of your own, probably stored in the folder *Spreadsheets*.

Exercise

1   Cell A2 contains the word *Men*. What are the names of the cells that contain the words:
   a *Gold*   **b** *Silver*   **c** *Women*

2   On your computer, open the Excel program. Alternatively, click on the CW icon on the previous page and go to Chapter 17. It will open at a new spreadsheet that is called Book 1.

3   In cell A1, type the heading *Australian Swimmers: Medals Won, Olympics 2000*. Press **Enter**. Click on A1, hold your finger down and drag from cell A1 to cell F1. This will highlight all those cells. On the menu press **merge and centre** ⊞ and then press **centre** ▤.

4   In A2, type **Men**; in B2, type **Gold**; in C2 type **Silver**; In D2 type **Bronze**. Now highlight all four of these cells by clicking A2 and dragging across to D2. Make these cells **bold** by pressing **B** in the toolbar.

5   Type in the rest of the table above including the number of medals won in each category.

6   Make bold the contents of cells A10, A12 and A16.

7   Select the cells A3 to D9 by clicking on A3 and dragging down to cell D9. Use ⬧ to **colour** these cells.

8   Highlight cell A1 and use **font colour** **A** from the toolbar to make the heading orange.

9   When you have finished, print your spreadsheet and stick it into your book.

- Spreadsheets have many applications in the world of business.

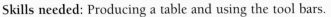

Spreadsheet 2: Operations with number

Skills needed: Producing a table and using the tool bars.

New skill: Using formulae for calculations.

Typing a formula into a cell

If we want our spreadsheet to calculate anything for us we need to use formulae.

- We must always start a formula with an equals sign.

  eg =A1−2   Here we are subtracting 2 from the contents of cell A1. If the active cell is C1, then the answer after this formula is applied will be placed in C1.

Formatting

- This is the process of making your spreadsheet look good by using tools such as *bold*, *italics*, *underline*, *centring*, *column width*, symbols like $ and %, *decimal places* and *colour*.

```
Microsoft Excel - Book 1                                                              _ □ ×
 File  Edit  View  Insert  Format  Tools  Data  Window  Help                          _ ⌐ ×
```

	A	B	C	D	E	F	G
1			Operation			Extension	
2	Number	Add 19	Subtract 20	Multiply by 7	Divide by 5	Divide by 3 then multiply by 10 then add 8 then subtract 1	
3	150	169	130	1050	30	507	
4	35	54	15	245	7	Fill down	
5							
6							
7						If you are not sure how to do something,	
8						look at Spreadsheet 1	
9							
10							

Sheet 1 / Sheet 2 / Sheet 3 /

Exercise

1   Open the Excel program as you did in the previous exercise. In B1, type the heading *Operation*. Click and drag from cell B1 to cell E1. This will highlight those 4 cells. On the toolbar press **merge and centre** and then press **centre** and then press **bold** **B**.

2   Type the rest of this table.

3   In B3 we want the answer when 19 has been added to the amount in A3. In B3 type =A3+19.

4   In C3 we want the answer when we subtract 20 from A3. So in C3 type =A3−20.

> In formulae like =A3−20 leave no spaces between symbols.

5   On the keyboard of a computer A3*7 means A3 *multiplied by* 7 and A3/5 means A3 *divided by 5*. So in D3 type =A3*7, and in E3 type =A3/5.

6   In B4 type =A4+19. Type in the formulae that will go into C4, D4 and E4.

7   Check your work by working out the answers and comparing them with the ones in the spreadsheet.

8   Click on A1 and drag the cursor to E4. Copy these cells by pressing **Ctrl + C** (or go to **Edit** at the top of the screen and press **Copy**). Highlight G1 and press **Ctrl + V** (or go to **Edit** at the top of the screen and press **Paste**).

9   Copy cells A1 to F4. Paste them at A7. Change the numbers in A9 and A10. Check the answers that appear in B9 to F10.

10   Save your work using the name *Operations* and print your spreadsheet.

Spreadsheet 3: Finding factors

Skills: Producing a table, using the toolbar (formatting), using formulae for calculations, inserting a row, correcting errors and highlighting a group of cells.

- **Click and drag** means to click on a cell and hold it down as you drag from that cell to another cell.
- **Edit   Clear   All**   removes everything from the highlighted cells.
  Edit   Clear   Formats   removes formats such as Colour, Bold, Number of decimal places, etc, but leaves the original typing.
- A **factor** of a number divides the number exactly, giving an answer that is a whole number.

Instructions

1   Open the Excel program as you did in the previous exercise. In A1, type the heading *Finding factors*. Click and drag from cell A1 to cell L1 and use [⊞] to make these into a single cell. In A2, type: *If the answer is a whole number, then the number and the answer are factors.* Click and drag from A2 to L2 and make these a single cell.

2   In cells A3 across to L3, type in: *Number, 1, 2, 3, 4, 5, 6, 7, 8, 9, 10.*
In A4, type 100. In A5, type 21. Use [**B**] to make these bold.

3   We need to divide the number in A4 by the numbers 1 to 10 (which are along the top of the tables) so: in B4 type =A4/1, in C4 type =A4/2, in D4 type =A4/3. Continue to fill the cells in this line in this way until you get to L4, where you will type =A4/10. Answers will appear in row 4.

4   Click and drag from cell B4 to cell B5. This highlights these two cells. Go to the Edit menu at the top of the page. Select Fill ▶ then click ↓Down (in the menu on the right). Repeat this procedure for C4 and C5, D4 and D5 and so on up to L4 and L5. You have told the computer to divide the number on the far left by 1, 2, 3, … 10 (the numbers at the top of the table).

5   Click and drag from cell C4 to cell L5. From the **Edit** menu, select Fill ▶ then ↓Down. The result of dividing the number on the far left by the numbers 2 to 10 should now be shown.

Exercise

1   Compare your table with the one below. If there are differences, check your work.

Finding factors										
If the answer is a whole number, then the number and the answer are factors.										
Number	1	2	3	4	5	6	7	8	9	10
100	100	50	33·3333	25	20	16·6667	14·2857	12·5	11·1111	10
21	21	10·5	7	5·25	4·2	3·5	3	2·625	2·333 33	2·1

2   **a**   Write the factors of 100 shown in the table.
   b   Write the factors of 21 shown in the table.

3   **a**   In A4 replace 100 by 36. What are the factors of 36?
   b   Use the method in **3a** to find the factors of:
      i 15   **ii** 28   **iii** 35   **iv** 99   **v** 29

Mathematical terms 5

calculator

- A machine that performs mathematical operations mechanically or electrically.

clear (the $\boxed{C}$, $\boxed{AC}$ or $\boxed{DEL}$ key)

- To remove the previous working from a calculator.

display

- What is shown on the screen of the calculator.

estimate

- To quickly calculate an answer that is close to the real one.

FIX ($\boxed{FIX}$ key)

- Used to round off answers to a given number of decimal places on a calculator.

inverse operation

- An inverse operation undoes what the original operation did.

$\boxed{INV}$, $\boxed{2nd\ F}$ or $\boxed{SHIFT}$ key

- This allows us to access the second function allocated to a key, usually written above it.

memory keys

- $\boxed{Min}$ or $\boxed{ST0\ A}$ enters the display replacing anything already in the memory.

- $\boxed{M+}$ adds the display to the memory.

- $\boxed{MR}$ or $\boxed{RCLA}$ recalls onto the screen whatever is in the memory.

reciprocal key $\boxed{^1/_x}$ or $\boxed{x^{-1}}$

- This is used to get the reciprocal of the display.

  eg 5 $\boxed{^1/_x}$ $\boxed{=}$ gives 0·2 (ie $\frac{1}{5}$).

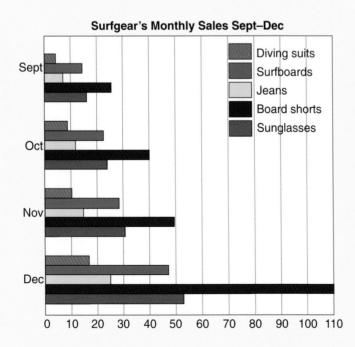

Surfgear's Monthly Sales Sept–Dec

Legend:
- Diving suits
- Surfboards
- Jeans
- Board shorts
- Sunglasses

- Spreadsheet data can be used to generate useful charts and graphs.

Diagnostic Test 5: | The Calculator

- Each section of the test has similar items that test a certain type of question.
- Errors made will indicate areas of weakness.
- Each weakness should be treated by going back to the section listed.

Use your calculator whenever necessary, estimating where possible.	Section
1 a $100 + 4 \times 7$ b $97 \cdot 3 + 13 \cdot 6 \times 9 \cdot 5$	5:01
2 a $935 \cdot 6 - 9 \cdot 817 + 37 \cdot 85$ b $57\,486 - 19\,954 + 147\,365$	5:01
3 a $80 \cdot 94 \div 3 \cdot 8 \times 45$ b $15 \cdot 96 \div 1 \cdot 9 + 1 \cdot 6$	5:01
4 a $81 \cdot 75 \times (2 \cdot 47 + 6 \cdot 53)$ b $(3 \cdot 7696 + 1 \cdot 886) \div (5 \cdot 028 - 1 \cdot 886)$	5:01
5 a $\dfrac{4862}{4 \cdot 81 + 8 \cdot 19}$ b $\dfrac{14 \cdot 375}{78 \cdot 09 - 71 \cdot 84}$	5:01
6 a Add the answers to 9×8, 6×9, $81 \div 0 \cdot 3$. b Add the answers to $1 \cdot 3 \times 0 \cdot 9$, $4 \cdot 65 \div 16$, $13 \cdot 08 - 6 \cdot 9$ and $0 \cdot 6 \times 0 \cdot 6$.	5:01

7 Without using a calculator, select the best estimate from A, B or C.
  a $432 \cdot 8 \div 16 \cdot 95$ b $41 \cdot 85 \times 19 \cdot 3$
     A 2 **B** 20 **C** 200   **A** 8 **B** 80 **C** 800
	5:02

8 a $6 \times (-3)$ b $-81 \cdot 76 + 1 \cdot 877$ c $-20 \cdot 65 \div -0 \cdot 08$	5:03
9 a 3^4 b $(-1 \cdot 8)^5$ c $2 \cdot 9^4$	5:03

10 Use your calculator to:
  a round off $53 \cdot 1427$ correct to 2 decimal places
  b round off $19 \cdot 9998$ correct to 3 decimal places
  c find $84 \cdot 79 \times 3 \cdot 1856$ correct to 4 decimal places.
	5:03

11 a $\sqrt{179 \cdot 56}$ b $\sqrt{9} + \sqrt{100}$ c $15 - \sqrt{96 \cdot 04}$	5:05
12 a $\sqrt[3]{4096}$ b $6 \times \sqrt[3]{27}$ c $72 \div \sqrt[3]{46 \cdot 656}$	5:05
13 a $\dfrac{3}{4} \times \dfrac{5}{8}$ b $3\dfrac{1}{2} + 4\dfrac{7}{8}$ c $4\dfrac{3}{5} \div 5$	5:05
14 Use the reciprocal key to evaluate these. a $\dfrac{1}{6 \cdot 4}$ b $\dfrac{1}{1 \cdot 4 + 1 \cdot 8}$ c $\dfrac{1}{17 \div 1 \cdot 36}$	5:05

Chapter 5 | Revision Assignment

1 A toy soldier is approximately $\frac{1}{32}$ of a real soldier's height. Estimate the height of the toy soldier.

2 The table below shows the temperature and the demand for electricity on a hot day for an island in the South Pacific.

EST means Eastern Standard Time.

EST	°C	Megawatts	EST	°C	Megawatts
0030	23·7	7 738	1230	42·3	12 131
0100	23·5	7 431	1300	42·2	12 148
0130	23·3	7 080	1330	43	12 167
0200	22·9	6 795	1400	43·6	12 154
0230	22·8	6 570	1430	43·5	12 207
0300	21·8	6 460	1500	43·4	12 214
0330	21·3	6 393	1530	43·7	12 331
0400	21·3	6 448	1600	43·7	12 317
0430	21·1	6 657	1630	44	12 229
0500	21·1	6 916	1700	42·4	12 170
0530	20·8	7 513	1730	37·7	11 929
0600	21·2	8 055	1800	36·1	11 744
0630	22·8	8 577	1830	35·2	11 470
0700	24·7	9 181	1900	33·8	11 371
0730	25·9	9 558	1930	32·7	11 384
0800	27·9	9 880	2000	32·1	11 344
0830	31·8	10 337	2030	31·3	10 859
0900	34	10 731	2100	30·9	10 388
0930	36·1	11 124	2130	30	10 277
1000	38	11 353	2200	29·6	9 881
1030	39·3	11 577	2230	29·1	9 743
1100	40·4	11 764	2300	28·7	9 431
1130	41·1	11 879	2330	28·5	9 066
1200	41·5	12 024	000	26·6	8 720

a Draw a graph showing the change in temperature (in degrees Celsius) as time changed. Use the title Temperature.

b Draw a graph showing the electricity demand (in Megawatts) as time changed. Use the title Electricity Demand.

c Write a paragraph explaining the changes that occurred referring to the graphs drawn or to the table above.

3 In the game of *Take Two*, the 100 Scrabble tiles are used. Each player starts with 4 tiles and when someone completes their crossword using all tiles they have taken, that person says 'Take Two!' and each person draws 2 more tiles. This continues until insufficient tiles remain for each player to take 2. Scoring is similar to *Scrabble*. If three people played in the game, how many times would each person draw only 2 tiles?

6

Patterns and Algebra

Chapter Contents

Learning Outcomes

Students will be able to:

- Use letters to represent numbers and translate between words and algebraic symbols.
- Create, record, analyse and generalise number patterns using words and algebraic symbols in a variety of ways.
- Use the algebraic symbol system to simplify, expand and factorise simple algebraic expressions.

Areas of Interaction

Approaches to Learning (Knowledge Acquisition, Problem Solving, Communication Skills, Thinking Skills), Human Ingenuity

6:01 | Patterns and Rules Review

If $a = 6$, find the value of:

1 $a + a$ **2** $2 \times a$ **3** $2a$ **4** $3a - a$

Write the next two numbers in each pattern.

5 10, 21, 32, ..., ...   **6** 12, 9, 6, ..., ...

7 3, 6, 9, ..., ...   **8** $1^2 + 1, 2^2 + 1, 3^2 + 1,$ ..., ...

Use the rule given to complete the table.

9 $M = 2n + 1$

n	0	1	2	3
M				

10 $y = 10 - x$

x	4	5	6	7
y				

Discussion

 ,  , 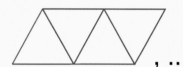 , ...

Examine the number of sides used for each group of triangles.

1 Complete a table of values that shows how *the number of sides* used is related to *the number of triangles*.

Number of triangles (x)	1	2	3	4	5
Number of sides (y)	3	5			

2 Describe the pattern in words and symbols.
The number of sides increases by 2 each time, so the number of sides is 2 times the number of triangles plus the one red side.
$$y = \ldots x + 1$$

3 We show this relationship on a graph.
$$y = 2x + 1$$

x	1	2	3	4
y	3	5	7	9

4 How would you describe in words, the pattern of points we have drawn?

5 What other points will belong to this pattern? Does this graph represent an increasing or decreasing number pattern?

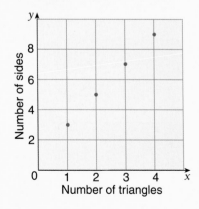

Find a rule to describe the pattern shown in this table.

x	2	3	4	6	12
y	6	4	3	2	1

All of these are ways of describing the pattern.

Solution

As x increases y decreases. In this case the two variables always have a product of 12.

Here $x \times y = 12$ or $xy = 12$

or $y = 12 \div x$ or $y = \dfrac{12}{x}$

or $x = 12 \div y$ or $x = \dfrac{12}{y}$

Exercise 6:01

Foundation Worksheet 6:01

Patterns and rules

1 Use the rule to fill in the table.

a $y = x + 1$

x	1	2	3	4
y				

1 Dipesh and Idris noticed that during a recent celebration in Kochi, a large number of colourful flags were flown from wire joining poles along the main street. They drew up the following table showing the number of poles (p) and the number of flags (f) as they walked along the street.

Poles (p)	1	2	3	4	5
Flags (f)	0	3	6	9	12

   a Find a rule connecting the number of flags (f) and the number of poles (p).
   b If the city of Bathurst had 96 flags, how many poles would they need?
   c If the poles were 10 m apart, how far would the colourful display extend?

2 Use the rule given to complete the table.

   a $F = P - 1$

P	1	2	3	4
F				

   b $F = 2P - 2$

P	1	2	3	4
F				

   c $F = 4P - 4$

P	1	2	3	4
F				

   d $y = x + 3$

x	1	2	3	4
y				

   e $y = 3x$

x	1	2	3	4
y				

   f $y = 2x + 1$

x	1	2	3	4
y				

3 With each table there is an incomplete rule. Complete the rules using the tables.

a

x	4	5	6	7
y	3	2	1	0

$y = \square - x$

b

d	1	2	3	4
m	24	12	8	6

$m = \square \div d$

c

w	0	1	2	3
p	7	17	27	37

$p = \square w + 7$

d

x	0	1	2	3
y	−5	−2	1	4

$y = \square x - 5$

e

a	−4	−3	−2	−1
b	23	16	11	8

$b = a^2 + \square$

f

n	0	1	2	3
p	50	42	34	26

$p = 50 - \square n$

4 Find the rule to describe each pattern.

a

x	0	1	2	3
y	0	7	14	21

b

d	8	9	10	11
b	3	4	5	6

c

v	4	5	6	7
M	9	11	13	15

d

a	0	1	2	3
M	0	1	4	9

e

d	2	3	4	5
e	11	10	9	8

f

x	1	2	3	4
y	12	6	4	3

5 Sandy paid $70 to enter a tennis competition. She had to play eight other players and received $25 prize money for each player she beat.
She worked out that her total profit (P) could be written in terms of the number of sets won (S) as $P = 25S - 70$.

a Use the rule to complete this table.

S	3	4	5	6	7	8
P						

b What happens to P if no sets are won?
c How many sets must Sandy win to be sure of winning money rather than losing money overall?

6

 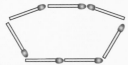 

Base length L	1	2	3
Perimeter P	5	7	9

The rule for the pattern above is $P = 2L + 3$.

a Explain why the rule works.
b Find the perimeter when the base length is:
   i 4   ii 5   iii 10   iv 100   v 68
c Can the base length ever be zero? Explain your answer.

Technology Applications

6:01 Magic squares

Activities

Investigation 6:01 | Making sense of algebra

Please use the Assessment Grid on the following page to help you understand what is required for this Investigation.

From Ireland I was sent small and large boxes of toy figures. If each small box contains x figures and each large box contains y figures, we could write an algebraic expression for the number of figures present in a group.

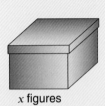

x figures

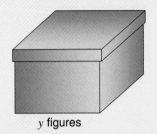

y figures

3 figures

We do not know how many soldiers are in each box. That is why we can say that they contain x and y soldiers respectively. In the picture above we have $x + y + 3$ figures.

Exercise

1 Use an algebraic expression to write the number of toy figures present.

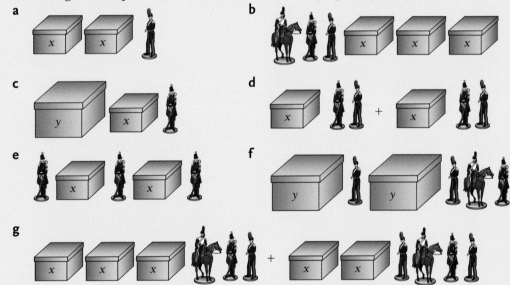

2 Find the number of toy figures present for each part of Question 1:
  a if the red boxes contain 10 figures and the blue boxes contain 16.
  b if the red boxes contain 7 figures and the blue boxes contain 11.

3 Draw some pictures of your own, like those above, to show:
  a $x + 2$ toy figures   b $3x + 1$ toy figures   c $x + y$ toy figures

4 Describe how algebra might help in solving more complex problems of the same type.

Appendix B **B:01 Challenge: Finite differences**

Assessment Grid for Investigation 6:01 | **Making sense of algebra**

The following is a sample assessment grid for this investigation. You should carefully read the criteria *before* beginning the investigation so that you know what is required.

		Assessment Criteria (B, C, D)		Achieved ✓
Criterion B Investigating Patterns	a	Expressions have been found for question 1 with few errors.	1	
			2	
	b	Simplified expressions have been found for question 1 with few errors.	3	
			4	
	c	Correct simplified expressions have been found for question 1 and the answers to question 2 have been found, with some patterns described.	5	
			6	
	d	Further examples demonstrate a good understanding of algebraic patterns, with clear explanations for all solutions and patterns found.	7	
			8	
Criterion C Communication	a	Answers may have been obtained but no working out is shown.	1	
			2	
	b	Working out is shown, showing the steps involved in both questions 1 and 2.	3	
			4	
	c	Algebraic setting out follows a logical sequence and an understanding of the solution has been demonstrated.	5	
			6	
Criterion D Reflection in Mathematics	a	An attempt has been made to explain and check the reasonableness of answers obtained.	1	
			2	
	b	The answers obtained in question 2 are compared and possible patterns are described.	3	
			4	
	c	An appreciation of the usefulness of algebra is given in question 4, with further possible applications given.	5	
			6	

6:02 | Addition and Subtraction of Like Terms

prep quiz

6:02

Simplify each expression:

1 $5x + 2x$	**2** $10a - 7a$	**3** $3p + 7p + 2p$	**4** $9m + m$	**5** $6m - m$
6 $3a^2 + 5a^2$	**7** $2mn + 6mn$	**8** $9ab + 2ba$	**9** $19x - 10x$	**10** $6p - 5p$

In Year 7 you were introduced to algebra. This Prep Quiz should have reminded you of the types of expressions you were asked to simplify.

Collecting like terms

> **Remember!**
> When adding or subtracting terms in algebra, the sign belongs to the term after it.

worked examples

see

1:12, A:12E

1 $\boxed{5x}\ \boxed{-2y}\ \boxed{-3x}\ \boxed{+7y}$

$= \boxed{5x}\ \boxed{-3x}\ \boxed{-2y}\ \boxed{+7y}$

$= 2x + 5y$

2 $\underline{4a\ +6\ -5\ -a}$

$= \underline{4a - a\ +6 -5}$

$= 3a + 1$

3 $7ab - 3bc + 2ab$
$= 7ab + 2ab - 3bc$
$= 9ab - 3bc$

4 $8x^2 + 2x - 6x^2 - 5x$
$= 8x^2 - 6x^2 + 2x - 5x$
$= 2x^2 - 3x$

5 $5a - 7 + a + 5b$
$= 6a - 7 + 5b$

6 $6x + 7y - 9x + 2y$
$= -3x + 9y$ OR $9y - 3x$

When you move a term, don't forget to move its sign too!

$-5x$

Only *like terms* can be added or subtracted together.

Exercise 6:02A (Easier types)

> **Foundation Worksheet 6:02**
>
> Addition and subtraction
> **1** Simplify each expression.
>   **a** $x + x$ **b** $6a - 2a$
> **2** Find the value when $x = 10$.
>   **a** $3x$ **b** $3x + 4$

1 Simplify each expression.

a $5x + 3x$	**b** $2y + 7y$	**c** $6a + a$
d $b + 7b$	**e** $7m - 2m$	**f** $9n - 4n$
g $10a - a$	**h** $x - x$	**i** $4l^2 + 9l^2$
j $21x^2 + 9x^2$	**k** $5xy + 7xy$	**l** $8pq + 6pq$

2 Complete these two tables.

a

+	a	$2a$	$5a$	$6a$	$10a$
$3a$					
$5a$			$11a$		
a					
$6a$					
$10a$					

b

−	$3a$	a	$2a$	$5a$	$4a$
$5a$					
$7a$			$5a$		
$12a$					
$8a$					
$10a$					

> Subtract the terms along the top from the terms in the left–hand column.

3 Simplify:

a $5a + 2a + 3a$
b $10y - 3y + 2y$
c $5m^2 + 2m^2 + 4m^2$
d $6x^2 - 3x^2 + 2x^2$
e $5pq + 2pq - 3pq$
f $7p - 4p - 2p$
g $7a + 3a + 2a + 6a$
h $6k + 3k - 2k + k$
i $7q^2 - 2q^2 - 3q^2 + q^2$

4 Simplify each expression, then let $a = 3$ to find its value.

a $5a + 2a$
b $3a + 2a$
c $5a + a$
d $9a - 7a$
e $6a - 5a$
f $16a - 11a$
g $2a^2 + 3a^2$
h $a^2 + 7a^2$
i $5a^2 - 3a^2$

> ▓ $8a$ means $8 \times a$, so if $a = 3$, then $8a = 8 \times 3$.

5 Simplify these expressions by collecting like terms.

a $2x + 3y + 4x$
b $6m + 2n + 3m$
c $a + 8a + a$
d $5x + 4y - 2x$
e $7p - p + 4m$
f $5t - 4t + 3w$
g $3a + 2b + 4a + 2b$
h $8t + 4w - 6t + 2w$
i $9p + 3q - 7p + 2q$

6 Simplify each expression, then let $x = 3$ and $y = 5$ to find its value.

a $2x + y + 3x$
b $3y + 4y + 10$
c $5x + 4y - 35$
d $3x + 2y + 2x + y$
e $5x - 2x + 3y + y$
f $4x + 3y - 2x - y$

Exercise 6:02B (Harder types)

1 Simplifying these expressions may involve negative numbers.

a $10a - 3a$
b $3a - 10a$
c $6a - 7a$
d $-6x + 8x$
e $-3p + 2p$
f $-4y + 9y$
g $6m - 9m$
h $a - 5a$
i $2y - 12y$
j $-3x - 2x$
k $-2y - 5y$
l $-4p - 6p$
m $8x - (-3x)$
n $6y - (-2y)$
o $5t - (-2t)$
p $-3ab + 5ab$
q $9xy - 15xy$
r $-5x^2 - 7x^2$
s $-3x - (-2x)$
t $-7x - (-10x)$
u $-4p - (-4p)$

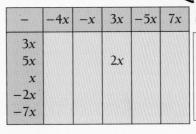

$-7 -8 = -15$
... I think!

2 Complete these tables.

a

+	$-4x$	$-x$	$3x$	$-5x$	$7x$
$3x$					
$5x$		$8x$			
x					
$-2x$					
$-7x$					

b

−	$-4x$	$-x$	$3x$	$-5x$	$7x$
$3x$					
$5x$			$2x$		
x					
$-2x$					
$-7x$					

> ▓ In Question **2b** subtract the terms at the top from the terms in the left-hand column.

3 Simplify these expressions by collecting the like terms.

a $5x + 2y - 4x$
b $9m + 4n - 5n$
c $8p + 3q - 9p$
d $5x - 7 - 3x$
e $10 - 4p + 2p$
f $9q - 3p + 7p$
g $9a - 3b - 9a$
h $-6m + 2n + 4m$
i $-3n + 2q + 7n$
j $-3x + 2x - 5y$
k $-5t - 2t + 3w$
l $m - 7m - 2n$
m $-5a - 2b - a$
n $6xy - 3x + 2xy$
o $5ab - 7ab + 6$
p $7x^2 + 9x - 8x^2$
q $-8p + 7pq - 2p$
r $5 - 2x^2 + x^2$

4 Simplify:

   a $2a + 4b + 6a + 2b$

   b $7x + 3y - 3x + 4y$

   c $9m - 2n + 7n + 2m$

   d $9p - 7 + 6p - 5$

   e $8a + 10 - 5a + 2$

   f $12 - 6q - 5q + 3$

   g $9k + 6l - 7k - 4l$

   h $3m - 5m + 9l - 7l$

   i $x + 7y - 5y + 2x$

   j $3ab + 4a + 2ab + 3a$

   k $6xy + 2 - 4xy - 5$

   l $3x^2 + 2x + 7x^2 - x$

   m $5a + 7 - 2a + 3a$

   n $10 + 13a - 7a + 2a$

   o $9y + 7y + 4x - 10y$

   p $3a + 2b + a - 4b$

   q $9l - 2q - 6l + 4q$

   r $10t + 2w - 11t - 6w$

   s $5ab - 4bc + 2ab + 3bc$

   t $6mn - 3m + 4mn - 6m$

   u $6 - 4kl - 9 - 3kl$

   v $7x^2 + 6x - 6x^2 - 9x$

   w $9q - 6q^2 + 5q^2 - 7q$

   x $7 + 4h - 10h - 16$

5 Simplify the following:

   a $5xy - 2yx$

   b $4ab - 10ba + a$

   c $-2mn + 8nm + 6$

   d $10 - ba - 5ab$

   e $5m^2 + 7m + 3 - 2m^2 - 5m$

   f $6a^2 + 9a - 1 + 5a^2 - 10a$

   g $2xy - 5yz + 3yx - 7yz$

   h $2a^2 + 3ab + a^2 - 2ba$

   i $6 + 2mn - 5 + m + 3nm$

   j $9k^2 - 8kt + 7t^2 + 8tk$

   k $10ab - 9ba + 3a - 4b + 6a$

   l $9m^2 + 6n^2 - m^2 - 10n - n$

> ▨ $a \times b = b \times a$
> so $ab = ba$

6:03 | Multiplication of Pronumerals

prep quiz

6:03

Simplify these products by writing them without the multiplication signs.

  1 $5 \times a$ **2** $p \times q$ **3** $3 \times a \times b$ **4** $5 \times x \times 3 \times y$ **5** $2 \times x \times x$

Find the value of each expression if $a = 3$ and $b = 4$.

  6 ab **7** $3a$ **8** $2a + 4b$ **9** b^2

  10 Put in the '×' signs to show the meaning of the expression mv^2.

The Prep Quiz should have reminded you that a term like mn means $m \times n$, so when we multiply, say, $3a \times 6b$, we simply multiply the numbers together and then the pronumerals without any multiplication signs.

$$3a \times 6b = (3 \times a) \times (6 \times a)$$
$$= 3 \times 6 \times a \times b$$
$$= 18ab$$

> When multiplying:
> two 'like' signs give a '+',
> two 'unlike' signs give a '–'.

worked examples

1 **a** $6 \times 4a = 24a$ **b** $3m \times 2n = 6mn$

     c $3a \times bc = 3abc$ **d** $4 \times 2x \times 3x = 24x^2$

2 **a** $-3 \times 2y = -6y$ **b** $-5p \times -4q = 20pq$

     c $3a \times -3a = -9a^2$ **d** $-2p \times 3q \times -4p = 24p^2q$

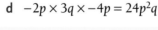

  Multiply the numbers first, then the pronumerals.

Exercise 6:03

1 Simplify each product.

  a $5 \times 2a$ b $7 \times 3x$ c $8 \times 2m$

  d $10 \times 6y$ e $8p \times 7$ f $6n \times 5$

  g $3q \times 7$ h $4 \times 11k$ i $3b \times 5$

  j $6 \times 2a$ k $3 \times 6y$ l $12a \times 4$

  m $\frac{1}{2} \times 6a$ n $12b \times \frac{1}{4}$ o $\frac{1}{3} \times 15m$ p $100y \times \frac{1}{100}$

2 Simplify:

  a $3m \times 2n$ b $6x \times 2y$ c $5t \times 5w$ d $7a \times 3b$

  e $7a \times b$ f $p \times 5q$ g $3k \times 4l$ h $3b \times a$

  i $4m \times 10n$ j $6x \times 3x$ k $9a \times 4y$ l $5x \times x$

  m $3y \times 5y$ n $6m \times 7m$ o $k \times 7k$ p $\frac{1}{2}y \times 4y$

3 Simplify these products.

  a $5ab \times 4n$ b $3 \times 2xy$ c $6 \times 3mn$

  d $7 \times 2a \times 3$ e $3 \times 4b \times 2$ f $2 \times 2a \times b$

  g $a \times b \times 5$ h $3 \times b \times 2c$ i $m \times 5 \times n$

  j $3a \times 2b \times 4$ k $a \times 5b \times 6c$ l $x \times 4y \times 3$

Note!
$a \times a$ **could be written as** aa, **but it is better to write** a^2.

4 Simplify:

  a $a \times ab$ b $mn \times m$ c $3x \times ax$

  d $2ab \times 3a$ e $4pq \times 3q$ f $5k \times 3kl$

  g $3a \times 4bc$ h $9ab \times 10bc$ i $4xy \times 5xz$

  j $3a \times 4b \times 2c$ k $mn \times np \times mp$ l $2ab \times b \times 3a$

5 Complete these multiplication tables.

  a

×	6	a	$2b$	$9m$	$3ab$
$2a$					
$3b$					
7					
a					
ab					

  b

×	x	$2y$	xy	$5x$	$2xz$
$4x$					
y					
$5y$					
$2xy$					
yz					

6 Simplify these products.

  a $(-3x) \times 5$ b $7 \times (-2m)$ c $(-4) \times (-3a)$

  d $9m \times (-3)$ e $(-5) \times (-6k)$ f $(-7a) \times (-2)$

  g $(-a) \times 2b$ h $(-p) \times (-q)$ i $5n \times (-2m)$

  j $(-6t) \times (-w)$ k $(-8x) \times 7y$ l $10m \times (-3m)$

  m $(-6y) \times (-6y)$ n $3a \times (-4a)$ o $(-3x) \times (-x)$

  p $6 \times 2a \times (-5)$ q $5 \times (-3y) \times (-2)$ r $6a \times (-4) \times a$

  s $9m \times 2n \times (-3)$ t $(-8k) \times 4 \times k$ u $(-3p) \times 4 \times (-2p)$

  v $5xy \times (-2x)$ w $(-4a) \times (-6ab)$ x $(-5mn) \times mp$

7 Complete these tables.

a

×	−3	5	2x	−4x	−y
7					
−2					
−x					
4x					
−3y					

b

×	2a	3b	−a	−4b	−ab
6a					
−3b					
−b					
3a					
2ab					

8 Simplify these miscellaneous products.

	A	**B**	**C**	**D**
a	$5x \times 3y$	$-2 \times 4m$	$6x \times (-3x)$	$2y \times y$
b	$6 \times 5ab$	$a \times b \times c$	$-3a \times (-2b)$	$mn \times m$
c	$2a \times 4b$	$-4p \times 3q$	$3xy \times 2y$	$5 \times 2a \times 3a$
d	$-4m \times (-4m)$	$\frac{1}{2} \times 10ab$	$5mn \times 6mn$	$ab \times 4b$
e	$2x^2 \times 3y$	$3t \times 5w$	$a \times (-3a)$	$3mn \times 2n \times 4$
f	$(-6k) \times 3k$	$(-2l) \times (-3l)$	$2a \times 5b \times 10c$	$7xy \times 5$
g	$7ab \times 2a \times 0$	$x \times (-x)$	$-4h \times 2k$	$9a \times (-3a) \times 2$
h	$(-3x) \times (-3) \times 2x$	$-a \times 2a \times 4b$	$7mn \times 4mp$	$(-2x) \times (-3) \times (-4y)$

6:03

Fun Spot 6:03A | Why do people laugh up their sleeves?

Simplify each part and put the letter for that part in the box above the correct answer.

A $6a + a$
B $15m - m$
C $8 \times 3k$
E $10 - x - x$
E $7a \times 0$
E $4x + 5 + 2x$
F $3a \times 2b$
H $16a \div 2$
R $7a - 6a$
S $6ab \times 4$
E $8a \times \frac{1}{2}$
H $xy + yx$

A $9x - x$
B $14x \div 2$
E $3k - 2t - t$
N $6a \times a$
Y $6a - 1$
S $7 + x - 7$
T $\frac{1}{3} \times 9a$
T $4p + 6p + 7$
T $a \times ab$
E $-5a + 2a$
H $(2a)^2$
U $101x - x$

E $9x - 5y - 2x$
E $9p + 3q - 7p - 2q$
I $16m - m - m - m$
K $8m + 3b - 2m + b$
N $6a - 7a$
O $10x - 8x$
P $b \times 7b$
S $10x + 8 - 10x$
T $3x - (-2x)$
E $-4x - x$
H $-4 \times k$
U $x - x + 1$

N $7x - 3y + 2x - 4y$
W $3x^2 \times 1$
Y $3a^2 + 5a^2$
R $6ab + b - 2ba + b$

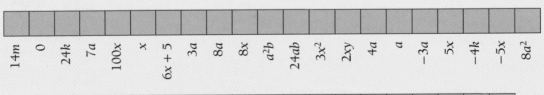

14m	0	24k	7a	100x	x	6x + 5	3a	8a	8x	a^2b	24ab	$3x^2$	2xy	4a	a	−3a	5x	−4k	−5x	$8a^2$

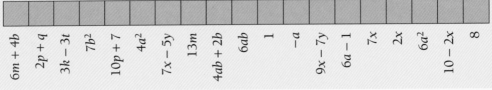

6m + 4b	2p + q	3k − 3t	$7b^2$	10p + 7	$4a^2$	7x − 5y	13m	4ab + 2b	6ab	1	−a	9x − 7y	6a − 1	7x	2x	$6a^2$	10 − 2x	8

6:04 | Division of Pronumerals

Simplify these divisions.

1 $12x \div 6$ **2** $20y \div 5$ **3** $10a \div 2$ **4** $100m \div 5$

5 $\dfrac{12x}{6}$ **6** $\dfrac{20y}{5}$ **7** $\dfrac{10a}{2}$ **8** $\dfrac{100m}{5}$

6:04

If $m = 20$ and $n = 5$, find the value of: **9** $m \div n$ **10** $\dfrac{m}{n}$

The Prep Quiz should have reminded you that a division can be written as a fraction.

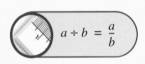

$$a \div b = \frac{a}{b}$$

$$x \div x = \frac{x}{x}$$
$$= 1$$

If a division is written as one term 'over' the other, we simply divide the numbers and then **cancel** the pronumerals that are common in the 'top' and 'bottom'. (When we cancel, we are really dividing top and bottom by that pronumeral.)

worked examples

1

a $\dfrac{20x}{5} = \dfrac{\overset{4}{\cancel{20}}x}{\cancel{5}_1}$

     $= 4x$

b $\dfrac{15x}{3x} = \dfrac{\overset{5}{\cancel{15}}x^1}{\cancel{3}x_1}$

     $= 5$

c $\dfrac{12ab}{6a^2} = \dfrac{\overset{2}{\cancel{12}}\cancel{a}^1 b}{\cancel{6}\cancel{a}_1 a}$

     $= \dfrac{2b}{a}$.

How many lots of 7y are there in 14y?

2

a $14y \div 7$
     $= 2y$

> Divide 14y into 7 parts.

b $14y \div 7y$
     $= 2$

3

a $9x^2 \div 3x$

     $= \dfrac{\overset{3}{\cancel{9}}\cancel{x}x}{\cancel{3}\cancel{x}}$

     $= 3x$

b $ab^2 \div ab$

     $= \dfrac{\overset{1}{\cancel{a}}\cancel{b}^1 b}{\cancel{a}\cancel{b}_1}$

     $= b$

c $3xy \div 6y$

     $= \dfrac{\overset{1}{\cancel{3}}x\cancel{y}^1}{\cancel{6}\cancel{y}_1 \, 2}$

     $= \dfrac{x}{2}$ [or $\frac{1}{2}x$ or $0.5x$]

 Divide the number first, then the pronumerals.

Remember this when dividing...

$(+ \; +) = +$
$(- \; -) = +$
$(+ \; -) = -$

4

a $\dfrac{-6x}{2x} = -3$

b $\dfrac{-12ab}{-4b} = 3a$

c $18m \div (-6) = -3m$

Exercise 6:04

1 Simplify each division.

a $\dfrac{6a}{3}$

b $\dfrac{10m}{5}$

c $\dfrac{16p}{4}$

d $\dfrac{12x}{4x}$

e $\dfrac{18k}{6k}$

f $\dfrac{20a}{10a}$

g $\dfrac{9mn}{3m}$

h $\dfrac{6ab}{a}$

i $\dfrac{8pq}{2q}$

j $\dfrac{5x}{10}$

k $\dfrac{6a}{10}$

l $\dfrac{4m}{20}$

m $\dfrac{4n}{12}$

n $\dfrac{10m}{20m}$

o $\dfrac{6p}{12p}$

p $\dfrac{7x}{21x}$

q $\dfrac{9m}{12m}$

r $\dfrac{12mn}{6m}$

s $\dfrac{8ab}{4b}$

t $\dfrac{6x^2}{3x}$

u $\dfrac{15a^2}{5a}$

2 Simplify:

a $12m \div 6$ b $10x \div 2$ c $20p \div 4$ d $16a \div 8$
e $15n \div 5$ f $24p \div 12$ g $30l \div 10$ h $25k \div 5$
i $6m \div 3m$ j $20a \div 10a$ k $12m \div 2m$ l $18l \div 3l$
m $24p \div 8p$ n $35x \div 7x$ o $28k \div 7k$ p $14t \div 7t$
q $5ab \div a$ r $6mn \div 2m$ s $8pq \div pq$ t $6tw \div 3t$
u $10mn \div 10n$ v $8x^2 \div 8x$ w $12xy \div xy$ x $18a^2 \div 9a$

3 Simplify these divisions which involve negative terms.

a $\dfrac{-10a}{5}$

b $\dfrac{-6m}{2}$

c $\dfrac{-8q}{-4}$

d $\dfrac{-12p}{-4}$

e $\dfrac{20p}{-10p}$

f $\dfrac{-15k}{5k}$

g $\dfrac{-18n}{-9n}$

h $\dfrac{-24x}{-8x}$

i $\dfrac{-6xy}{3x}$

j $\dfrac{12mn}{-3n}$

k $\dfrac{-9kl}{-3l}$

l $\dfrac{-20mn}{-5}$

m $12x \div (-3)$ n $15m \div (-5)$ o $-20t \div 10$ p $-24n \div (-8)$
q $10m \div (-5m)$ r $-14x \div 2x$ s $-9w \div (-3w)$ t $-18p \div (-9p)$
u $6ab \div (-3b)$ v $-16mn \div 8$ w $-12ab \div (-3a)$ x $-ab \div (-a)$

4 Simplify these miscellaneous divisions.

	A	B	C	D
a	$25x \div 5x$	$10pq \div p$	$-3m \div 3$	$6p \div (-3)$
b	$60t \div 20$	$-5a \div 5a$	$12pq \div 4pq$	$-30m \div (-6m)$
c	$\dfrac{8ab}{4b}$	$\dfrac{3m}{2m}$	$\dfrac{7ab}{3a}$	$\dfrac{2x^2}{x}$
d	$12xy \div 6xy$	$-15a^2 \div 5a$	$6m \div (-6)$	$24pq \div 12q$

6:05 | Multiplication and Division of Pronumerals

prep quiz

6:05

Simplify each expression.

1 $6m \times 3$　　　**2** $6m \div 3$　　　**3** $8a \times 2a$　　　**4** $8a \div 2a$　　　**5** $10p \times 5q$

6 $2ab \times 4a$　　**7** $12p \div p$　　　**8** $\dfrac{10a}{5a}$　　　**9** $\dfrac{6mn}{6n}$　　　**10** $\dfrac{9x^2}{3x}$

Now use this exercise to increase your skill in multiplying and dividing algebraic expressions. First, examine the following examples.

worked examples

1 $6m \times 3 \div 9m$

$= 18m \div 9m$

$= 2$

2 $16x^2 \div 8x \div 2$

$= 2x \div 2$

$= x$

3 $\dfrac{3a \times 2b}{6a}$

$= \dfrac{6ab}{6a}$

$= b$

Exercise 6:05

Foundation Worksheet 6:05
Multiplication and division of pronumerals
Simplify:
1 a $6 \times 2 \times 5$　　**b** $8 \times 5 \div 10$
2 a $10a \times 3 \times 6$　**b** $3x \times 4 \times 2$
3 a $12y \div 4$　　　**b** $12y \div 4 \times 3$
4 a $8m \div m$　　　**b** $10ab \div 2b$

1 Simplify these expressions which involve 3 terms.

a $2 \times 3x \times 5y$　　**b** $4a \times 5b \times 2c$　　**c** $6x \times 2 \div 4x$

d $6 \times 5m \div 10$　　**e** $20p \div 4 \times 3q$　　**f** $10a \div 2a \times 3a$

g $15t \div 5t \div 3$　　**h** $24pq \div 6p \div 2q$　　**i** $24m \div 6m \times m$

j $6ab \times 2a \div 4b$　　**k** $ab \times 7a \times 3b$　　**l** $28tw \div 7w \times 2t$

2 Simplify each expression.

	A	B	C
a	$5m \times 2m$	$6p \div 3p$	$16p \div 8$
b	$12ab \div 6b$	$3pq \times 2p$	$6p \div 6p$
c	$-3p \times 2q$	$24m \div (-6)$	$3xy \times x$
d	$(3m)^2$	$(5a)^2$	$(4x)^2$
e	$(-2m) \times (-3n)$	$-24l \div (-6)$	$a \times 3a$
f	$6pq \times 2p$	$-5x \times 2xy$	$48mn \div 12m$
g	$(3pq)^2$	$(7mn)^2$	$(2tw)^2$
h	$3p \times 2 \times 4q$	$2a \times 3b \times 4c$	$9 \times 2p \times m$
i	$7ab \times 0 \times 5b$	$a \times 3x \times 2a$	$-3t \times 2t \times 5$
j	$-25xy \div 5x$	$9ab \div (-9ab)$	$-18x^2 \div (-9x)$
k	$12a \div 6 \times 3a$	$9p \div 3p \times 2p$	$24x^2 \div 6x \times 2$
l	$\dfrac{6a \times 3b}{9ab}$	$\dfrac{5x \times 4x}{10x}$	$\dfrac{4p \times 5q}{10p}$
m	$\dfrac{2m \times 6n}{3n \times 4m}$	$\dfrac{10x \times 3x}{6x \times 5}$	$\dfrac{(4ab)^2}{8ab^2}$

> ■ Notice:
> $(5xy)^2$
> $= 5xy \times 5xy$
> $= 25x^2y^2$

Remember your 'order of operations'.

3 See if you can work out the simplest expressions for these.

a $(2a)^2 \times (3b)^2 \div 18ab$　　　　**b** $[6m^2 \times 6n^2 \div 9mn \div 2m]^2$

Fun Spot 6:05 | Why didn't the boy drink his milk after his bath?

Simplify each part and put the letter for that part in the box above the correct answer.

F $10x + 7x$

B $2p \times 9$

T $6m - 10m$

H $12k - 6l + 2k$

N $15y \div (-3y)$

H $-12k + 10k$

E $(-18ab) \div 9b$

H $3x - 7x$

A $16mn \div 8$

H $8x \times 3xy$

D $8pq + 7pq - 3p$

O $13k \times 2k \div k^2$

I $-m + n + m - n$

K $(-2x) \times 5x \times (-3)$

E $(-6m) \times (-6m)$

H $6m - 5m$

M $20b \div b$

I $(-3) \times 6q$

O $8t \times 7t$

A $5x^2 + 2x - 3x^2$

A $9a - 7a - a$

F $ab \times ac$

I $-3m + 10m$

M $(-6a) \times (-3b)$

R $14m^2 \div (-7m)$

N $4m \times 2n \times 5$

R $3m^2 + m^2 - 6m^2$

F $3a \times 4b \times 5c$

L $24ab \div 6a \times 2b$

L $5ab + (6a \times 2b)$

E $3a + 2a + 6a$

R $2a \times a$

E $(-40n) \div (-10)$

T $36pq \div 9q$

D $7m - (-3m)$

T $9a \times 7b$

S $2x \times \frac{1}{2}x$

K $9p - 2q - 7p$

O $7m - 3m + 2n$

G $5ab + 7ba$

R $16x \div 4x \times 2x$

T $3x + 7y - 2y + x$

I $100bc \div 20b$

O $6y^2 + 7y - 8y^2 + 2y$

N $(32x^2 \div 4x) - 7x$

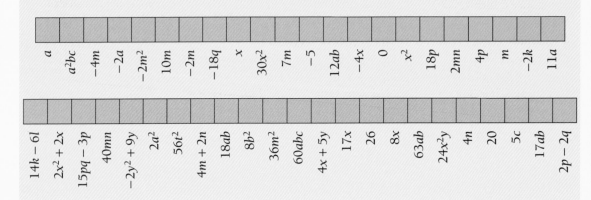

a	a^2bc	$-4m$	$-2a$	$-2m^2$	$10m$	$-2m$	$-18q$	x	$30x^2$	$7m$	-5	$12ab$	$-4x$	0	x^2	$18p$	$2mn$	$4p$	m	$-2k$	$11a$

$14k - 6l$	$2x^2 + 2x$	$15pq - 3p$	$40mn$	$-2y^2 + 9y$	$2a^2$	$56t^2$	$4m + 2n$	$18ab$	$8b^2$	$36m^2$	$60abc$	$4x + 5y$	$17x$	26	$8x$	$63ab$	$24x^2y$	$4n$	20	$5c$	$17ab$	$2p - 2q$

If you're having trouble, use Drag and Drops 4 and 5 on page 147.

6:06 | Using Algebra

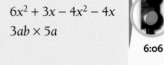
Simplify each expression.

1 $5x + 2x + 3x$ 2 $2a + 7b + 6a$ 3 $9m - 12m$ 4 $6x^2 + 3x - 4x^2 - 4x$

5 $3 \times 7x$ 6 $12p \div 6p$ 7 $-10x \times 3x$ 8 $3ab \times 5a$

9 $\dfrac{10x^2}{5x}$ 10 $\dfrac{24ab}{6b}$

The usefulness of algebra lies in solving problems. With any good tool, we have to learn to use it properly before we can put it to good use.

worked examples

1 Write expressions for the perimeter and area of each figure.

a
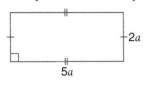

b
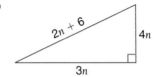

Perimeter $= 5a + 2a + 5a + 2a$
      $= 14a$ units
Area $= 5a \times 2a$
    $= 10a^2$ square units

Perimeter $= 3n + 4n + 2n + 6$
      $= 9n + 6$ units
Area $= \frac{1}{2} \times 3n \times 4n$
    $= 6n^2$ square units

2 If I bought 6 apples which cost k cents each and 4 pears which cost $2k$ cents each, find an expression for the total cost of the fruit.

Cost of apples $= 6 \times k$ Cost of pears $= 4 \times 2k$
      $= 6k$ cents $= 8k$ cents

∴ Total cost $= 6k + 8k = 14k$ cents

Exercise 6:06

1 Write an expression for each perimeter.

a
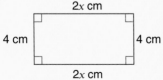

b
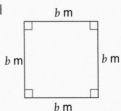

c
2x cm
4 cm   4 cm
2x cm

d
b m
b m   b m
b m

e
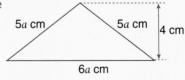

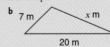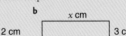

2 Write an expression for the area of each part of Question 1.

3 Write down an expression, in its simplest form, for the perimeter of each figure. All measurements are in millimetres. (Similar markings on sides of a figure mean that their lengths are equal.)

a

x

b
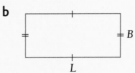
B
L

c

$3q$
p

d
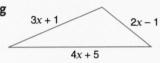
$5k$

e
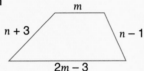
$2x$

f
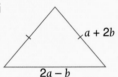
$3m$
$5n$

g
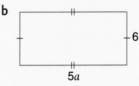
$3x + 1$ $2x - 1$
$4x + 5$

h
m
$n + 3$ $n - 1$
$2m - 3$

i
$a + 2b$
$2a - b$

4 Find a simple expression for the area of each figure below. All measurements are in centimetres.

a
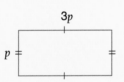
$2m$

b
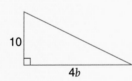
6
$5a$

c
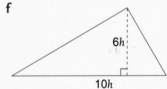
$2x$
$7y$

d
$3p$
p

e
10
$4b$

f
$6h$
$10h$

5 Find the simplest expression for each of the following problems.
  a If I bought p pens and $3q$ pencils and my sister bought $2p$ pens and q pencils, how many pens and pencils did we buy altogether?
  b I had $10a$ pears, I ate $3a$ of them, then bought $7a$ more. How many do I have now?
  c Three different types of sweets cost $5x$, $3x$ and $2x$ cents each. If I buy 4 of each type, what will be the total cost?
  d Box A contains m chocolates and $2n$ lollies. Box B contains $3m$ chocolates and n lollies. If I buy 3 of box A and 2 of box B, how many sweets will I have altogether?

6:07 | Index Notation

prep quiz

6:07

Evaluate:

1 2^2 **2** 5^2 **3** 10^4 **4** 2^3 **5** 3^3

Write these as powers.

6 $3 \times 3 \times 3$ **7** $a \times a \times a \times a \times a$ **8** $10 \times 10 \times 10 \times 10$

9 $x \times x \times x \times x \times x \times x \times x \times x \times x$ **10** $y \times y \times y \times y \times y \times y \times y \times y$

When a pronumeral is multiplied by itself a number of times we can simplify the expression using index notation.

worked examples

1 $x \times x \times x \times x \times x \times x \times x \times x = x^8$
(eight xs multiplied together)

2 Evaluate $10a^2b^3$ if $a = 2$ and $b = 3$.
$$10a^2b^3 = 10 \times a \times a \times b \times b \times b$$
$$= 10 \times 2 \times 2 \times 3 \times 3 \times 3$$
$$= 1080$$

The index belongs to the t only.

$3t^4$

Exercise 6:07

1 Simplify the following, using index notation.

  a $m \times m$ **b** $a \times a \times a \times a \times a \times a$ **c** $x \times x \times x \times x \times x$

  d $5 \times n \times n \times n$ **e** $7 \times a \times a \times 3$ **f** $8 \times y \times y \times y \times 2$

  g $p \times p \times q$ **h** $8 \times x \times 7 \times y \times y$ **i** $4 \times m \times m \times m \times n \times n$

2 Rewrite in expanded form (eg $2y^4 = 2 \times y \times y \times y \times y$).

  a x^3 **b** $8b^2$ **c** $7m^6$ **d** y^5 **e** $3a^4$

  f x^2y^2 **g** am^4 **h** x^3y^3 **i** a^3b **j** ap^3

  k $2ap^2$ **l** $4ap^3$ **m** $6x^2y^2$ **n** $5a^5b$ **o** $10m^3n^4$

3 Find the value of each if $a = 2$, $b = 4$, $c = -5$, $x = 10$ and $y = 3$.

  a b^2 **b** c^2 **c** a^4 **d** x^6 **e** y^3

  f $3x^2$ **g** $2a^3$ **h** $4y^2$ **i** $2y^4$ **j** $5x^3$

  k x^2a^2 **l** $3b^2c$ **m** $4a^2y^3$ **n** $2a^2x^2$ **o** $3c^3$

6:08 | Grouping Symbols

prep quiz

6:08

Evaluate:

1 $4 \times (2 + 3)$	**2** $4 \times 2 + 4 \times 3$
3 $3 \times (5 - 3)$	**4** $3 \times 5 - 3 \times 3$
5 $-2 \times (4 + 3)$	**6** $(-2) \times 4 + (-2) \times 3$

Simplify:

7 $5 \times a + 5 \times 2$	**8** $3 \times 2x + 3 \times 5y$
9 $2x \times 3x + 2x \times 5$	**10** $3a \times 4a - 3a \times 2b$

In Year 7 we saw that an expression like $3(2 + 5)$ meant $3 \times (2 + 5)$, which in turn is equal to $3 \times 2 + 3 \times 5$. Similarly, in algebra:

see

$$a(b + c) = ab + ac \quad \text{OR} \quad a(b - c) = ab - ac$$

> ■ *Grouping Symbols*
> - parentheses ( )
> - brackets [ ]
> - braces { }

1:12, A:12F This means that to write an expression without grouping symbols, we multiply each term inside the grouping symbols by the term outside.

worked examples

1 a $5(a + 2) = 5 \times a + 5 \times 2$
$\qquad = 5a + 10$

b $6(2x - 3y) = 6 \times 2x - 6 \times 3y$
$\qquad = 12x - 18y$

c $x(x + 7) = x^2 + 7x$

d $3a(5 - 2a) = 15a - 6a^2$

Look what happens when the term outside is negative!

e $-3(x + 5) = -3 \times x + (-3) \times 5$ ◀
$\qquad = -3x - 15$

f $-2x(3 - 5x) = -2x \times 3 - (-2x) \times 5x$ ◀
$\qquad = -6x + 10x^2$

■ Watch out for these types with negative signs.

g An expression like $-(x + 3)$ is the same as $-1(x + 3)$, ◀
$\quad$ so $-1(x + 3) = -1 \times x + (-1) \times 3$
$\qquad\qquad\quad = -x - 3$

2 Expand and simplify:

> ■ 'Expand' means to rewrite without grouping symbols.

a $5(x + 3) + 2x$
$= 5x + 15 + 2x$
$= 7x + 15$

b $3(a + 4) + 2(5 - a)$
$= 3a + 12 + 10 - 2a$
$= a + 22$

c $2(5x + 3) - (4x - 3)$
$= 10x + 6 - 4x + 3$
$= 6x + 9$

d $x(2x - 3) - 4(x + 5)$
$= 2x^2 - 3x - 4x - 20$
$= 2x^2 - 7x - 20$

Watch out for the minus sign.

Exercise 6:08A

1 Rewrite these expressions without grouping symbols.

a $3(a + 2)$ b $4(x + 3)$ c $2(x + 7)$ d $5(v + 1)$
e $6(m - 5)$ f $5(n - 2)$ g $4(b - 3)$ h $6(l - 1)$
i $2(3 + a)$ j $3(4 + x)$ k $6(6 + t)$ l $7(2 + w)$
m $7(1 - x)$ n $5(2 - y)$ o $4(3 - p)$ p $9(8 - y)$
q $3(a + b)$ r $2(x + y)$ s $6(p + q)$ t $7(m + n)$
u $4(p - q)$ v $5(a - b)$ w $10(t - w)$ x $8(x - y)$

2 Expand these expressions.

a $2(2a + 3)$ b $5(3x + 1)$ c $4(2m + 3)$ d $6(3n + 2)$
e $5(2m - 1)$ f $4(4n - 5)$ g $2(5p - 2)$ h $7(5t - 3)$
i $6(2 + 3m)$ j $7(1 + 4x)$ k $3(3 + 4n)$ l $4(2 + 5t)$
m $10(2 - 3x)$ n $4(1 - 3p)$ o $3(2 - 5w)$ p $8(1 - 2x)$
q $2(3a + 2b)$ r $3(4m + n)$ s $5(4x + 3y)$ t $10(x + 3y)$
u $5(2x - y)$ v $4(2a - 3b)$ w $2(7m - 2n)$ x $3(6t - 2w)$

3 Expand:

a $x(x + 2)$ b $y(y + 3)$ c $a(a + 5)$ d $m(m + 10)$
e $a(a - 1)$ f $m(m - 5)$ g $n(n - 3)$ h $y(y - 8)$
i $x(y + 2)$ j $a(b + 2)$ k $m(t - 3)$ l $n(x - 6)$
m $a(x + a)$ n $x(x + y)$ o $m(m + n)$ p $t(w + t)$
q $k(k + l)$ r $p(q - p)$ s $t(x + y)$ t $a(b - c)$

4 Expand:

a $2a(a + 2)$ b $3x(x + 5)$ c $5n(n + 2)$ d $4m(m + 4)$
e $3p(p - 4)$ f $4q(q - 1)$ g $10m(m - 7)$ h $8a(a - 5)$
i $6x(4 - x)$ j $2m(1 + m)$ k $9t(t + 2)$ l $5n(5 - n)$
m $2a(a + b)$ n $4p(p + q)$ o $3x(x + y)$ p $7m(n + m)$
q $3y(2y + 4)$ r $3a(b + 2a)$ s $3m(2m + 5n)$ t $4p(3q - 2p)$

5 Expand and simplify each expression by collecting like terms.

a $2(x + 3) + 4x$ b $3(m + 2) + 4m$ c $5(a + 5) - 3a$
d $4(n - 2) + 3n$ e $5(a - 4) - 2a$ f $3(m - 1) + 4m$
g $6(a + 2) + 2a + 4$ h $3(x + 3) + 2x - 7$ i $4(y + 3) - 2y + 5$
j $5x + 4(x + 3)$ k $5a + 3(a - 2)$ l $8m + 4(m - 2)$

6 Expand all grouping symbols, then simplify each expression.

a $2(x + 3) + 3(x + 2)$ b $4(x + 2) + 2(x + 3)$ c $5(a + 2) + 3(a + 1)$
d $5(m + 2) + 2(m - 1)$ e $6(y + 1) + 3(y - 2)$ f $5(m + 1) + 2(m - 1)$
g $4(3 + a) + 5(2 + a)$ h $7(m + 3) + 2(2 - m)$ i $6(2 + y) + 3(4 - y)$
j $9(x + 1) + 3(x - 3)$ k $8(p + 1) + 3(2 + p)$ l $7(a + 2) + 5(3 - a)$
m $2(m + n) + 2(m + n)$ n $5(x + y) + 5(x - y)$ o $3(p + q) + 2(p - q)$

1 Noting that $-3(x - 4) = -3 \times x - (-3) \times 4$ **and** $-5(2y + 7) = -5 \times 2y + (-5) \times 7$
$$= -3x + 12 \qquad\qquad = -10y - 35,$$

expand the following:

a $-2(x + 3)$	**b** $-3(a + 5)$	**c** $-5(y + 1)$	**d** $-9(k + 2)$
e $-4(a - 2)$	**f** $-2(p - 3)$	**g** $-7(t - 6)$	**h** $-5(x - 1)$
i $-3(6 + x)$	**j** $-9(7 - q)$	**k** $-2(10 + y)$	**l** $-6(8 - h)$

2 Rewrite the following without grouping symbols. [*Note:* $-(x + 7)$ is the same as $-1(x + 7)$.]

a $-(a + 2)$	**b** $-(x + 3)$	**c** $-(p + 7)$	**d** $-(q + 1)$
e $-(x - 3)$	**f** $-(t - 2)$	**g** $-(w - 6)$	**h** $-(y - 1)$
i $-(2x + 7)$	**j** $-(3x - 2)$	**k** $-(4x + 5)$	**l** $-(7y - 3)$

3 Expand the following.

a $-x(x + 2)$	**b** $-a(a + 3)$	**c** $-m(m - 4)$	**d** $-n(n - 1)$
e $-a(b + 3)$	**f** $-p(q + 5)$	**g** $-t(x - 3)$	**h** $-m(n - 10)$
i $-2m(m + 4)$	**j** $-5a(2a + 5)$	**k** $-6x(x - 7)$	**l** $-4t(5t + 3)$

4 Expand and then collect like terms.

a $2(a + 4) - 4a$	**b** $6(p - 4) + 19$	**c** $5(a - 1) - 6a$
d $2a + 3(1 - a)$	**e** $6x + 2(3 - 4x)$	**f** $10 + 6(a - 2)$
g $6 - 4(a + 2)$	**h** $5x - 2(x + 3)$	**i** $6m - 2(m - 1)$
j $10x - (x + 3)$	**k** $16 - (x + 5)$	**l** $5y - (2 + 3y)$
m $6m - 3(m + 2) + 5$	**n** $7a + 6 - 2(a + 4)$	**o** $20 - (10 + 3a) + 5a$

5 Expand all grouping symbols, then simplify each expression.

a $3(x + 2) - 2(x + 3)$	**b** $4(a + 2) - 2(a + 3)$	**c** $6(y + 4) - 5(y + 1)$
d $5(a + 4) - 4(a - 1)$	**e** $6(m + 5) - 2(m - 2)$	**f** $8(t + 3) - 6(t - 4)$
g $2(m - 2) - 3(m + 2)$	**h** $5(y - 2) - 6(y + 4)$	**i** $3(p - 6) - 2(p + 2)$
j $5(p - 2) - 3(p - 1)$	**k** $6(t - 1) - 4(t - 2)$	**l** $8(q - 3) - 6(q - 1)$
m $3(p + 7) - (p - 7)$	**n** $6(q + 2) - (q + 3)$	**o** $2(m - 5) - (4 - m)$

6 Try simplifying these expressions by first expanding all grouping symbols and then collecting like terms. Be careful!

a $3(x + 5) + 4(x + 2) - 5(x + 1)$	**b** $6(m - 2) - 3(m + 2) + 5(2 - m)$
c $5(2a + 4) - (6 - 3a) - 2(a + 1)$	**d** $10(a - 4) - 6(4 - a) - (a + 4)$
e $x(x + 7) - 5(x - 7) + 2(1 - x)$	**f** $a(2a + 3b) + b(3a - 2b)$
g $3y(y - 2) + 4y(x - 7) - 2x(y + 4)$	**h** $3a(2a + 4b) - 3b(4a + c) - 3c(3a - 2b)$

challenge

6:10

■ See **Challenge 6:10** on page 141 for more fun with grouping symbols!

6:09 | Factorising

Expand: **1** $2(x + 3)$ **2** $5(a - 7)$

3 $p(p + 4)$ **4** $2m(m - n)$

Write down the factors of: **5** 6   **6** 12   **7** 20

What is the highest common factor (HCF) of:

8 6 and 9?   **9** 8 and 12?   **10** 20 and 25?

> ■ *Factors* are numbers that will divide into a given number, leaving no remainder, eg {1, 2, 3, 6, 9, 18} is the set of factors of 18.

prep quiz
6:09

If we expand the expression $3(x + 4)$, we get $3x + 12$.

To factorise $3x + 12$ we reverse this procedure. We need to see that 3 is the highest common factor of $3x$ and 12, and then write it outside the grouping symbols. The remainder is then written inside the grouping symbols.

worked examples

> Factorising is the reverse of expanding.

1 $3x + 12 = 3 \times x + 3 \times 4$
$= 3(x + 4)$

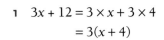

expand

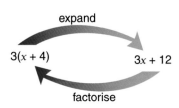

$3(x + 4)$ $3x + 12$

factorise

2 $6m + 9 = 3 \times 2m + 3 \times 3$ (HCF is 3)   **3** $5x - 20y = 5 \times x - 5 \times 4y$ (HCF is 5)
$= 3(2m + 3)$ $= 5(x - 4y)$

4 $2m^2 + 3m = m \times 2m + m \times 3$ (HCF is m)   **5** $8ab - 6a = 2a \times 4b - 2a \times 3$ (HCF is $2a$)
$= m(2m + 3)$ $= 2a(4b - 3)$

6 $ax + a = a \times x + a \times 1$ (HCF is a)   **7** $2a + 4b - 6c = 2 \times a + 2 \times 2b - 2 \times 3c$ (HCF is 2)
$= a(x + 1)$ $= 2(a + 2b - 3c)$

$$ab + ac = a(b + c) \quad \textbf{OR} \quad ab - ac = a(b - c)$$

Exercise 6:09

> **Foundation Worksheet 6:09**
>
> **Factorising**
> **1 a** Expand $2(x + 4)$.
> **b** Factorise $2x + 8$.
> **2** Complete:
> **a** $3x - 3 = 3(\dots - \dots)$
> **3** Factorise $8x + 16$.

1 Write the missing number in each case.

a $2x + 4 = \dots (x + 2)$ **b** $5a + 10 = \dots (a + 2)$

c $6y - 3 = \dots (2y - 1)$ **d** $10p - 5 = \dots (2p - 1)$

e $4n + 6 = \dots (2n + 3)$ **f** $6 - 8m = \dots (3 - 4m)$

g $ab + a = \dots (b + 1)$ **h** $xy + 3x = \dots (y + 3)$

i $p^2 - 2p = \dots (p - 2)$ **j** $a^2 + ab = \dots (a + b)$

2 Write the part that goes within the parentheses.

a $2m + 10 = 2(\quad)$
b $5x + 10 = 5(\quad)$
c $4a + 4 = 4(\quad)$
d $3y - 9 = 3(\quad)$
e $7k - 14 = 7(\quad)$
f $10m - 10 = 10(\quad)$
g $4x + 6 = 2(\quad)$
h $6n + 9 = 3(\quad)$
i $8k + 6 = 2(\quad)$
j $6y - 4 = 2(\quad)$
k $4x - 10 = 2(\quad)$
l $10a - 15 = 5(\quad)$
m $ax + 3a = a(\quad)$
n $mn + 5n = n(\quad)$
o $4y + xy = y(\quad)$
p $ab - bc = b(\quad)$
q $xy - y = y(\quad)$
r $p - pq = p(\quad)$
s $x^2 + 3x = x(\quad)$
t $5a + a^2 = a(\quad)$
u $5y - 10xy = 5y(\quad)$

3 Factorise the following by taking out the HCF.

a $2y + 6$
b $3x + 6$
c $5m + 20$
d $6k + 12$
e $9n - 18$
f $6a - 3$
g $4y - 12$
h $14p - 7$
i $10 + 5a$
j $6 + 4p$
k $10 + 6g$
l $8 + 8y$
m $20 - 10m$
n $12 - 4a$
o $15 - 3q$
p $7 - 7p$
q $6m + 6n$
r $5x + 10y$
s $6n - 12m$
t $8p - 8q$
u $4p - 6$
v $9a + 12$
w $8 + 14x$
x $10 - 8k$

4 Factorise:

a $ax + 2x$
b $xy + 5y$
c $ab + 3b$
d $9x + xy$
e $5m - mn$
f $pq - 3q$
g $10x - ax$
h $tw - w$
i $ax + bx$
j $pq + qr$
k $mn - np$
l $ab - bc$
m $x^2 + 3x$
n $y^2 + 2y$
o $m^2 + m$
p $t^2 + tx$
q $p^2 - 5p$
r $6m - m^2$
s $2x^2 - 3x$
t $9l - 7l^2$
u $5m + 2mn$
v $7xy - 3x$
w $3ab + 5bc$
x $8pq - 7pr$

5 Factorise completely:

a $5x + 10xy$
b $4m + 8mn$
c $6p + 4pq$
d $10t + 15tw$
e $9mn - 3m$
f $6pq - 12q$
g $8t - 4tw$
h $6a - 3ab$
i $2x^2 + 4x$
j $9m^2 - 6m$
k $10n + 5n^2$
l $8pq - 4q^2$
m $3mn + 6nr$
n $4pq + 8pr$
o $6ab + 3bc$
p $8xy + 2xz$
q $9xy - 3xz$
r $6ab - 12ac$
s $5mn - 15mp$
t $8tw - 4xw$
u $a^2b - ab$
v $5x^2 - 10xy$
w $9mn + 6m^2$
x $6pq - 20q^2$

6 Factorise these by taking out the factor common to all three terms.

a $3x + 3y + 3z$
b $6a + 6b - 6c$
c $5m + 5n + 5$
d $5a + 10b - 15c$
e $6p - 3q + 9r$
f $12x + 6y - 9$
g $3a^2 + 3a + 3$
h $5m^2 + 10m + 15$
i $4p^2 - 2p + 8$
j $ax + ay + az$
k $xp + xq + xr$
l $5t + tw - tx$
m $5x^2 - 10x + 15xy$
n $6m + 15mn + 9mp$
o $10a^2 + 15ab - 5a$

7 Factorise the following by taking out a negative common factor.
Remember that $-2(x + 3) = -2x - 6$ and $-x(x - 3) = -x^2 + 3x$.

a $-2x - 4$
b $-6m - 12$
c $-3p - 9$
d $-5p + 10$
e $-3q + 3$
f $-7n + 21$
g $-20 - 10a$
h $-12 - 4p$
i $-9 + 6q$
j $-6a - 12b$
k $-5m + 15n$
l $-10a + 2b$
m $-x^2 + 3x$
n $-ax - 5a$
o $-6ax + 3bx$

6:10 | Algebraic Fractions

Simplify:

1. $\dfrac{2}{5} + \dfrac{3}{5}$ 2. $\dfrac{7}{10} - \dfrac{3}{10}$ 3. $\dfrac{2}{3} + \dfrac{1}{6}$ 4. $\dfrac{3}{5} + \dfrac{1}{4}$ 5. $\dfrac{3}{5} \times \dfrac{5}{6}$

6. $\dfrac{2}{3} \div \dfrac{5}{6}$ 7. $5x + x$ 8. $7m - 6m$ 9. $2x + 3y$ 10. $2x \times 3y$

6:10A Addition and subtraction

worked examples

The rules for adding and subtracting numerical fractions still apply.

1. $\dfrac{2x}{5} + \dfrac{x}{5} = \dfrac{2x + x}{5}$

   $= \dfrac{3x}{5}$

■ If the denominators are the same, simply add or subtract the numerators.

2. $\dfrac{7m}{3} - \dfrac{5m}{3} = \dfrac{7m - 5m}{3}$

   $= \dfrac{2m}{3}$

3. $\dfrac{3a}{5} + \dfrac{2a}{4} = \dfrac{3a \times 4}{5 \times 4} + \dfrac{2a \times 5}{4 \times 5}$

   $= \dfrac{12a}{20} + \dfrac{10a}{20}$

■ Cancel if possible.

   $= \dfrac{22a}{20}$

   $= \dfrac{11a}{10}$

4. $\dfrac{2n}{5} - \dfrac{n}{10} = \dfrac{2n \times 2}{5 \times 2} - \dfrac{n}{10}$

   $= \dfrac{4n}{10} - \dfrac{n}{10}$

   $= \dfrac{3n}{10}$

■ If the denominators are different, rewrite each fraction with a common denominator, then add or subtract the numerators.

 Always look for the lowest common denominator!

Exercise 6:10A

Foundation Worksheet 6:10A

Algebraic fractions A
Simplify:

1 a $\dfrac{1}{3} + \dfrac{1}{3}$ b $\dfrac{7}{8} - \dfrac{6}{8}$

2 a $\dfrac{x}{3} + \dfrac{x}{3}$ b $\dfrac{7x}{8} - \dfrac{6x}{8}$

3 a $\dfrac{14m}{100} + \dfrac{13m}{100}$

1 Simplify each addition or subtraction.

a $\dfrac{x}{5} + \dfrac{x}{5}$ b $\dfrac{3m}{7} + \dfrac{2m}{7}$ c $\dfrac{5n}{4} + \dfrac{2n}{4}$

d $\dfrac{4x}{5} - \dfrac{3x}{5}$ e $\dfrac{9t}{8} - \dfrac{4t}{8}$ f $\dfrac{6m}{7} - \dfrac{4m}{7}$

g $\dfrac{5a}{6} + \dfrac{a}{6}$ h $\dfrac{5p}{10} + \dfrac{p}{10}$ i $\dfrac{3t}{8} + \dfrac{t}{8}$

j $\dfrac{5w}{12} + \dfrac{5w}{12}$ k $\dfrac{6a}{8} - \dfrac{a}{8}$ l $\dfrac{x}{5} + \dfrac{2x}{5}$ m $\dfrac{9m}{12} - \dfrac{3m}{12}$

n $\dfrac{5y}{9} - \dfrac{y}{9}$ o $\dfrac{7n}{3} - \dfrac{4n}{3}$ p $\dfrac{7x}{10} - \dfrac{2x}{10}$ q $\dfrac{7t}{8} - \dfrac{3t}{8}$

r $\dfrac{7x}{12} + \dfrac{7x}{12}$ s $\dfrac{5m}{16} + \dfrac{9m}{16}$ t $\dfrac{11y}{12} - \dfrac{5y}{12}$ u $\dfrac{17x}{20} - \dfrac{12x}{20}$

2 Simplify the following.

a $\dfrac{2a}{3} + \dfrac{a}{4}$ b $\dfrac{m}{2} + \dfrac{2m}{5}$ c $\dfrac{x}{3} + \dfrac{x}{2}$ d $\dfrac{2t}{3} + \dfrac{t}{2}$

e $\dfrac{2m}{3} - \dfrac{m}{2}$ f $\dfrac{3w}{5} - \dfrac{w}{3}$ g $\dfrac{a}{2} - \dfrac{a}{3}$ h $\dfrac{3n}{2} - \dfrac{3n}{5}$

i $\dfrac{x}{2} + \dfrac{x}{4}$ j $\dfrac{2a}{3} + \dfrac{a}{6}$ k $\dfrac{2m}{5} + \dfrac{m}{10}$ l $\dfrac{3y}{2} + \dfrac{5y}{6}$

m $\dfrac{3t}{5} - \dfrac{3t}{10}$ n $\dfrac{3y}{4} - \dfrac{y}{2}$ o $\dfrac{4m}{3} - \dfrac{5m}{6}$ p $\dfrac{7n}{9} - \dfrac{2n}{3}$

q $\dfrac{7x}{10} + \dfrac{x}{4}$ r $\dfrac{m}{6} + \dfrac{m}{9}$ s $\dfrac{3a}{4} + \dfrac{a}{6}$ t $\dfrac{3n}{8} + \dfrac{n}{6}$

u $\dfrac{7y}{12} - \dfrac{3y}{8}$ v $\dfrac{3x}{4} - \dfrac{3x}{10}$ w $\dfrac{5m}{6} - \dfrac{m}{4}$ x $\dfrac{7p}{9} - \dfrac{2p}{3}$

6:10B Multiplication and division

worked examples

■ Cancel any common factors, then multiply the 'tops' and then multiply the 'bottoms'.

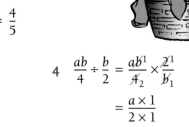
Multiply and divide in the same way as for numerical fractions.

1   $\dfrac{a}{2} \times \dfrac{b}{3} = \dfrac{a \times b}{2 \times 3}$

       $= \dfrac{ab}{6}$

2   $\dfrac{2x}{3} \times \dfrac{6}{5x} = \dfrac{2x^1}{{}_1 3} \times \dfrac{6^2}{5x_1}$

       $= \dfrac{2 \times 2}{1 \times 5} = \dfrac{4}{5}$

When dividing, don't forget to 'invert' the second fraction and then multiply.

3   $\dfrac{x}{5} \div \dfrac{x}{3} = \dfrac{{}^1 x}{5} \times \dfrac{3}{x_1}$

       $= \dfrac{1 \times 3}{5 \times 1}$

       $= \dfrac{3}{5}$

4   $\dfrac{ab}{4} \div \dfrac{b}{2} = \dfrac{ab^1}{{}_2 4} \times \dfrac{2^1}{b_1}$

       $= \dfrac{a \times 1}{2 \times 1}$

       $= \dfrac{a}{2}$

Exercise 6:10B

1 Simplify these products.

a $\dfrac{x}{2} \times \dfrac{y}{3}$ b $\dfrac{a}{5} \times \dfrac{b}{6}$ c $\dfrac{m}{3} \times \dfrac{n}{4}$

d $\dfrac{a}{3} \times \dfrac{2}{x}$ e $\dfrac{5}{m} \times \dfrac{n}{3}$ f $\dfrac{2p}{3} \times \dfrac{5}{q}$

g $\dfrac{2m}{3} \times \dfrac{m}{4}$

h $\dfrac{3x}{2} \times \dfrac{y}{6}$

i $\dfrac{a}{10} \times \dfrac{5}{6}$

j $\dfrac{t}{4} \times \dfrac{6}{w}$

k $\dfrac{2x}{3} \times \dfrac{9}{x}$

l $\dfrac{5n}{2} \times \dfrac{4m}{15}$

m $\dfrac{p}{6} \times \dfrac{3}{2p}$

n $\dfrac{3x}{5y} \times \dfrac{2y}{3}$

o $\dfrac{a}{b} \times \dfrac{b}{a}$

p $\dfrac{2x}{y} \times \dfrac{3y}{x}$

q $\dfrac{ab}{5} \times \dfrac{a}{b}$

r $\dfrac{3x}{4y} \times \dfrac{2y}{9}$

2 Simplify these divisions.

a $\dfrac{m}{3} \div \dfrac{m}{2}$

b $\dfrac{x}{4} \div \dfrac{x}{3}$

c $\dfrac{p}{6} \div \dfrac{p}{5}$

d $\dfrac{t}{2} \div \dfrac{t}{5}$

e $\dfrac{5}{x} \div \dfrac{x}{2}$

f $\dfrac{a}{3} \div \dfrac{2}{a}$

g $\dfrac{m}{3} \div \dfrac{4}{n}$

h $\dfrac{5}{t} \div \dfrac{w}{3}$

i $\dfrac{2a}{3} \div \dfrac{a}{5}$

j $\dfrac{5m}{4} \div \dfrac{3}{m}$

k $\dfrac{2a}{3} \div \dfrac{4}{a}$

l $\dfrac{3p}{4} \div \dfrac{p}{2}$

m $\dfrac{a}{b} \div \dfrac{x}{y}$

n $\dfrac{m}{n} \div \dfrac{n}{m}$

o $\dfrac{3p}{q} \div \dfrac{2p}{q}$

p $\dfrac{2a}{b} \div \dfrac{3a}{c}$

q $\dfrac{ab}{3} \div \dfrac{a}{b}$

r $\dfrac{5a}{3} \div 3a$

s $\dfrac{ab}{3} \div \dfrac{ac}{2}$

t $\dfrac{9xy}{2w} \div \dfrac{3x}{4w}$

Challenge 6:10 | Expanding binomial products

A binomial product is the product of two such expressions.

A binomial expression has two terms.

$(x + 7)(x + 3)$

$x + 7$

Note that if $(b + c)a$ is expanded the result would be $ba + ca$.

Now if a was replaced by another binomial expression, say $x + 3$, we would have:

$$(b + c)(x + 3) = b(x + 3) + c(x + 3)$$

Of course this can be further expanded: $= bx + 3b + cx + 3c$

A binomial product when expanded gives an expression with four terms, but sometimes two of these may be added together. Study the following examples carefully.

Examples

1 $(x + 2)(x + 3) = x(x + 3) + 2(x + 3)$
$\qquad\qquad\quad = x^2 + 3x + 2x + 6$
$\qquad\qquad\quad = x^2 + 5x + 6$

2 $(a + 5)(a - 3) = a(a - 3) + 5(a - 3)$
$\qquad\qquad\quad = a^2 - 3a + 5a - 15$
$\qquad\qquad\quad = a^2 + 2a - 15$

3 $(m + 3)^2 = (m + 3)(m + 3)$
$\qquad\qquad = m(m + 3) + 3(m + 3)$
$\qquad\qquad = m^2 + 3m + 3m + 9$
$\qquad\qquad = m^2 + 6m + 9$

4 $(p - 7)(p + 7) = p(p + 7) - 7(p + 7)$
$\qquad\qquad\quad = p^2 + 7p - 7p - 49$
$\qquad\qquad\quad = p^2 - 49$

5 $(a + b)(c + d) = a(c + d) + b(c + d)$
$\qquad\qquad\quad = ac + ad + bc + bd$

6 $(2x + 3)(3x - 1) = 2x(3x - 1) + 3(3x - 1)$
$\qquad\qquad\qquad = 6x^2 - 2x + 9x - 3$
$\qquad\qquad\qquad = 6x^2 + 7x - 3$

Now try this next set of challenging exercises.

■ *Remember!*
There are no problems, just challenges!

Exercise

1 Expand the following.
- **a** $(a + 2)(a + 4)$
- **b** $(x + 2)(x + 5)$
- **c** $(y + 1)(y + 2)$
- **d** $(p + 7)(p + 2)$
- **e** $(x + 3)(x - 1)$
- **f** $(q + 4)(q - 2)$
- **g** $(a + 3)(a - 4)$
- **h** $(m + 5)(m - 2)$
- **i** $(y - 3)(y + 2)$
- **j** $(x - 1)(x + 3)$
- **k** $(n - 5)(n + 4)$
- **l** $(a - 3)(a + 3)$
- **m** $(x - 1)(x - 2)$
- **n** $(a - 4)(a - 4)$
- **o** $(t - 4)(t - 7)$
- **p** $(x - 5)(x - 6)$

2 Expand:
- **a** $(a + 2)^2$
- **b** $(m + 5)^2$
- **c** $(x + 7)^2$
- **d** $(m + 10)^2$
- **e** $(x - 1)^2$
- **f** $(a - 3)^2$
- **g** $(n - 4)^2$
- **h** $(y - 8)^2$

3 Expand and simplify:
- **a** $(a + x)(b + y)$
- **b** $(p + q)(x + y)$
- **c** $(a + b)(c - d)$
- **d** $(m - n)(x - y)$
- **e** $(3 + x)(5 + y)$
- **f** $(a + 4)(b + 5)$
- **g** $(x + 7)(y - 3)$
- **h** $(t - 5)(w - 3)$

4 Expand and simplify:
- **a** $(2x + 1)(x + 7)$
- **b** $(3a + 5)(a + 1)$
- **c** $(y + 7)(3y + 2)$
- **d** $(m + 1)(3m + 1)$
- **e** $(3y + 2)(2y + 5)$
- **f** $(4n + 3)(2n + 1)$
- **g** $(3p + 4)(2p + 5)$
- **h** $(5y + 2)(2y - 3)$
- **i** $(2m + 1)^2$
- **j** $(5x + 3)^2$
- **k** $(2m - 3)^2$
- **l** $(5 - 2a)^2$

Mathematical terms 6

algebra (algebraic)
- The use of pronumerals in solving problems and expressing ideas.

cubed
- Used three times as a factor.
  eg $a^3 = aaa$

directed numbers
- Numbers that use direction (+ and −).

evaluate
- To find the value of . . .

expand
- To remove grouping symbols.
  eg $3(2x − 7) = 6x − 21$

expression
- Algebraic expressions are made up of one or more terms joined by + or − signs.
  eg $2x − 7$, $5x + 2y + 1$, $a^2 − 2a + 1$

formula
- A number sentence (or equation) written using pronumerals and numerals.
  eg $C = 50M + 6$, $A = L × B$

grouping symbols
- These group numbers or terms.
  eg parentheses ( ), brackets [ ],
  braces { }, fraction bar $\dfrac{x+1}{2}$,
  square root sign $\sqrt{4x+1}$

index (indices)
- The raised symbol when a number is written as a power.

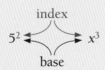

$$\text{index}$$
$$5^2 \longleftrightarrow x^3$$
$$\text{base}$$

index notation
- The use of powers to write a number or algebraic expression.

like terms
- These have the same pronumeral parts.
  eg $3xy$ and $7xy$, $8x^2$ and $−x^2$
- Unlike terms have different pronumeral parts.
  eg x^2 and x, $5xy$ and $2y$

power
- Repeated as a factor.
  eg 3 to the power of $5 = 3^5$
     $= 3 × 3 × 3 × 3 × 3$

pronumeral
- A symbol (usually a letter) that takes the place of a numeral.
  eg x or $θ$

rule
- An instruction or formula that explains how the numbers in a pattern are related.

simplify
- To give the shortest or simplest answer.

squared
- Multiplied by itself.
  eg $5^2 = 5 × 5$
- Used twice as a factor.

substitute (substitution)
- 'To put in place of.'
- Usually a numeral replaces a pronumeral.
  eg Substitute $x = 7$ in $2x + 3$.

value
- The number represented by a pronumeral.
  eg For the rule $y = x + 7$, find the value of y if x is given the value of 4.

Technology Applications

Mathematical terms 6

Drag and Drops

Diagnostic Test 6: | Further Algebra

- Each section of the test has similar items that test a certain type of example.
- Failure in more than one item will identify an area of weakness.
- Each weakness should be treated by going back to the section listed.

	Section

1 Use the rule given to complete the table.   6:01

  a $P = 2S + 4$ **b** $F = 3P - 3$

S	0	2	4	6
P				

P	1	2	3	4
F				

2 Find the rule that describes each pattern.   6:01

x	0	1	2	3
y	0	4	8	12

a	5	6	7	8
b	12	14	16	18

3 Simplify: 6:02
  a $5x + 3x$ **b** $2xy + 7xy$ **c** $3x^2 + 6x^2$

4 Simplify: 6:02
  a $9m - m$ **b** $5ab - 3ab$ **c** $7a^2 - 6a^2$

5 Simplify: 6:02
  a $3x + 4x + 2x$ **b** $7a + 5a - 3a$ **c** $10m - 7m + 2m$

6 Simplify: 6:02
  a $6a - 9a$ **b** $-3m + 4m$ **c** $-2x - 3x$

7 Simplify by collecting the like terms.   6:02
  a $5x + 2y + 3x$ **b** $7m - 3m + 2n$ **c** $6a + 3b + 4a - 2b$

8 Simplify by collecting the like terms.   6:02
  a $7m + 6n - 9n$ **b** $6a + 3b - 7a$ **c** $5m + 2n - 3m - 4n$

9 Simplify: 6:03
  a $6 \times 3m$ **b** $5x \times 3$ **c** $4 \times 7k$

10 Simplify: 6:03
  a $3m \times n$ **b** $6a \times 3b$ **c** $5x \times 7y$

11 Simplify: 6:03
  a $-2x \times 7$ **b** $5m \times (-3)$ **c** $-3x \times (-2y)$

12 Simplify: 6:04
  a $\dfrac{10x}{5}$ **b** $\dfrac{15m}{5m}$ **c** $12x \div 4$

13 Simplify: 6:04
  a $\dfrac{ab}{b}$ **b** $\dfrac{4pq}{2q}$ **c** $9xy \div 3x$

14 Simplify, using index notation.
   a $a \times a \times a \times a \times a$ **b** $x \times x \times x \times y$ **c** $8 \times m \times m \times m \times m$

15 Rewrite in expanded form.
   a x^4 **b** $x^3 y^5$ **c** $6a^6 b$

16 Expand:
   a $3(x + 2)$ **b** $5(a - 7)$ **c** $a(a + 3)$

17 Expand and simplify:
   a $3(m + 3) - 2m$ **b** $4(x - 2) + 3x + 5$ **c** $2(x + 4) + 3(x - 1)$

18 Expand:
   a $-3(x + 3)$ **b** $-2(a - 5)$ **c** $-x(x + 7)$

19 Expand and simplify:
   a $5(x + 3) - 2(x + 1)$ **b** $4(a + 3) - 2(a - 1)$ **c** $3(x - 4) - 2(x + 1)$

20 Factorise:
   a $2x + 8$ **b** $5y - 5$ **c** $6 + 12m$

21 Factorise:
   a $ax + 3x$ **b** $6m - mn$ **c** $y^2 + 3y$

22 Simplify completely:
   a $\dfrac{3a}{5} + \dfrac{a}{5}$ **b** $\dfrac{5m}{7} - \dfrac{3m}{7}$ **c** $\dfrac{x}{6} + \dfrac{2x}{6}$

23 Simplify:
   a $\dfrac{a}{3} + \dfrac{a}{4}$ **b** $\dfrac{2m}{5} - \dfrac{m}{3}$ **c** $\dfrac{3x}{4} + \dfrac{x}{2}$

24 Simplify completely:
   a $\dfrac{x}{3} \times \dfrac{y}{4}$ **b** $\dfrac{a}{5} \times \dfrac{a}{2}$ **c** $\dfrac{2a}{5} \times \dfrac{10}{a}$

25 Simplify completely:
   a $\dfrac{m}{3} \div \dfrac{m}{4}$ **b** $\dfrac{a}{5} \div \dfrac{2}{a}$ **c** $\dfrac{3p}{4} \div \dfrac{p}{2}$

Niagara Falls

- Use the Internet to find the height, width and water flow of the Niagara Falls.

Chapter 6 | Revision Assignment

1 Change each of the following to its basic fraction.
   a 20%   b 25%   c 60%   d 72%

2 Change each fraction to a percentage.
   a $\frac{5}{100}$ b $\frac{27}{100}$ c $\frac{100}{100}$ d $\frac{110}{100}$

3 Write each fraction as a percentage.
   a $\frac{3}{10}$ b $\frac{9}{25}$ c $\frac{7}{20}$ d $\frac{11}{40}$

4 Write each percentage as a decimal.
   a 15%   b 7%   c 108%   d 74%

5 a Change 0·375 to a percentage.
   b Change 0·025 to a percentage.
   c Change $\frac{15}{16}$ to a percentage.
   d Change $10\frac{3}{4}\%$ to a decimal.

6 Find:
   a 15% of $28   b 3% of 920 L
   c 150% of 10 500   d 4·5% of $21 500

7 a Don Nash scored 75 runs out of a total of 225. What percentage of the total did he score?
   b A farmer sells off 3% of her flock of 5200 sheep. How many sheep does she sell?

   c A man runs 1 km in 4 min 40 s. After one month of practice he improves his time to 4 min 15 s. What is his percentage improvement?
   d An alloy is made of 7 kg of silver, 18 kg of lead and 15 kg of zinc. What percentage of the metal is silver?

8

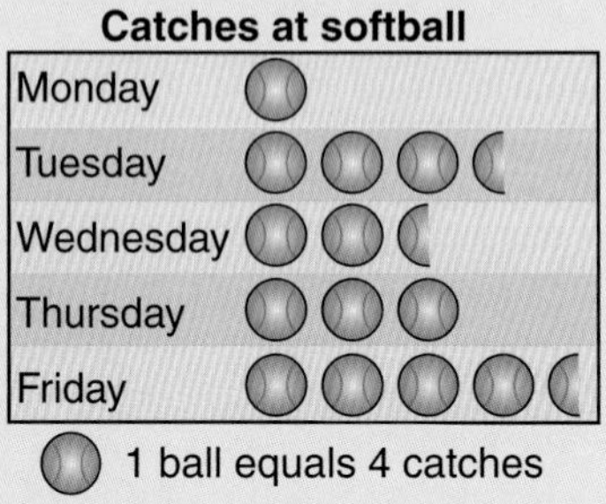

Catches at softball

Monday	◐
Tuesday	◐◐◐◐◑
Wednesday	◐◐◑
Thursday	◐◐◐
Friday	◐◐◐◐◑

◐ 1 ball equals 4 catches

   a How many catches were there on Tuesday?
   b How many catches were there altogether?
   c Which day had one-third as many balls caught as another day?
   d Which day had four more catches than Wednesday?

Chapter 6 | Working Mathematically

1 Larry has to make a handrail by fixing 40 vertical posts, which are 25 mm wide, between two walls which are 5000 mm apart. If the posts are to be equally spaced, how far apart should the posts be? (Answer to the nearest millimetre.)

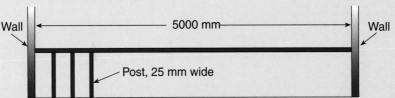

Wall ←————————— 5000 mm —————————→ Wall

Post, 25 mm wide

2 Four teams are to play in a soccer competition. The competition is a double round-robin, where each team plays each other team twice on a home-and-away basis. Make up a draw for this competition, calling the teams 1, 2, 3 and 4, and making the first-mentioned team in each match the home team.

3 In the cube shown you can move from corner to corner along the edges of the cube only. You wish to go from A to H.
   a What is the shortest possible path? How many different paths are there?
   b If you cannot pass through any corner more than once, what is the length of the longest path from A to H?

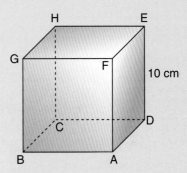

10 cm

4 Five positive whole numbers add up to 15.
   a What is the largest of the five numbers if it is known that the numbers are all different?
   b What is the largest possible number if the numbers do not have to be all different?

5 Card towers can be made from playing cards as shown in the diagram below.

Level 1
(2 cards)

Level 2
(7 cards)

Level 3
(15 cards)

How many cards would be needed to build a:
   a Level 4 tower?   b Level 10 tower?

Technology
Applications

Drag and Drops

7

Equations, Formulae and Inequations

Chapter Contents

Learning Outcomes

Students will be able to use algebraic techniques to solve linear equations and simple inequalities.

Areas of Interaction

Approaches to Learning (Knowledge Acquisition, Problem Solving, Communication Skills, Thinking Skills), Human Ingenuity

An **equation** is a number sentence in which one (or more) of the numbers is missing or unknown and is represented by a pronumeral.

 Equations are sometimes called algebraic sentences.

7:01 | Inverse Operations

prep quiz

7:01

Write an algebraic expression for each of the following sentences.

1 Add 5 to x.   **2** Multiply a by 3.   **3** Divide y by 8.   **4** Take 2 away from p.

5 Multiply x by 3 and then add 2.   **6** Subtract 2 from y and then multiply the result by 7.

What is the opposite of:

7 adding 8?   **8** subtracting 5?   **9** multiplying by 4?   **10** dividing by 3?

• We build algebraic expressions by starting with the pronumeral.

Algebraic Expression	Meaning	Arrow Diagram
$x + 5$	x has had 5 added to it.	$\boxed{x} \xrightarrow{+5} \boxed{x+5}$
$x - 5$	x has had 5 subtracted from it.	$\boxed{x} \xrightarrow{-5} \boxed{x-5}$
$5x$	x has been multiplied by 5.	$\boxed{x} \xrightarrow{\times 5} \boxed{5x}$
$\dfrac{x}{5}$	x has been divided by 5.	$\boxed{x} \xrightarrow{\div 5} \boxed{\dfrac{x}{5}}$

• Arrow diagrams can be used to show how the expression has been made.
• The operation that has caused the change is written above the arrow.
• When solving equations, we need to reverse the steps to get back to the pronumeral. In other words, we need to perform the **inverse** operations. For instance, if:

$\boxed{x} \xrightarrow{+5} \boxed{x+5}$ then $\boxed{x+5} \xrightarrow{-5} \boxed{x}$

$\boxed{x} \xrightarrow{-5} \boxed{x-5}$ then $\boxed{x-5} \xrightarrow{+5} \boxed{x}$

$\boxed{x} \xrightarrow{\times 5} \boxed{5x}$ then $\boxed{5x} \xrightarrow{\div 5} \boxed{x}$

$\boxed{x} \xrightarrow{\div 5} \boxed{\dfrac{x}{5}}$ then $\boxed{\dfrac{x}{5}} \xrightarrow{\times 5} \boxed{x}$

Inverse means *opposite*.

$\boxed{2} \xrightarrow{+5} \boxed{7}$

$\boxed{7} \xrightarrow{-5} \boxed{2}$

Adding 5 and subtracting 5 are inverse operations.

1 Note how each expression has been built from the pronumeral.

a $\boxed{y} \xrightarrow{-8} \boxed{y-8}$

b $\boxed{a} \xrightarrow{\times 3} \boxed{3a} \xrightarrow{+5} \boxed{3a+5}$

c $\boxed{q} \xrightarrow{+6} \boxed{q+6} \xrightarrow{\times 2} \boxed{2(q+6)}$

d $\boxed{m} \xrightarrow{\div 2} \boxed{\dfrac{m}{2}} \xrightarrow{-4} \boxed{\dfrac{m}{2}-4}$

e $\boxed{n} \xrightarrow{-11} \boxed{n-11} \xrightarrow{\div 7} \boxed{\dfrac{n-11}{7}}$

2 Note the inverse operations used to get back to the pronumeral.

a $\boxed{9m} \xrightarrow{\div 9} \boxed{m}$

b $\boxed{8x+15} \xrightarrow{-15} \boxed{8x} \xrightarrow{\div 8} \boxed{x}$

c $\boxed{4(y+3)} \xrightarrow{\div 4} \boxed{y+3} \xrightarrow{-3} \boxed{y}$

d $\boxed{\dfrac{a-1}{5}} \xrightarrow{\times 5} \boxed{a-1} \xrightarrow{+1} \boxed{a}$

Order of operations is very important!

Exercise 7:01

1 Complete the following arrow diagrams by writing the correct operation above the arrow.

a $\boxed{x} \rightarrow \boxed{9x}$

b $\boxed{a} \rightarrow \boxed{a+2}$

c $\boxed{q} \rightarrow \boxed{q-7}$

d $\boxed{y} \rightarrow \boxed{5y} \rightarrow \boxed{5y-1}$

e $\boxed{m} \rightarrow \boxed{\dfrac{m}{10}}$

f $\boxed{n} \rightarrow \boxed{n+6} \rightarrow \boxed{\dfrac{n+6}{5}}$

g $\boxed{a} \rightarrow \boxed{\dfrac{a}{3}} \rightarrow \boxed{\dfrac{a}{3}+9}$

h $\boxed{a} \rightarrow \boxed{a-8} \rightarrow \boxed{\dfrac{a-8}{7}}$

i $\boxed{n} \rightarrow \boxed{\dfrac{n}{-5}} \rightarrow \boxed{\dfrac{n}{-5}+3}$

j $\boxed{p} \rightarrow \boxed{p+3} \rightarrow \boxed{2(p+3)}$

k $\boxed{x} \rightarrow \boxed{-3x} \rightarrow \boxed{-3x+5}$

2 Complete these arrow diagrams, showing how to get back to the pronumeral.

a $\boxed{3m} \rightarrow \boxed{m}$ b $\boxed{\dfrac{x}{2}} \rightarrow \boxed{x}$ c $\boxed{n+5} \rightarrow \boxed{n}$

d $\boxed{p-7} \rightarrow \boxed{p}$ e $\boxed{10x} \rightarrow \boxed{x}$ f $\boxed{\dfrac{a}{3}} \rightarrow \boxed{a}$

g $\boxed{8+t} \rightarrow \boxed{t}$ h $\boxed{q-5} \rightarrow \boxed{q}$ i $\boxed{2m+1} \rightarrow \boxed{2m} \rightarrow \boxed{m}$

j $\boxed{5p-2} \rightarrow \boxed{5p} \rightarrow \boxed{p}$ k $\boxed{7x+3} \rightarrow \boxed{7x} \rightarrow \boxed{x}$ l $\boxed{9q-4} \rightarrow \boxed{9q} \rightarrow \boxed{q}$

m $\boxed{6+3x} \rightarrow \boxed{3x} \rightarrow \boxed{x}$ n $\boxed{7+\dfrac{m}{2}} \rightarrow \boxed{\dfrac{m}{2}} \rightarrow \boxed{m}$ o $\boxed{\dfrac{x}{5}-2} \rightarrow \boxed{\dfrac{x}{5}} \rightarrow \boxed{x}$

p $\boxed{\dfrac{a+7}{3}} \rightarrow \boxed{a+7} \rightarrow \boxed{a}$ q $\boxed{\dfrac{b-2}{5}} \rightarrow \boxed{b-2} \rightarrow \boxed{b}$ r $\boxed{5-3x} \rightarrow \boxed{-3x} \rightarrow \boxed{x}$

s $\boxed{8-2p} \rightarrow \boxed{-2p} \rightarrow \boxed{p}$ t $\boxed{5-\dfrac{x}{3}} \rightarrow \boxed{\dfrac{-x}{3}} \rightarrow \boxed{x}$

3 Draw arrow diagrams to show how the following expressions were made from the pronumeral.

a $8m$ b $\dfrac{p}{7}$ c $5+x$ d $q-10$

e $3x+2$ f $5n-3$ g $6p+7$ h $9a-1$

i $\dfrac{x}{3}+5$ j $7+\dfrac{a}{4}$ k $\dfrac{y+3}{4}$ l $\dfrac{n-1}{5}$

m $7(m+2)$ n $9(x-3)$ o $5(2+x)$ p $3(q-4)$

q $3-2x$ r $-5a+7$ s $6-\dfrac{x}{3}$ t $10-9p$

4 Complete the following arrow diagrams.

a $\boxed{a} \overset{-2}{\rightarrow} \boxed{}$ b $\boxed{x} \overset{\times 4}{\rightarrow} \boxed{}$ c $\boxed{m} \overset{\div 3}{\rightarrow} \boxed{}$

d $\boxed{t} \overset{+9}{\rightarrow} \boxed{}$ e $\boxed{p} \overset{\times 5}{\rightarrow} \boxed{} \overset{+2}{\rightarrow} \boxed{}$ f $\boxed{x} \overset{\times 6}{\rightarrow} \boxed{} \overset{-4}{\rightarrow} \boxed{}$

g $\boxed{y} \overset{+1}{\rightarrow} \boxed{} \overset{\times 7}{\rightarrow} \boxed{}$ h $\boxed{b} \overset{\div 4}{\rightarrow} \boxed{} \overset{+2}{\rightarrow} \boxed{}$ i $\boxed{q} \overset{-3}{\rightarrow} \boxed{} \overset{\div 3}{\rightarrow} \boxed{}$

j $\boxed{n} \overset{\times (-2)}{\rightarrow} \boxed{} \overset{+6}{\rightarrow} \boxed{}$ k $\boxed{b+10} \overset{-10}{\rightarrow} \boxed{}$ l $\boxed{a-7} \overset{+7}{\rightarrow} \boxed{}$

m $\boxed{5m} \overset{\div 5}{\rightarrow} \boxed{}$ n $\boxed{\dfrac{n}{4}} \overset{\times 4}{\rightarrow} \boxed{}$ o $\boxed{2x+3} \overset{-3}{\rightarrow} \boxed{} \overset{\div 2}{\rightarrow} \boxed{}$

p $\boxed{5p-4} \overset{+4}{\rightarrow} \boxed{} \overset{\div 5}{\rightarrow} \boxed{}$ q $\boxed{6+7t} \overset{-6}{\rightarrow} \boxed{} \overset{\div 7}{\rightarrow} \boxed{}$ r $\boxed{\dfrac{m+5}{4}} \overset{\times 4}{\rightarrow} \boxed{} \overset{-5}{\rightarrow} \boxed{}$

s $\boxed{\dfrac{a}{3}-5} \overset{+5}{\rightarrow} \boxed{} \overset{\times 3}{\rightarrow} \boxed{}$ t $\boxed{5-2x} \overset{-5}{\rightarrow} \boxed{} \overset{\div (-2)}{\rightarrow} \boxed{}$

5 What operations must be performed on x to get the following expressions?

a $x - 6$ b $\dfrac{x}{3}$ c $x + 5$ d $7x$

e $2x + 3$ f $5x - 2$ g $6 + 3x$ h $7x - 1$

i $\dfrac{x + 7}{5}$ j $\dfrac{x - 4}{3}$ k $\dfrac{x}{8} + 5$ l $\dfrac{x}{3} - 4$

m $2(x + 3)$ n $5(x - 9)$ o $-6x + 8$ p $10 - 3x$

I love operations!

6 What must be done to these expressions to make them equal to a?

a $a - 7$ b $5a$ c $6 + a$ d $\dfrac{a}{3}$ e $-4a$

f $2a + 5$ g $3a - 1$ h $5 + 7a$ i $5a - 6$ j $8 - 3a$

k $\dfrac{a + 3}{7}$ l $\dfrac{a}{7} + 3$ m $5(a + 2)$ n $3(a - 1)$ o $\dfrac{a - 9}{5}$

7 What order of inverse operations must be performed to get back to the pronumeral?

a $\dfrac{2a + 3}{5}$ b $6(3x + 7)$ c $\dfrac{7 - 3p}{6}$ d $9 + \dfrac{2m}{3}$

e $5(2 - 3m)$ f $\dfrac{5 - n}{7}$ g $6 - \dfrac{5q}{3}$ h $\dfrac{7(3y + 4)}{5}$

7:02 | Solving Equations

7:02

Simplify the following: **1** $7x \div 7$ **2** $x + 4 - 4$ **3** $a - 7 + 7$ **4** $\dfrac{m}{5} \times 5$

What is the inverse of: **5** multiplying by 3?   **6** adding 7?

7 subtracting 1?   **8** dividing by 5?

Complete these arrowing diagrams, putting operations above each arrow.

9 $\boxed{5m + 3} \rightarrow \boxed{5m} \rightarrow \boxed{m}$

10 $\boxed{8a - 2} \rightarrow \boxed{8a} \rightarrow \boxed{a}$

• Solving equations is like balancing scales.
• With equations, we know that one side is equal to the other.
• The solution of the equation therefore is the value of the pronumeral that 'balances' the equation.

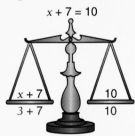

$x + 7 = 10$

| $x + 7$ | 10 |
| $3 + 7$ | 10 |

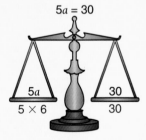

$5a = 30$

| $5a$ | 30 |
| 5×6 | 30 |

$x = 3$ balances the scale so $x = 3$ is the solution.

$a = 6$ balances the scale so $a = 6$ is the solution.

- Often, solving an equation requires us to change the equation into a simpler one. We can do this by adding (+), subtracting (−), multiplying (×) or dividing (÷) both sides of the equation by the same number.
- Look at the solutions of these two equations, noting that both sides remain balanced because the same operation is done to both sides.

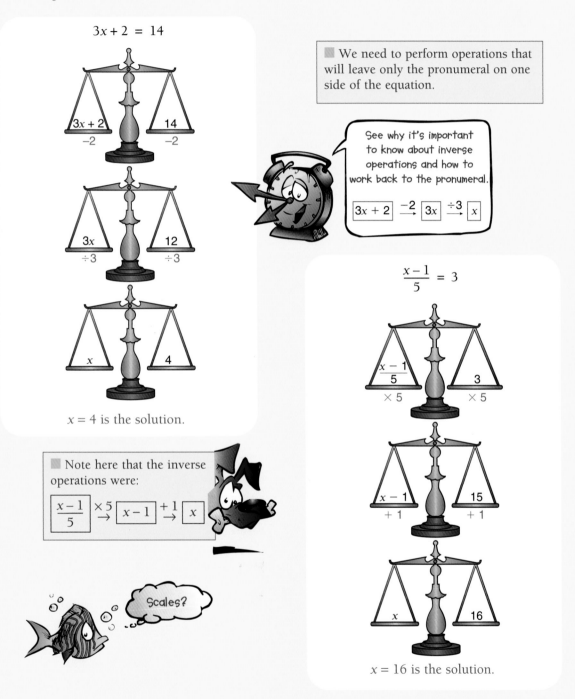

$3x + 2 = 14$

We need to perform operations that will leave only the pronumeral on one side of the equation.

See why it's important to know about inverse operations and how to work back to the pronumeral.

$$\boxed{3x + 2} \xrightarrow{-2} \boxed{3x} \xrightarrow{\div 3} \boxed{x}$$

$x = 4$ is the solution.

$$\frac{x - 1}{5} = 3$$

Note here that the inverse operations were:

$$\boxed{\dfrac{x-1}{5}} \xrightarrow{\times 5} \boxed{x-1} \xrightarrow{+1} \boxed{x}$$

Scales?

$x = 16$ is the solution.

Now examine the solutions to the equations in the following worked examples, noting the operations that have been done to both sides (shown in colour).

worked examples

1 These solutions involve only one step.

a $m + 27 = 59$
$\qquad -27 \quad -27$
$\qquad m = 59 - 27$
$\qquad \therefore m = 32$

b $a - 16 = 9$
$\qquad +16 \quad +16$
$\qquad a = 9 + 16$
$\qquad \therefore a = 25$

c $3p = 23$
$\qquad \div 3 \quad \div 3$
$\qquad p = \frac{23}{3}$
$\qquad \therefore p = 7\frac{2}{3}$

d $\frac{x}{7} = 12$
$\qquad \times 7 \quad \times 7$
$\qquad x = 7 \times 12$
$\qquad \therefore x = 84$

2 The solutions of these equations involve two steps.

a $2a + 5 = 7$
$\qquad -5 \quad -5$
$\qquad 2a = 2$
$\qquad \div 2 \quad \div 2$
$\qquad \therefore a = 1$

b $\frac{x+3}{5} = 2$
$\qquad \times 5 \quad \times 5$
$\qquad x + 3 = 10$
$\qquad -3 \quad -3$
$\qquad \therefore x = 7$

c $\frac{p}{3} - 6 = 15$
$\qquad +6 \quad +6$
$\qquad \frac{p}{3} = 21$
$\qquad \times 3 \quad \times 3$
$\qquad \therefore p = 63$

d $10 - 3m = 25$
$\qquad -10 \quad -20$
$\qquad -3m = 15$
$\qquad \div -3 \quad \div -3$
$\qquad \therefore m = -5$

Exercise 7:02

Foundation Worksheet 7:02

Solving equations 1
1 Solve these equations.
  a ☐ + 7 = 10   **b** ☐ − 1 = 6
  c 6 × ☐ = 18   **d** ☐ ÷ 2 = 3
2 Which of the numbers
  2, 7 and 10 are solutions?
  a ☐ + 4 = 11   **b** 3 × ☐ = 30

1 Solve each of these one-step equations.

a $x + 7 = 15$	**b** $p + 9 = 11$	**c** $y + 7 = 21$
d $15 + n = 18$	**e** $7 + q = 15$	**f** $20 + k = 29$
g $y - 5 = 3$	**h** $m - 7 = 2$	**i** $x - 10 = 3$
j $5x = 15$	**k** $7x = 42$	**l** $3p = 36$
m $12 = 3y$	**n** $18 = 9y$	**o** $24 = 8x$
p $\frac{n}{3} = 2$	**q** $\frac{x}{5} = 3$	**r** $\frac{m}{4} = 4$

2 These one-step equations involve negative integers.

a $x + 3 = 2$	**b** $m + 5 = 1$	**c** $n + 6 = 4$
d $7 + p = -1$	**e** $6 + q = 0$	**f** $10 + y = -2$
g $a - 7 = -2$	**h** $x - 10 = -3$	**i** $p - 9 = -4$
j $q - 2 = -1$	**k** $y - 4 = -4$	**l** $t - 6 = -2$
m $3m = -6$	**n** $8p = -16$	**o** $6w = -6$
p $-2n = 12$	**q** $-3q = 27$	**r** $-4m = -8$
s $\frac{x}{3} = -2$	**t** $\frac{m}{4} = -20$	**u** $\frac{n}{7} = -28$
v $x - (-2) = 5$	**w** $-5 - y = 3$	**x** $6 - (-x) = 3$

■ *Notice:*
If $-a = 3$,
then $a = -3$
(Multiply both
sides by -1)

3 The solution to an equation can be checked by substituting it into the equation.
Check to see if the solution to each equation below is correct.

a $x + 16 = 43$	**b** $9 + y = 13$	**c** $m - 10 = 3$	**d** $n - 12 = 15$
$\quad x = 27$	$\quad y = 5$	$\quad m = 13$	$\quad n = 27$
e $6 - q = 4$	**f** $8 - y = 10$	**g** $7m = 10$	**h** $3a = 2$
$\quad q = 2$	$\quad y = 2$	$\quad m = \frac{10}{7}$	$\quad a = \frac{3}{2}$

i $-5y = -15$ **j** $\dfrac{x}{3} = 6$ **k** $\dfrac{m}{5} = 10$ **l** $\dfrac{n}{6} = 3$

       $y = -3$ $x = 18$ $m = 2$ $n = \frac{1}{2}$

4 Solving these equations involves two steps. Clearly show each step in your working. (All the answers are integers.)

   a $2x + 1 = 5$ **b** $3a + 2 = 8$ **c** $2m + 7 = 13$
   d $3n - 2 = 7$ **e** $5k - 1 = 24$ **f** $6t - 4 = 8$
   g $6 + 5a = 26$ **h** $10 + 3w = 13$ **i** $12 + 4q = 16$
   j $10 - 3x = 1$ **k** $15 - 2m = 11$ **l** $20 - 5q = 0$
   m $15 = 2x - 3$ **n** $7 = 5y - 3$ **o** $10 = 2 - 4a$
   p $4 - x = -7$ **q** $-3 - x = -2$ **r** $2 = 4 - x$

5 Solving these equations also involves two steps. (The solutions are all positive integers.)

   a $\dfrac{3x}{2} = 3$ **b** $\dfrac{2x}{5} = 4$ **c** $\dfrac{3m}{4} = 6$

   d $\dfrac{x + 1}{4} = 3$ **e** $\dfrac{a + 2}{3} = 1$ **f** $\dfrac{n + 7}{2} = 10$

   g $\dfrac{m - 4}{2} = 5$ **h** $\dfrac{n - 1}{3} = 6$ **i** $\dfrac{a - 2}{4} = 10$

   j $\dfrac{y}{3} + 1 = 3$ **k** $\dfrac{x}{4} + 2 = 1$ **l** $\dfrac{m}{5} - 3 = 2$

   m $5 + \dfrac{a}{2} = 10$ **n** $2 + \dfrac{x}{3} = 8$ **o** $5 + \dfrac{m}{2} = 7$

▨ $\dfrac{3x}{5} = 6$
     $\times 5$ $\times 5$
     $3x = 30$
     $\div 3$ $\div 3$
     $x = 10$

▨ Multiply each term on *both sides* by the denominator.

6 The solutions to these equations involve fractions.

   a $2x + 1 = 4$ **b** $2a + 5 = 10$
   c $3m + 4 = 5$ **d** $5n + 2 = 8$
   e $2p - 3 = 2$ **f** $4q - 1 = 2$
   g $5n - 5 = 4$ **h** $6y - 3 = 1$
   i $5 + 2k = 12$ **j** $7 + 3x = 9$
   k $8 + 3a = 10$ **l** $1 + 2a = 4$
   m $2m + 6 = 3$ **n** $5p + 7 = 1$
   o $3 - 2a = 6$ **p** $5 - 3a = 1$

Opposite operations are the key.

▨ $3a + 2 = 6$
     -2 -2
     $3a = 4$
     $\div 3$ $\div 3$
      $a = \frac{4}{3}$ or $1\frac{1}{3}$

7 Now try this set of equations, which are either one- or two-step types.

   a $5x = 35$ **b** $m + 7 = 11$ **c** $2x + 1 = 3$ **d** $5 - n = 0$
   e $3a + 1 = 10$ **f** $a - 2 = -3$ **g** $y + 3 = 1$ **h** $3m - 1 = 5$
   i $-4x = 16$ **j** $5 + 3n = 10$ **k** $3x = 2$ **l** $6 - q = 10$
   m $\dfrac{x}{5} = 10$ **n** $\dfrac{3p}{2} = 6$ **o** $\dfrac{x + 2}{5} = 1$ **p** $\dfrac{a}{3} - 4 = 2$

   q $6 + \dfrac{a}{3} = 8$ **r** $\dfrac{5 + a}{2} = 1$ **s** $\dfrac{m - 4}{7} = 6$ **t** $\dfrac{5m}{2} = 3$

   u $6 - 2a = 8$ **v** $3p + 5 = 2$ **w** $\dfrac{q + 6}{2} = 1$ **x** $\dfrac{3 - x}{2} = 5$

Fun Spot 7:02A | Why did the tooth get dressed up?

Work out the answer to each part and put the letter for that part in the box above the correct answer.

Solve these equations.

T $x + 8 = 15$ **A** $a = -4 - 6$ **A** $a = (\frac{1}{2})^3$

T $3 + x = 1$ **T** $8m = -56$ **D** $11x = 121$

A $x + x = 1$ **T** $75 \div a = 15$ **E** $0{\cdot}2x = -1$

E $8a = 0$ **S** $8 + x = 12$ **H** $1 - x = 4$

U $60 - n = 0$ **O** $35 \div n = 1$ **N** $5(x - 9) = 0$

T $n = 20 - n$ **U** $7 - x = 8$ **O** $\dfrac{100}{m} = 5$

O $6 \div x = 2$ **W** $\frac{1}{4} + n = 1$ **T** $7a = 7$

I $-3 - 3 = a$ **K** $1 - x = -1$ **S** $4x = 1$

B $-a = -8$ **T** $a - 8 = 2a$ **I** $\dfrac{x}{3} = 2$

T $10 - n = -2$ **E** $\dfrac{m}{20} = 5$

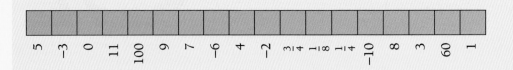

| 5 | −3 | 0 | 11 | 100 | 9 | 7 | −6 | 4 | −2 | $\frac{3}{4}$ | $\frac{1}{8}$ | $\frac{1}{4}$ | −10 | 8 | 3 | 60 | 1 |

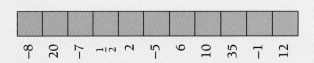

| −8 | 20 | −7 | $\frac{1}{2}$ | 2 | −5 | 6 | 10 | 35 | −1 | 12 |

How heavy is one box?

7:03 | Equations with Pronumerals on Both Sides

- To solve these equations we may have to add or subtract pronumerals as well as numerals. Follow the steps in each diagram.

$9x + 6 = 8x + 9$

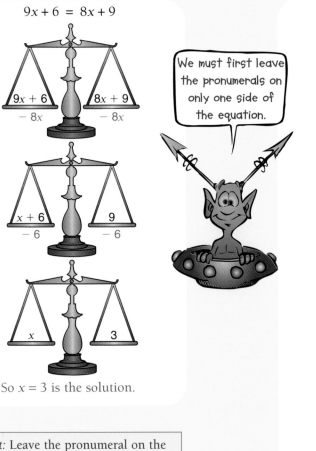

We must first leave the pronumerals on only one side of the equation.

So $x = 3$ is the solution.

Hint: Leave the pronumeral on the side where the term will be positive.

$5 - 3x = 2x + 3$

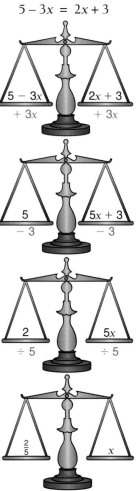

So $x = \frac{2}{5}$ is the solution.

1 $3a + 5 = 2a + 7$
$\quad -\,2a \quad\; -\,2a$
$\quad a + 5 = 7$
$\quad\; -\,5 \quad -\,5$
$\quad\quad \therefore a = 2$

2 $5x - 3 = 2x + 9$
$\quad -\,2x \quad\; -\,2x$
$\quad 3x - 3 = 9$
$\quad\; +\,3 \quad +\,3$
$\quad\quad 3x = 12$
$\quad\quad \div\,3 \quad \div\,3$
$\quad\quad \therefore x = 4$

3 $2 - 2x = 8 + x$
$\quad +\,2x \quad +\,2x$
$\quad\quad 2 = 8 + 3x$
$\quad\; -\,8 \quad -\,8$
$\quad\; -\,6 = 3x$
$\quad\; \div\,3 \quad \div\,3$
$\quad\; -\,2 = x$
$\quad\quad \therefore x = -2$

| ▨ Therefore! |
| :∴ |

Exercise 7:03

Foundation Worksheet 7:03

Solving equations 2
1 Solve by inspection:
  a $x + 15 = 16$ **b** $a - 9 = 2$
  c $4m = 32$ **d** $\frac{x}{2} = 7$
2 Solve by inspection:
  a $3 + a = 9$ **b** $10 + y = 11$
  c $m \times 3 = 6$ **d** $10 \div x = 2$

1 Solve the following equations. (The answers are all integers.)

  a $2a + 5 = a + 7$ **b** $3x + 1 = 2x + 8$

  c $7p - 2 = 6p + 1$ **d** $10q - 3 = 9q + 5$

  e $7n = 6n + 5$ **f** $8x = 7x - 3$

  g $5m + 2 = 4m - 1$ **h** $3a + 7 = 2a + 5$ **i** $3x + 1 = x + 7$

  j $5m + 2 = 3m + 8$ **k** $5y - 4 = y + 12$ **l** $3x + 7 = x + 1$

  m $2x + 5 = 3x - 1$ **n** $4m + 2 = 6m + 10$ **o** $x + 7 = 5x - 1$

  p $3x + 2 = 7 - 2x$ **q** $6m - 1 = 15 - 2m$ **r** $5 - 3p = p + 5$

2 Check to see if the given solution is correct or incorrect by seeing if it 'fits' the equation.

  a $5m - 2 = 4m + 1$ **b** $3p + 7 = 2p + 12$ **c** $10q + 3 = 11q + 1$
        $m = 3$ $p = 5$ $q = -2$

  d $7a + 3 = 5a + 1$ **e** $8q - 7 = 5q + 5$ **f** $x + 10 = 5x - 2$
        $a = 2$ $q = 4$ $x = 2$

  g $3n + 1 = n - 7$ **h** $2m + 5 = 5m - 1$ **i** $8a + 1 = 3a - 4$
        $n = -3$ $m = 2$ $a = -1$

  j $5x = 2x + 6$ **k** $5a + 8 = 3a$ **l** $3x = 10 + 2x$
        $x = 2$ $a = 4$ $x = 2$

  m $3 + 2x = 7 + 3x$ **n** $5 - 2m = 6 + m$ **o** $5p - 2 = 5 - 2p$
        $x = 4$ $m = -1$ $p = 1$

3 Solve these equations.

  a $3x + 1 = x + 2$ **b** $5m + 2 = 3m + 5$ **c** $4p + 2 = p + 4$

  d $5m = 2m + 1$ **e** $3a = a - 1$ **f** $6n + 2 = n + 8$

  g $5a - 1 = 3a + 4$ **h** $12n - 9 = 9n + 1$ **i** $8q - 5 = 5q + 3$

  j $6n + 4 = 4n + 3$ **k** $8a + 5 = 5a + 7$ **l** $4k - 2 = k - 6$

  m $2a + 5 = 4a + 2$ **n** $x + 6 = 4x + 2$ **o** $2q + 7 = 6q - 2$

  p $8t = 5t + 8$ **q** $3m = 6m - 2$ **r** $6x = 5 - 2x$

  s $3a + 2 = 5a + 6$ **t** $w - 3 = 7w + 5$ **u** $2m - 3 = 5m + 1$

  v $5 - 2y = 3 + y$ **w** $10 + 3x = 9 - 5x$ **x** $3 - p = 16 - 4p$

7:04 | Equations with Grouping Symbols

Rewrite these expressions without grouping symbols.

1 $2(x + 3)$ **2** $3(a - 5)$ **3** $2(4a + 6)$ **4** $5(2p - 1)$ **5** $7(3 - 2q)$

Solve these one-step equations.

6 $x + 7 = 12$ **7** $x + 7 = 2$ **8** $5p = 10$ **9** $10p = 5$ **10** $8 - x = -3$

- If you remember how to 'expand' grouping symbols, these equations are no harder than the ones you have already seen.

worked examples

see

7:08

1 Expand the grouping symbols and then solve the equation.

a $2(x + 4) = 10$
$$2x + 8 = 10$$
$$\quad -8 \quad -8$$
$$2x = 2$$
$$\div 2 \quad \div 2$$
$$\therefore x = 1$$

b $5(a - 3) = 3$
$$5a - 15 = 3$$
$$\quad +15 \quad +15$$
$$5a = 18$$
$$\div 5 \quad \div 5$$
$$\therefore a = \frac{18}{5} \text{ or } 3\frac{3}{5}$$

c $3(2m - 4) = 4m - 6$
$$6m - 12 = 4m - 6$$
$$\quad -4m \quad -4m$$
$$2m - 12 = -6$$
$$\quad +12 \quad +12$$
$$2m = 6$$
$$\div 2 \quad \div 2$$
$$\therefore m = 3$$

2 Expand each set of grouping symbols and then solve the equations.

a $3(a + 7) = 4(a - 2)$
$$3a + 21 = 4a - 8$$
$$\quad -3a \quad -3a$$
$$21 = a - 8$$
$$\quad +8 \quad +8$$
$$29 = a$$
$$\therefore a = 29$$

b $3(x + 4) + 2(x - 5) = 4$
$$3x + 12 + 2x - 10 = 4$$
Collect like terms.
$$5x + 2 = 4$$
$$\quad -2 \quad -2$$
$$5x = 2$$
$$\div 5 \quad \div 5$$
$$x = \frac{2}{5}$$

Exercise 7:04

1 Expand the grouping symbols and then solve each equation.

a $2(x + 3) = 4$
c $7(n + 2) = 14$
e $3(a - 2) = 6$
g $9(x - 1) = 18$
i $2(a + 3) = 7$
k $2(x - 2) = 1$
m $2(3 - a) = 4$

b $3(a + 2) = 12$
d $6(p + 2) = 24$
f $2(m - 3) = 8$
h $5(q - 2) = 10$
j $3(x + 1) = 8$
l $5(t - 1) = 2$
n $4(7 - x) = 12$

2 Solve each equation by first expanding the grouping symbols. (Answers are all integers.)

- **a** $3(2x + 1) = 9$
- **b** $2(3a + 4) = 20$
- **c** $5(2m + 1) = 25$
- **d** $4(3a - 1) = 8$
- **e** $5(2p - 3) = 5$
- **f** $4(3q - 2) = 16$
- **g** $2(x + 2) = x + 5$
- **h** $3(a + 3) = 2a + 12$
- **i** $5(m + 2) = 3m + 12$
- **j** $3(m - 1) = 2m - 1$
- **k** $4(n - 2) = 2n + 4$
- **l** $3(2a + 1) = 4a + 7$
- **m** $2m + 5 = 3(m - 1)$
- **n** $6x + 3 = 3(x + 2)$
- **o** $5 - 2x = 3(x - 5)$

3 Solve each equation.

- **a** $2(x + 1) = 5$
- **b** $3(a + 3) = -10$
- **c** $5(p + 3) = 2$
- **d** $3(a - 2) = 0$
- **e** $5(q - 1) = -3$
- **f** $7(t - 2) = 5$
- **g** $2(3x + 1) = 5$
- **h** $3(2p + 3) = 12$
- **i** $5(2w + 3) = -20$
- **j** $3(x - 1) = x + 2$
- **k** $2(q - 3) = 4q - 9$
- **l** $5(k + 2) = 2k + 11$
- **m** $3m + 2 = 5(m - 1)$
- **n** $7x = 5(2x - 1)$
- **o** $3n - 7 = 6(2n - 2)$

4 Find the solution to each equation by expanding all grouping symbols first.

- **a** $3(a + 2) = 2(a + 1)$
- **b** $5(x - 1) = 4(x + 2)$
- **c** $5(p - 2) = 4(p + 2)$
- **d** $3(q + 2) = 2(q + 5)$
- **e** $3(m + 1) = 5(m - 1)$
- **f** $6(x + 2) = 4(x + 6)$
- **g** $2(a - 7) = 5(a - 4)$
- **h** $7(t + 2) = 4(t + 5)$
- **i** $3(2a + 1) = 5(a + 2)$
- **j** $4(3p - 1) = 5(2p + 1)$
- **k** $6(t + 7) = 4(t + 10) + 8$
- **l** $5(2a - 1) = 3(a + 6) - 7$
- **m** $3(2 + m) = 5(2 - m) + 6m$
- **n** $6(p + 3) = 5(2 - p) + 7p - 12$

5 Solve each equation. (See Worked Example **2b** on p 250.)

- **a** $3(a + 2) + a + 5 = 15$
- **b** $5(m - 1) + 2m = 2$
- **c** $2(m + 3) + 5(m + 2) = 23$
- **d** $3(x + 2) + 2(x - 3) = 10$
- **e** $5(p + 1) + 2(p + 4) = 20$
- **f** $4(t - 2) + 2(t + 5) = 14$
- **g** $4(2a + 3) + 2(a - 5) = 22$
- **h** $2(2m + 3) + 3(m - 5) = 5$
- **i** $5(a - 3) + 3(2 + 3a) = 19$
- **j** $7(a + 5) + 2(6 - 3a) = 1$

6 Try solving these equations, but first read the warning sign!

- **a** $3(a + 2) - 2(a + 1) = 6$
- **b** $5(m + 3) - 4(m + 2) = 10$
- **c** $5(n + 4) - 3(n - 2) = 30$
- **d** $6(a + 2) - 4(a - 1) = 20$
- **e** $4(a + 3) - (a + 2) = 13$
- **f** $4(p + 5) - (p + 3) = 23$
- **g** $5(2a + 1) - 2(a - 4) = 2$
- **h** $6(2x + 5) - 5(3x + 2) = 10$

> ▨ *Warning!*
> Remember how to expand
> with a negative term:
> $$-2(x + 4) = -2x - 8$$
> or
> $$-3(a - 1) = -3a + 3$$

Technology Applications

Activities

7:04 Equations

- At half past 10 what is the angle between the hands of a clock?
- What would be the angle between the hands two hours later?

7:05 | Formulae

If $a = 5$ and $b = 3$, find the value of each of these expressions.

1 $a - b$ **2** $b - a$ **3** $2a + 3b$ **4** $3a - 2b$ **5** $a^2 + b^2$

Find the value of the expression $2x - y$ if:

6 $x = 3, y = 4$ **7** $x = 2, y = 5$ **8** $x = -2, y = 4$ **9** $x = 5, y = -2$ **10** $x = -3, y = -4$

- A **formula** is a type of equation which may represent a special relationship. For instance, the formula $A = L \times B$ represents the relationship between the area (A) of a rectangle and its length (L) and breadth (B).
- A formula is different to an equation because it will have more than one pronumeral. To find the value of one pronumeral, we must know the values of every other pronumeral in the formula.
- There are two types of questions. These are as shown by the following examples.

worked examples A

For these formulae we need to find the value of the pronumeral that is by itself.

1 If $P = 2L + 2B$, find P
  if $L = 4$ and $B = 3$.

2 If $v = u + at$, find v
  if $u = 1 \cdot 2$, $a = 0 \cdot 5$ and $t = 12 \cdot 6$.

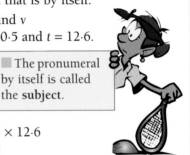

■ The pronumeral by itself is called the **subject**.

Solutions

1 $P = 2L + 2B$
     $= 2 \times 4 + 2 \times 3$
     $= 8 + 6$
     $= 14$
     $\therefore P = 14$

■ Substitute
$L = 4$ and
$B = 3$.

2 $v = u + at$
     $= 1 \cdot 2 + 0 \cdot 5 \times 12 \cdot 6$
     $= 1 \cdot 2 + 6 \cdot 3$
     $= 7 \cdot 5$
     $\therefore v = 7 \cdot 5$

worked examples B

For these formulae we need to find the value of the pronumeral that is *not* by itself.

1 If $y = 3x - 2$, find x if $y = 10$.

2 If $A = \dfrac{a + b}{2}$, find a if $A = 7$ and $b = 10$.

Solutions

1 $y = 3x - 2$
     $10 = 3x - 2$
     Solving this equation:
     $12 = 3x$
       $4 = x$
     $\therefore x = 4$

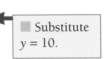

■ Substitute
$y = 10$.

■ *Notice:*
For this type of
question we
need to solve
an equation.

2 $A = \dfrac{a + b}{2}$

     $7 = \dfrac{a + 10}{2}$

     so $14 = a + 10$
       $4 = a$
     $\therefore a = 4$

7:05A Finding the subject of a formula

Exercise 7:05A

1 The formula for the area of a rectangle is $A = lb$.
Find the value of A if:

    a $l = 5, b = 3$ **b** $l = 6, b = 2$ **c** $l = 15, b = 9$
    d $l = 20, b = 2$ **e** $l = 15, b = 5$ **f** $l = 7, b = 4$

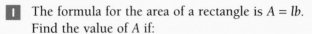

2 The perimeter of a rectangle is given as $P = 2l + 2b$. Find the
value of P for the values of l and b given in Question **1**.

3 The average of two numbers, m and n, is given by the formula
$A = \dfrac{m + n}{2}$. Find A if:

    a $m = 6, n = 10$ **b** $m = 12, n = 18$ **c** $m = 6, n = 9$
    d $m = 2 \cdot 1, n = 1 \cdot 7$ **e** $m = 1 \cdot 6, n = 3 \cdot 2$ **f** $m = 4 \cdot 5, n = 3 \cdot 1$

> ■ *Remember!*
> • Replace the pronumerals with the numerals given.
> • Then find the value of the remaining pronumeral.

4 Given the formula $v = u + at$, find the value of v if:

    a $u = 3, a = 2, t = 4$ **b** $u = 5, a = 4, t = 8$ **c** $u = 12, a = 1, t = 9$
    d $u = 6, a = 10, t = 0 \cdot 5$ **e** $u = 20, a = \frac{1}{2}, t = 12$ **f** $u = 8, a = \frac{1}{4}, t = 20$

5 For the formula $y = mx + b$, find y if:

    a $m = 2, x = 7, b = 3$ **b** $m = 0, x = 3, b = 2$ **c** $m = 4, x = 1, b = -3$
    d $m = \frac{1}{2}, x = 4, b = 2$ **e** $m = 4, x = 1, b = 0$ **f** $m = -1, x = 4, b = 5$

6 **a** If $A = \frac{1}{2}bh$, find A if $b = 6, h = 10$.

    b Given $C = 2\pi r$, $\pi = 3 \cdot 14$ and $r = 1 \cdot 2$, find C.

    c If $D = ST$, find D if $S = 1 \cdot 3, T = 0 \cdot 9$.

    d For $A = \pi rs$, find A if $\pi = \frac{22}{7}$, $r = 3\frac{1}{2}$ and $s = 5$.

    e If $C = \frac{5}{9}(F - 32)$, find C if $F = 86$.

    f Given $T = a + (n - 1)d$, find T when $a = 10$, $n = 4, d = 3$.

    g If $I = \dfrac{PRN}{100}$, find I given $P = 2000, R = 8$ and $N = 3$.

    h $v = \sqrt{u^2 + 2aS}$; find v if $u = 8, a = 10$ and $S = 4$.

> Do you recognise the formulae in (a), (b) and (c)?

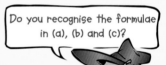

7 The formula $A = \frac{1}{2}h(a + b)$ gives the area (A) of a trapezium when the height (h) and the length
of the two parallel sides (a and b) are known. Find the area when:

    a $h = 3\,\text{cm}, a = 8\,\text{cm}, b = 6\,\text{cm}$ **b** $h = 20\,\text{m}, a = 4\,\text{m}, b = 9\,\text{m}$
    c $h = 30\,\text{m}, a = 80\,\text{m}, b = 70\,\text{m}$ **d** $a = 10\,\text{mm}, b = 8\,\text{mm}, h = 3\,\text{mm}$

8 'Young's Rule' is used to calculate a child's medicine dose.
It is $C = \dfrac{nA}{n + 12}$, where: C is the child's dose in mL
                           n is the child's age in years
                           A is the adult dose in mL.
The adult dose is 30 mL. Find the dose for a child aged:

    a 3 years   **b** 8 years   **c** 12 years

9 The cartoon below illustrates the fact that the energy of a moving vehicle depends on two things, its mass and its velocity (or speed).

The formula connecting E (energy), m (mass) and v (velocity) is $E = \frac{1}{2}mv^2$.
(In this formula it is only the v that is squared.)
Energy is measured in joules, mass in kilograms and velocity in metres per second.
Find the energy of the object in each part below.

a $m = 4\,kg$, $v = 2\,m/s$ b $m = 10\,kg$, $v = 3\,m/s$ c $m = 2\,kg$, $v = 10\,m/s$
d $m = 2.6\,kg$, $v = 4\,m/s$ e $m = 6\,kg$, $v = 1.2\,m/s$ f $m = 8\,kg$, $v = \frac{1}{2}\,m/s$

7:05B Finding the value of a pronumeral that is not the subject

Exercise 7:05B

1 For the formula $A = lb$, find the value of b if:
a $A = 20$, $l = 5$ b $A = 256$, $l = 16$
c $A = 6$, $l = 1.5$ d $A = 9.3$, $l = 0.6$

2 Given the formula $v = u + at$, find:
a u if $v = 20$, $a = 3$, $t = 6$ b u if $v = 36$, $a = 9$, $t = 3$
c u if $v = 12$, $a = -3$, $t = 2$ d a if $v = 10$, $u = 2$, $t = 4$

3 Using the formula $A = \dfrac{m + n}{2}$, find m if:
a $A = 12$, $n = 16$ b $A = 20$, $n = 8$ c $A = 12.6$, $n = 14.3$

4 Using the formula for the perimeter of a rectangle, $P = 2l + 2b$, find the length l if:
a perimeter = $20\,m$, breadth = $4\,m$ b perimeter = $32\,cm$, breadth = $6\,cm$
c perimeter = $8.4\,km$, breadth = $2.1\,km$ d perimeter = $0.8\,m$, breadth = $0.1\,m$

5 Given the formula $y = mx + b$, find:
a b if $y = 12$, $m = 4$, $x = 3$ b b if $y = 20$, $m = 4$, $x = 3$ c b if $y = 6$, $m = 4$, $x = 3$

6 **a** If $A = \frac{1}{2}h(a + b)$, find a if $A = 10$, $h = 5$, $b = 2$.

  b If $M = a(x + y)$, find y if $M = 25$, $a = 5$, $x = 3$.

  c For $T = a + (n - 1)d$, find n if $T = 70$, $a = 7$, $d = 9$.

  d If $F = 32 + \frac{9}{5}C$, find C if $F = 86$.

  e Given $c^2 = a^2 + b^2$, find a if $c = 17$ and $b = 15$.

  f Given $A = \frac{1}{2}bh$, find b if $A = 9$, $h = 6$.

  g For the formula $E = \frac{1}{2}mv^2$, find m when $E = 16$ and $v = 4$.

> Do you recognise the formulae in (a), (e), (f) and (g)?

7 Emma's pay (P) each week depends on the number of sales (s) she makes. The formula is $P = 20(3s + 4)$.

  a How much is Emma paid if she makes no sales?

  b How much is she paid if she makes 10 sales?

  c How many sales must she make to earn $500 in a week?

8 The Pioneer bus company calculates its charge for excursions using the formula $C = \dfrac{11n}{2}$, where C is the cost in dollars and n is the number of students.
Excursions must have at least 20 students. No more than 40 students can go on the one excursion.

  a What is the smallest charge?

  b What is the greatest charge?

  c Why do you think they insist on at least 20 students?

  d If the cost is $143, how many students are involved?

9 A factory makes n closets each day and its daily profit, P, can be calculated from the formula $P = 200n - 400$.

  a How many closets must be made to make $1000 profit in one day?

  b How many must be made to 'break even' in one day?

  c If only one closet is made in a day, what is the profit? Explain your answer.

- The formula connecting average **speed** (S) with the **total distance travelled** (D) and the **total time taken** (T), is $S = \dfrac{D}{T}$.
  - (a) Find the speed of the train if it covered a distance of 481 km in 3 h 15 min.
  - (b) Find the time taken if the train travelled at an average speed of 122 km/h for $4\frac{1}{2}$ hours.

7:06 | Solving Problems Using Equations

Solve these simple equations.

1 $7x = 56$ **2** $9 + a = 6$ **3** $\dfrac{m}{3} = 6$ **4** $n + 6 = 4$ **5** $3x = -12$

Write expressions for:

  6 the sum of a and b **7** the product of 5 and y

  8 the number 5 bigger than x **9** the number 6 less than m

10 the next even number after n, if n is an even number.

- The main use of equations is to help us solve problems. To do this we must be able to translate or rewrite a problem given in words into an equation, where the pronumeral will represent the number we are trying to find. Follow the steps below.

Solving problems
Step 1 Introduce a pronumeral.
Step 2 Write down an equation.
Step 3 Solve the equation.
Step 4 Answer the problem.

worked examples

1 The product of a certain number and 6 is 72. What is the number?

Solution

Let the number be n.	← Step 1 →
$6n = 72$	← Step 2 →
∴ $n = 12$	← Step 3 →
∴ The number is 12.	← Step 4 →

2 If a number is multiplied by 6, and 7 is subtracted from the product, the answer is 23. What is the number?

Solution

Let the number be x.
$$6x - 7 = 23$$
$$6x = 30$$
$$∴ x = 5$$
∴ The number is 5.

3 The sum of three consecutive integers is 30. What are the integers?

Solution

Let the smallest integer be n.
So $n + (n + 1) + (n + 2) = 30$
$$3n + 3 = 30$$
$$3n = 27$$
$$∴ n = 9$$
∴ The integers are 9, 10 and 11.

'Consecutive' means 'one after the other', so the next consecutive integer after n would be $n + 1$.

4 A rectangle is twice as long as it is wide. If the perimeter is 144 cm, what are its dimensions?

5 Find the value of x in this diagram.

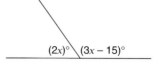

$(2x)°$ $(3x - 15)°$

Solution

Let the width of the rectangle be x.
Then the length will be $2x$.
So $2x + x + 2x + x = 144$
ie $\qquad\qquad 6x = 144$
$\qquad\qquad \therefore x = 24$
$\therefore$ The width of the rectangle is 24 units.
$\quad$ The length of the rectangle is 48 units.

Solution

To solve this problem you need to remember that the two angles add to give $180°$ (angles on a straight line).
So $2x + (3x - 15) = 180$
ie $\qquad 5x - 15 = 180$
$\qquad\qquad 5x = 195$
$\qquad\qquad x = 39$
$\therefore$ The value of x is 39.

Exercise 7:06

1 Solve these number problems by first writing an equation.
- **a** The sum of a certain number and 11 is 23. What is the number?
- **b** A certain number minus 9 is equal to 13. What is the number?
- **c** 15 minus a certain number is equal to 8. What is the number?
- **d** The product of 9 and a certain number is 108. What is the number?
- **e** The sum of a certain number and 3 is −5. What is the number?
- **f** A certain number is bigger than 10 and the difference from 10 is 7. What is the number?

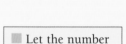
Let the number be n.

2 **a** If a number is multiplied by 3, and 5 is added to the product, the result is 17. What is the number?
- **b** When 6 is subtracted from the product of 4 and a certain number, the answer is 14. What is the number?
- **c** The sum of a certain number and 3 is then multiplied by 7. If the answer is 63, what is the number?
- **d** The product of a certain number and 5 is subtracted from 90. If the answer is 25, what is the number?
- **e** 9 is subtracted from a certain number and the result is multiplied by 4. If the answer is 24, what is the number?
- **f** The sum of two consecutive integers is 23. What are the integers?
- **g** The sum of three consecutive integers is 51. What are the integers?

■ • These will be two-step equations!
• Also, you may need grouping symbols.

■ If n is an even number, then the next one will be $n + 2$.

3 The equation for each of these problems will have the pronumeral on both sides.
- **a** The result of adding 12 to a certain number is the same as multiplying the number by 4. Find the number.
- **b** Twice a number plus seven is the same as three times the number plus one. What is the number?
- **c** Five times a number less seven is the same as three times the number plus five. Find the number.
- **d** If the sum of a number and 3 is multiplied by 4, the answer is the same as twice the number plus 16. Find the number.

4 Use the information given with each figure to form an equation and then solve it to find the value of the pronumeral.

a
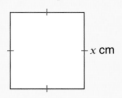
Perimeter = 64 cm

b
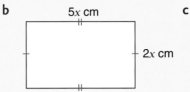
Perimeter = 98 cm

c
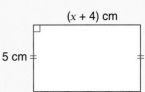
Area = 45 cm²

d
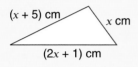
Perimeter = 22 cm

e
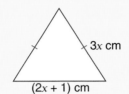
Perimeter = 57 cm

f
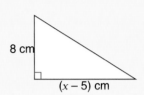
Area = 24 cm²

5 From the properties of the figures, write down equations and solve them for each pronumeral.

a
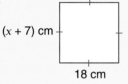

b
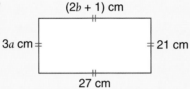

c

d
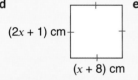

e
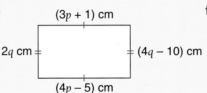

f
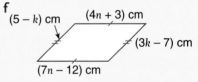

6 Find the value of *a* in these figures. You will need to remember some geometry.

a
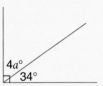

b

c
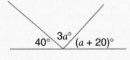

see

Appendix A:o6D

d

e
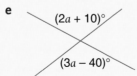

f

7 Try solving these assorted problems by first forming an equation.

a My mother is three times as old as I am. If she is 24 years older than me, what are our ages? (*Hint:* Let my age be *x*.)

b Eun Kyung and Vy have $35 between them. If Vy has 4 times as much as Eun Kyung, how much does each girl have? (*Hint:* Let Eun Kyung's amount be *a*.)

c Four pens and five pencils cost a total of $3.70. If a pen costs 25 cents more than a pencil, find the cost of each item.

d The perimeter of a rectangle is 44 cm. If its length is three times its width, find the dimensions of the rectangle. Also find its area.

e Determine the dimensions of this rectangle and hence its area.

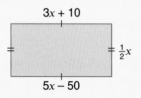

Dimensions are length and breadth.

The rectangle is labelled: top side $3x + 10$, bottom side $5x - 50$, right side $\frac{1}{2}x$.

f Vinh has $6 more than Tuan, and Jakob has $13 less than Vinh. How much does each person have if they have $29 altogether? (*Hint:* Let Vinh's amount be *x*.)

g When Juan was 12 his father was three times his age. Now his father is only twice Juan's age. How old are they now? (Let Juan's age, now, be *x*.)

8 Two sides of a garden bed are to be lined with logs as shown. Three logs are needed for each side but 1 m is cut off the third log to make sure that the logs don't extend beyond the garden. The width of the garden is 3 m and its area is 42 m². How long is each log? (*Hint:* Let *x* be the length of each log.)

Challenge worksheet **7:06 Oranges for sale**

7:07 | Graphing Inequations

An inequation is a number sentence where the 'equals' sign has been replaced by an inequality sign.
The most common inequality signs are:

>	<	≥	≤
is greater than	is less than	is greater than or equal to	is less than or equal to

Write *true* or *false*.

1 $7 > 3$ **2** $6 \times 2 \leq 12$ **3** $-5 < 2$ **4** $-3 > -4$

Write the set of numbers graphed on each number line.

5
```
  ← ─┼──┼──●──●──●──●─→
    -2  -1  0  1  2  3
```
6
```
  ← ─┼──●──●──●──●──●─→
       1  2  3  4  5  6
```
7
```
  ← ─┼──●──●──●──┼──┼─→
    -4  -3  -2  -1  0  1
```

On separate number lines, graph each set.

8 {1, 2, 3}   **9** {−4, −3, −2, −1}   **10** {6, 7, 8, 9, 10, 11}

Inequations usually have more than one solution.
- The equation $x + 8 = 10$ has one solution, namely $x = 2$.
- The inequation $x + 8 > 10$ has an infinite number of solutions.
  Some solutions would be: $2\frac{1}{2}$, 2·9, 12, 20 etc.
  The full set of solutions is written as $x > 2$.
  This infinite set of answers can be
  graphed on the number line as:
```
  ← ─┼──┼──┼──○──┼──┼──┼─→
    -1  0  1  2  3  4  5
```

Make sure that you know how to graph inequalities.

1
```
  ← ─┼──┼──┼──●──┼──┼──┼─→
    -1  0  1  2  3  4  5 x
```
This shows the solution $x = 2$.

2
```
  ← ─┼──┼──┼──●━━┿━━┿━→
    -1  0  1  2  3  4  5 x
```
This shows the solution $x \geq 2$.

3
```
  ← ─┼━━┿━━┿━━●──┼──┼──┼─→
    -1  0  1  2  3  4  5 x
```
This shows the solution $x \leq 2$.

4
```
  ← ─┼━━┿━━┿━━○──┼──┼──┼─→
    -1  0  1  2  3  4  5 x
```
This shows the solution $x < 2$.

5
```
  ← ─┼──┼──┼──○━━┿━━┿━→
    -1  0  1  2  3  4  5 x
```
This shows the solution $x > 2$.

'2' is not included in the solution set.
'2' is included in the solution set.

Exercise 7:07

1 Choose one of $x = 3$, $x \leq 3$, $x < 3$, $x > 3$ or $x \geq 3$ to describe each graph.

a
```
  ← ─┼──┼──┼──┼──○━━┿━→
    -1  0  1  2  3  4  5 x
```
b
```
  ← ─┼──┼──┼──┼──○──┼──┼─→
    -1  0  1  2  3  4  5 x
```
c
```
  ← ─┼──┼──┼──┼──●──┼──┼─→
    -1  0  1  2  3  4  5 x
```
d
```
  ← ─┼━━┿━━┿━━┿━━●──┼──┼─→
    -1  0  1  2  3  4  5 x
```

2 Write an inequation (using <, >, ≤ or ≥) to describe each graph.

a

$$\xleftarrow{\quad\begin{array}{cccccccc} | & | & | & ⊕ & | & | & | & | \\ 0 & & 2 & & 4 & & 6 & & 8 \end{array}\quad}_{x}$$

b

$$\xleftarrow{\quad\begin{array}{cccccccc} | & | & | & | & | & | & ● & | & | \\ 0 & & 2 & & 4 & & 6 & & 8 \end{array}\quad}_{x}$$

c

$$\xleftarrow{\quad\begin{array}{cccccccc} | & | & | & ● & | & | & | & | \\ -4 & & -2 & & 0 & & 2 & & 4 \end{array}\quad}_{a}$$

d

$$\xleftarrow{\quad\begin{array}{cccccccc} | & | & | & ⊕ & | & | & | & | \\ -4 & & -2 & & 0 & & 2 & & 4 \end{array}\quad}_{a}$$

e

$$\xleftarrow{\quad\begin{array}{cccccccc} | & | & | & | & | & | & ⊕ & | \\ 20 & & 22 & & 24 & & 26 & & 28 \end{array}\quad}_{m}$$

f

$$\xleftarrow{\quad\begin{array}{cccccccc} | & | & | & | & | & | & ⊕ & | \\ 20 & & 22 & & 24 & & 26 & & 28 \end{array}\quad}_{m}$$

g

$$\xleftarrow{\quad\begin{array}{cccccccc} | & | & | & ● & | & | & | & | \\ -10 & & -8 & & -6 & & -4 & & -2 \end{array}\quad}_{x}$$

h

$$\xleftarrow{\quad\begin{array}{cccccccc} | & | & | & ● & | & | & | & | \\ -6 & & -4 & & -2 & & 0 & & 2 \end{array}\quad}_{x}$$

3 Graph each of the following solutions on a separate number line.

a $x > 2$	**b** $x \leq -1$	**c** $x < 10$	**d** $x \geq 7$
e $x \leq 12$	**f** $x > 15$	**g** $x \geq -20$	**h** $x < 32$
i $a \geq -5$	**j** $a < 6$	**k** $m > -3$	**l** $m \leq -8$

7:08 | Solving Inequations

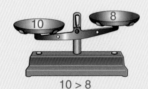

10 > 8

x < 10

The scales on the left show that 10 > 8.
Would the scales stay as they are if:

1 the same amount is added to both sides?

2 the same amount is subtracted from both sides?

3 the mass on each side is doubled?

4 the mass on each side is halved?

The scales on the left show that x < 10.
Would the scales stay as they are if:

5 the same amount is added to both sides?

6 the same amount is subtracted from both sides?

7 the mass on each side is doubled?

8 the mass on each side is halved?

What sign must be placed in the box
to make the final statement true?

9
$$\begin{array}{ccc} 8 & > & 4 \\ \div(-2) & & \div(-2) \\ -4 & \Box & -2 \end{array}$$

10
$$\begin{array}{ccc} 2 & < & 10 \\ \times(-3) & & \times(-3) \\ -6 & \Box & -30 \end{array}$$

• The rules below have been discovered in the prep quiz.

Solving inequations
When solving inequations, we can use the *same rules* as for equations except for
one important exception:
• **When multiplying or dividing an inequation by a negative number, the inequality**
  sign must be reversed to obtain an equivalent inequation.
  eg < is changed to > and ≥ is changed to ≤.

worked examples

Solve the following inequalities and graph their solutions.

1 $6x \le 18$

   $\div 6 \quad \div 6$

   $x \le 3$

2 $x - 15 > 7$

   $+ 15 \quad + 15$

   $x > 22$

3 $\dfrac{t}{5} \ge -2$

   $\times 5 \quad \times 5$

   $t \ge -10$

4 $3x + 4 < 19$

   $-4 \quad -4$

   $3x < 15$

   $\div 3 \quad \div 3$

   $x < 5$

5 $6 - 2x \le 22$

   $- 6 \quad - 6$

   $-2x \le 16$

   $\div(-2) \quad \div(-2)$

   $x \ge -8$

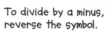

To divide by a minus, reverse the symbol.

Exercise 7:08

1 From the set $\{-8, -6, -4, -2, 0, 2, 3\cdot5, 6, 8\}$ choose all answers that would satisfy:

   a $x < -2$

   b $x > 7$

   c $x \le 2$

2 Solve each inequation and graph the solution on a number line.

   a $6a \le 12$

   b $7x > 14$

   c $5y \ge 25$

   d $11x < 99$

   e $\dfrac{m}{5} > 3$

   f $\dfrac{x}{10} \le 11$

   g $\dfrac{x}{4} < 8$

   h $\dfrac{x}{6} \ge 7$

   i $m + 3 > 10$

   j $y + 8 \le 20$

   k $x + 3 \ge 4$

   l $x + 11 < 11$

   m $x - 1 \le 7$

   n $y - 2 > 2$

   o $x - 7 < 20$

   p $x - 14 \ge 18$

3 Solve the following inequations.

a $3a > 11$
b $5y \le 14$
c $10x \ge 13$
d $7m < 7.7$

e $8x \le 10$
f $4x > 1$
g $9y < 0$
h $11x \ge 4$

i $\dfrac{x}{10} < 1.1$
j $\dfrac{x}{3} \ge \dfrac{1}{2}$
k $\dfrac{m}{2} \le \dfrac{1}{5}$
l $\dfrac{x}{7} > 9.8$

m $a + 1.1 \ge 8.6$
n $y + \dfrac{1}{2} < \dfrac{3}{4}$
o $x + 9.8 > 12$
p $x + \dfrac{3}{4} \le 2$

q $x - \dfrac{2}{5} > 1$
r $m - 0.8 \le 1.6$
s $x - \dfrac{3}{4} \ge 1\dfrac{1}{4}$
t $y - 0.1 = 10$

4 Solve each inequation.

a $x + 3 < 1$
b $x - 8 \ge -2$
c $7x > -14$

d $8m \ge -1$
e $y + 3 < 0$
f $x - 15 \le 1$

g $y - 1 \le -8$
h $a + 7 > 7$
i $6x < -7$

j $\dfrac{x}{8} > -3$
k $\dfrac{m}{7} \le \dfrac{1}{2}$
l $\dfrac{x}{3} \ge -1$

These may involve negative numbers.

5 Solve:

a $-6x < 12$
b $-2m > 20$
c $-4x \ge 36$

d $-3m \ge -12$
e $-x \le -8$
f $-x < 8$

g $\dfrac{x}{-2} > 4$
h $\dfrac{m}{-5} < 7$
i $\dfrac{x}{-8} \le -3$

6 Solve each of these inequations. Then substitute one of the answers into the original inequation to test your solution.

a $4x + 3 > 11$
b $7m - 4 \le 52$
c $15 + 3x < 48$

d $6 + 2x \le 22$
e $5x + 21 \ge 41$
f $40 + 7x > 61$

g $\dfrac{x}{2} - 4 < 16$
h $\dfrac{x}{4} + 3 > 4$
i $\dfrac{x}{3} - 1 \le -4$

If you multiply or divide by a negative, reverse the symbol.

7 Solve each equation, check the solution and then graph the solution on a number line.

a $8 - 2x \le 4$
b $9 - 6x > 25$
c $-6x + 3 \le 21$

d $-3x - 8 > 11$
e $-x - 5 < 14$
f $8(4 - x) \ge 8$

Set these out just like equations.

Appendix E **E:01 Fun Spot: The Tower of Hanoi**

Mathematical terms 7

algebraic expression
- An algebraic expression consists of one or more terms joined together by operation signs.
  eg $a + 5$, $x^2 - x + 4$, $\dfrac{3m - 1}{7}$
- An expression does *not* have an 'equals' sign like an equation.

equation
- A number sentence where one or more of the numbers is missing or unknown.
- The unknown number is represented by a pronumeral.
  eg $x + 5 = 8$, $\dfrac{3x + 1}{7} = \dfrac{x - 5}{2}$

evaluate
- To find the value of an expression.
  eg Find the value of $3a + 7$ if $a = 3$.
- To find the answer (usually after substitution).

formula (formulae)
- A formula represents a relationship between physical quantities.
- It will always have more than one pronumeral.
  eg $A = l \times b$ represents the relationship between the area (A) of a rectangle and its length (l) and breadth (b).

grouping symbols
- The most common types are:
  parentheses ( )
  brackets   [ ]
  braces   { }
- Used to 'group' a number of terms together in an expression.
  eg $5(x + 3)$

inequality signs
- $>$ *is greater than*, $<$ *is less than*
- $\geq$ *is greater than or equal to*,
  $\leq$ *is less than or equal to*
  eg $x + 3 < 4$ means that
  $x + 3$ *is less than 4*

inequation
- An *equation* where the 'equals' sign has been replaced by an inequality sign.
  eg $4x - 1 > 5$ or $\dfrac{x}{3} \leq 4$

inverse operation
- The operation that will reverse or 'undo' a previous operation.
  eg Addition is the inverse operation of subtraction; division is the inverse operation of multiplication.

pronumeral
- A symbol used to represent a number.
- Usually a letter such as x.

solution
- Method of finding the answer to a problem
  OR
  the answer to a problem.
- The solution to an equation or inequation is the number or numbers that make it a true sentence.
  eg $x = 3$ is the solution to $x + 2 = 5$.

solve
- Find the *solution* or answer to a problem or equation.

substitute
- To replace a pronumeral with a numeral.
  eg To substitute 3 for a in the expression
  $4a - 2$ would give:
  $4(3) - 2$
  $= 12 - 2$
  $= 10$

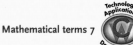

Mathematical terms 7

Diagnostic Test 7: | Equations, Formulae and Inequations

- Each section of the test has similar items that test a certain type of question.
- Errors made will indicate areas of weakness.
- Each weakness should be treated by going back to the section listed.

	Section
1 Solve: **a** $x + 11 = 27$ **b** $p - 5 = 2$ **c** $5 + a = 3$ **d** $y - 7 = -2$	7:02
2 Solve: **a** $6m = 54$ **b** $3x = 5$ **c** $\dfrac{n}{4} = 8$ **d** $\dfrac{a}{3} = -2$	7:02
3 Solve these two-step equations. (Answers are integers.) **a** $2x + 3 = 7$ **b** $3m - 1 = 8$ **c** $6 + 4y = 22$ **d** $4 - 2a = 6$	7:02
4 The answers to these equations involve fractions. **a** $2x + 1 = 6$ **b** $4y - 3 = 4$ **c** $7 + 5k = 3$ **d** $9 - 2t = 6$	7:02
5 Solve these two-step equations. **a** $\dfrac{5m}{4} = 10$ **b** $\dfrac{m+2}{3} = 4$ **c** $\dfrac{x}{2} + 4 = 6$ **d** $\dfrac{w-2}{5} = 2$	7:02
6 Solve: **a** $2a + 1 = a + 7$ **b** $3m + 2 = m - 6$ **c** $4k - 1 = 5 - 2k$ **d** $7x = 5x + 9$	7:03
7 Solve: **a** $2(a + 4) = 8$ **b** $6(m - 3) = 12$ **c** $2(2y + 1) = 6$ **d** $3(5m - 1) = 27$	7:04
8 Solve: **a** $3(n + 2) = 2n + 7$ **b** $9p + 1 = 7(p + 3)$ **c** $2(x + 1) = 5(x - 5)$ **d** $3(2x - 1) = 4(3x - 1)$	7:04
9 **a** If $A = lb$, find A if $l = 6$ and $b = 7$. **b** For $y = mx + b$, find y if $m = 3$, $x = 5$ and $b = -2$. **c** Given that $p = q^2 + r^2$, find p if $q = 4$ and $r = 6$. **d** For $A = \frac{1}{2}h(a + b)$, find A when $h = 8$, $a = 4$, $b = 3$.	7:05A
10 **a** If $A = lb$, find b when $A = 24$ and $l = 8$. **b** Given that $P = 2l + 2b$, find l if $P = 40$ and $b = 8$. **c** For $A = \dfrac{x + y}{2}$, find x if $A = 17$ and $y = 21$. **d** If $v = u + at$, find t if $v = 6$, $u = 12$ and $a = -2$.	7:05B
11 Form an equation for each number problem, letting the number be n, and solve it. **a** The product of a number and 7 is 63. Find the number. **b** The sum of a number and 5 is 2. What is the number?	7:06

c When 7 is added to the product of 3 and a number, the answer is 19. What is the number?

d 6 is subtracted from a number and the result is multiplied by 5. The answer is 15. What is the number?

12 Form an equation from the information with each figure and solve it to find x.

7:06

a

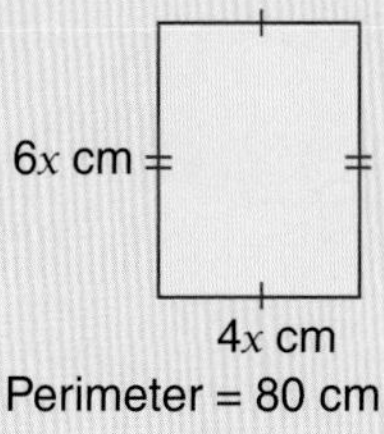

6x cm

4x cm

Perimeter = 80 cm

b (3x + 5) cm

3 cm

Area = 60 cm²

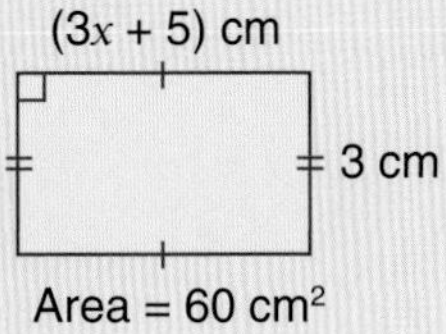

c

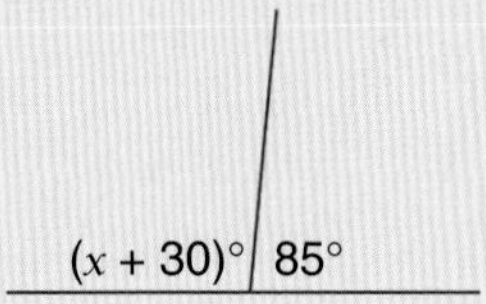

$(x + 30)°$ | $85°$

13 Graph each inequality on a separate number line.

7:07

a $x < 4$ b $x \geq -2$ c $x \leq 0$

14 Solve each inequation.

7:08

a $3x \leq 14$ b $x + 8 > 2$ c $\dfrac{x}{8} < 5$

Chapter 7 | Revision Assignment

7A

1 Before they played, Sandy had 15 marbles and Luke had 10. Luke lost 5 marbles to Sandy.

a What percentage of his marbles did Luke lose?

b By what percentage did the number of Sandy's marbles increase?

2 Find the value of x in each case.

a

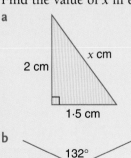

x cm

2 cm

1·5 cm

b

132°

$x°$

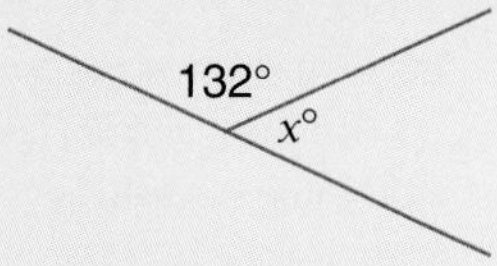

3 The probability that I will be allowed to leave before 10 am is 0·35. What is the probability that I won't be allowed to leave before 10 am?

4 Calculate the area of each of these figures.

a

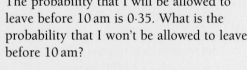

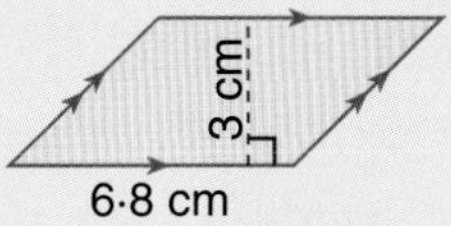

3 cm

6·8 cm

b

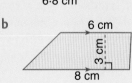

6 cm

3 cm

8 cm

c

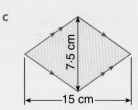

7·5 cm

15 cm

5 **a** Expand $6(x - 3)$.
    b Factorise $12a - 20$.
    c Expand $4a(a + 2)$.
    d Factorise $6ab + 12b$.

6 **a** Convert 17 000 t to kg.
    b Change 7800 m to km.
    c Write 800 min in hours and minutes.

7 Simplify:
    a $-3 - 4 - 2$ **b** $12 - 6 - 8$
    c $-3 \times 2 \times -4$ **d** $(-4 + 6) \times -2$

8 **a** If 40% of a fertiliser is superphosphate, how many kilograms of superphosphate are needed for 1 tonne of fertiliser?
    b A real estate agent receives $4\frac{1}{2}\%$ commission on the value of each house that she sells. How much does she receive for a house valued at \$125 000?

9 Find the volume of each prism.
    a

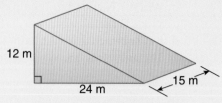

    b

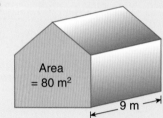

7B

Chapter 7 | Working Mathematically

1 I purchased 15 boxes of matches. If each box contains between 47 and 54 matches, choose which of the following answers could be the total number of matches.
    A 615   **B** 705   **C** 763   **D** 810

2 One can of food has a mass of 250 g, while another has a mass of 450 g. A third can has a mass of 675 g and a fourth can has the second largest mass of these four cans. Choose which of the answers could be the total mass of the four cans.
    A 1675   **B** 1825   **C** 1826   **D** 2125

3 To celebrate the birth of a new nation, 3400 people link hands to reach across the city of Auckland. If the space between bodies is 1·3 metres and the width of each body is 0·5 metres, how far will the people stretch?

4 The total number of votes cast in three electorates was 648 493. If in one of these electorates 249 306 votes were cast and in another 198 486 votes were cast, how many votes were cast in the third electorate?

5 Sophia is 28 years younger than Alec. Roman is one-quarter the age of Sophia. Maria is 18 years older than Roman. If Maria is 28, how old is Alec?

6 Use ID Card 1 (Metric Units) on page xiv to identify:
    a 2   **b** 4   **c** 5   **d** 7   **e** 9
    f 11   **g** 12   **h** 20   **i** 22   **j** 24

1 Solving equations by inspection
2 Substitution in formulae
3 Graphing inequations

8

The Number Plane

Chapter Contents

Learning Outcomes

Students will be able to graph and interpret linear relationships on the number plane.

Areas of Interaction

Approaches to Learning (Knowledge Acquisition, Problem Solving, Communication Skills, Thinking Skills, Information and Communication Technology Skills), Environments, Community and Service, Human Ingenuity

8:01 | Reading Maps

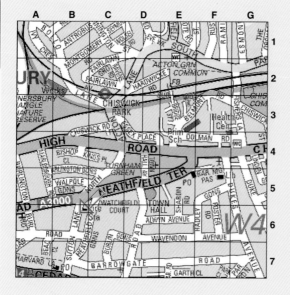

See if you can remember how to read a street directory by completing this Prep Quiz.

1 What park has the coordinates D4?

2 Is Narva Place at B5?

3 What is located at D5?

Name the roads closest to:

4 A1   5 F7   6 F3

What would be the reference coordinates of:

7 Chiswick Park Railway Station?

8 Acton Green Common?

9 The Health Centre?

10 Sutton Lane Fire Station?

To give positions on a street directory, a letter and a number are used. This is not the only way of reading a map. Work through the following exercise which will show you some other types of coordinates.

Exercise 8:01

1 a What road is in the centre of square J12?

b What feature has reference coordinates of G11?

c What grid references could be used for Mary St?

d If you were to give one grid reference for Cannon St, what would it be?

e How are major roads represented on the map?

f How are railway lines represented on the map?

g A church has reference coordinates K11. What street do you think it would be in?

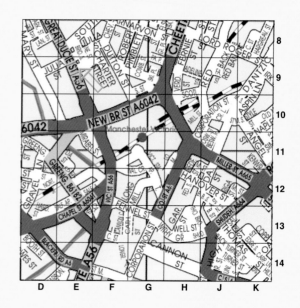

2

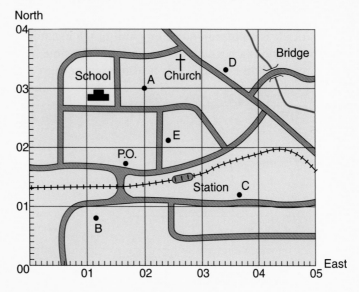

A | 01 02 03 04 05 06 07 08   09 10 11 12 13 14 15 16

This is a plan of a theatre. The seat number of the hexagon is E04 (ie row E seat 4).
What shape is shown on the following seats?

a C16   b C01   c E04   d A13

What is the seat number of the:

e triangle?   f star?   g square?   h pentagon?

3 A better and more accurate
method than the 'street directory'
method is to use numbers in both
directions. Here the numbers are
on the lines and not in the
middle of the square.

Each square is further divided
into 10 divisions. This enables
positions to be given as two
3-digit 'coordinates'. The
reference to the east is given
first, the reference to the north
given second.

For example, on this map,
point A has 020 for an east
reference and 030 for a north
reference, so the 'grid reference'
for point A would be 020030.

Can you see that the grid reference for point B would be 011008?

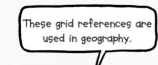

These grid references are
used in geography.

Give a six-figure grid reference for point:

a C   b D   c E

What feature is located at each of the following grid reference
points?

d 012029   e 026016   f 026035
g 042032   h 016017

4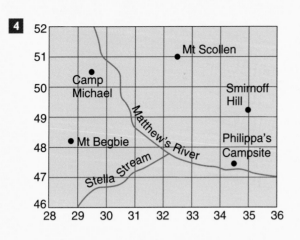

Usually when reading a map, the 'tenth' divisions have to be estimated. Can you see that the grid reference for Mt Begbie would be 288482? What feature is at:

a 345475?
b 323478?

Give grid references for:

c Camp Michael
d Mt Scollen
e Smirnoff Hill

Sometimes it's difficult to be exact.

5 Of course, another way of reading maps is by using **latitude** and **longitude**.
Latitude is a position north or south of the **equator**, given in degrees.
Longitude is a position east or west of the **prime meridian**, which runs through Greenwich in England. This is also given in degrees.

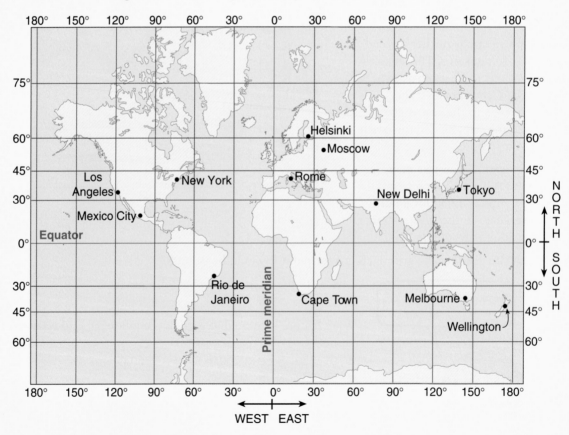

The position of Melbourne is 38°S 145°E. Look at the map and make sure you can see why Melbourne has these coordinates.

As a second example, Los Angeles is 34°N 118°W.

That means Melbourne is 38° south of the equator and 145° east of the prime meridian.

Match the following cities with the correct latitude and longitude in the list given.

a	Rome	**b**	Moscow	**A**	61°N 25°E	**B**	41°S 175°E
c	New York	**d**	New Delhi	**C**	19°N 99°W	**D**	42°N 12°E
e	Cape Town	**f**	Wellington	**E**	34°S 18°E	**F**	29°N 77°E
g	Mexico City	**h**	Rio de Janeiro	**G**	23°S 43°W	**H**	56°N 36°E
i	Helsinki	**j**	Tokyo	**I**	36°N 140°E	**J**	41°N 74°W

6 All countries in Central America are north of the equator and west of the prime meridian. San Jose has the approximate coordinates 10°N 84°W.

Write down (to the nearest degree) the coordinates that would locate these places:

a Guatemala City   **b** Managua   **c** Panama City   **d** Belmopan
e San Salvador   **f** Tegucigalpa   **g** San Andres Island   **h** Coiba Island
i Maiz Islands   **j** Ambergris Cay

8:02 | Coordinates and the Number Plane

When reading maps, positions are always located by using a pair of coordinates, either a letter and a number, or two numbers. You should remember how to give a position on the number plane by using a pair of numbers or coordinates.

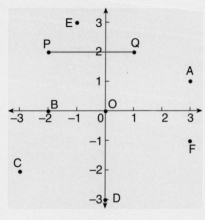

1 What name is given to the horizontal axis?

2 What name is given to the vertical axis?

3 Give the name and coordinates of point O.

What are the coordinates of point: 4   A?

                                        5   B?

                                        6   C?

                                        7   D?

What point is at: 8   (3, −1)?   9   (−1, 3)?

10 How long is interval PQ?

The Prep Quiz should have reminded you about the following ideas.

> (−2, 4) is called an *ordered pair* or the *coordinates* of a point.
> The first number, −2, is the *x*-coordinate, which is the reading on the horizontal axis.
> The second number, 4, is the *y*-coordinate, which is the reading on the vertical axis.

worked examples

1 Plot the points given by this table.

x	−1	0	1	2
y	−1	1	3	5

This table is a list of points.

Solution

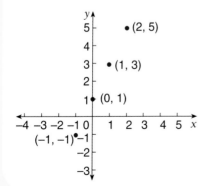

2 Plot these points and join them in the order given:
(−1, 1), (0, 3), (4, 4), (3, 2), (−1, 1)
What shape is formed?

Solution

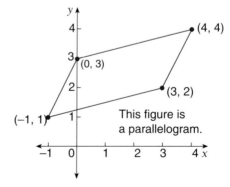

This figure is a parallelogram.

3 a Plot the points A(1, 1), B(5, 1) and C(5, 3) and join them to form triangle *ABC*.
b What is the length of each side of the triangle? (Use Pythagoras' Theorem.)

Solution

a

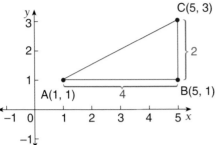

b The length of *AB* is $5 - 1$, ie 4 units.
The length of *BC* is $3 - 1$, ie 2 units.

Because triangle *ABC* is a right-angled triangle, we can calculate the length of *AC* using Pythagoras' Theorem:

$$AC^2 = AB^2 + BC^2$$
$$= 4^2 + 2^2$$
$$= 16 + 4$$
$$= 20$$
$$\therefore AC = \sqrt{20}$$

$\therefore$ Length of side $AC = \sqrt{20}$ units.

$c^2 = a^2 + b^2$

Exercise 8:02

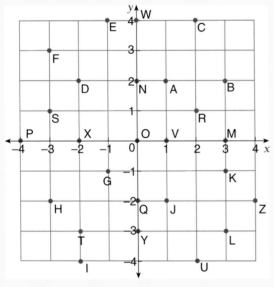

1 Write down the letter of the point with these coordinates:

a	(2, 4)	**b**	(3, 2)
c	(0, 2)	**d**	(−2, 2)
e	(−3, 1)	**f**	(−4, 0)
g	(−3, −2)	**h**	(−2, −4)
i	(0, −2)	**j**	(1, −2)
k	(3, −3)	**l**	(3, 0)

2 Write down the coordinates of each point.

a	A	**b**	E	**c**	F
d	K	**e**	O	**f**	R
g	T	**h**	U	**i**	V
j	W	**k**	X	**l**	Y
m	Z	**n**	G	**o**	J

3 The number plane can be divided into four sections called **quadrants**, as shown in the diagram.
Looking at the number plane for Questions 1 and 2, point **D** would be in the 2nd quadrant. In which quadrant would each of the following points belong?

a	A	**b**	E	**c**	H	**d**	J
e	S	**f**	K	**g**	C	**h**	T
i	G	**j**	Z	**k**	F	**l**	B

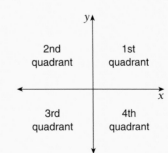

4 a Plot these points on a number plane:
(1, –1), (1, 3), (3, 3), (3, –1).

b By joining the points in order and then back
to the first point again, what type of figure
is formed?

c What are the lengths of the sides of this figure?

d What is its perimeter?

e What is its area?

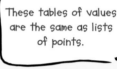
Just **look** at my
wrecked angle!

5 The points in each table represent a straight line.
Draw the four lines on one number plane.

x	–4	–3	–2	–1
y	0	1	2	3

x	–3	–2	–1	0
y	–1	–2	–3	–4

x	0	1	2	3
y	4	3	2	1

x	1	2	3	4
y	–3	–2	–1	0

These tables of values
are the same as lists
of points.

a What shape is enclosed by these lines?

b Where do the diagonals cross?

6 a Plot these points and join them to form a triangle: $X(0, 1)$, $Y(4, 1)$, $Z(4, 4)$.

b What type of triangle is $\triangle XYZ$?

c What is the length of side: **i** XY?   **ii** YZ?

7 Plot each set of points on separate number planes and join them to form right-angled triangles.
By first finding the length of each shorter side, calculate the length of the hypotenuse in each.

a (–4, –2), (4, –2), (4, 4)   **b** (–5, –1), (7, –1), (7, 4)

c (3, 0), (–1, 0), (–1, 4)   **d** (3, 4), (–2, 4), (–2, 0)

e (–3, 4), (2, 4), (2, –1)   **f** (–2, –2), (3, 4), (3, –2)

■ Leave your answers as
square roots if necessary.

8

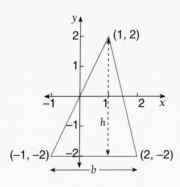

This triangle has been formed by joining the points shown.

a What is the height
h of this triangle?

b What is the length of
the base b?

c Therefore what is the
area of this triangle?

That's pretty
clever!

9 Use the method shown in Question 8 to find the area of the triangle formed by joining each set of points.

a (−1, −1), (3, −1), (2, 4)   b (−2, 0), (5, 0), (5, 3)
c (−2, 3), (4, 3), (1, −1)   d (0, 1), (3, 1), (−1, 4)

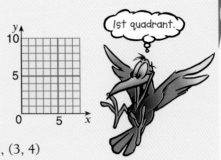

- Would you know where my dart landed if I told you I threw triple twenty?
- How does the dartboard resemble a number plane?

8:03 | Introducing Straight Line Graphs

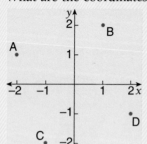

What are the coordinates of point:

1 A?   **2** B?   **3** C?   **4** D?

If $x = 3$, what is the value of:

5 $4x$?   **6** $2x + 1$?   **7** $1 - x$?

8 What value has $x - 5$ when $x = 4$?

9 If $x = 0$, what is the value of $2x - 3$?

10 Solve $4 + y = 9$.

- Most of the equations we have met have had only one solution.
  For example, the solution to $y + 7 = 10$ is $y = 3$.
- When an equation has two different pronumerals, more than one solution usually exists.

Discussion

Try to find ten different solutions to $\boxed{x + y = 7}$.

We know that $3 + 4 = 7$, so one solution would be $x = 3, y = 4$. We could write this as (3, 4).

Substitute values of x to find other solutions.

When $x = 0, y = 7$. The point is (0, 7).
When $x = 1, y = 6$. The point is (1, 6).
When $x = 2, y = 5$. The point is (2, 5).
When $x = 3, y = 4$. The point is (3, 4).
We could write these points in a table.

x	0	1	2	3
y	7	6	5	4

If we plot these points on the number plane they all fall on the same straight line. Test the other solutions you have found to see if they lie on this same straight line.

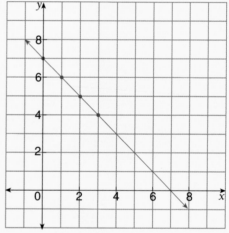

All points are on the same line.

What we have done above is to graph the straight line $x + y = 7$.

Exercise 8:03

1 In each case substitute the value of x to find the value of y and fill in the table.

a $x + y = 4$
If $x = 0, y = 4$
$x = 1, y = \ldots$
$x = 2, y = \ldots$
$x = 3, y = \ldots$
$x = 4, y = \ldots$

x	0	1	2	3	4
y	4				

b $y = 2x$
If $x = 0, y = 0$
$x = 1, y = \ldots$
$x = 2, y = \ldots$
$x = 3, y = \ldots$
$x = 4, y = \ldots$

x	0	1	2	3	4
y	0				

c $y = 3x - 2$
If $x = 0, y = -2$
$x = 1, y = \ldots$
$x = 2, y = \ldots$
$x = 3, y = \ldots$
$x = 4, y = \ldots$

x	0	1	2	3	4
y	-2				

d $y = 10x + 36$
If $x = 0, y = 36$
$x = 1, y = \ldots$
$x = 2, y = \ldots$
$x = 3, y = \ldots$
$x = 4, y = \ldots$

x	0	1	2	3	4
y	36				

e $y = 8 - x$
If $x = 0, y = \ldots$
$x = 1, y = \ldots$
$x = 2, y = \ldots$
$x = 3, y = \ldots$
$x = 4, y = \ldots$

x	0	1	2	3	4
y					

f $2x + y = 16$
If $x = 0, y = \ldots$
$x = 1, y = \ldots$
$x = 2, y = \ldots$
$x = 3, y = \ldots$
$x = 4, y = \ldots$

x	0	1	2	3	4
y					

2 State whether the values given for x and y make the equation *true* or *false*.

a $y = 4x$
$x = 5, y = 20$

b $x + y = 6$
$x = 4, y = -2$

c $x + 2y = 12$
$x = -4, y = 8$

d $2x + y = 7$
$x = 3, y = 1$

e $5x + 10y = 105$
$x = 9, y = 6$

f $y = 2x + 8$
$x = 0, y = 6$

g $y = 36x - 10$
$x = 1, y = 26$

h $3x - 2y - 8 = 0$
$x = 10, y = 11$

i $8x - y + 10 = 0$
$x = 4, y = 12$

3 Find an equation linking x and y.

a

x	0	1	2	3	4
y	0	3	6	9	12

b

x	0	1	2	3	4
y	2	3	4	5	6

c

x	0	1	2	3	4
y	-5	-4	-3	-2	-1

d

x	0	1	2	3	4
y	8	7	6	5	4

e

x	0	1	2	3	4
y	1	11	21	31	41

f

x	0	1	2	3	4
y	8	12	16	20	24

Consider the straight line $y = 7x + 5$.
- The *coefficient of x* is **7**. (The coefficient of y is 1.)
- The *constant term* is **5**.

8:04 | Graphing Straight Lines

- To draw a straight line, we need to know *two* points through which it passes.
- When we graph the equation of a straight line, we find *three* points, just in case we make a mistake with one of them.

 Notes on graphing straight lines
1 **In this section the equations will always represent straight lines, and all the answers to one equation will lie on the one line.**
2 **Two points are needed to draw a straight line but we usually find three points so that we can check the answers.**
3 **If the three points are not in line, at least one answer is wrong.**
4 **Any other point on the straight line will also be a solution to the equation.**
5 **We may choose any three values for *x*, but it is usually best to let *x* be 0, 1 and 2.**

worked examples

Draw the graph of each straight line.

1 $3x + y = 12$ 2 $y = 2x + 5$ 3 $y = 3x - 2$

Solutions

1 When $x = 0$, $0 + y = 12$
   $\therefore y = 12$
   $x = 1$, $3 + y = 12$
   $\therefore y = 9$
   $x = 2$, $6 + y = 12$
   $\therefore y = 6$

2 When $x = 0$, $y = 0 + 5$
   $\therefore y = 5$
   $x = 1$, $y = 2 + 5$
   $\therefore y = 7$
   $x = 2$, $y = 4 + 5$
   $\therefore y = 9$

3 When $x = 0$, $y = 0 - 2$
   $\therefore y = -2$
   $x = 1$, $y = 3 - 2$
   $\therefore y = 1$
   $x = 2$, $y = 6 - 2$
   $\therefore y = 4$

x	0	1	2
y	12	9	6

x	0	1	2
y	5	7	9

x	0	1	2
y	-2	1	4

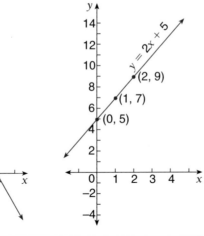

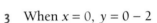

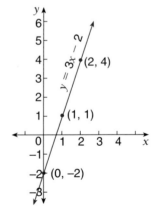

Straight line equations are called *linear equations*.

1 Complete each table of values and then graph the equation on a number plane.

a $y = x + 3$

x	−1	0	1	2
y				

b $y = x - 1$

x	−1	0	1	2
y				

c $y = \frac{1}{2}x$

x	−2	0	2	4
y				

d $y = -x$

x	−1	0	1	2
y				

e $y = 5 - x$

x	−1	0	1	2
y				

f $y = 4 - 2x$

x	−1	0	1	2
y				

2 Graph each equation on a separate number plane by first completing a table of values.

a $y = x + 1$ **b** $y = x - 2$

c $y = 3 - x$ **d** $y = -1 - x$

e $y = 2x - 3$ **f** $y = 3x + 1$

g $x + y = 4$ **h** $x - y = 2$

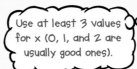

Use at least 3 values for x (0, 1, and 2 are usually good ones).

3 Complete the table of values

x	−1	0	1	2
y				

for each graph below, and also work

out what its equation must be. They can all be written in the form $y = \square \, x + \triangle$.

a

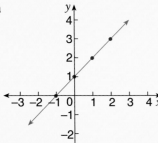

b

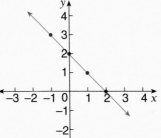

c

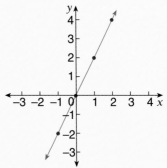

d

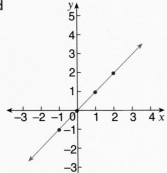

e

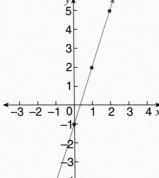

f

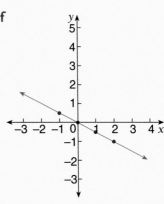

4 To see if a point will lie on a certain graph, we substitute the coordinates into the equation. The point (2, 3) lies on $y = 2x - 1$ because $3 = 2(2) - 1$ is a true statement. State whether each of the following points lies on the given equation.

a	(1, 2)	$y = 2x - 1$	**b**	(3, 1)	$y = x - 1$	**c**	(1, 3)	$y = x + 2$
d	(5, 0)	$y = 2x + 3$	**e**	(0, 2)	$y = 2x + 2$	**f**	(4, 1)	$x + y = 3$
g	(−1, 2)	$y = 2x - 5$	**h**	(1, −2)	$y = x + 1$	**i**	(−1, −2)	$y = 3 - x$
j	(−3, 2)	$y = 2x - 1$	**k**	(4, −3)	$x + y = 1$	**l**	(−3, −4)	$y = 1 + x$

5 By completing tables of values or just by examining the points on each graph below, match each graph with the correct equation from the list below.

A $x + y = 3$ **B** $y = 2x - 3$ **C** $x - y = 3$ **D** $y = \frac{1}{2}x + 2$

a 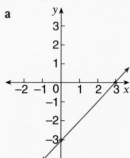   **b** 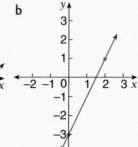   **c** 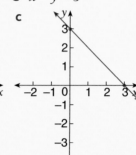   **d**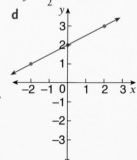

8:05 | Lines Parallel to the Axes

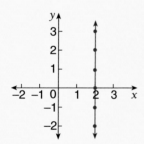

This line is parallel to the y-axis.
- Below, we have put the points on the line at left into a table.

x	2	2	2	2	2	2
y	−2	−1	0	1	2	3

- There seems to be no connection between x and y.
  However, x is always 2, no matter what value y has.
  So the equation is $x = 2$.

Lines parallel to the y-axis have equations of the form
$$x = a,$$
where a is the point at which the line cuts the x-axis.

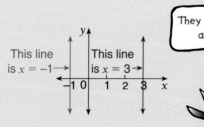

They cut the x–axis at –1 and 3.

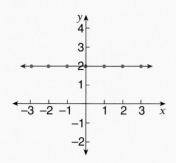

This line is parallel to the *x*-axis.
- Below, we have put the points on the line into a table.

x	-2	-1	0	1	2	3
y	2	2	2	2	2	2

- There seems to be no connection between *x* and *y*.
  However, *y* is always 2, no matter what value *x* has.
  So the equation is $y = 2$.

Lines parallel to the *x*-axis have equations of the form
$$y = b,$$
where *b* is the point at which the line cuts the *y*-axis.

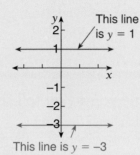

This line is $y = 1$

This line is $y = -3$

They cut the y-axis at –3 and 1.

Exercise 8:05

1 Write down the equation of each line.

a 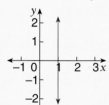   b 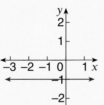   c 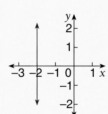   d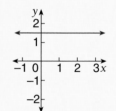

2 For each number plane write down the equations of the lines Ⓐ to Ⓕ.

a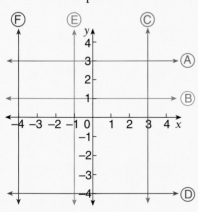

b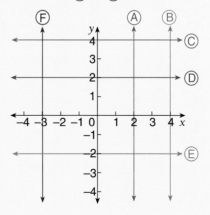

3 a What is the equation of the *y*-axis?   b What is the equation of the *x*-axis?

4 Using values from −5 to 5 on each axis, draw the graphs of the following straight lines.

  a $y = 4, x = 5, y = -1, x = 0$
  b $x = 1, y = 0, x = 2, y = 3$
  c $y = 4, x = 2, y = -2, x = -4$
  d $x = 5, y = -5, x = 2, y = 2$
  e $y = -2, y = 0, x = 0, x = 3$
  Which of these encloses a square region?

5 Give the point where each pair of lines cross. (You can use the graphs in Question **2**.)

  a $x = 3$ and $y = 1$ **b** $x = -4$ and $y = 3$ **c** $x = -1$ and $y = -4$
  d $x = 2$ and $y = -2$ **e** $x = -3$ and $y = 2$ **f** $x = 4$ and $y = 4$
  g $x = 0$ and $y = 3$ **h** $x = 2$ and $y = 0$ **i** $x = 0$ and $y = 0$

Fun Spot 8:05 | Why should you never tell secrets in a vegetable garden?

Work out the answer to each part and put the letter for that part in the box above the correct answer.

If $x = 3$, find the value of:

A $2x$ **B** $1 - x$ **C** x^2 **D** $5x - 4$ **E** $-x$

Give the coordinates of:

  A A   **B** B
  C C   **E** E
  H H   **K** K
  L L   **O** O

Where does the line
$3x + 2y = 6$ cut:

  A the x-axis?   **E** the y-axis?
  U What is the equation of the x-axis?
  S What is the equation of the y-axis?

Simplify:

A $5 \times x$ **A** $y + y$ **A** $y \times y$ **E** $x + 2x$ **R** $2 \times 5x$ **R** $4y \times 3$
N $8x - x$ **N** $2y \div 2$ **N** $2x - 2x$ **S** $8x \div x$ **S** $2x \div 2x$ **S** $3x - 3$
T $5x - 3y + 3$ if $x = 5$ and $y = 7$

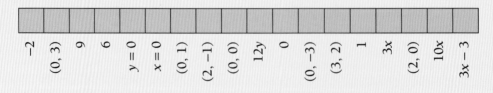

Row 1 answers: -2, $(0, 3)$, 9, 6, $y = 0$, $x = 0$, $(0, 1)$, $(2, -1)$, $(0, 0)$, $12y$, 0, $(0, -3)$, $(3, 2)$, 1, $3x$, $(2, 0)$, $10x$, $3x - 3$

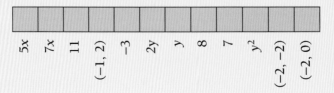

Row 2 answers: $5x$, $7x$, 11, $(-1, 2)$, -3, $2y$, y, 8, 7, y^2, $(-2, -2)$, $(-2, 0)$

8:06 | Further Graphing

Graph this pair of equations and find where they intersect on the number plane.

$y = 4 - x$
$y = 2x - 2$

Solution

First complete a table of values for each equation.

$y = 4 - x$

x	0	1	2
y	4	3	2

$y = 2x - 2$

x	0	1	2
y	-2	0	2

Then graph both equations on the same number plane.

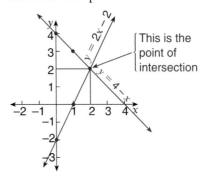

This is the point of intersection

∴ The point of intersection is (2, 2)

Exercise 8:06

Foundation Worksheet 8:06

Graphing straight lines
1 See Exercise 12:02 **1**.
2 See Exercise 12:03 **1**.
3 See Exercise 12:04 **1**.
4 See Exercise 12:05 **1**.

1 Give the coordinates of the point of intersection for each pair of lines.

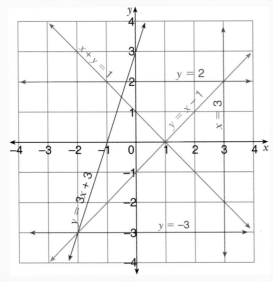

a $x = 3$	**b** $x = 3$
$y = 2$	$y = x - 1$
c $x + y = 1$	**d** $x = 3$
$y = 2$	$y = -3$
e $y = -3$	**f** $x + y = 1$
$y = 3x + 3$	$y = x - 1$
g $x + y = 1$	**h** $y = 3x + 3$
$x = 0$	$y = x - 1$
i $y = x - 1$	**j** $y = 2$
$y = 0$	$y = x - 1$

■ *Note:*
$x = 0$ must be the y-axis and $y = 0$ must be the x-axis.

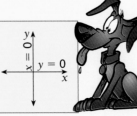

2 Graph each pair of lines and find their point of intersection.

a $x = -1$	**b** $x = 2$	**c** $x = -3$	**d** $y = x + 1$
$y = 1$	$y = 3$	$y = x$	$y = -3$
e $y = x$	**f** $y = x - 2$	**g** $y = 2x - 1$	**h** $x + y = 4$
$y = 2x$	$y = 2 - x$	$y = 5 - x$	$y = 3x - 4$

■ *Discuss:*
Is the point of intersection a solution of both equations?

3 a On the same number plane, graph the lines $y = 3x$, $y = 3x + 2$ and $y = 3x - 2$. What kind of lines have you drawn? For these lines, does the value of y increase or decrease as x gets bigger?

b On the same number plane, graph the lines $y = -x + 4$ and $y = x + 2$. What kind of lines have you drawn?

c On the same number plane, graph the lines $y = x$, $y = 2x - 1$ and $y = 3x - 2$. What do these lines have in common?

d On the same number plane, graph the lines $y = -2x$, $y = -2x + 2$ and $y = -2x + 4$. What kind of lines have you drawn? For these lines, does the value of y increase or decrease as x gets bigger?

4 Not all graphs in the number plane are straight lines. If the equation $y = x^2$ is plotted, we get a curve as shown. Complete the table of values for $y = x^2$.

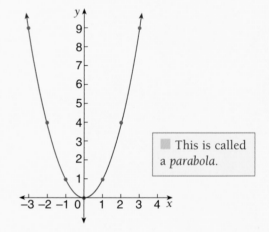

This is called a *parabola*.

$$y = x^2$$

x	-3	-2	-1	0	1	2	3
y							

5 Here is a table of values for the equation $y = x^3$. Complete the table and graph the points on a number plane.

$$y = x^3$$

x	-2	$-1\frac{1}{2}$	-1	$-\frac{1}{2}$	0	$\frac{1}{2}$	1	$1\frac{1}{2}$	2
y		$-3\frac{3}{8}$				$\frac{1}{8}$			

6 Complete the table of values for the equation $y = \dfrac{1}{x}$ and draw its graph.

x	-4	-3	-2	-1	$-\frac{1}{2}$	$-\frac{1}{4}$	0	$\frac{1}{4}$	$\frac{1}{2}$	1	2	3	4
y													

You can't have a y value for x = 0. Do you know why?

Investigation 8:06 | Straight line graphs

Please use the Assessment Grid on the following page to help you understand what is required for this Investigation.

On this number plane we have graphed two 'families' of lines; one set red, one set blue.

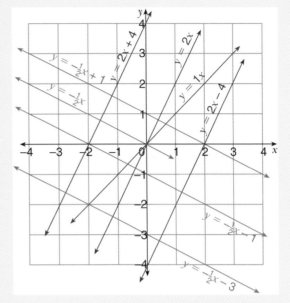

1 a How are the red lines alike?
  b How are the red equations alike?

2 a How are the blue lines alike?
  b How are the blue equations alike?

3 a Which lines intersect at the origin?
  b How are the equations of these lines alike?

4 a Which lines would be parallel to $y = -\frac{1}{2}x + 4$? (Graph this line.)
  b Which lines would be parallel to $y = 2x + 1$? (Graph this line.)

5 The equation of a line can be written in different ways. All of those graphed here are written in the form $y = mx + b$.

  a Would all lines that have a negative x term (eg $y = -\frac{1}{2}x + 4$) (slope down) or increase (slope up) as x increases in value?

  b Would all lines that have a positive x term (eg $y = 2x + 1$) increase or decrease?

  c By investigating these graphs, can you find some connection between the constant b in each equation (eg $y = 2x + 4$) and the graph of the line?

■ Graphics calculator or spreadsheet software could be used to graph and compare a range of linear relationships.

• A professional golfer was paid appearance money for each day that she took part in the tournament. She also won $32 600 in prize money. She played for 5 days and the total amount paid to her was $43 350. What was the daily appearance money?

Assessment Grid for Investigation 8:06 | Straight line graphs

The following is a sample assessment grid for this investigation. You should carefully read the criteria *before* beginning the investigation so that you know what is required.

			Assessment Criteria (B, C, D)		Achieved ✓
Criterion B Investigating Patterns		a	Some of the given similarities of the equations are correct.	1	
				2	
		b	The given similarities between the equations and the lines are correct and have been described in writing.	3	
				4	
		c	The similarities have been extended to matching lines in the diagram that are parallel to those in question 4.	5	
				6	
		d	Patterns have been discovered in question 5 and have led to a correct description about the slope of the line and the effect of the constant term.	7	
				8	
Criterion C Communication		a	The working out is not very clear and there are few explanations of method or results.	1	
				2	
		b	The working out is clear and there is a reasonable explanation of the results obtained.	3	
				4	
		c	Working out is well organised and easy to follow. Some diagrams have been used to help explain the results in question 5.	5	
				6	
Criterion D Reflection in Mathematics		a	An attempt has been made to explain the method used and some results have been checked against each other.	1	
				2	
		b	The method is well explained and results have been checked against one another by the use of diagrams or in some other way.	3	
				4	
		c	The results in question 5 have been checked to make sure they follow a pattern and two alternative ways to graph lines may be given with the relative advantages of each.	5	
				6	

Fun Spot 8:06 | The game of Sprouts

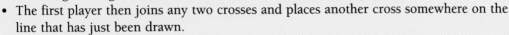

This game is played by two people. All you need is a pen and a piece of paper.

Before the game begins, a number of crosses are drawn on the paper.

8:06

- The first player then joins any two crosses and places another cross somewhere on the line that has just been drawn.
- The second player then does the same.
- Each player then takes it in turns until one player can't go.

The two rules that must be observed are:

- A line cannot be drawn so that it cuts another line.
- If a cross has three lines coming from it, then it can't be used again — it is 'dead'.

You should also take it in turns to go first.

A sample game is shown below, starting with 3 crosses.

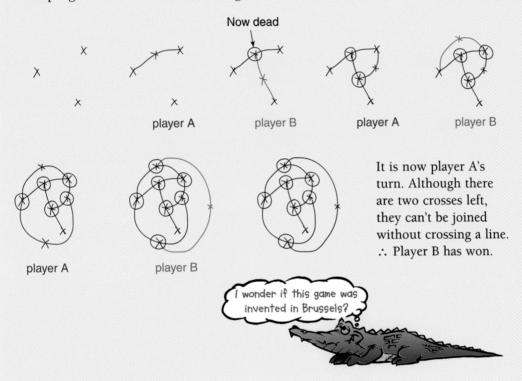

It is now player A's turn. Although there are two crosses left, they can't be joined without crossing a line.
∴ Player B has won.

I wonder if this game was invented in Brussels?

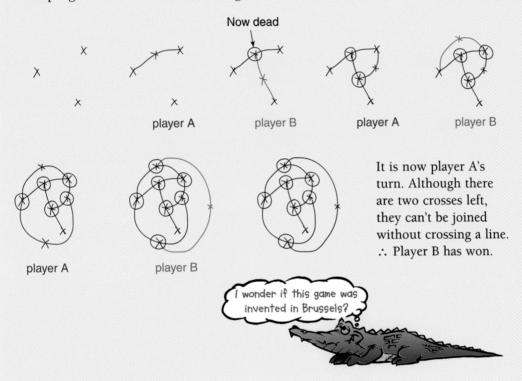

Mathematical terms 8

number plane

- A rectangular grid that allows the position of points in a plane to be identified by an ordered pair of numbers.

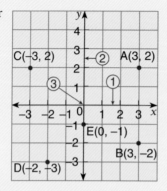

axis (axes)

- The number lines ① and ② on the number plane, used to give the position of points.
- *x*-axis: The horizontal axis, ①.
- *y*-axis: The vertical axis, ②.

coordinates

- A pair of numbers that gives the position of a point in a number plane relative to the origin. See (3, 2), (3, −2), (−3, 2), (−2, −3) and (0, −1) under **number plane**.
- *x*-coordinate: The first of the coordinates. It tells how far right (or left) the point is from the origin.
- *y*-coordinate: The second of the coordinates. It tells how far the point is above (or below) the origin.

graph (a line)

- All the points on a line.
- To plot the points that lie on a line.

intercept

- The point where a graph cuts an axis.
- *x*-intercept: The point where a graph cuts the *x*-axis.
- *y*-intercept: The point were a graph cuts the *y*-axis.

intersection

- The point where two graphs cross.

linear equation

- The equation of a straight line.
  eg $y = 3x - 4$, $x + y = 5$
- coefficient: The number placed before (ie multiplying) a pronumeral (or pronumerals).
  eg 3 is the coefficient of $3x$ in $y = 3x - 4$.
- constant term: The term containing no pronumerals.
  eg −4 is the constant term in $y = 3x - 4$.

plot

- To mark the position of a point on the number plane.

quadrants

- The four quarters that the number plane is divided into by the *x*- and *y*-axes.

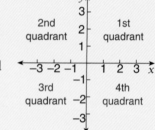

latitude

- One of the two coordinates used to read maps.
- A position north or south of the equator, given in degrees.

longitude

- One of the two coordinates used to read maps.
- A position east or west of the prime meridian, which runs through Greenwich in England. This is also given in degrees.

Diagnostic Test 8: | The Number Plane

- Each section of the test has similar items that test a certain type of question.
- Errors made will indicate areas of weakness.
- Each weakness should be treated by going back to the section listed.

	Section

1 Write down the coordinates of these points.   8:02
  a B   b D   c F   d G

2 Which points have these coordinates?   8:02
  a $(1, 0)$ b $(2, 3)$ c $(-3, -1)$ d $(3, -1)$

3 In which quadrant is point: 8:02
  a D?   b H?   c C?   d E?

4 What is the distance between the points: 8:02
  a B and H   b B and D   c D and F   d E and H

5 a What is the equation of the red line?   8:05
  b What is the equation of the blue line?

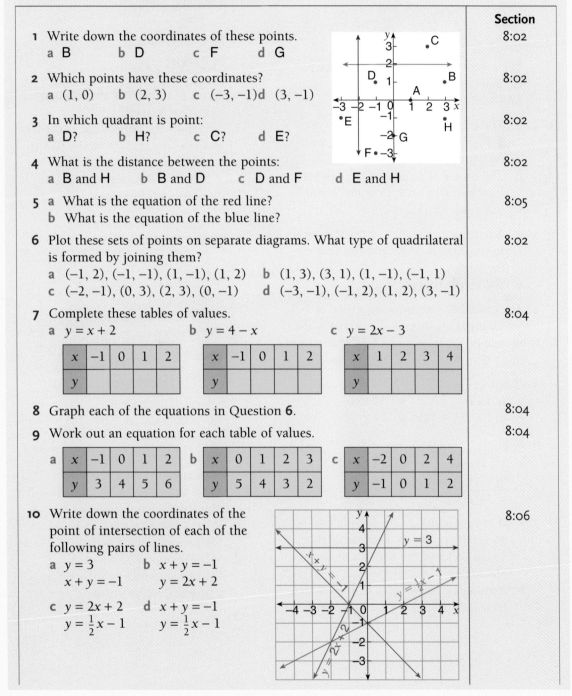

6 Plot these sets of points on separate diagrams. What type of quadrilateral   8:02
is formed by joining them?
  a $(-1, 2), (-1, -1), (1, -1), (1, 2)$ b $(1, 3), (3, 1), (1, -1), (-1, 1)$
  c $(-2, -1), (0, 3), (2, 3), (0, -1)$ d $(-3, -1), (-1, 2), (1, 2), (3, -1)$

7 Complete these tables of values.   8:04
  a $y = x + 2$ b $y = 4 - x$ c $y = 2x - 3$

x	−1	0	1	2
y				

x	−1	0	1	2
y				

x	1	2	3	4
y				

8 Graph each of the equations in Question 6.   8:04

9 Work out an equation for each table of values.   8:04

a x	−1	0	1	2
y	3	4	5	6

b x	0	1	2	3
y	5	4	3	2

c x	−2	0	2	4
y	−1	0	1	2

10 Write down the coordinates of the   8:06
point of intersection of each of the
following pairs of lines.
  a $y = 3$ b $x + y = -1$
    $x + y = -1$ $y = 2x + 2$

  c $y = 2x + 2$ d $x + y = -1$
    $y = \frac{1}{2}x - 1$ $y = \frac{1}{2}x - 1$

Chapter 8 | Revision Assignment

1

A

2 m

D _____ C
   4 m

3 m

B ┄┄┄┄┄┄┄┄┄

Use a scale drawing to calculate the distance from **A** to **B**, correct to one decimal place.

2 a The council rates on a property are 3·8% of its value. What are the rates on a property valued at $68 000?

b The owner of a shop sells goods for their cost plus 60%. How much will he sell a cup for if he pays $12 for it?

3 a A triangle has angles whose sizes are in the ratio $1:2:3$. Find the sizes of the angles.

b Sketch the triangle in Part **a**.

4 The probability of throwing a total of 5 or less using three dice, is $\frac{5}{108}$. What is the probability of throwing a total that is more than 5?

5 Simplify:
a $6(a + b) - b$ **b** $3x \times 8x$
c $6(7 - 2b) - 12b$ **d** $6x \times -3$

6 Find:
a $\sqrt{13^2 - 12^2}$ **b** $\sqrt{(13 - 12)^2}$

c $\dfrac{6 - 51}{-7 + 2}$ **d** $\dfrac{6 - 51}{-(7 + 2)}$

7 a A rectangle that is 20 cm long has an area the same as a square of side 15 cm. What is the breadth of the rectangle?

b A rectangle has an area of 120 cm². If its length is 15 cm, what is its breadth?

8 **Pasture Usage**

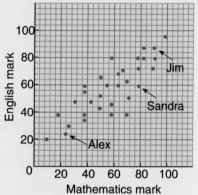

a What percentage of the total pasture is taken up by oats?

b Calculate the percentage of the total pasture that is taken up by barley.

c If the farm has a total size of 150 hectares, how many hectares are planted with turnips?

9 **Comparison of Marks for English and Mathematics: Year 8**

a What were Jim's marks in Mathematics and English?

b What were Sandra's marks in Mathematics and English?

c What were Alex's marks in Mathematics and English?

d What relationship between Mathematics and English marks is suggested by this scatter diagram?

10   **People in the Classroom**

Boys	Girls	

Teachers ⟶

a What kind of graph is this?
b What is the percentage of boys in the classroom? (*Hint:* Measure the graph.)
c If 40 people are in the classroom, how many teachers are there?

Chapter 8 | Working Mathematically

1 Use ID Card 6 on page xviii to identify:
   a 8   b 10   c 11   d 12
   e 14   f 15   g 16

2 A 7 m rope is cut in half and one half is kept. This is cut in half and, again, one half is kept. The remaining piece of rope is cut into quarters and one of the quarters is kept. What length of the rope has finally been kept? (Give your answer in millimetres.)

3 A cake was cut into slices of equal size. Three-quarters of the cake was eaten and eight slices remained. Into how many slices was the cake originally cut?

4 All boxes of Green Head Matches hold between 47 and 55 matches. Heather, my two-year-old daughter, emptied a number of unused boxes of matches. These she put in a pile. If there were 386 matches, how many boxes had Heather emptied?

8B

id

8

5 A block of land is rectangular in shape. Its perimeter is 15 m and it is known to be four times longer than it is wide. Find its length.

6 Eight people wish to volunteer for a medical experiment involving two people. How many different pairs of volunteers could be chosen?

1 Points on a line
2 Addition and subtraction of directed numbers
3 Multiplication and division of directed numbers

Technology Applications
Drag and Drops

Chapter Review
Questions

Teacher's Resource
Practice Test

• Mathematics is used in the design of structures in industry and technology.

9

Graphs and Tables

Chapter Contents

Learning Outcomes

Students will be able to construct, read and interpret graphs, tables, charts and statistical information.

Areas of Interaction

Approaches to Learning (Knowledge Acquisition, Thinking Skills, Reflection Skills, Information and Communication Technology Skills), Health and Social Education, Environments, Community and Service, Human Ingenuity

9:01 | Graphs and Their Features

- This section is meant to be used as a reference section and for later revision. Cover the *Features* and *Details* sections below and see how many you can list.
- Discuss each type of graph as a class or in a small group.
- The features and details for the **pictogram** (picture graph) and the **column graph** are shown in Appendixes I:01 and I:02 respectively.

9:01A The divided bar graph

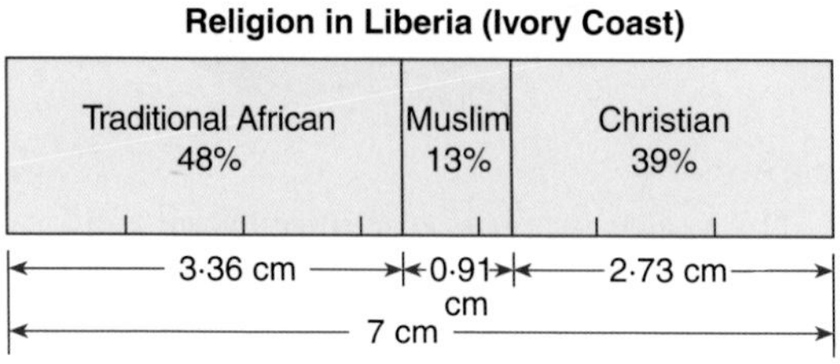

Religion in Liberia (Ivory Coast)

Traditional African 48%	Muslim 13%	Christian 39%

←————— 3·36 cm —————→|←0·91→|←———2·73 cm———→
                            cm
←————————————— 7 cm —————————————→

> ■ *Note:* 48% of 7 cm = 3·36 cm
> 13% of 7 cm = 0·91 cm
> 39% of 7 cm = 2·73 cm

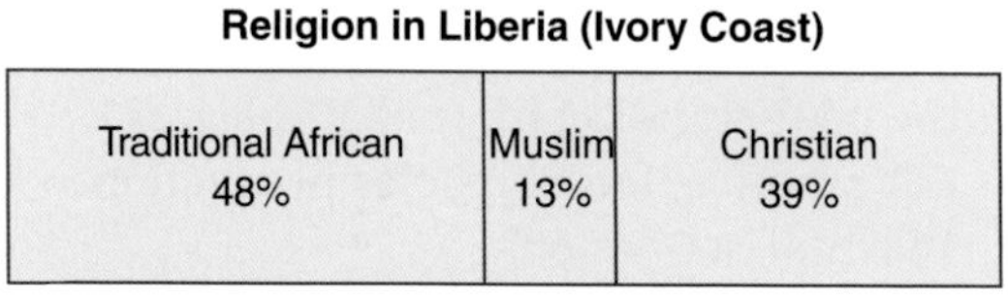

Religion in Liberia (Ivory Coast)

Traditional African 48%	Muslim 13%	Christian 39%

Features

1 The bar graph makes use of a rectangle.
2 The bar graph is uncomplicated in its appearance and takes up little space. (The measurements shown here are usually not given.)
3 It shows how the whole is divided into its parts. The large 'bar' is divided up according to the size of its parts.
4 You can compare the sizes of the categories easily.
5 It doesn't attempt to communicate details except through percentages which may be given on the graph.

Details

1 The bar graph must have a title or heading.
2 No axes are necessary.
3 When drawing the graph, decide on a length for the bar (10 cm is a desirable length) and use mathematics to find the length of each part. That is, find what fraction or percentage each category is of the whole, then give that fraction or percentage of the bar to that category.
4 Marks to show centimetres or units are not usually placed on the graph and percentages are often shown, as in this case.

9:01B The sector graph (or pie graph)

If you could bend a bar graph into a circle, you would have a sector graph.

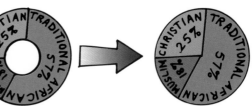

Example

If 25% of people in Obarti are Christian, then $\frac{1}{4}$ of the circle (90° at the centre) should be used for this category.

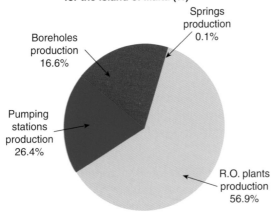

Average water production by source for the Island of Malta (%)

- Springs production 0.1%
- Boreholes production 16.6%
- Pumping stations production 26.4%
- R.O. plants production 56.9%

Features

1 The sector graph is uncomplicated and appeals to people because it's like cutting up a pie.
2 Like the divided bar graphs, one whole (360° at the centre) is divided into parts according to the size of the categories.
3 Sizes of categories are easily compared.
4 The sector graph is attractive yet takes up little space.

Details

1 The sector graph must have a title or heading.
2 No axes are necessary.
3 Use mathematics to find the centre angle for each category. That is, find what fraction or percentage a category is of the whole. Give that fraction or percentage of the 360° at the centre to that category. For example, for 'Boreholes production': 16·6% of 360° ≑ 60°.

- How could you estimate the amount of water produced each year in Malta? (Would the graph above help you?)

9:01C The line graph

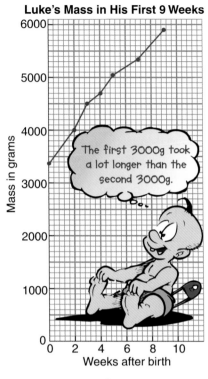

Luke's Mass in His First 9 Weeks

The first 3000g took a lot longer than the second 3000g.

Features

1 The line graph conveys more information than most graphs, and is often quite detailed.
2 It shows trends and relationships clearly.
3 The line graph has a large variety of forms and applications. (Examples include travel graphs, conversion graphs, graphs describing physical phenomena, step graphs, lines of best fit, number plane graphs etc.)
4 The graphs are read in the same way that number plane graphs are read, in that the value of x is linked to the value of y.
5 The 'lines' on a line graph may be curved.

Details

1 The line graph must have a title or heading.
2 Both axes must be labelled.
3 Different scales may need to be used on the two axes. Each axis may need a different range of numbers or a different type of unit.
4 Each point on the graph represents a pair of readings, one on the horizontal axis and one on the vertical axis.
5 Once given information has been used to draw a line graph, other useful information can be taken from the graph. For example, even though Luke's weight was not taken at 1 week old, we can estimate his mass then to have been 3650 g.
6 Line graphs should be used for continuous data only (ie points between the dots on the graph also have meaning).

9:01D The conversion graph

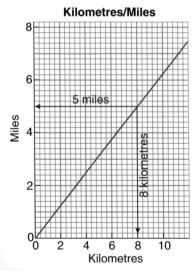

Kilometres/Miles

5 miles

8 kilometres

Features

1 The conversion graph allows us to convert from one measurement to another.
2 The graph is read in the same way as other line graphs. eg 8 kilometres = 5 miles.

Details

1 The details listed above for line graphs apply to conversion graphs.
2 Conversion graphs are straight lines.

9:01E The step graph

Parking cost on a city street

Cost / Time in hours

Features

1 The step graph is made up of several horizontal intervals or *steps*.
2 The end of one horizontal step and the start of the next one are in the same vertical line.
3 Each horizontal step has an open circle ○ at its start and a coloured-in circle or dot ● at its end. An open circle excludes that point from the step. A coloured-in circle includes that point in the step. So when 'time' equals '2', the 'cost' is €3·60 not €5·40.

■ *Note:* When a gap or jump appears in a graph we say that the graph is *discontinuous*.

Details

1 The details listed in **9:01C** for line graphs apply to step graphs.
2 Every point on the graph has meaning in that it has a reading on both axes. The *data* is continuous.
3 The ends of steps should be considered carefully: *Is this end included or not?*

I'll have to watch my step!

It is important to realise that graphs rarely stand alone. They are usually part of an article which refers to the graph, possibly giving some explanation of how information was obtained. The article may attempt to draw conclusions based on the information presented.

Exercise 9:01

Foundation Worksheet 9:01

Picture graphs and column graphs
1 Using picture graphs.
2 Using column graphs.

1 Write answers in your own words.
Refer to the previous pages if necessary.
  a What is a divided bar graph?
  b What is a sector graph?
  c What is a line graph?
  d What is a conversion graph?
  e What is a step graph?
  f What is a discontinuous graph?

2 a What is another name for a conversion graph?
  b What is another name for a sector graph?
  c List three different types of the line graph.

You could write down the features and details.

3 Refer to the divided bar graph on page 203.
  a What is the title of this graph?
  b If the population of Liberia is 3 500 000, how many people are Muslim?
  c What percentage (to the nearest whole percent) would be represented by 1 cm of the 7 cm bar?
  d What length of the bar would represent 10 per cent?

4 Refer to the sector graph on page 204 that refers to Malta's water consumption.
  a Which category was responsible for the greatest water production?
  b Are you able to say how much water was produced by springs? Why or why not?
  c What angle at the centre should be allocated to borehole production? Has it been? Is the graph accurate?
  d What angle at the centre should be allocated to Pumping stations?

5 Refer to the line graph on page 205.
  a What was Luke's mass at the end of 9 weeks?
  b At what age did Luke have a mass of 4000 g?
  c Within which week did Luke's mass first pass 5000 g?
  d Use the graph to estimate what Luke's mass might have been at the end of the tenth week.

6 Refer to the conversion graph on page 205.
  a How many miles are in 8 kilometres?
  b How many kilometres are in 5 miles?
  c To the nearest kilometre, how many kilometres are in:
    i 7·5 miles?   **ii** 2 miles?   **iii** 5·5 miles?
  d To the nearest mile, how many miles are in:
    i 2 km?   **ii** 5 km?   **iii** 11 km?
  e How many kilometres would be in 10 miles?

7 Refer to the step graph on page 206.
  a What unit is used on the horizontal axis?
  b How would money be paid if you wanted to park on a city street?
  c How much should it cost to park for:
    i 20 minutes?   **ii** 3 hours?   **iii** 3 hours 2 minutes?
  d What is the longest time allowed for a cost of:
    i €1.80?   **ii** €7.20?   **iii** €3.60?

Investigation 9:01 | Collecting graphs

Please use the Assessment Grid on the following page to help you understand what is required for this Investigation.

Collect as many different types of graphs as you can and display them for discussion with your class. On your display include a description of the type of graph and how suitable it is for displaying the information. Make sure that you have at least three graphs. Graphs may be found in:

- newspapers
- car, science, financial, geographical or research magazines
- atlases and encyclopaedias
- medical journals
- booklets accompanying products purchased.

On the back of each graph write the source and date of publication. Include with each graph the article of which it is a part.

If you can't find any graphs, you might like to draw your own.

9:02 | Reading Graphs

When reading graphs, remember to read the accompanying information as well.

Exercise 9:02A

Foundation Worksheet 9:02

Reading graphs
1 Reading picture graphs.
2 Reading column graphs.
3 Reading other graphs.

1 In both pictograms and divided bar graphs, one symbol or column is divided into parts. What mass of wheat would be represented by these symbols?

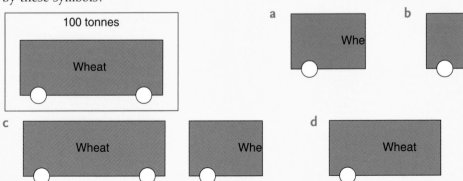

Assessment Grid for Investigation 9:01 | **Collecting graphs**

The following is a sample assessment grid for this investigation. You should carefully read the criteria *before* beginning the investigation so that you know what is required.

			Assessment Criteria (B, C, D)		Achieved ✓
Criterion B Investigating Patterns	a		Only one type of graph has been collected.	1	
				2	
	b		A variety of graphs have been collected but there is no description or source information.	3	
				4	
	c		A variety of graphs have been collected and each graph has a description and source.	5	
				6	
	d		The description of the graph includes its type and suitability for the information presented.	7	
				8	
Criterion C Communication	a		The graphs are displayed in a disorganised manner and no description of the graphs is given.	1	
				2	
	b		Graphs are displayed in an organised way and some description of the graphs is given.	3	
				4	
	c		Graphs are displayed in an organised way and a full description for each graph is given.	5	
				6	
Criterion D Reflection in Mathematics	a		No evaluation of the suitability of each graph is given.	1	
				2	
	b		Some evaluation of the suitability of each graph to display the information is given.	3	
				4	
	c		A full evaluation of the suitability of each graph is given, with alternatives suggested for those described as unsuitable.	5	
				6	

2 Graphs are sometimes drawn carelessly or are drawn to deceive us. We need to be able to notice errors in graphs. For each part below, select the graph that correctly matches the information given.

a Jan spent 10 days of her holiday at the seaside, 4 days visiting her parents and 2 days at home.

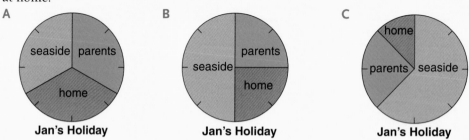

b 100 people were asked to spell 'hypotenuse'. 40 spelt it correctly, 35 would not try and 25 spelt it incorrectly.

c To send a package, it costs me 1.25 Swiss francs (CHF) for a weight of up to 100 g and CHF2.00 for a weight more than 100 g and up to 200 g.

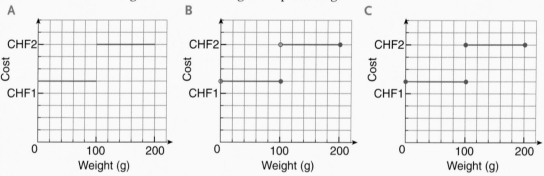

d Of 60 school band members on the bus, 30 were in full uniform, 20 were partly in uniform and 10 were not in uniform.

A

| full | part | none |

Uniform

B

| full | part | none |

Uniform

3 Upon reaching the Eiffel Tower, 50 people climbed to the top, 30 people began the climb but turned back before reaching the top and 20 people did not attempt the climb. Copy and complete the sector graph to the right to show this information about 'Climbing the Eiffel Tower'.

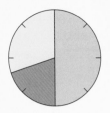

4 Each graph below shows Tom's distance from home as time passes.
  a Which graph shows Tom moving away from home as time passes?
  b Which graph shows Tom moving closer to home as time passes?
  c Which graph shows Tom staying the same distance from home as time passes?

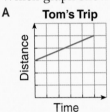

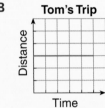

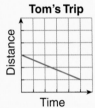

5

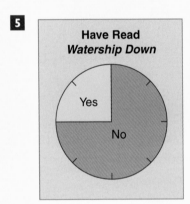

Our librarian wanted to know whether her students had read the novel, *Watership Down* by Richard Adams.
She asked 200 students and graphed the results.
  a What kind of graph did she use?
  b What fraction of her students had read the book?
  c How many of the students asked had not read the book?
  d What angle at the centre of the circle has been used to show the group that had not read the book?

6 The sector graph shows the top ten destinations of Japanese emigrants. What percentage of Japanese emigrated to:
  a China?
  b The United States?
  c Australia or Hong Kong?
  d What was the second most popular destination?

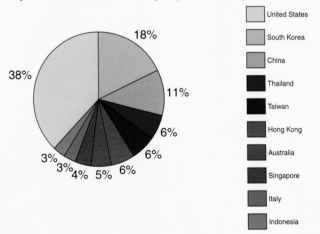

Top 10 Destinations Among Japanese Emigrants in 2000

7

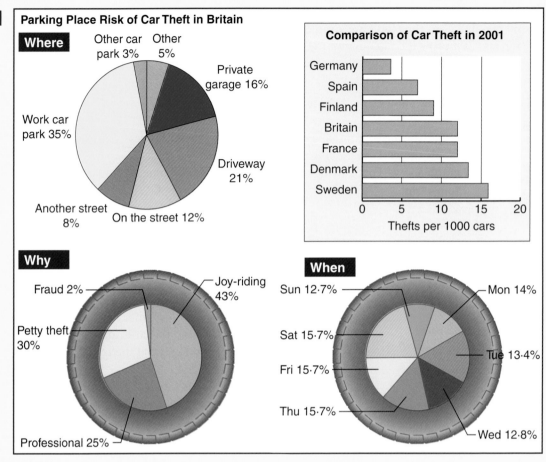

Parking Place Risk of Car Theft in Britain

Where
- Other car park 3%
- Other 5%
- Private garage 16%
- Driveway 21%
- On the street 12%
- Another street 8%
- Work car park 35%

Comparison of Car Theft in 2001

Germany, Spain, Finland, Britain, France, Denmark, Sweden

Thefts per 1000 cars (0, 5, 10, 15, 20)

Why
- Fraud 2%
- Joy-riding 43%
- Petty theft 30%
- Professional 25%

When
- Sun 12·7%
- Mon 14%
- Sat 15·7%
- Tue 13·4%
- Fri 15·7%
- Thu 15·7%
- Wed 12·8%

Use the graphs above to answer the following questions.
a In Britain, what percentage of cars were stolen if the cars were parked:
  i in driveways? **ii** in private garages? **iii** on the street?
  iv on another street? **v** in work car park? **vi** in some other car park?
b What other places could fit the category 'Other' on the graph showing where thefts occur?
c What percentage of stolen cars were taken by joy riders?
d What fraction of all thefts were carried out by professional thieves?
e On which day was the least number of cars stolen?
f Why do you think two of the sector graphs are drawn as tyres?
g How many cars per thousand (to the nearest whole car) were stolen in:
  i Germany? **ii** Spain? **iii** Finland?
  iv France? **v** Denmark? **vi** Sweden?
h Are we told when these statistics were collected?

8 This conversion graph converts between degrees Celsius and degrees Fahrenheit.

Use the graph to change these temperatures from °C to °F.

a 0°C   **b** 100°C
c 25°C   **d** 50°C
e 15°C   **f** 110°C

Change these temperatures from °F to °C.

g 32°F   **h** 176°F
i 160°F   **j** 104°F
k 16°F   **l** 0°F

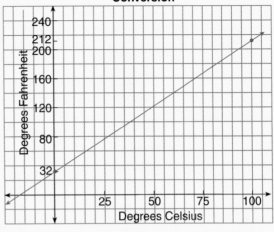

Degrees Celsius/Degrees Fahrenheit Conversion

9

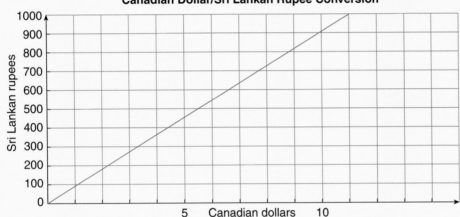

Canadian Dollar/Sri Lankan Rupee Conversion

What is the value in Sri Lankan rupees (correct to 2 significant figures) of:

a $10?   **b** $5?   **c** $3?   **d** $6.50?
e $30?   **f** $75?   **g** $300?   **h** $750?

What is the value in Canadian dollars (to 1 significant figure) of:

i 200 Rs?   **j** 700 Rs?   **k** 900 Rs?   **l** 100 Rs?
m 660 Rs?   **n** 1800 Rs?   **o** 3000 Rs?   **p** 30 000 Rs?

10 The parking charges for a parking station are shown in this step graph.

a Find:
    i the cost of parking for 2 h
    ii the cost of parking for $1\frac{1}{2}$ h.
b What is the longest time a car can be parked for €8?
c What is the cost of parking a car from Monday to Friday if it is parked for periods of $1\frac{1}{4}$ h, $2\frac{1}{2}$ h, 3 h, $\frac{1}{2}$ h and 2 h on those days respectively?

Parking Costs

11 Jeong Hyun decided to start a fast food restaurant. At first it was unsuccessful but, as word got around that his Korean food was some of the best in Seoul, business improved.

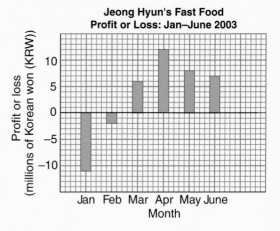

**Jeong Hyun's Fast Food
Profit or Loss: Jan–June 2003**

a In which month was the greatest profit made? What was the profit then?
b In which month did the shop make a profit of 6 million Korean won (KRW)?
c What was the profit or loss for January?
d What was the reason for the continued improvement from January to April?
e In which month was the greatest improvement made on the previous month?
f For the six months January to June, what was the total profit made?

12

Make-up of Homeroom 8B

Mr Curtois and his students are called Homeroom 8B.
The length of Mr Curtois' section of the bar is 3 mm.
a How long is:
   i the whole bar?　**ii** the girls' section?　**iii** the boys' section?
b How many teachers are in the group?
c How many times as long as the teacher's section is the girls' section?
d How many girls are in the group?
e How many times as long as the teacher's section is the boys' section?
f What percentage of the group:
   i are girls?　**ii** is the teacher?　**iii** are boys?

13

Company Profits

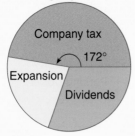

Company profits are used to pay company tax, to expand the company's assets (through the modernisation of plant, expansion of productive capacity and provision of additional employment) and to pay dividends (which are again taxed through personal income tax).

The angle at the centre for 'Company tax' is 172° and the angle at the centre for 'Expansion' is 79°.
a What kind of graph is this?
b What category receives the smallest part of the profits?
c What angle at the centre is used to represent 'Dividends'?
d Find the percentage of company profits that is allocated to 'Expansion'.

14 A carrier's charges for delivering a parcel are set out in the graph.

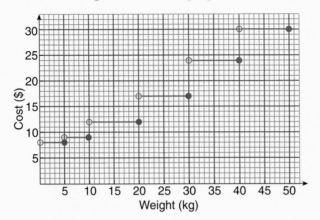

What does it cost to deliver a parcel weighing:

a 25 kg?   **b** 8 kg?   **c** 40 kg?

What is the heaviest parcel that can be delivered for:

d $8?   **e** $17?   **f** $24?

For each additional 10 kg, or part thereof, in excess of 50 kg an extra $2.40 is charged.

g What would be the cost of sending a parcel weighing 75 kg?

15 Over the years machinery has done more and more of the work previously carried out by unskilled labour. This has led to a greater need for skilled and well-educated workers. These figures are based on data from the Committee of Inquiry into Education and Training, 1979.

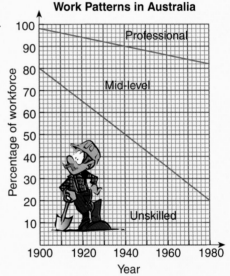

Work Patterns in Australia

a What kind of graph would this be?

b What percentage of workers in 1900 were professional?

c What percentage of workers in 1900 were unskilled?

d What percentage of workers in 1900 were in the mid-level category?

e What percentage of each category was present in 1920?

f What percentage of each category was present in 1980?

g Do you think the percentages for each of the years mentioned on the horizontal axis have been researched? Why or why not?

h If the trend of this graph continued to the year 2010, what would be the percentage of unskilled workers? Is this likely?

i On the basis of the information on this graph, do you think it is important for young people to develop skills which they could use in the workplace? Where can these skills be developed?

16 The graph below shows an attempt to represent the data in the table provided.

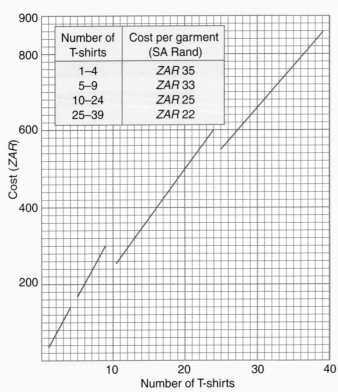

Number of T-shirts	Cost per garment (SA Rand)
1–4	ZAR 35
5–9	ZAR 33
10–24	ZAR 25
25–39	ZAR 22

Is that a step graph?

a Why are there gaps on the graph, for example, between 4 and 5, 9 and 10, etc?

b Considering your answer to Part **a**, do the points between any two successive integers on the horizontal axis have any meaning?

c Strictly speaking, the graph above is not a correct representation of the data in the table. What should the graph really look like?

d Can you see any advantage in drawing the graph in this way rather than the correct way?

e Using the graph, what is the maximum number of T-shirts that can be bought for:
  i ZAR 160?   **ii** ZAR 300?   **iii** ZAR 620?

• What kind of graph would you use to show the percentage of men, women, boys and girls at this match?

1 A block of ice was placed in a large cylinder and the level of water was recorded as the cylinder was heated.

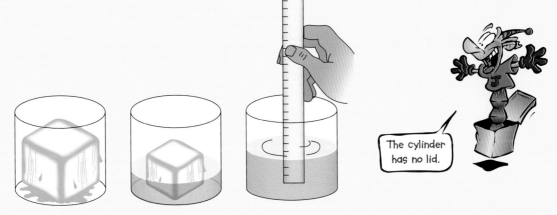

The cylinder has no lid.

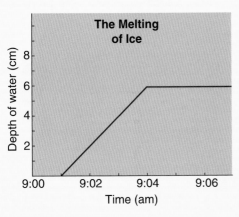

The Melting of Ice

The results of this experiment are shown on the graph.

a When did the experiment begin?

b What was the depth of water at 9:02 am?

c When was the depth of water 4 cm?

d What was the greatest depth of water during the experiment?

e At what time did the last of the ice melt?

f If the experiment continued, allowing the water to boil for some time, what would happen to the water level in the cylinder? How would this be shown on the graph?

2 Water from a tap flowed into a barrel which had been partly filled with water. The depth of water was measured as time passed and the results were graphed. The tap was turned off after 10 minutes.

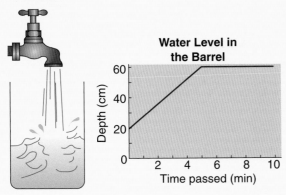

Water Level in the Barrel

a What depth of water was in the barrel at the beginning of the experiment?

b What depth of water was in the barrel after 1 minute?

c After how many minutes was the depth of water 40 cm?

d Why does the graph level out after the 5th minute?

e When was the tap turned off?

f By how much did the water level rise in the first 5 minutes?

3

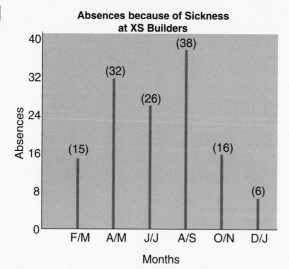

Absences because of Sickness at XS Builders

(graph showing: F/M (15), A/M (32), J/J (26), A/S (38), O/N (16), D/J (6))

Vertical axis: Absences (0, 8, 16, 24, 32, 40)
Horizontal axis: Months

a What kind of graph is this?
b What does J/J stand for on the horizontal axis?
c How many absences occurred in April/May?
d How many absences occurred in October/November?
e What was the greatest number of absences and in what time period did this occur?
f Why do you think the absences were so low in December/January?
g What was the total number of absences in these 12 months?

4 Marni and her parents wanted to throw a surprise party for Marni's husband. During the day these three prepared food and decorated the living room. The friends, two carloads full, arrived before James, the guest of honour, arrived. After the party, Marni's parents stayed for a while to help clean up the house.

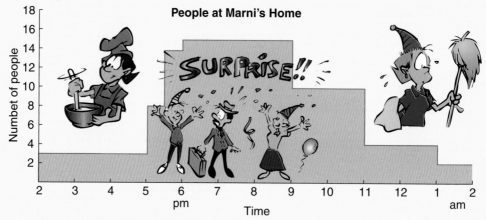

People at Marni's Home

Vertical axis: Number of people (2, 4, 6, 8, 10, 12, 14, 16, 18)
Horizontal axis: Time (2 pm, 3, 4, 5, 6, 7, 8, 9, 10, 11, 12, 1, 2 am)

a At what time did the first guests arrive? How many came then?
b How much time passed before the other guests arrived?
c How many guests were there altogether?
d When did James arrive home? How many people were at the party then?
e When did the first guests leave? How many left then?
f At what time did Marni's parents leave?
g See if you can make up a different story which fits this graph. The name of the graph and the titles of the axes may change if you wish.

5

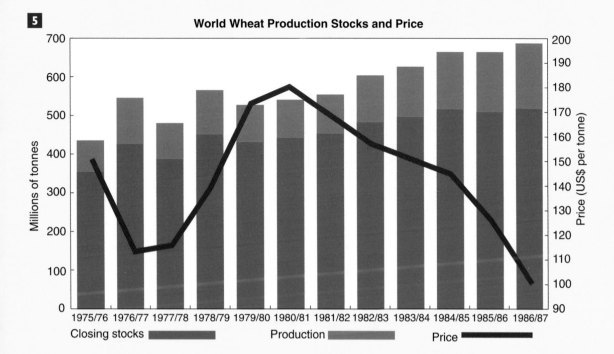

World Wheat Production Stocks and Price

Closing stocks ▬▬▬ Production ▭▭▭ Price ▬▬▬

Often one graph is drawn on top of another so that comparisons can be made. Here 'Production' refers to the wheat grown in that year while 'Closing stocks' refers to the total amount of wheat available at the end of the period, including what was unused in the previous time period.

a In which time period was the price of wheat at its highest?
b How many millions of tonnes, to the nearest 50 million, were produced in the period:
  i 1975/76?   ii 1977/78?   iii 1982/83?   iv 1986/87?
c In which time period was the price of wheat at its lowest? What was the price then?

6

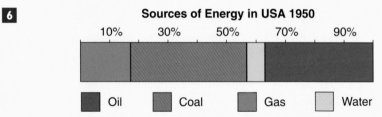

Sources of Energy in USA 1950

■ Oil   ■ Coal   ■ Gas   ▨ Water

a What kind of graph is this?
b What was the greatest source of energy in 1950?
c What percentage of energy came from oil?
d What percentage of energy came from gas?
e List the sources of energy in order of size, from largest to smallest.
f Would you expect the sources of energy now to be in the same percentages as in 1950? Why or why not?
g In the 2000s, what other sources of energy might be included?

7 Mrs O'Neill asked her science class to carry out an experiment. They were to use a special light (a *stroboscope*) and a camera to take pictures of a falling ball as it rolled off the top of a stand.

One picture was obtained which showed the position of the ball in each $\frac{1}{20}$ of a second. An *x*- and *y*-axis were drawn on the photograph to give the graph shown to the right.

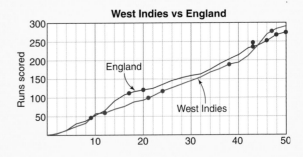

The Path of a Ball

a At the beginning of the experiment what was the height of the ball?

b What horizontal distance had the ball travelled in $\frac{8}{20}$ of a second?

c What was the height of the ball when $\frac{8}{20}$ of a second had passed?

d How far had the ball fallen in $\frac{8}{20}$ s?

e What was the height of the ball when it had moved through a horizontal distance of 50 cm?

f How far had the ball moved in the horizontal direction when its height was 75 cm?

8 These line graphs show how the West Indies and the English performed in a one-day cricket match. The West Indies were the first to bat, and after batting for 50 overs (6 balls are bowled in each over), the English had to bat for 50 overs. If the English had been able to pass the West Indies' total number of runs, they would have won. When a person batting gets out, a heavy dot is placed on the graph at that point.

West Indies vs England

a How many runs had the West Indies scored after 20 overs?

b How many runs had the English scored after 20 overs?

c How many of the English were out after 20 overs?

d How many West Indies got out altogether?

e How many English got out altogether?

f What was the West Indies' total score?

g What was the total score for the English?

h Who won the game?

i Which team had scored more runs after 30 overs, and how many more had that team scored than the other team?

j How many runs did the West Indies score in the 11th over?

k During which over did the West Indies reach 200?

l In which over did the English lose their 5th wicket?

9:03 | Unusual Graphs

Some newspapers and magazines use unusual ways of presenting graphs. Sometimes too, they use pictures or illustrations which resemble graphs but may lack accuracy or some of the features of a graph.

Exercise 9:03

1 **Exports of Coffee from the Philippines**

The destination of Philippine exports of coffee in 1998:

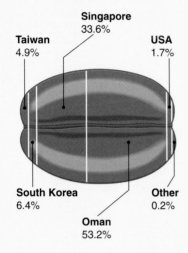

Singapore 33.6%
Taiwan 4.9%
USA 1.7%
South Korea 6.4%
Other 0.2%
Oman 53.2%

a Which graph does this most resemble?
b Why have they chosen to divide a picture rather than a bar or rectangle?
c What percentage of Philippine coffee exports go to South Korea?
d How much more (as a percentage of coffee exported) did Oman buy than Singapore?
e What is the title of this graph?

2

Parking Costs

The parking charges for the Kowloon Car Care Corner are shown here.

a What is the cost for 2 hours?
b For how long can you park for HKD36?
c What is the maximum charge shown here?
d What is the cost for half an hour?
e Why do you think that this type of graph is called a step graph?

Temperature in Beijing, 13 October 1993

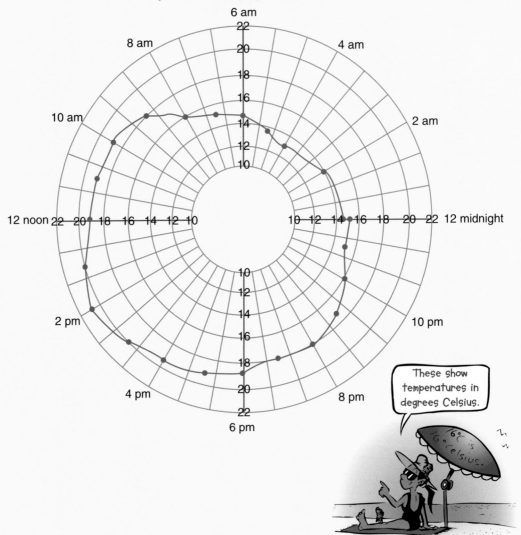

This unusual graph shows the temperature over a 24-hour period on the day Ming How was born.

a How old was Ming How on:
   i 2 August 1998?   **ii** 3 November 2005?
b What type of graph is this?
c What angle at the centre is used to represent:
   i 6 hours?   **ii** 1 hour?
d What are the least and greatest temperatures that could be shown on this graph?
e What was the temperature at:
   i 9 am?   **ii** 3 am?   **iii** 3 pm?
f At what time(s) was the temperature 16°C?
g On 13 October 1993, what were the least and greatest temperatures?

4

The Irresistible Rise of Steffi Graf

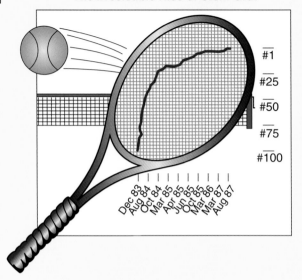

It took teenager Steffi Graf $3\frac{1}{2}$ years to lift her world tennis computer ranking from 100 to 1. At 18 years of age she was the No. 1 seed for the 1988 Ford Australian Open.

a What kind of graph is this?

b What does the symbol # stand for?

c Is this graph easy to read?

d Is the graph meant to give detailed information or is it meant to create an impression?

e What was Steffi's ranking in December 1983?

f What was her ranking in August 1984?

Is that a Graf graph?

5

Evolution of the men's 100 m World Record

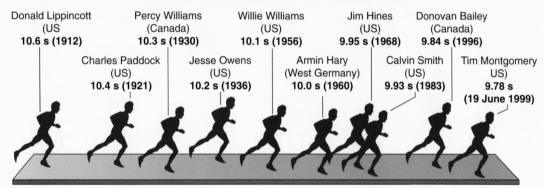

Donald Lippincott (US 10.6 s (1912)

Charles Paddock (US) 10.4 s (1921)

Percy Williams (Canada) 10.3 s (1930)

Jesse Owens (US) 10.2 s (1936)

Willie Williams (US) 10.1 s (1956)

Armin Hary (West Germany) 10.0 s (1960)

Jim Hines (US) 9.95 s (1968)

Calvin Smith (US) 9.93 s (1983)

Donovan Bailey (Canada) 9.84 s (1996)

Tim Montgomery US) 9.78 s (19 June 1999)

a Why is this an impressive way to show the information gathered?

b Which of the graphs does this most resemble? Why?

c Who was the first man to run 100 metres in less than 10 seconds?

d By how much did Donovan Bailey break the world record when he won the final of the 100 m at the Atlanta Olympics?

e How many athletes from the United States of America have held this record since 1920?

f How much faster did Donovan Bailey run than the other Canadian, Percy Williams?

g What has been the smallest margin by which the 100 m record has been broken since 1912?

h Research the evolution of this world record after 1999.

6

Population of Smallville

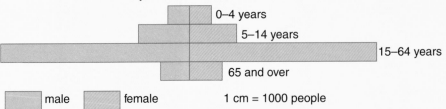

0–4 years
5–14 years
15–64 years
65 and over

☐ male   ▨ female   1 cm = 1000 people

This graph resembles a column graph where each column is a divided bar graph.

a Which of the population group used has:
  i the smallest size?   **ii** the largest size?

b By measuring each column (which is lying on its side) using the scale given, find the number of:
  i 0–4 year olds   **ii** 5–14 year olds   **iii** 15–64 year olds
  iv 65 year olds and over.
  (Give answers to the nearest 50.)

c Use your answers to Part **b** to find the population of Smallville.

d Which is the only category in which the females outnumber the males? Why is this?

7

Percentage Divisions of Faith (in Singapore, 2000)

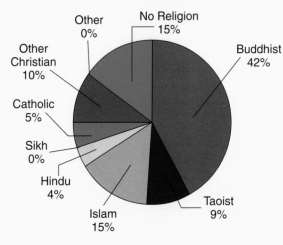

Other 0%
No Religion 15%
Other Christian 10%
Buddhist 42%
Catholic 5%
Sikh 0%
Hindu 4%
Islam 15%
Taoist 9%

a What type of graph does this resemble?

b Are the angles at the centre the correct size?

c Is the information presented in an eye-catching way?

d What percentage of Singaporeans claimed to have no religion?

e What percentage of Singaporeans surveyed were Christian?

f What percentage were grouped together under 'Other'?

g What percentage were Buddhists?

h What percentage followed Islam?

9:04 | Drawing Graphs

9:04A The column graph

Information and reasoning
Details of births in Peaceful Cove are given below.

Year	Births
1998	80
1999	110
2000	115
2001	116
2002	120
2003	130

Step 1 Choose a title. We could use 'Births in Peaceful Cove 1998–2003'.

Step 2 Choose a scale and name for each axis. The horizontal axis is usually used for time.

The greatest number of births is 150. We choose a scale (such as 1 cm = 20 births) so that the graph will fit our space.

Step 3 Choose a width for each column and draw the graph. Draw the columns equal distances apart.

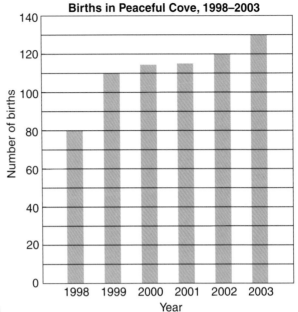

9:04B The divided bar graph

Information and reasoning
Details concerning the sport preferences of Grade 8 at Sundown Internatioinal School are given below.

Sport chosen	Tennis	Football	Softball	Swimming	Total number of students
Number of students	42	46	52	70	210

Step 1 Choose a title.
We could use 'Grade 8 Sport: Sundown International'.

Step 2 Choose an appropriate length for the bar.
Usually the number in each category is converted to a percentage of the whole and a bar of length 10 cm is used.
This allows each millimetre to represent 1% of students.

$$\text{Tennis} = \frac{42}{210} \times 100\% = 20\% \qquad \text{Football} = \frac{46}{210} \times 100\% \doteqdot 22\%$$

$$\text{Softball} = \frac{52}{210} \times 100\% \doteqdot 25\% \qquad \text{Swimming} = \frac{70}{210} \times 100\% \doteqdot 33\%$$

Step 3 Draw the graph.
We will make the length 100 mm (ie 10 cm) so that 1% = 1 mm.

Grade 8 Sport: Sundown International

Tennis	Cricket	Softball	Swimming

9:04C The sector graph (or pie graph)

Information and reasoning

Details of the make-up of New Town International School are given below.

Infants	Primary	Secondary	Adults	Total
30	44	60	10	144

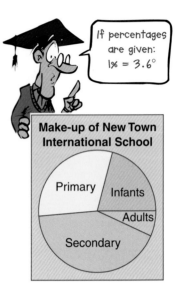

If percentages are given:
1% = 3.6°

Step 1 Choose a title.

We could use 'Make-up of New Town International School'.

Step 2 Work out the angles at the centre.

Ask: 'What fraction is this category of the whole?' Then find this fraction of 360° to calculate the angle at the centre.

$$\text{Infants} = \frac{30}{144} \times 360° = 75°$$
$$\text{Primary} = \frac{44}{144} \times 360° = 110°$$
$$\text{Secondary} = \frac{60}{144} \times 360° = 150°$$
$$\text{Adults} = \frac{10}{144} \times 360° = 25°$$

Step 3 Draw the graph.

Choose a suitable radius for the circle.

9:04D The line graph

Information and reasoning

While in hospital, Rocco's temperature was taken every 4 hours. The details are shown below. 37°C is normal temperature.

Time	4 pm	8 pm	12 pm	4 am	8 am	12 noon	4 pm	8 pm
Temp.	38·2	39·4	39·8	40	39	37·6	36·6	37

←——— Thursday ———→ ←——— Friday ———→

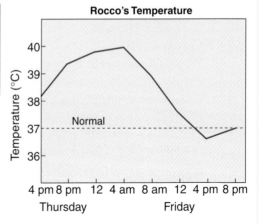

Step 1 Choose a title.

We could use 'Rocco's Temperature'.

Step 2 Choose a scale and name for each axis.

We will need 8 divisions on the time axis. We could name the vertical axis 'Temperature (°C)' and use 5 divisions, one for each °C.

Step 3 Draw the graph.

9:04E The conversion graph

Information and reasoning

We know that 20 acres = 8·1 hectares and that
0 acres = 0 hectares.

Step 1 Choose a title.
'Acres/Hectares Conversion' would be a
good title.

Step 2 Choose a scale and name for each axis.
We need to go up to 20 on the *acres* axis and
8·1 on the *hectares* axis. The scales used could
be: 1 cm = 5 acres and 1 cm = 2 hectares.

Step 3 Draw the graph.
Plot the points (0, 0) and (20, 8·1).
Join these two points.

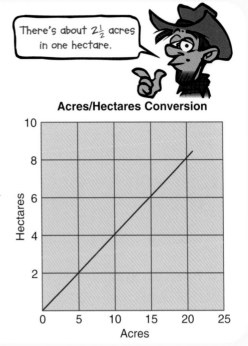

9:04F The step graph

Information and reasoning

Travelling by boat costs $3 for travelling up to 5 km,
$10 for travelling more than 5 km and up to 10 km,
and $18 for travelling more than 10 km.

Step 1 Choose a title.
'Boat Fares' would be a good title.

Step 2 Choose a scale and a name for each axis.
Kilometres travelled, using 1 cm = 5 km,
could be used on the horizontal axis.
Fare (up to $20) could be used on the
vertical axis with a scale of 1 cm = $5.

Step 3 Draw the graph.
Realise that there are three different fares.
Check that for each the empty circle
is on the left. Note that the top step
continues on.

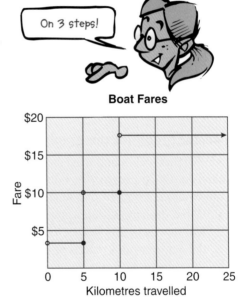

When graphing the information in a table:
• **Determine how big you want the graph to be.**
• **Look at the range of numbers on both axes.**
• **Determine the scales needed.**
• **Work out the heights of the columns for a column graph OR the heights of the
points which will need to be joined for a line graph.**

Exercise 9:04

The column graph

1 Draw a column graph for each of the following sets of data, referring to page 225 if necessary.

a These are the numbers of road accidents in Peaceful Cove from 1999 till 2003.

Year	1999	2000	2001	2002	2003
Number of accidents	100	130	140	170	200

b These are the favourite colours of 1000 Grade 8 students.

Colour preference	Green	Pink	Yellow	Blue	Red	Other
Number of students	228	208	90	200	114	150

The divided bar graph

2 Draw a divided bar graph for each of the following sets of data, referring to page 225 if necessary.

a These show the favourite pets of 200 children at New Town International School.

Favourite pet	Guinea pig	Cat	Dog	Bird	Other
Number of children	40	30	84	20	26

b Grade 8 students were asked to choose one of four subjects as a course for Grade 9. Their responses are shown below.

Course chosen	Photography	Music	Art	Computing
Number of students	15	36	42	57

The sector graph (or pie graph)

3 Sandwiches, cakes and fried rice were sold at the canteen. Of 36 people who bought lunch, 18 bought sandwiches, 9 bought pies and 9 bought sausage rolls.

a When drawing a sector graph, 360° at the centre will represent 36 choices. How many degrees at the centre would represent one choice?

b What fraction of the people ordered:
  i sandwiches? **ii** cakes? **iii** fried rice?

c What angle at the centre must be used to represent the choice of:
  i sandwiches? **ii** cakes? **iii** fried rice?

d Draw the sector graph, referring to page 226 if necessary.

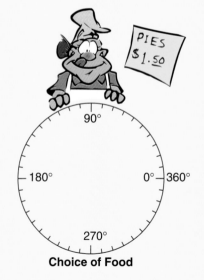

Choice of Food

4 Draw a sector graph for each of the following sets of data, referring to page 226 if necessary.

a Of the ARS 200 Argentinian Pesos that Juan took on his trip from the countryside to Buenos Aires to visit his aunt, ARS 120 was spent on fares, ARS 40 was spent on food, ARS 10 was spent on a gift and the remainder was spent on entertainment.

b Percentages (by mass) of ingredients I used to make concrete are given below.

Type of ingredient	Gravel	Sand	Cement
Percentage used	45	36	19

c The methods of travel to school of 90 students are given below.

Methods of travel	Bus	Car	Walk	Train
Number	40	22	20	8

d The table below gives the favourite swimming strokes of 80 swimmers.

Favourite stroke	Freestyle	Breaststroke	Backstroke	Butterfly
Number	40	20	14	6

The line graph

5 Draw a line graph for each of the following sets of data, referring to page 226 if necessary.

a While in hospital, Angelina's temperature was taken every 4 hours. The details are shown below. 37°C is normal temperature.

Time	4 pm	8 pm	12 am	4 am	8 am	12 pm	4 pm	8 pm
Temperature	39	39·6	40	39·2	38·4	37·8	37	37·2

b Using an electronic device, Tracey measured the distance of a penguin from its burrow. It would search for food in the ocean all day then return at night to the burrow to feed its young. The details are shown below for an 18-hour period.

Time	4 am	6 am	8 am	10 am	noon	2 pm	4 pm	6 pm	8 pm	10 pm
Distance	0	2 km	8 km	15 km	20 km	18 km	16 km	10 km	8 km	0

c At 7 pm Fred put the plug in the bath, turned on the water and let it run steadily for 6 minutes. He turned the tap off and then took 3 minutes to prepare to get into his bath. Before he got in the bath, the water was 15 cm deep. After he sat in the water, the depth was 18 cm. He bathed for 9 minutes before getting out of the bath. He immediately removed the plug, allowing the water to escape. The bath was empty in 3 minutes. Let each centimetre on the vertical axis represent 5 cm of water, and each centimetre on the horizontal axis represent 3 minutes.

The conversion graph

6 Use the fact that 0 kilograms = 0 pounds and 5 kg = 11 pounds to draw a conversion graph that converts between kilograms (kg) and pounds (lb).

7 The exchange rate between Russian rubles (RUB) and Chinese yuan renmimbi (CHY) is RUB 1 = CHY 0.30. Draw a conversion graph that converts up to RUB 100 into CHY.

The step graph

8 Draw a step graph to show the delivery charges for parcels shown below. If two charges are possible, the lower one is used.

Mass (kg)	0–5	5–10	10–20	20–30	30–40	40–50
Cost	$5.50	$7	$8.50	$10	$12.50	$15

9 Draw a step graph of these parking costs.

Time	Cost
1 hour or less	$10
More than 1 h and up to 2 h	$15
More than 2 h and up to 3 h	$20
More than 3 h and up to 4 h	$22
More than 4 h and up to 5 h	$25
More than 5 h	$27

These graphs could be easily drawn on 2 mm or 5 mm grid paper.

10 The cost of sending mail to my parents' home is given below. Draw a graph of this information.

Mass	Cost
Up to 20 g	$1.50
Over 20 g up to 50 g	$2.00
Over 50 g up to 100 g	$2.50
Over 100 g up to 250 g	$6.00
Over 250 g up to 500 g	$10.00

9:05 | Travel Graphs

- The travel graph is a line graph that relates distance and time.
- *Time* is shown on the horizontal axis and *distance from a particular place* is shown on the vertical axis.
- The steeper the graph, the greater the speed.
- If the graph is horizontal, the person has stopped. Speed is zero, as it is assumed that travel is along a straight road.

worked examples

Pascal travelled from Alicante to her home along the Western Highway. Her distance from Alicante as time passed is given by the graph. During the trip Pascal stopped for a while, then returned to Alicante, then travelled to her home where she arrived at 12 noon.

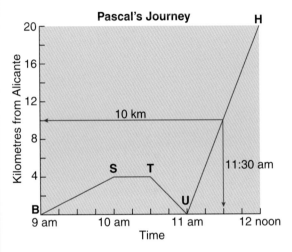

a Pascal travelled 4 km from Alicante (BS) before she stopped. She had travelled slowly (4 km/h), stopping at 10 am.

b She waited for half an hour (ST), then returned to Alicante more quickly than she had come away (TU).

c She then, very quickly (20 km in one hour) went home (UH) arriving at 12 noon.

Note:
- The distance from Alicante is shown on the vertical axis, so when Pascal reaches home (H) she is 20 km from Alicante.
- When the graph slopes up as time passes, Pascal is travelling away from Alicante. When the graph slopes down, Pascal is moving towards Alicante.
- The steeper the line the greater is her speed.
- When the line is horizontal she has stopped.
- She is 10 km from Alicante at 11:30 am.

It's cycle–logical!

$$\text{Speed} = \frac{\text{distance travelled}}{\text{time taken}} \qquad S = \frac{D}{T} \qquad \begin{array}{l} T = \dfrac{D}{S} \\[2mm] D = S \times T \end{array}$$

Exercise 9:05

Foundation Worksheet 9:05

1

Luke's Journey Home

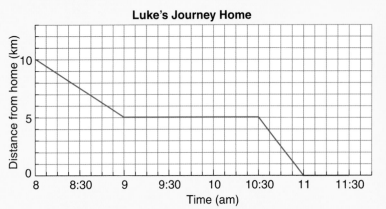

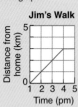

Jim's Walk

How far from home was Jim at:
a 2 pm?   **b** 3 pm?   **c** 4 pm?
d 5 pm?   **e** 1 pm?
At what time was Jim:
f 2 km from home?

How far from home was Luke at:

a 8 am?   **b** 9 am?   **c** 10 am?   **d** 11 am?
e 9:30 am?   **f** 11:30 am?   **g** 10:30 am?   **h** 8:30 am?

During what times was Luke:

i resting (or stationary)?   **j** travelling towards home?

2

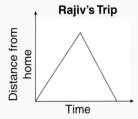

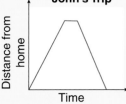

From these three graphs:
a who did not rest?   **b** who did not start from home?

3 Alana left home at 5 am and travelled out
of town by bicycle until it got a flat tyre.
She had to push the bike to her uncle's
home, which she reached at 8 am.
How far from the school is:

a Alana's home?   **b** her uncle's home?

How far did Alana travel between:

c 5 am and 6 am?   **d** 6 am and 8 am?

e Was Alana travelling faster between 5 am
and 6 am or between 6 am and 8 am?

f When did Alana's bicycle get a flat tyre?

g How far did Alana travel altogether?

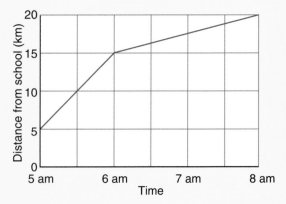

4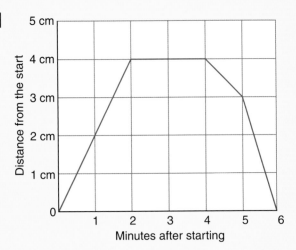

We placed a snail at one end of a 5 cm long stick. This graph shows the progress of the snail. How far from the start was the snail after:

a 2 minutes? **b** 4 minutes?
c 1 minute? **d** 6 minutes?

When was the snail:

e 3 cm from the start?
f 4 cm from the start?
g not moving?

How far did the snail travel:

h in the first minute?
i in the first 6 minutes?
j in the sixth minute?

5 Eun Sung and Thao are competing in a 40-km bicycle race over rough country.

a How far did Thao travel in the first 2 hours? What was her speed?

b How far did Eun Sung travel in the first 2 hours? What was his speed?

c When did Thao have an accident? How long did it take her to fix her bicycle? What was her speed in the last 5 hours?

d Who won the race? How long afterwards did the second person finish?

e How many hours after the start (to the nearest half hour) did Eun Sung pass Thao?

6 Draw a travel graph to describe this story. The hare and the tortoise agreed to race over 4 km. In the first $\frac{1}{2}$ hour, the tortoise travelled 500 m. It continued at this speed until it had finished the race. The hare, who had run 2 km in the first $\frac{1}{2}$ hour, looked back and couldn't see the tortoise so it sat down to rest and fell asleep. It woke up just as the tortoise crossed the finish line.

a What was the tortoise's average speed and when did it pass the hare?

b What was the hare's average speed:

  i in the first $\frac{1}{2}$ hour?   **ii** in the first 4 hours?

9:06 | Reading Tables

The ability to read tables is an important skill which you will use often. Tables are used to inform, and to record information. You have already been asked to read tables in books 1 and 2, and you will meet even more in books 3 and 4. As you examine the tables you meet, ask:

They said to use a table to find when the tide changes.

- Is this information interesting or unusual?
- Why is the writer using a table and why is the information being given?
- What questions can I think of that relate to this information? eg Why are these results occurring? What is the likely cause of trends?
- Can I use information in the table to solve the problems presented?

Applications of Tables

- Weather records, such as temperature, rainfall, air pressure, wind speed, humidity.
- Conversion tables, eg for foreign currency, garment sizes, times.
- Tables in the community, eg of STD charges, postal charges, bus and train timetables, cookbooks, tidal information.

Types of data

A Quantitative Data

- Numerical categories are used. This data tells you *how much*.
- Quantitative data is either *discrete* or *continuous*.

   Discrete quantitative data uses separate ordered numerical data. An example is the *number of goals scored*. Here $2\frac{1}{2}$ goals is not possible. Only whole goals can be scored.

   Continuous quantitative data could use any numerical value within a certain range. Examples include *height, distance travelled, time taken* and *mass*.

B Categorical Data

- Non-numerical categories are usually used. Each bit of data fits into a category.
- Examples of categorical data include *gender* (male or female), *quality* (poor, average, good or excellent), *country*, and *animal type*.

1·6 m
1·4 m
1·2 m

Exercise 9:06

1 For each type of data listed say whether it is discrete quantitative, continuous quantitative or categorical data.

- religion
- distance
- number of shirts made
- amount of water used
- cost
- mass
- test mark
- depth of water
- time
- country of birth

2 This information has been presented in table form so that it can be easily read.

When Do You Eat Your Evening Meal?

Time	Total per cent	Blue collar	White collar	Retired	Student	Unemp.	Washing-ton	San Diego
Before 5:29 pm	5	4	1	13	7	6	5	3
5:30 to 5:59 pm	8	8	3	17	2	19	6	10
6 to 6:29 pm	28	31	21	28	13	15	25	30
6:30 to 6:59 pm	24	28	25	17	27	27	21	25
7 to 7:29 pm	18	16	24	15	20	27	17	18
7:30 to 7:59 pm	7	5	13	2	13	—	13	7
8 to 8:29 pm	4	3	6	3	13	—	5	2
8:30 to 8:59 pm	1	1	2	1	—	—	2	2
9 to 9:29 pm	1	—	1	—	—	6	1	1
9:30 to 9:59 pm	1	1	1	1	3	—	1	—
10 pm or later	—	—	—	—	—	—	1	—
No answer	3	3	3	3	3	—	3	2
Average time (pm)	6:21	6:16	6:37	6:02	6:40	6:29	6:25	6:18

Do You Watch Television with Dinner?

	Total	Blue collar	White collar	Retired	Student	Unemp.	18–24	25–54	55+
Usually	47	49	44	50	32	72	51	43	55
Sometimes	22	25	26	12	16	5	18	28	13
Seldom	12	12	14	7	27	7	14	13	9
Never	18	13	16	30	25	16	17	16	23
Don't know	1	—	1	1	—	—	1	—	1

a For the total population, which was the most popular time category for eating the evening meal?

b Do people in San Diego tend to eat their evening meal earlier or later than people in Washington? Why would this be so?

c Which category of people tended to eat their meals earlier than any other category? Why do you think this might be so?

d What percentage of students ate their meal between 5:30 pm and 5:59 pm?

e What percentage of people in San Diego ate their evening meal between 6 pm and 7:30 pm?

f What percentage of the total usually watch television as they eat dinner?

g What harmful effects might watching television with meals have on family life?

h Which group tends least of all to watch television with meals?

i Examine both tables closely and write down four interesting observations, giving possible reasons for each if you can.

j Would choices from the responses *usually*, *sometimes*, *seldom*, *never* or *don't know* be quantitative or categorical data?

3 A thermometer that shows both Celsius and Fahrenheit readings is a conversion table.

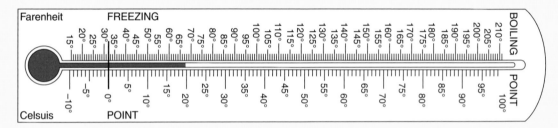

a Use the thermometer above to give (to the nearest degree) the Celsius temperature equivalent to:
  i 200° Fahrenheit
  ii 162° Fahrenheit
  iii 74° Fahrenheit
  iv 36° Fahrenheit

b Give the Fahrenheit temperature (to the nearest degree) equivalent to:
  i 0° Celsius
  ii 100° Celsius
  iii 37° Celsius
  iv 22° Celsius

c Does the thermometer record data that is:
  i quantitative or categorical?
  ii discrete or continuous?

4 The top ten batsmen in World Test Cricket as of March 2006 are given in the table below.

Batsman	Country	Test matches	Innings	Not outs	Runs	High score	Average	100s	50s
B C Lara	West Indies	121	214	6	11 204	400*	53.87	31	46
A R Border	Australia	156	265	44	11 174	205	50.56	27	63
S R Waugh	Australia	168	260	46	10 927	200	51.06	32	50
S R Tendulkar	India	129	206	21	10 386	248*	56.14	35	41
S M Gavaskar	India	125	214	16	10 122	236*	51.12	34	45
G A Gooch	England	118	215	6	8900	333	42.58	20	46
Javed Miandad	Pakistan	124	189	21	8832	280*	52.57	23	43
I V A Richards	West Indies	121	182	12	8540	291	50.24	24	45
A J Stewart	England	133	235	21	8463	190	39.55	15	45
R T Ponting	Australia	100	166	23	8253	257	57.71	28	32

* indicates 'not out'.

a What criterion has been used to rank the batsmen?
b Which batsman has the highest average?
c The statistics for Sir Garfield Sobers are:

Tests	Innings	Not outs	Runs	HS	50	100	Average
93	160	21	8032	365*	30	26	57.78

How would you rank his performance with those in the table above?
d In what percentage of his times at bat (Innings) did Sir Garfield Sobers score 50 runs or more?
e If the batsmen in the table were ranked according to average, who would the top three batsmen be?
f Sir Donald Bradman is regarded as the greatest batsman of all time yet he is not on the top ten list. His career figures were:

Tests	Innings	Not outs	Runs	HS	50	100	Average
52	80	10	6996	334	13	29	99·94

If Sir Donald had batted as many times as Alan Border (ie they had the same number of Innings), estimate how many runs he would have scored.

• Brian Lara

Population of Costa Rica by Province

	Alajuela	Cartago	Guanacaste	Heredia	Limón	Puntarenas	San José
1844	12 600	21 600	8 200	16 700	1 500	2 800	28 900
1883	53 100	35 600	17 200	31 100	3 400	8 100	65 300
1914	100 000	64 000	38 000	45 000	24 000	21 000	128 000
1927	97 600	70 200	51 100	38 400	32 300	28 700	153 200
1944	152 700	109 400	87 100	54 000	39 400	47 800	235 600

a Do you think that these figures are exact, or rounded off?
b By how much did the population of Cartago grow from 1844 to 1914?
c Which provinces had a population decline in the years shown?
d Which province has had the greatest population throughout these records? Why do you think this is so?
e By how much is the population figure for Cartago in 1883 greater than the figure for Puntarenas in 1883?
f Is the data given for the population of Costa Rica quantitative or categorical? Is it discrete or continuous?

6 The Central Division is one of three divisions that compete for the National Baseball League Pennant. Statistics for the Central Division of the National Baseball League (USA) are given in the following table.

	First season	No of seasons	No of playoff appearances	No of National League Pennants	Year of first Pennant
St Louis Cardinals	1900	106	20	16	1926
Houston Astros	1965	41	8	0	0
Milwaukee Brewers	1970	36	2	1	0
Chicago Cubs	1903	103	14	10	1906
Cincinnati Reds	1890	116	12	9	1919
Pittsburgh Pirates	1891	115	14	9	1901

a Which teams have played more than 100 seasons in the National League?
b Which team has won the most National League Pennants?
c In which season did the St Louis Cardinals first play?
d Which team has the best record for playoff appearances per season?
e Which team had to wait the least time to win a Pennant after joining the National League?
f For how many years did the Cincinnati Reds have to wait tow in their first Pennant?

7 These tables allow us to find the distance between two places and the cost of sending parcels over various distances. The coloured rectangle shows the distance between Lisbon and Prague.

Amsterdam

Distance Between Cities (km)

Amsterdam									
648	Berlin								
209	782	Brussels							
2300	3165	2080	Lisbon						
1782	2527	1562	638	Madrid					
876	604	811	2515	1877	Munich				
514	1094	294	1786	1268	827	Paris			
973	354	911	2945	2307	363	1094	Prague		
1835	1573	1615	2737	2099	969	1531	1370	Rome	
1196	666	1134	3255	2617	458	1285	312	1168	Vienna
861	863	641	2302	1664	313	557	676	986	784	Zurich

Cost of Sending Parcels by Courier in Europe €

Distance (km)	Mass (kg)							Each additional 10 kg or part thereof
	1–5	*6–10*	*11–15*	*16–20*	*21–30*	*31–40*	*41–50*	
0–500	24.50	27.50	30.50	33.50	37.00	42.00	47.00	6.00
501–1000	25.50	28.50	32.00	35.50	40.50	45.00	50.50	7.00
1001–2000	27.00	30.50	33.50	37.50	43.00	48.50	55.00	8.00
Over 2500	28.00	32.50	35.50	39.50	45.00	51.00	58.50	8.50

The coloured cell shows the cost of sending an article for a distance exceeding 2500 km if its mass is between 21 and 30 kg.

a Find the distance between Vienna and Madrid.

b Find the cost of sending a 16 kg parcel from Vienna to Madrid.

c What is the distance from:

    i Lisbon to Amsterdam?   **ii** Munich to Rome?

    iii Madrid to Brussels?   **iv** Prague to Berlin?

d Find the cost of sending a 7 kg parcel from Lisbon to Amsterdam.

e Find the cost of sending a 19 kg parcel from Munich to Rome.

f Find the cost of sending a 4 kg parcel from Madrid to Brussels.

g Find the cost of sending a 35 kg parcel from Prague to Berlin.

8 Almost 10% of Canada's population are of Asian origin. The following table shows the ethnic origin of Canada's Asian immigrants by province.

The Origin of Canada's Asian Immigrants by Province (%)									
	British Colombia	Alberta	Saskatchewan	Manitoba	Ontario	Quebec	New Brunswick	Nova Scotia	Prince Edward Is.	Newfoundland
Chinese	47.5	39.7	42.5	20.2	34.0	30.1	41.1	35.3	41.3	38.3
East Indian	23.3	22.5	14.9	17.2	27.1	16.3	26.1	27.5	18.3	32.5
Filipino	8.8	13.3	15.0	44.9	10.8	9.4	7.8	7.5	6.4	11.7
Vietnamese	3.5	7.9	8.6	5.3	4.4	11.1	4.6	7.6	3.7	2.4
Korean	4.1	2.9	3.0	1.6	3.6	2.1	1.5	4.9	–	2.9
Japanese	4.7	4.4	2.9	2.7	1.9	1.5	4.5	5.2	14.7	2.2
Pakistani	0.8	2.0	2.3	0.8	3.5	3.8	1.4	2.9	–	1.0
Sri Lankan	0.3	0.4	0.5	0.6	3.2	4.1	2.0	1.6	–	1.9
Punjabi	2.1	1.4	0.9	0.9	1.6	1.0	1.8	0.3	2.8	–
Tamil	0.2	0.1	0.1	0.1	2.3	1.4	–	0.1	–	0.5
Other Asian*	4.8	5.4	9.5	5.6	7.8	16.7	9.1	7.1	12.8	6.4

* Other Asian includes: Afghan, Pashtun, Bangladeshi, Bengali, Burmese, Cambodian, East Indian, Goan, Gujarati, Hmong, Indonesian, Kashmiri, Khmer, Laotian, Malaysian, Mongolian, Nepali, Sinhalese, Taiwanese, Thai and Tibetan.

a What percentage of Canada's Asian population come from China in:
  i Alberta?   **ii** Quebec?   **iii** Newfoundland?
b Apart from China, which is the most common origin of Canada's Asian population in:
  i Saskatchewan?   **ii** Manitoba?   **iii** Quebec?
c In which province was the percentage highest for those who were:
  i Filipino?   **ii** Vietnamese?   **iii** Korean?   **iv** Japanese?
  v Pakistani?   **vi** Pujabi?   **vii** Sri Lankan?   **viii** Tamil?
d What does the * denote?

9:07 | Misuse of Graphs

Because graphs and tables are based on information gathered and not on opinion, people tend to believe the impressions they give. Dishonest people, therefore, often try to mislead people by misusing statistics. Others, through carelessness, can give a false impression.

Ask: **'How was the information collected?'**
'Was it a biased sample?'
'Is all the information reported or just what favoured one point of view?'
'Have the graphs been drawn so as to mislead or confuse?'

In the following exercise you will see some common ways of drawing graphs that may be used to deceive. (Sometimes the use of these techniques might be reasonable, but if they give a false impression we must ask why the graph was drawn.)

Exercise 9:07

Using area or volume will mislead when only height is intended.

1

Boxit's Production of Boxes 2001–2003

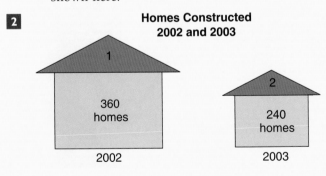

a How many times greater is the height of box 2 than the height of box 1?
b How many times greater is the area of box 2 than the area of box 1?
c How many times greater is the volume of box 2 than the volume of box 1?
d How many times greater is the height of box 3 than the height of box 1?
e How many times greater is the area of box 3 than the area of box 1?
f How many times greater is the volume of box 3 than the volume of box 1?
g Draw a column graph using simple columns of equal width to represent the information shown here.

> • Box 2 is meant to represent twice what box 1 represents, but it appears to be 8 times as big.
> • Box 3 is meant to represent 3 times what box 1 represents, but it appears to be 27 times as big.

2

Homes Constructed 2002 and 2003

Here no axes are given, although the number of homes is given for each year.

a What fraction of the height of Figure 1 is the height of Figure 2?
b What fraction of the number of homes constructed in 2002 is the number constructed in 2003?
c The area of Figure 2 is $\frac{4}{9}$ of the area of Figure 1. Would this graph tend to give a false impression?
d Draw a column graph to correctly represent this information.

The choice of scales will determine the appearance of a line graph.

3 The same information is represented in all three of these graphs.

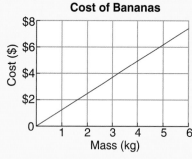

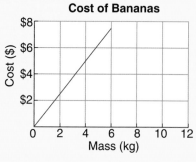

Here, the scale on the horizontal axis is different.

■ *Warning!* Irregular scales

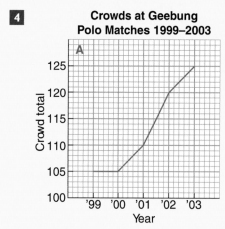

a Use the graphs to find the cost of 4 kg of bananas.
b Do all three graphs show the same cost for 4 kg?
c Does each graph agree on the mass of bananas that could be bought for $7.50? What is this mass?
d If the graphs show the same information, why do they look different?

If an axis does not start from zero, or the zero is put in the wrong place, it can mislead people.

4

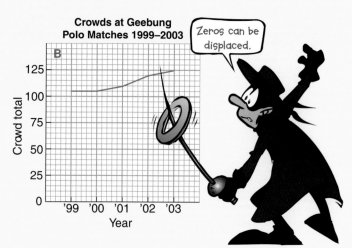

Zeros can be displaced.

a On graph A, at what number does the vertical axis start?
b On graph B, at what number does the vertical axis start?
c On graph A, what does one small unit on the vertical axis represent?
d On graph B, what does one small unit on the vertical axis represent?
e Which graph suggests that the crowds are increasing rapidly?
f Do the graphs represent exactly the same information?

5 How do the following graphs mislead?

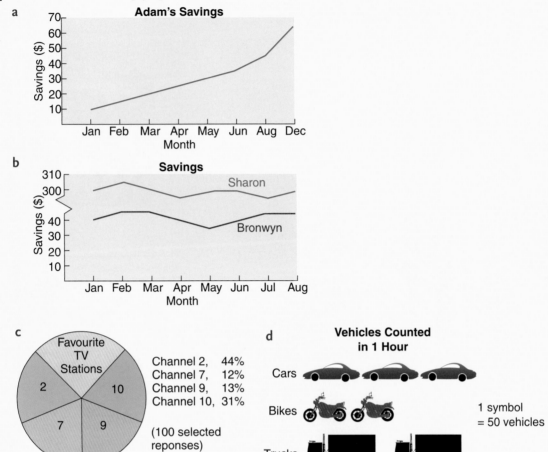

a Adam's Savings

b Savings

c Favourite TV Stations

Channel 2, 44%
Channel 7, 12%
Channel 9, 13%
Channel 10, 31%

(100 selected reponses)

d Vehicles Counted in 1 Hour

Cars
Bikes
Trucks

1 symbol = 50 vehicles

e Sales of Suntan Oil

f Wool Exports from Australia

Wool for Europe 27%
Wool for China 15%
Wool not exported 5%

Percentage of total wool clip

6 What is wrong with the following examples of collecting information?

a I phoned 1000 people and discovered that 92 per cent of people have a telephone.

b I interviewed 100 people who came out to Zac's Discount and found that 63 per cent of people use Zac's Toothpaste.

c I interviewed three people and found that 100 per cent of people voted Liberal.

d I asked 50 people to answer Yes or No to the question 'Have you stopped insulting your neighbours?', and found that 80 per cent of people have stopped insulting their neighbours.

Fun Spot 9:07 | Anyone for tennis?

Six couples took part in a tennis tournament.

The husbands' names were:

Humberto   Duarte   Maureo   Ramiro   Justino   Mateus

The wives' names were:

Izabel   Morela   Yelena   Mirari   Aitana   Fia

Each of the wives came from a different town in Brazil. They were:

Sao Paulo   Rio de Janeiro   Recife   Campinas   Brasilia Belo Horizonte

Also, each wife had a different hair colour, namely:

black   brown   grey   red   blonde   white

Use the information given above and below to work out for each lady:

- the name of her husband
- her home town
- her hair colour.

We play tennis for the 'love' of it!

You should be able to find the husband's name, the home town, and the hair colour of each lady.

These doubles games took place:

- Humberto and Duarte played Aitana and Morela.
- Maureo and Ramiro played Yelena and Morela.
- The ladies with black and brown hair played Humberto and Maureo, then Ramiro and Duarte.

Then these singles games took place:

- Aitana played Maureo, Ramiro and Justino.
- The lady with grey hair played Izabel, Mirari and Fia.
- The lady from Belo Horizonte played Izabel, Yelena and Mirari.
- Izabel played the ladies with white and blonde hair.
- The lady from Rio de Janeiro played Humberto and Maureo.
- Duarte played Yelena and Fia.
- Maureo played Mirari and Fia.
- The lady from Recife played ladies with red and black hair.
- The lady from Campinas played the lady with grey hair.
- Mateus played the lady with black hair.
- Mirari played the lady with white hair.
- Justino played the lady from Belo Horizonte.
- Yelena played the lady from Recife.
- The lady from Belo Horizonte played the lady with white hair.
- The lady from Rio de Janeiro played Fia.
- Ramiro played the lady from Recife.
- The lady from Sao Paulo played the lady with red hair.
- Ramiro played the ladies from Campinas and Brasilia.

I'm glad I knew this!

Note: No married couple ever played in the same game!

Mathematical terms 9

axis (axes)
- A fixed line adopted for reference.
- Scales on the axes allow us to *read* the graph.

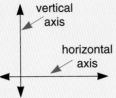

data
- The pieces of information to be examined.
- categorical: data that uses non-numerical categories.
  eg man, woman, boy, girl.
- quantitative: data that uses numbers to show *how much*.
  — *continuous* data can have any reasonable numerical value.
    eg height.
  — *discrete* data uses only some of the numerical values.
    eg age in years or number of points scored.

scale
- The value and size of units used on each axis.
- On the horizontal axis the scale might be 1 cm represents 1 hour.

table
- Information is often condensed and shown in table form.

title
- The name or heading of a graph.
- Each graph should be given a title that describes its content.

graphs
- column graphs
  The heights of columns are compared.

- conversion graph
  A line graph that allows us to change from one unit to another.

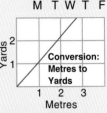

- divided bar graph
  A bar is divided to show the make up of the data.

- line graph
  A continuous line shows the connection between the variables.

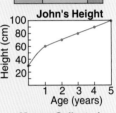

- picture graph
  A picture is used as a unit to show *how many*.

- sector graph
  A circle is cut into sectors to show the parts of a whole.

- step graph
  Several sections or *steps* are used. This line graph is not continuous.

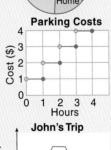

- travel graph
  This line graph relates distance and time to show progress on a trip.

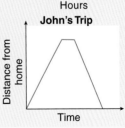

Mathematical terms 9

Diagnostic Test 9: | Graphs and Tables

- Each section of the test has similar items that test a certain type of question.
- Failure in more than one item will identify an area of weakness.
- Each weakness should be treated by going back to the section listed.

		Section
1 Draw a column graph to display the following data.		9:04A

Eastern US Stock of Adult and Juvenile Steller Sea Lions

Year	1980	1990	1991	1992	1994	1996
Number of Sea Lions (1000s)	110	31	29	27	24	22

2 Draw a divided bar graph to display the following information.   9:01A
                                                                       9:04B

Choice of Breakfast Cereal

Cereal	Vita Brits	Corn Flakes	Wheet Bix	Total
Number of students	50	120	30	200

3 Draw a sector graph (ie pie graph) to display the following information.   9:01B
                                                                                 9:04C

Choice of Flavours

Flavour	Strawberry	Chocolate	Vanilla	Others
Number of people	80	60	36	24

4 The temperature was measured in degrees Celsius every four hours.   9:01C
Draw a line graph to display the following information.   9:04D

Temperature Over a 24-hour Period

Time	mid-night	4 am	8 am	noon	4 pm	8 pm	mid-night
Temperature	15°C	12°C	16°C	19°C	20°C	18°C	16°C

5 Draw a conversion graph using the fact that: 9:01D
20 centimetres = 12·4 inches.   9:04E

6 Draw a step graph using the information: 9:01E
For up to one hour the cost is $6.   9:04F
For more than one hour and up to two, the cost is $10.
For more than two hours and up to three, the cost is $14.
For more than three hours the cost is $18.

7 Draw a travel graph to show Heather's journey.   9:05
She left home at 7 am to walk to Naomi's place, 10 km away.
After walking steadily for 2 hours she had covered 8 km.
She then stopped to rest for 30 minutes before continuing to
walk steadily for 1 more hour until she reached her goal.

Chapter 9 | Revision Assignment

1 On a number line, graph the set of counting numbers between 2 and 6.

2 Write these Roman numerals as basic numerals in our number system.
- **a** CXXIII
- **b** XLIV
- **c** MDCIX
- **d** MCMLXXXVIII

3 Simplify:
- **a** $7 \times 2 + 8 \times 10$
- **b** $14 - (15 - 1)$
- **c** $7 - 36 \div 4$
- **d** $100 \div (80 \div [20 - 16])$
- **e** $(7 \times 10\,000) + (2 \times 1000) + (1 \times 100) + (8 \times 10) + (5 \times 1)$

4
- **a** $\frac{7}{10} + \frac{9}{10}$
- **b** $\frac{3}{8} + \frac{2}{5}$
- **c** $\frac{9}{10} - \frac{1}{4}$
- **d** $\frac{3}{5} \times \frac{3}{4}$
- **e** $\frac{17}{100} \times \frac{1}{2}$
- **f** $4 \times \frac{3}{8}$
- **g** $\frac{9}{10} \div \frac{3}{4}$
- **h** $\frac{3}{4} \div 5$

5
- **a** $18 \cdot 65 + 4 \cdot 4$
- **b** $10 - 3 \cdot 15$
- **c** $41 \cdot 5 \div 100$
- **d** $1 \cdot 3 \times 0 \cdot 5$
- **e** $4 \cdot 5 \div 3$
- **f** $8 \cdot 26 \div 8$
- **g** $4 \cdot 6 \div 0 \cdot 02$
- **h** $(0 \cdot 05)^2$
- **i** Round off $0 \cdot \dot{6}$ correct to 2 decimal places.

6 Write as a percentage:
- **a** $\frac{3}{4}$
- **b** $1\frac{2}{5}$
- **c** $0 \cdot 145$
- **d** $2 \cdot 05$

7
- **a** Find 8% of $43 000.
- **b** Find 13% of 800 km.
- **c** Increase $1600 by 5%.
- **d** Decrease $1680 by 5%.
- **e** 20% of my wages is $130. How much are my wages?

8 Use a scale drawing to find the value of each pronumeral, correct to 1 decimal place.

a

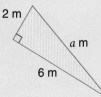

b

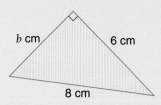

9 Simplify:
- **a** $8x + 3x$
- **b** $10a - 9a$
- **c** $3x^2 + 5x^2$
- **d** $6m - m$
- **e** $10 \times 4y$
- **f** $20b \div 2$
- **g** $\frac{1}{4} \times 16a$
- **h** $2a \times 7b$
- **i** $\frac{x}{5} + \frac{x}{5}$
- **j** $\frac{15m}{20} - \frac{2m}{20}$
- **k** $\frac{2x}{7} \times \frac{y}{5}$
- **l** $\frac{m}{4} \div \frac{m}{5}$

10 a Of 200 tickets sold in a raffle, Rachel bought 10, Naomi bought 8 and Ben bought 2. A ticket was chosen at random to determine who won the prize. What is the probability that the prize will be won by:

   i Rachel?   **ii** Naomi?   **iii** Ben?

b The chance of our boat sinking as we cross the river is $\frac{3}{20}$. What is the chance that our boat will not sink?

c Find the value of each pronumeral giving a reason for your answer.

  i

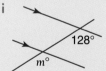

  ii

  iii

9B

Chapter 9 | Thinking Mathematically

1 Tom is eight years older than Clare. The sum of their ages is 54. How old is Tom?

2 Pirate Pete was drawing up a treasure map.
   a He arrived at X after walking 20 m north, then 30 m east, then 30 m south, then 10 m east and then 30 m north. From which point did he start?

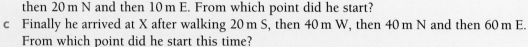

   b Later he arrived at X after walking 40 m E, then 10 m S, then 20 m W, then 20 m N and then 10 m E. From which point did he start?
   c Finally he arrived at X after walking 20 m S, then 40 m W, then 40 m N and then 60 m E. From which point did he start this time?

3 What six coins could be used to give a total of $3.40? Give two solutions.

4 Danny placed three of his building blocks in a row on the floor with ends touching.
   a How many of the faces would be visible?
   b How many faces would not be visible?
   c How many faces would be visible if there were 70 blocks?
   d How many faces would not be visible if there were 100 blocks?

5 A farmer has chickens and horses. If there are 16 heads and 40 legs on these altogether, how many horses are there?

 6 Use ID Card 4 on page xvi to identify:
   a 7   b 9   c 11   d 12   e 18
   f 19   g 20   h 21   i 22   j 23

9

 1 Types of graphs

10
Reasoning in Geometry

Chapter Contents

Learning Outcomes

Students will be able to:

- Identify and name angles formed by the intersection of straight lines, including those related to transversals on sets of parallel lines, and make use of the relationships between them.
- Classify, construct, and determine the properties of triangles and quadrilaterals.

Areas of Interaction

Approaches to Learning (Knowledge Acquisition, Problem Solving, Thinking Skills, Reflection Skills),Environments, Human Ingenuity

10:01 | Adjacent Angles

Last year many basic geometrical facts were discovered. These facts and others will be used to develop logical reasoning. It is important therefore that you revise past work.

Refer to Geometry ID Card 6 on page xviii. Identify (1) to (15).
Learn the terms you do not know.

prep quiz

1 What is the size of a right angle?

2 $30 + m = 90$. Find the value of m.

3 $x + 42 = 90$. Find the value of x.

4 What is the size of a straight angle?

5 $a + 50 = 180$. Find the value of a.

6 $135 + b = 180$. Find the value of b.

7

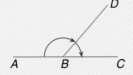

In the figure, $\angle ABC$ is a straight angle. What can you say about $\angle ABD + \angle DBC$?

8

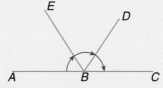

In the figure, $\angle ABC$ is a straight angle. What can you say about $\angle ABE + \angle EBD + \angle DBC$?

9

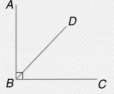

In the figure, $\angle ABC$ is a right angle. What can you say about $\angle ABD + \angle DBC$?

10

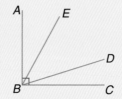

In the figure, $\angle ABC$ is a right angle. What can you say about $\angle ABE + \angle EBD + \angle DBC$?

The Prep Quiz illustrates two important basic facts.

> **1** If two adjacent angles make a right angle, then the sum of these angles is 90°.
> **2** If two adjacent angles make a straight angle, then the sum of these angles is 180°.

worked examples

Find the value of the pronumeral in each of the following, giving a reason for your answer.

1

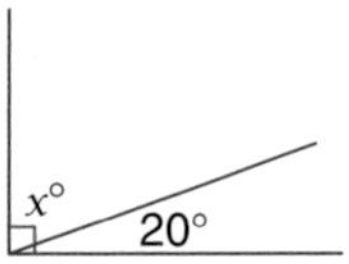

2

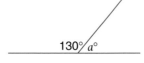

3

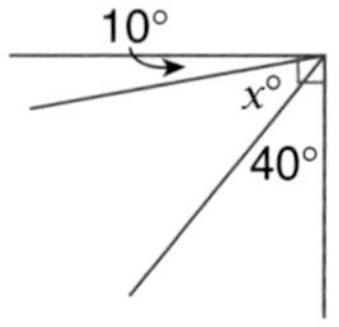

Solutions

1 $x + 20 = 90$ (adj. comp. $\angle$s)
   $\therefore x = 70$ or
       ($\angle$s make a right angle)

2 $a + 130 = 180$ (adj. supp. $\angle$s)
       $a = 50$ or
        ($\angle$s make a str. $\angle$)

3 $10 + x + 40 = 90$ (adj. comp. $\angle$s)
        $x = 40$

Word	Abbreviation
adjacent	adj.
angles	$\angle$s
complementary	comp.
supplementary	supp.
straight	str.
point	pt

Reasons are written using *abbreviations*.

Exercise 10:01

1 Write down the value of the pronumeral in each of the following.

a
20° 15° $x°$

b
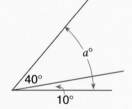
$a°$ 40° 10°

c

24° 21° $x°$

d
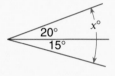
35° 20° $x°$

e
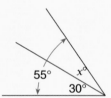
55° 30° $x°$

f
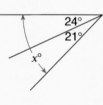
$a°$ 50° 90°

g
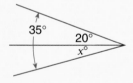
$a°$ 50° 80°

h
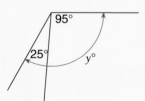
95° 25° $y°$

i
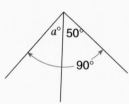
60° 65° $p°$

j
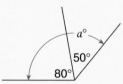
150° $a°$ 95°

k
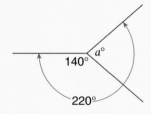
140° $a°$ 220°

l
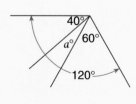
40° 60° $a°$ 120°

2 Find the value of the pronumeral in each of the following. Give a reason for your answer.

a

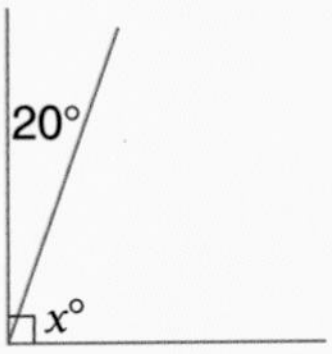

20°

$x°$

b

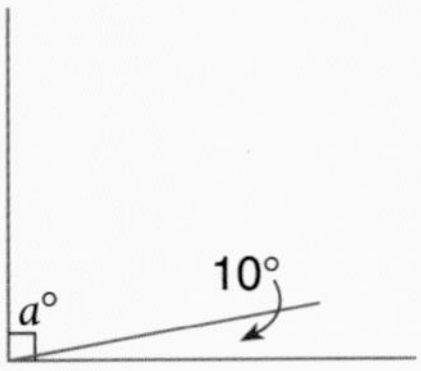

$a°$ 10°

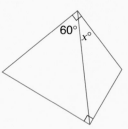

You should be able to fly through these!

c

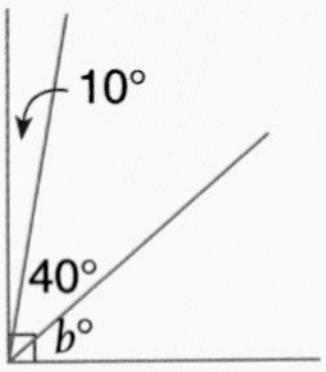

10°

40°

$b°$

d

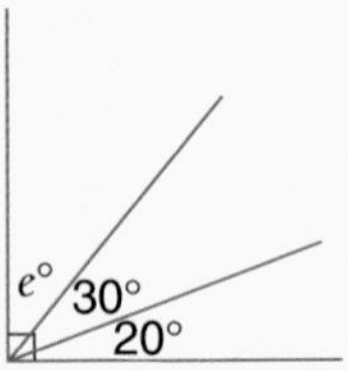

$e°$ 30°

20°

e

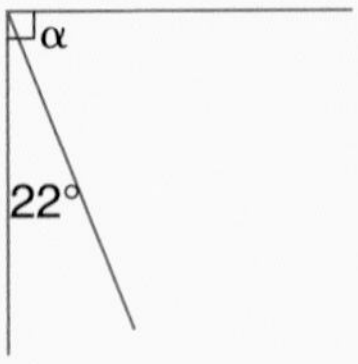

α

22°

f

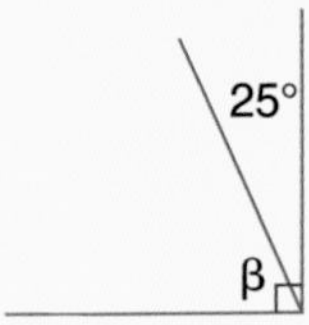

25°

β

g

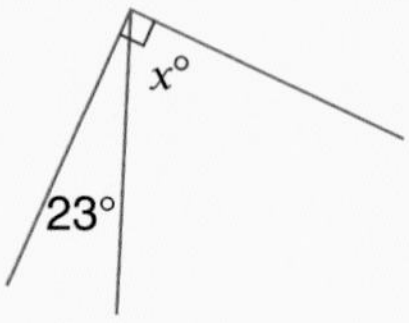

$x°$

23°

h

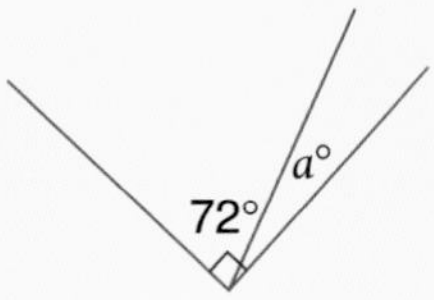

$a°$

72°

i

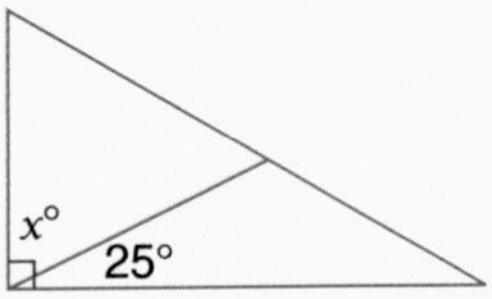

$x°$

25°

j

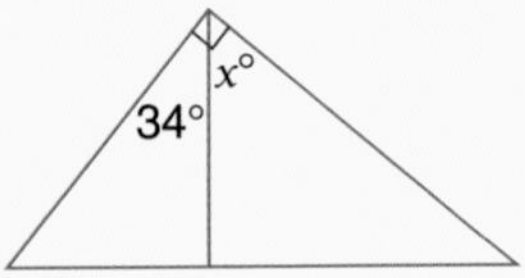

$x°$

34°

k

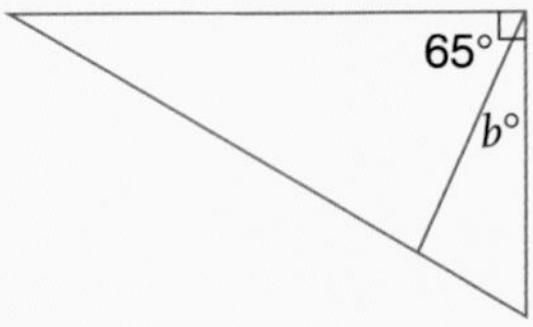

65°

$b°$

l

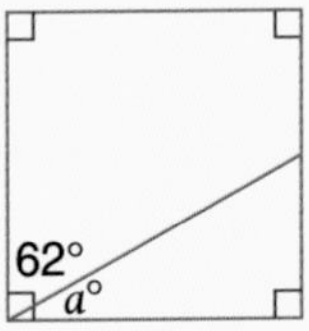

62°

$a°$

m

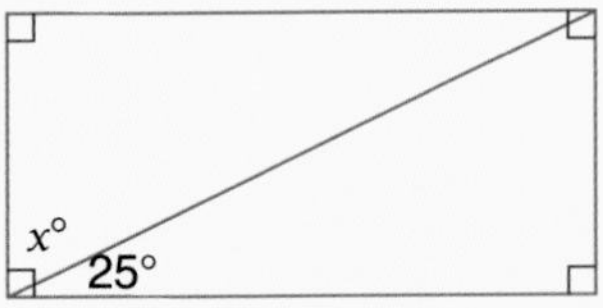

$x°$

25°

n

60°

$x°$

3 Find the value of the pronumeral in each of the following. Give a reason for your answer.

Are you sailing through these questions?

a

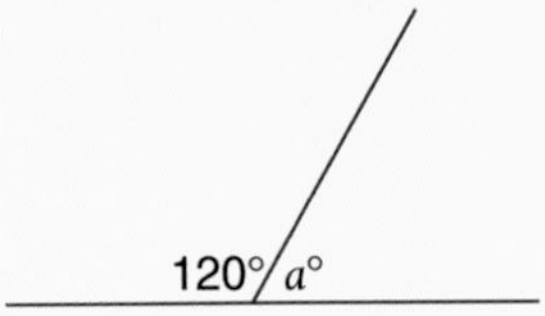

120° $a°$

b

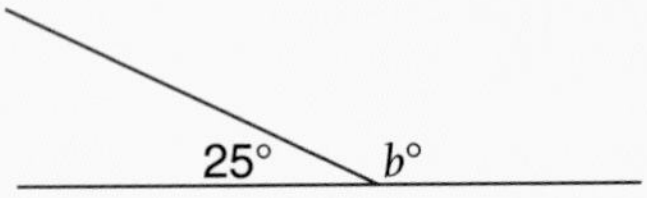

25° $b°$

c

d

e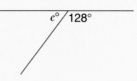

f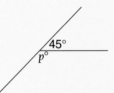

g

h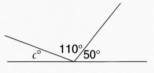

i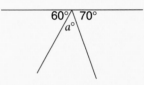

j

k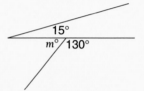

l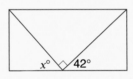

m

n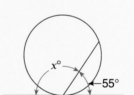

4 α (alpha) and β (beta) are Greek letters that stand for the measure of an angle. Write an equation for each of the following and solve it to find the values of α and β.

a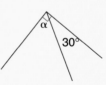

b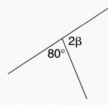

c

d

e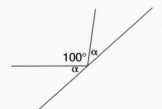

f

10:02 | Angles at a Point and Vertically Opposite Angles

 The Greek letters α, β, γ, δ and θ are used to stand for the *measure* or *size* of an angle.
• This means that the *degrees* symbol is not used with them.

Angles at a point

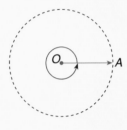

Figure 1

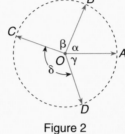

Figure 2

Here the arm *OA* can move around the fixed point *O*.

In Figure 1 the arm *OA* completes one revolution and so moves through an angle of 360°.

In Figure 2 the arm *OA* stops at *B*, *C* and *D* before continuing to its starting position. Despite these stops the arm *OA* has still completed one revolution.

Hence we can see that:

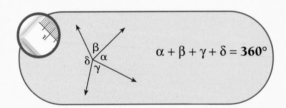

$$\alpha + \beta + \gamma + \delta = 360°$$

I hope you see the point!

Vertically opposite angles

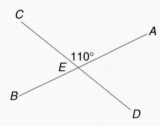

AB and *CD* are straight lines and $\angle CEA = 110°$. Using the knowledge gained in the last section, we can calculate the size of the other three angles.

By progressively covering up each of the arms *ED*, *AE*, *CE* and *BE*, we get the series of diagrams below. Each of these diagrams shows a pair of adjacent supplementary angles.

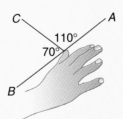

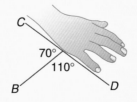

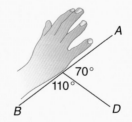

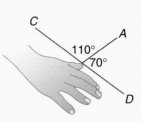

- Putting these results together, we can see that when two lines cross, two pairs of equal angles are formed. These angles, which are opposite each other, are called **vertically opposite angles**.

Two pairs of equal angles! That should be handy.

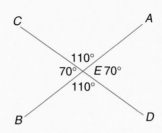

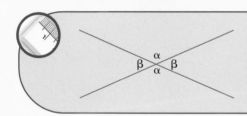

When two straight lines cross, two pairs of vertically opposite angles are formed. Vertically opposite angles are equal.

worked examples

Find the values of the pronumerals in each of the following.

1

2
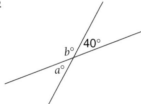

3
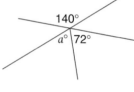

Solutions

1 $x + 140 + 125 = 360$
($\angle$s at a pt)
$\therefore x = 95$

2 $a = 40$ (vert. opp. $\angle$s)
$b + 40 = 180$ (adj. supp. $\angle$s)
$\therefore b = 140$

3 $a + 72 = 140$
(vert. opp. $\angle$s)
$\therefore a = 68$

Exercise 10:02

1 Find the value of the pronumeral in each of the following. Give reasons for your answers.

a
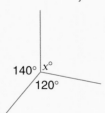

b
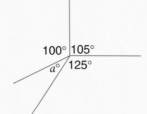

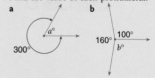

c

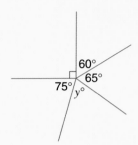

d

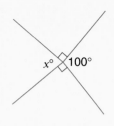

How can I worm my way around these?

2 Find the value of the pronumeral in each of the following. Give reasons for your answers.

a

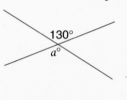

130°
a°

b

b°

25°

c

c° 100°

d

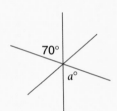

70°

a°

e

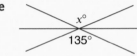

x°
135°

f

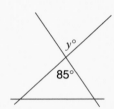

y°

85°

3 Find the values of the pronumerals in each of the following, giving reasons for your answers.

Use a ruler to check which sides are straight.

a

40°
70°
4α

b

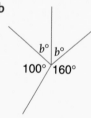

b° b°
100° 160°

c

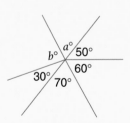

b° a° 50°
60°
30° 70°

d

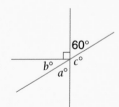

60°
b° c°
a°

e

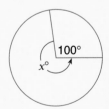

100°
x°

f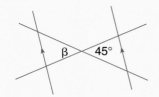

β   45°

g

2a°

100°

h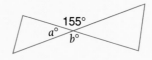

155°
a°
b°

i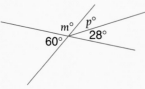

m° p°
60° 28°

j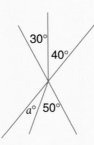

30°
40°

a° 50°

k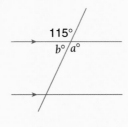

115°
b°/a°

4 Find the values of the pronumerals in each of the following, giving reasons for your answers.

a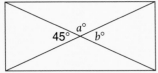

a°
45° b°

b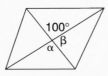

100°
β
α

c

α α
α α
α α

d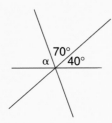

70°
α 40°

e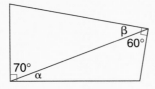

β
60°
70°
α

f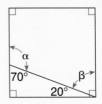

α
70°
β
20°

- What kind of angles are formed by the drumsticks?

10:03 | Angles Associated with Parallel Lines

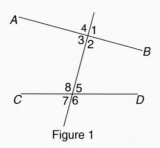

Figure 1

When two lines are cut by a third line (called a **transversal**), the eight angles shown in Figure 1 are formed. From what we have learned about vertically opposite angles, we can see that:

angle 1 = angle 3   angle 2 = angle 4

angle 5 = angle 7   angle 6 = angle 8

A model of this situation can be made from rulers or cardboard strips as shown.
- The rulers need to be pivoted at E and F.
- By moving the ruler AB into different positions, the relationships between the angles can be investigated.
- Of particular importance is the case when the lines AB and CD are parallel. When the lines are parallel, the angles that the lines make with the transversal are equal. This can be seen from the sequence of diagrams below.

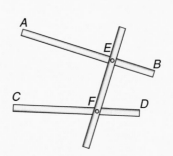

It should be easy to make one of these.

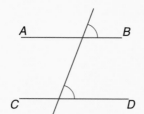		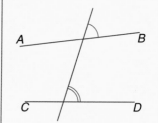
The top angle is bigger than the bottom angle. The lines will cross on the right of the transversal.	The top angle is equal to the bottom angle. The lines are parallel.	The top angle is smaller than the bottom angle. The lines cross on the left of the transversal.

Using the same notation as in Figure 1, we can see that when two parallel lines are cut by a transversal then:

angle 1 = angle 5   angle 4 = angle 8

angle 2 = angle 6   angle 3 = angle 7

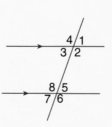

This means that:
- angles 1, 3, 5, 7 are equal; and
- angles 2, 4, 6, 8 are equal.

The special angle relationships that occur when two lines are parallel are set out in the following rule box.

What that says is that all the big angles are equal, and all the small angles are equal.

When a pair of parallel lines is cut by a transversal, four pairs of equal corresponding angles are formed.

When a pair of parallel lines is cut by a transversal, two pairs of equal *alternate* angles are formed.

When a pair of parallel lines is cut by a transversal, two pairs of *co-interior* angles are formed. Co-interior angles are supplementary.

worked examples

1 Copy the diagram and write in the values of all the other angles in the figure.

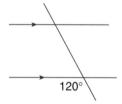

120°

2 Find the value of the pronumeral in each of the following, giving reasons for your answers.

a

a°
80°

b

b° 75°

c
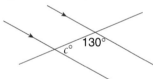
c° 130°

Solutions

1
60° \ 120°
120° \ 60°

60° \ 120°
120° \ 60°

Alternate angles (or 'Z' angles)

Corresponding angles (or 'F' angles)

Co-interior angles (or 'C' angles)

2 a
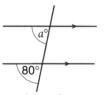
a°
80°

b

b° 75°

c
c° 130°

a = 80   (corres. ∠s and parallel lines)

b = 75   (alt. ∠s and parallel lines)

c = 50   (co-int. ∠s and parallel lines)

1 Copy each of the diagrams and then write down the sizes of all the angles.

a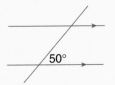

b

c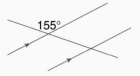

2 Copy each of the diagrams below and mark in the four pairs of equal corresponding angles using the symbols ●, ○, × and)).

a

b

c

3 Find the values of the pronumerals in each of the following, giving a reason for each answer.

a

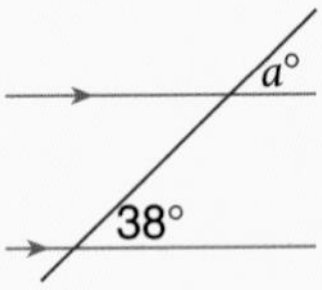

b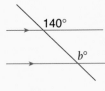

c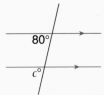

d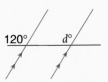

e

f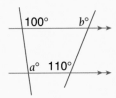

4 Copy each of the diagrams in Question **2** and mark in the two pairs of alternate angles, using the symbols × and ●.

5 Find the value of the pronumeral in each of the following, giving a reason for each answer.

a

b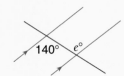

c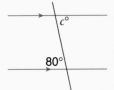

d

132° $f°$

e

$b°$ 42° $a°$ 83°

f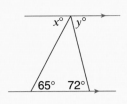

$x°$ $y°$ 65° 72°

6 Copy each of the diagrams in Question 2 and mark in the two pairs of co-interior angles.

7 Find the values of the pronumerals in each of the following, giving a reason for each answer.

'Interior' means 'inside'. I wonder why they're called co-interior angles?

a

$a°$ 60°

b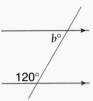

$b°$ 120°

c

35° $c°$

d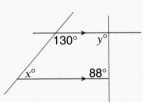

130° $y°$ $x°$ 88°

e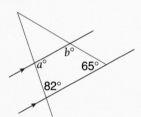

$a°$ $b°$ 65° 82°

8 Find the value of the pronumeral in each of the following. Give a reason for each answer.

a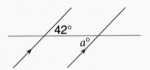

42° $a°$

b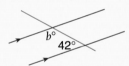

$b°$ 42°

c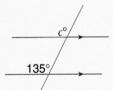

$c°$ 135°

d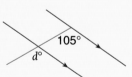

105° $d°$

e

68° $e°$

f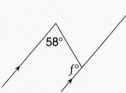

58° $f°$

g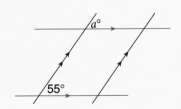

$a°$ 55°

h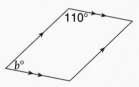

110° $b°$

i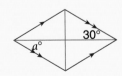

30° $a°$

9 Find the values of the pronumerals in each of the following. Give a reason for each answer.

a

b

Notice:
There may be
more than one
way to do these
questions.

c

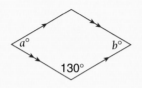

d

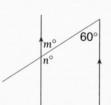

e

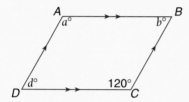

Parts **c** and **e** show this important fact:

 The opposite angles of a parallelogram are equal.

In the questions so far we have seen that if two lines are parallel, then corresponding angles are equal, alternate angles are equal, and co-interior angles are supplementary. The reverse is also true.

1 If corresponding angles are equal, *or*
2 if alternate angles are equal, *or*
3 if co-interior angles are supplementary, then the lines are parallel.

10 Give a reason why *AB // CD* in each case.

a

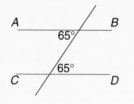

b

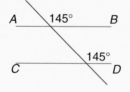

c

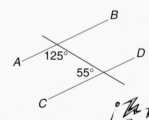

d

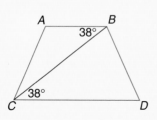

e

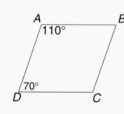

 The symbol
'//' means
'is parallel to'.

Fun Spot 10:03 | What did the canary say when its cage fell apart?

Answer each question and put the letter for that question in the box above the correct answer.

Find the value of the pronumeral in each of the following.

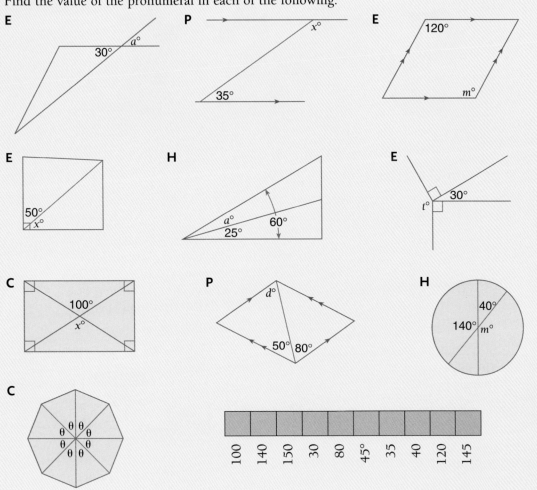

10:03 Angles in parallel lines

10:04 | Angle Sum of a Triangle

Last year you discovered that the angles of a triangle add up to 180°. This was done by cutting the angles of a triangle and rearranging them to form a straight angle.

The angle sum of a triangle

Using the work in this chapter, we can prove the result given above.

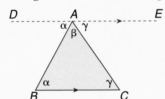

We want to prove that the angle sum of a triangle is 180°, ie $\alpha + \beta + \gamma = 180°$.

First we draw a line DE through A, parallel to BC.
$\angle BAD = \alpha$ (alternate to $\angle ABC$, DE // BC)
$\angle CAE = \gamma$ (alternate to $\angle ACB$, DE // BC)
Now $\alpha + \beta + \gamma = 180°$ ($\angle DAE$ is a straight angle)
∴ the angle sum of a triangle is 180°.

The angle sum of a triangle is 180°.
$\alpha + \beta + \gamma = \mathbf{180°}$

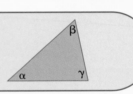

That means if you know two angles, you can work out the third.

The exterior angle of a triangle

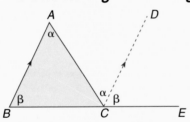

We want to find a relationship between the exterior angle ACE and others within the triangle.
First we draw a line CD through C, parallel to BA.
$\angle ACD = \alpha$ (alternate to $\angle BAC$, BA // CD)
$\angle DCE = \beta$ (corresponding to $\angle ABC$, BA // CD)
Now $\angle ACE = \alpha + \beta$ ($\angle ACE = \angle ACD + \angle DCE$)
∴ the exterior angle of a triangle is equal to the sum of the interior (or **remote**) opposite angles.

The exterior angle of a triangle is equal to the sum of the two remote interior angles.
$\gamma = \alpha + \beta$

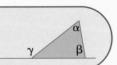

worked examples

Find the values of the pronumerals, giving reasons for your answers.

1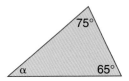

2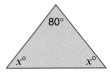

3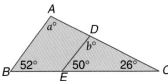

4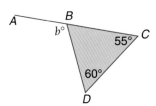

5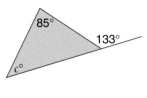

Solutions

1   $\alpha + 65° + 75° = 180°$
   (angle sum of a Δ)
       $\therefore \alpha = 40°$

2   $x + x + 80 = 180$
   (angle sum of a Δ)
   $\therefore 2x + 80 = 180$
       $\therefore 2x = 100$
         $\therefore x = 50$

3   $b + 50 + 26 = 180$
   (angle sum of ΔDEC)
       $\therefore b = 104$
   $a + 52 + 26 = 180$
   (angle sum of ΔABC)
       $\therefore a = 102$

4   $b = 55 + 60$
   (exterior angle of ΔBCD)
   $\therefore b = 115$

5   $c + 85 = 133$
   (exterior angle of a Δ)
     $\therefore c = 48$

Exercise 10:04

1 Find the value of the pronumeral in each of the following. Give a reason for each answer.

a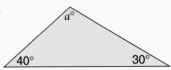

b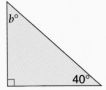

c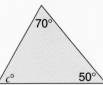

d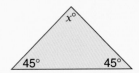

e

f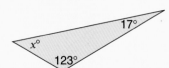

g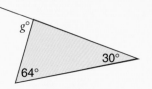

h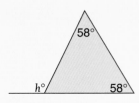

i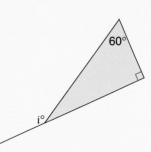

2 Write an equation for each of the following and solve it to find the value of the pronumeral.

a

b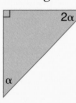

c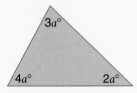

d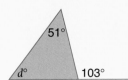

e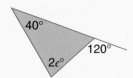

f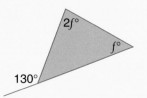

3 In each of the following there is more than one triangle. By finding the angle sum of the shaded triangle, find the value of the pronumeral.

a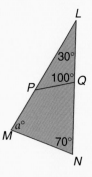

b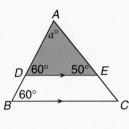

c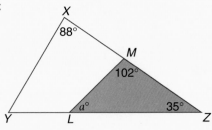

4 Examine each figure carefully and, by using the correct triangle, find the values of the pronumerals.

a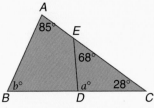

b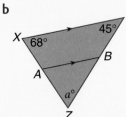

c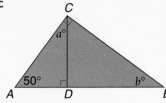

5 In each of the following find the value of x and then use this to find the value of y.
Give a reason for each statement in your answer.

a

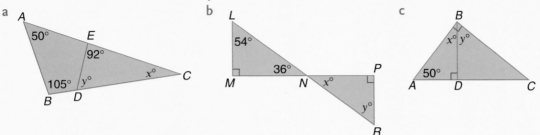

b

c

6 Find the values of the pronumerals in each of the following, giving reasons for your answers.

a

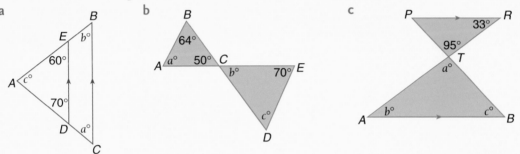

b

c

• Carpenters need an understanding of parallel lines in roof construction.

10:05 | Angle Sum of a Quadrilateral

In the last section we proved that the angles of a triangle have a sum of 180°.

Since all quadrilaterals can be divided into two triangles, we can conclude that the angle sum of a quadrilateral is $2 \times 180°$ or 360°.

In geometry, you continually build on previous knowledge.

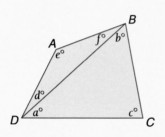

We want to prove that the angle sum of a quadrilateral is 360°.

$$\begin{aligned}
\text{Angle sum of } ABCD &= \angle DAB + \angle ABC + \angle BCD + \angle CDA \\
&= e + (f + b) + c + (a + d) \\
&= (a + b + c) + (d + e + f) \\
&= \begin{array}{c} \text{angle sum} \\ \text{of } \Delta DBC \end{array} + \begin{array}{c} \text{angle sum} \\ \text{of } \Delta DAB \end{array} \\
&= 180° + 180° \\
&= 360°
\end{aligned}$$

∴ the angle sum of a quadrilateral is 360°.

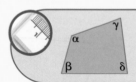

The angles of a quadrilateral add up to 360°.
∴ $\alpha + \beta + \gamma + \delta = 360°$

worked examples

Find the value of the pronumeral in each of the following.

1

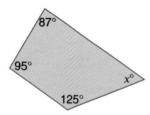

87°
95°
125°
$x°$

2

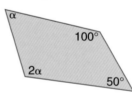

α
100°
2α
50°

Solutions

1   $x + 125 + 95 + 87 = 360$
    (angle sum of a quad.)
        ∴ $x + 307 = 360$
              ∴ $x = 53$

2   $2\alpha + \alpha + 100° + 50° = 360°$
    (angle sum of a quad.)
            ∴ $3\alpha + 150° = 360°$
                  ∴ $3\alpha = 210°$
                    ∴ $\alpha = 70°$

Exercise 10:05

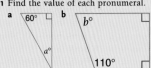

Foundation Worksheet 10:05

Triangles and quadrilaterals
1 Find the value of each pronumeral.

1 Find the value of the pronumeral in each of the following, giving a reason in each case.

a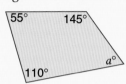

b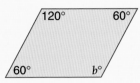

c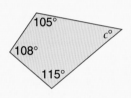

d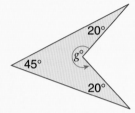

e

2 Write an equation for the angle sum of each of the following and then solve it to find the value of the pronumeral.

a

b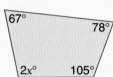

If you can solve equations, these questions are a piece of cake!

c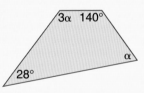

d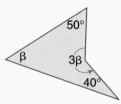

3 Use the angle sum of the quadrilateral *ABCD* to find the value of *x* and then find the value of *y*.

a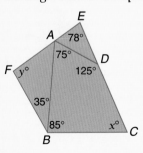

b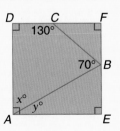

c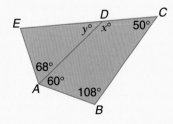

4 Find the values of the pronumerals in each of the following. Give reasons for your answers.

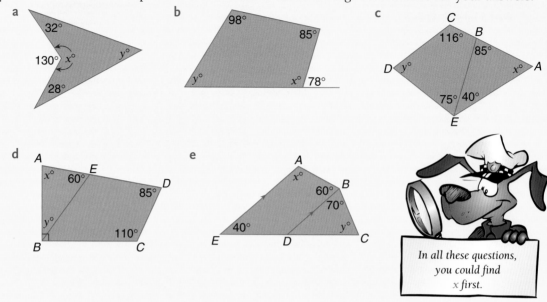

a

32°

130° x°

28°

y°

b

98°

85°

y°

x° 78°

c

C

116° B

85°

D y° A

75° 40°

E

d

A

x° 60° E

D

85°

y°

B 110° C

e

A

x°

60° B

70°

40°

E D y° C

In all these questions, you could find x first.

10:06 | Isosceles and Equilateral Triangles

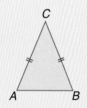

C

A B

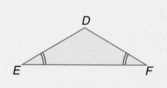

D

E F

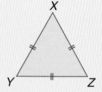

X

Y Z

1 Which of the triangles above are isosceles?
2 Which of the triangles above is equilateral?
3 In ΔABC, which angles are equal?
4 In ΔDEF, which sides are equal?

Complete the following:

5 'If a triangle has two sides equal, then it has …'
6 'If a triangle has two angles equal, then it has …'
7 'In ΔXYZ all angles are …'
8 'If a triangle has three equal angles, the sides are …'
9 'If a triangle has three sides equal, then its angles are …'
10 'If a triangle has three equal sides, then each of its angles will measure …'

My ladder forms an isosceles triangle. What other objects form isosceles triangles?

This Prep Quiz should have reminded you of some properties of isosceles and equilateral triangles.

worked examples

Find the values of the pronumerals in each of the following, giving reasons for your answers.

1

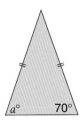

a°
70°

2

b°

3

x cm
80°
80°
7 cm

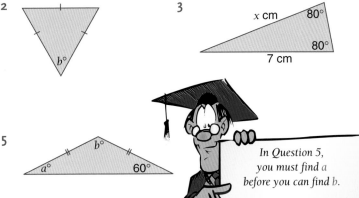

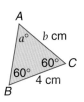

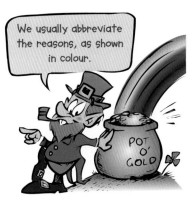

In Question 5, you must find a before you can find b.

4

A
a°
b cm
60°
C
60°
4 cm
B

5

b°
a°
60°

Solutions

1 $a = 70$
(equal angles of isosceles triangle)
(equal ∠s of isos. Δ)

2 $b = 60$
(angle of an equilateral triangle)
(∠ of equal. Δ)

3 $x = 7$
(equal sides of isosceles triangle)
(equal sides of isos. Δ)

4 $a + 60 + 60 = 180$
(angle sum of a triangle)
(∠ sum of Δ)
$\therefore a = 60$
$\therefore \Delta ABC$ is equilateral
$\therefore b = 4$
(sides of equilateral triangle)
(sides of equil. Δ)

5 $a = 40$
(equal ∠s of isos. Δ)
$a + b + 40 = 180$
(∠ sum of Δ)
$\therefore 40 + b + 40 = 180$
$b = 100$

We usually abbreviate the reasons, as shown in colour.
POT O' GOLD

Exercise 10:06

1 Find the values of the pronumerals, giving reasons for all answers.

a

33°
b°

b

c°
16 cm
28°
16 cm

c

70°
y m
70°
5·8 m

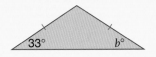

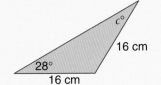

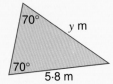

d

30°
4 cm
30°
$x°$
y cm

e

$a°$
x cm
$a°$
5 cm

f

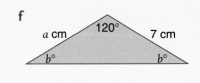

a cm
120°
7 cm
$b°$
$b°$

g

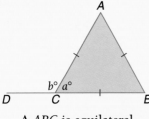

$a°$

h

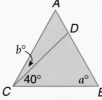

15 mm
$x°$
15 mm
15 mm

i

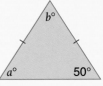

20 mm
60°
60°
y mm
z mm
60°

2 Find the value of a, then b, in each of the following. Give reasons for your answers.

a

70°
$a°$
$b°$

b

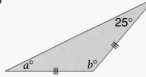

25°
$a°$
$b°$

c

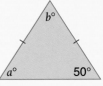

$b°$
$a°$
50°

3 Find the value of a, then b, in each of the following. Give reasons for your answers.

a

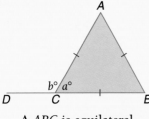

A
$b°$ $a°$
D   C   B

$\triangle ABC$ is equilateral.

b

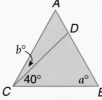

A
D
$b°$
40°
$a°$
C   B

$\triangle ABC$ is equilateral.

c

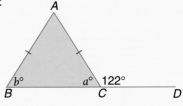

A
$b°$
$a°$ 122°
B   C   D

d

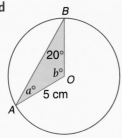

B
20°
$b°$
O
$a°$
5 cm
A

O is the centre of
the circle.

e

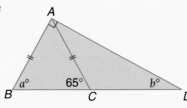

A
$a°$
65°
$b°$
B   C   D

f

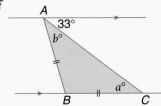

A
33°
$b°$
$a°$
B   C

10:07 | More Involved Numerical Problems

Many problems involve more than one step of reasoning. More than one geometrical fact may be used, or the same fact may be used in different situations.

Solving these geometry problems is going to require all my detective logic.

 When solving these problems, one must usually work backwards, asking questions such as:
1 What am I trying to find?
2 What information do I need to know to find it?
3 Can I find this other information by relating to it what I already know?

This approach is illustrated in the examples below.

worked examples

Find the values of the pronumerals, giving reasons for your answers.

1

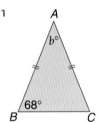

2

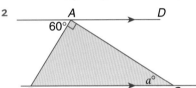

3

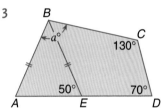

Solutions

1 $\angle ACB = 68°$
(equal $\angle$s of isos. Δ)
$\therefore b + 68 + 68 = 180$
(angle sum of Δ)
$\therefore b = 44$

2 $\angle ABC = 60°$
(alt. $\angle$s, $AD \parallel BC$)
$\therefore a + 60 + 90 = 180$
(angle sum of Δ)
$\therefore a = 30$

Now, number (1)...let's see. If I knew the 3rd angle, I'd add the 3 angles to give 180°... Ah! But the other angle is 68° because the triangle is isosceles...

THAT'S IT!

3 $\angle BAE = 50°$
(equal $\angle$s of isos. ΔBAE)
$\therefore a + 130 + 70 + 50 = 360$
(angle sum of quad.)
$\therefore a = 110$

1 Find the value of the pronumeral in each of the following, give reasons for your answers.

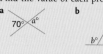

a

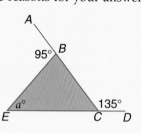

b

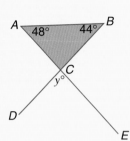

If you copy a diagram, you can do your working on it.

c

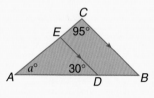

d

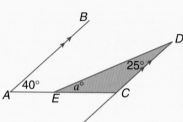

e

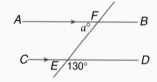

f

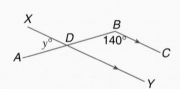

g

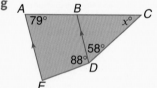

h

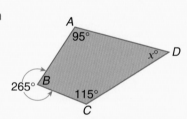

i

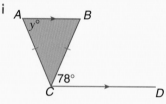

2 Find the values of the pronumerals in each of the following. Give reasons for your answers.

a

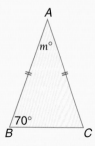

b

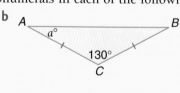

c

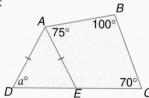

d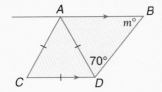

e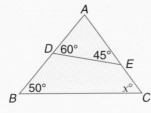

f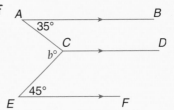

g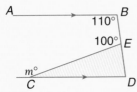

h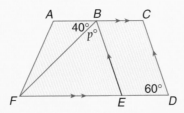

i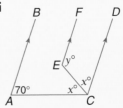

3 Find the value of the pronumeral in each of the following. Give reasons for your answers.

a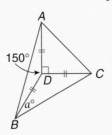

b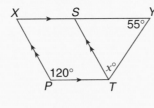

c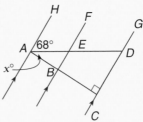

Appendix D D:01: Non-numerical geometrical reasoning (extension)

Challenge worksheet 10:07 The logical prisoner

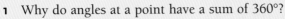

Reading mathematics 10:07 | Can you explain why?

A real test of your knowledge is to explain something in your own words.

For each part, read the explanation in this chapter and then try to explain it in your own words.

1   Why do angles at a point have a sum of 360°?
2   Why are vertically opposite angles equal?
3   Why are the opposite angles of a parallelogram equal?
4   Why is the angle sum of a triangle 180°?
5   Why is the exterior angle of a triangle equal to the sum of the two remote interior angles?
6   Why is the angle sum of a quadrilateral 360°?

Fun Spot 10:07 | Numbered boxes!

This is a variation on the well-known game of boxes.

Construct a lattice of dots as shown below and scatter numbers from 1 to 5 throughout the lattice.

You can make your grid as big or as small as you want.

```
. . . . . . . . . .
  2   2   3   1   2   5   1   4   2   3
. . . . . . . . . .
  3   5   2   4   5   4   2   3   5   4
. . . . . . . . . .
  5   3   1   4   1   5   1   4   3   1
. . . . . . . . . .
  3   2   4   1   2   3   5   4   2   2
. . . . . . . . . .
  4   1   5   2   3   4   5   1   5   3
. . . . . . . . . .
```

Players then take it in turns to join two dots together. If, when joining two dots, a square is completed, that player scores the points in that square and has another turn.

The game continues until all the squares, or boxes, have been formed. The points are then totalled and the player with the highest score wins.

A trickier game can be made by making some of the numbers negative.

```
.   .   .   .   .
  2   −1   3   2
.   .   .   .   .
  1   −5   4   −3
.   .   .   .   .
  −4   2   1   3
.   .   .   .   .
```

You must, of course, try to avoid the negative numbers.

- The front of this glockenspiel can be seen to be a transversal across parallel lines. What kind of angles are formed next to this transversal?

Mathematical terms 10

angles at a point
- The sum of all angles at a point is 360°.
$\alpha + \beta + \gamma = 360°$

angle sum
- Angle sum of a triangle is 180°.
- Angle sum of a quadrilateral is 360°.

isosceles triangle
- Two sides are equal.
- Base angles are equal.

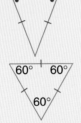

equilateral triangle
- All sides are equal.
- All angles are 60°.

exterior angle of a triangle
- It equals the sum of the two interior remote angles.

adjacent angles
- Angles that have the same vertex and a common arm. They lie on opposite sides of the common arm.

complementary angles
- Two angles that add up to 90°.

complement
- The angle that needs to be added to a given angle to give 90°.
eg The complement of 60° is 30°.

supplementary angles
- Two angles that add up to 180°.

supplement
- The angle that needs to be added to a given angle to give 180°.
eg The supplement of 120° is 60°.

vertically opposite angles
- These are equal angles, formed when two straight lines intersect.

parallel lines
- Straight lines, in the same plane, that do not meet.

transversal
- A line that crosses two or more other lines.

corresponding angles (and parallel lines)
- These are in corresponding or matching positions relative to the transversal and a parallel line.

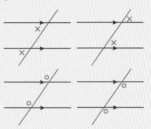

- They are equal if the lines are parallel.
- There are 4 pairs in the diagrams above.

alternate angles (and parallel lines)
- They lie 'inside' the parallel lines and on opposite sides of the transversal.
- They are equal if the lines are parallel.

co-interior angles (and parallel lines)
- They lie 'inside' the parallel lines and on the same side of the transversal.
- They are supplementary.

condition for lines to be parallel
- A pair of equal corresponding angles.
- A pair of equal alternate angles.
- A pair of co-interior angles that are supplementary.

Mathematical Terms 10

Diagnostic Test 10: | Reasoning in Geometry

- Each section of the test has similar items that test a certain type of question.
- Failure in more than one item will identify an area of weakness.
- Each weakness should be treated by going back to the section listed.

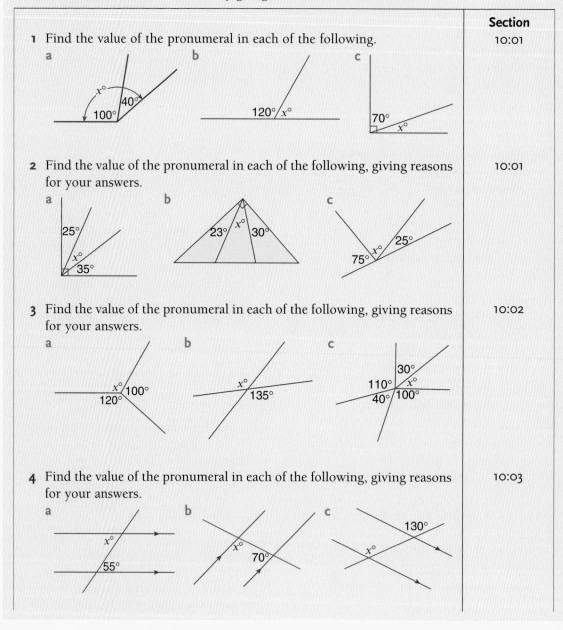

	Section
1 Find the value of the pronumeral in each of the following.	10:01
2 Find the value of the pronumeral in each of the following, giving reasons for your answers.	10:01
3 Find the value of the pronumeral in each of the following, giving reasons for your answers.	10:02
4 Find the value of the pronumeral in each of the following, giving reasons for your answers.	10:03

5 Find the value of the pronumeral in each of the following, giving reasons for your answers.

10:04

a

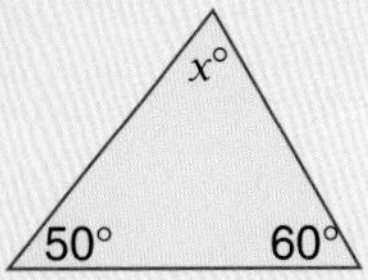

b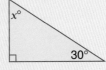

c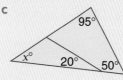

6 Find the value of the pronumeral in each of the following, giving reasons for your answers.

10:04

a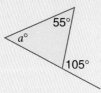

b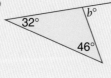

c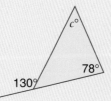

7 Find the value of the pronumeral in each of the following, giving reasons for your answers.

10:05

a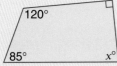

b

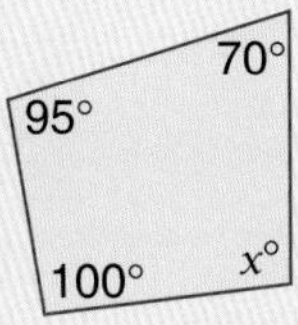

c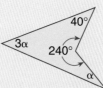

8 Find the value of the pronumeral in each of the following, giving reasons for your answers.

10:06

a

b

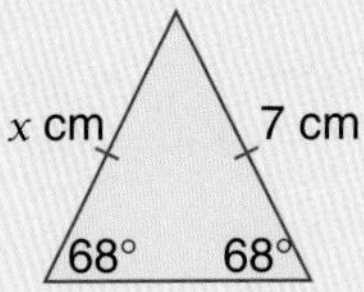

c

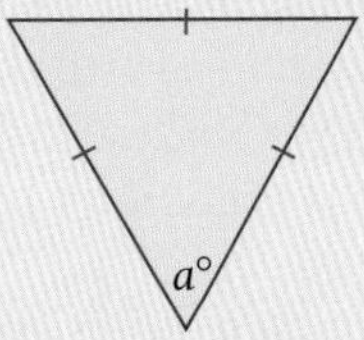

9 Find the value of the pronumeral in each of the following, giving reasons for your answers.

10:07

a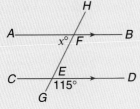

b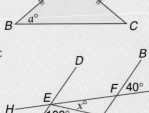

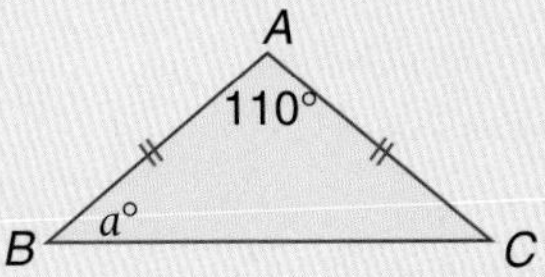

c

Chapter 10 | Revision Assignment

1 Find the value of the pronumeral in each of the following. Give reasons for your answers.

a

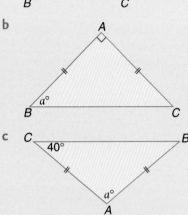

b

c

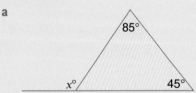

b

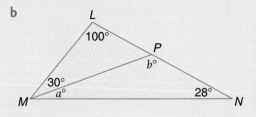

2 a A quadrilateral has three angles which measure 60°, 90° and 120°. What is the size of the fourth angle?

b A quadrilateral has two equal angles. The other two angles measure 70° and 30°. What is the size of the equal angles?

c Explain why it is impossible to draw a triangle that has side lengths of 10 cm, 6 cm and 3 cm.

3 Find the values of the pronumerals in each of the following. Give a reason for each answer.

a

4 Simplify:
a $2x \times 3x$ b $4ab \times 3ab$
c $12a \div 4a$ d $16ab \div 8a$

5 Factorise:
a $4a - 16$ b $a^2 - 6a$
c $2m^2 - 12m$ d $12ab - 6a$

6 Simplify:
a $\dfrac{3p}{4} + \dfrac{p}{2}$ b $\dfrac{m}{5} - \dfrac{m}{10}$
c $\dfrac{3a}{2} \times \dfrac{a}{4}$ d $(12a) \div \dfrac{a}{4}$

7 Use a calculator where necessary to evaluate the following, correct to 1 decimal place.

a $\sqrt{256 + 289}$ b $\sqrt{256} + \sqrt{289}$
c $\sqrt{256 \times 25}$ d $\sqrt{256} \times \sqrt{25}$

8 a Michelle earns $320 per week. She receives a wage rise of $14.40 per week. Express this rise as a percentage of her wage.

b Roberto invests $2000 and at the end of a year he receives an interest payment of $150. What is the percentage interest rate of his investment?

9 If I take three cards at random from a standard pack, the probability that I would select three picture cards is $\dfrac{11}{1105}$. What is the probability that I will not select three picture cards?

10 In our classroom there are 3 men, 2 women, 15 girls and 10 boys. If one person is selected at random, what is the probability that the person is:

    a a woman?   **b** a boy?   **c** a female?   **d** a baby?   **e** a human being?

11 A square and two equilateral triangles are joined as shown in the diagram. Find the size of:

    a $\angle AFE$ **b** $\angle ABC$

12 If in Question **11** a line was drawn from A to C, what would be the size of $\angle BAC$?

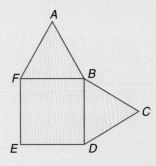

Chapter 10 | Working Mathematically

1 My sister Lyn has collected 48 different Christmas stamps while I have collected 75 different Christmas stamps. If 34 of Lyn's stamps are the same as 34 of mine, how many different stamps have we collected altogether?

2 How many counting numbers between 16 and 94 are even?

3 Five people meet and shake hands with one another. How many handshakes are necessary if each person shakes hands with every other person only once?

4 In order to play mixed doubles at tennis last week, we had to choose two ladies from the three who were there and two men from the four who were there. How many different groups of four could be chosen to play?

5 A machine can give a signal by using five lights which are in a row. Each light can be either on or off. How many different signals are possible?

6 Write down the value of 3^1, 3^2, 3^3, 3^4, 3^5 and 3^6. By examining the answers, find the last digit of 3^{2000}.

---

1 Finding the size of angles 1   Technology Applications

2 Finding the size of angles 2

3 Finding the size of angles 3   Drag and Drops

Chapter Review Questions

Area and Volume

Chapter Contents

Learning Outcomes

Students will be able to:

- Use formulae and Pythagoras' Theorem in calculating perimeter and area of circles and
  figures composed of rectangles and triangles.
- Calculate the surface area of rectangular and triangular prisms and volume of right prisms
  and cylinders.

Areas of Interaction

Approaches to Learning (Knowledge Acquisition, Problem Solving, Communication Skills,
Thinking Skills, Reflection Skills), Environments, Human Ingenuity

It is important to know how to calculate the areas of simple figures and the volumes of prisms. These are important skills for living in our society.

When we measure the area of a shape, we are measuring the amount of space inside that shape. We measure the number of square units inside the shape.

1 cm² is the area within a square that has 1 cm sides.
1 m² is the area within a square that has 1 m sides.
1 ha is the area within a square that has 100 m sides.

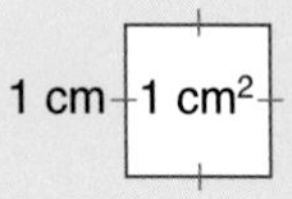

11:01 | Review of Area from Last Year

Last year you learned how to find the areas of squares, rectangles and triangles. The formulae for these are shown below.

Square	Rectangle	Triangle
$A = s^2$	$A = lb$	$A = \frac{1}{2}bh$ or $\frac{bh}{2}$

worked examples

Find the area of each figure below.

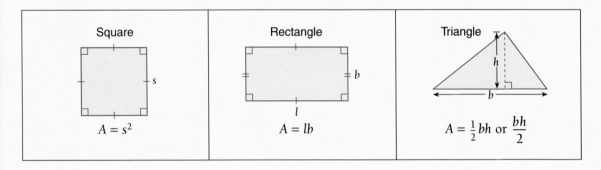

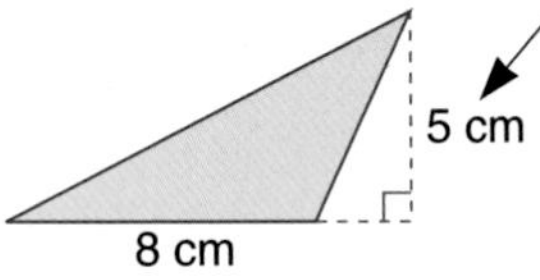

This is the vertical height of the triangle.

1 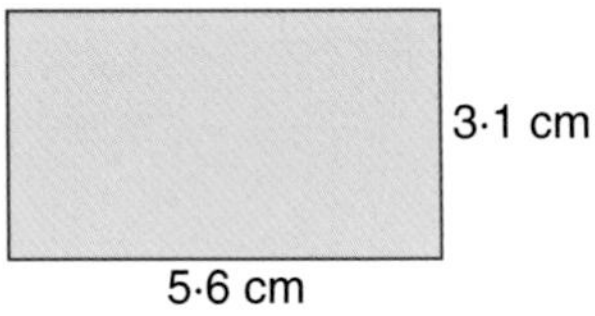   3·1 cm   5·6 cm

2 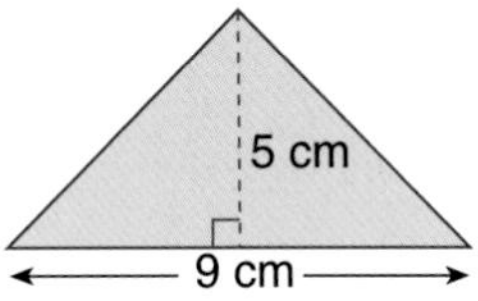   5 cm   9 cm

3   5 cm   8 cm

Solutions

1 $A = lb$
$= 5 \cdot 6 \times 3 \cdot 1$
$= 17 \cdot 36$
∴ Area of rectangle
$= 17 \cdot 36 \text{ cm}^2$

2 $A = \frac{1}{2} bh$
$= \frac{1}{2} \times 9 \times 5$
$= 22\frac{1}{2}$
∴ Area of triangle
$= 22\frac{1}{2} \text{ cm}^2$

3 $A = \frac{1}{2} bh$
$= \frac{1}{2} \times 8 \times 5$
$= 20$
∴ Area of triangle
$= 20 \text{ cm}^2$

prep quiz

11:01

Find the area of each figure in cm².

1 6 cm

2 4 cm

3 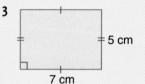 5 cm
7 cm

4 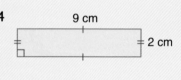 9 cm
2 cm

5 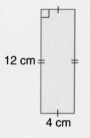 12 cm
4 cm

6 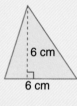 6 cm
6 cm

7 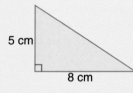 5 cm
8 cm

8 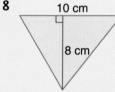 10 cm
8 cm

Find the areas of these figures in square units.

9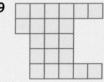

10

> **Remember!**
> Area is measured
> in 'square units'.

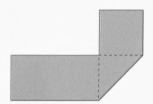

Sometimes a figure needs to be cut into more than one of the
basic shapes before its area can be found. Such a figure is called
a **composite figure**.

Measurements
- **All measurements are approximations.**
- **They are as accurate as the measuring instruments used to obtain them.**
- **The greatest possible error in a correct measurement is half of the smallest
  unit used.**

worked examples

4

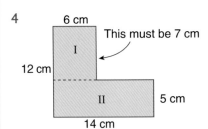

6 cm

This must be 7 cm

I

12 cm

II   5 cm

14 cm

5

This must be 4 cm

I

12 cm

II   8 cm

10 cm

Each of these composite figures has been cut into two simpler shapes.

Area of rectangle I = 6×7

           = $42\,cm^2$

Area of rectangle II = 14×5

           = $70\,cm^2$

$\therefore$ Total area = $42 + 70$

           = $112\,cm^2$

Area of triangle I = $\frac{1}{2} \times 10 \times 4$

           = $20\,cm^2$

Area of rectangle II = 10×8

           = $80\,cm^2$

$\therefore$ Total area = $20 + 80$

           = $100\,cm^2$

Exercise 11:01

1 Calculate the area of each figure.

Note: The 'base' of the triangle may not be on the bottom.

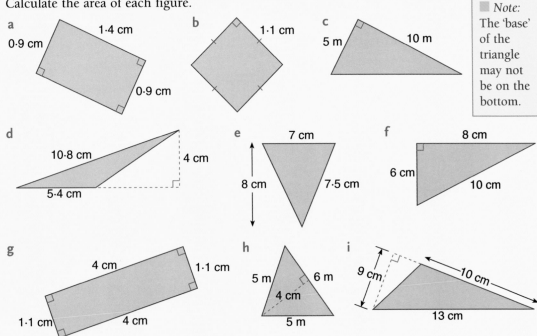

a 1·4 cm, 0·9 cm, 0·9 cm

b 1·1 cm

c 5 m, 10 m

d 10·8 cm, 4 cm, 5·4 cm

e 7 cm, 8 cm, 7·5 cm

f 8 cm, 6 cm, 10 cm

g 4 cm, 1·1 cm, 1·1 cm, 4 cm

h 5 m, 6 m, 4 cm, 5 m

i 9 cm, 10 cm, 13 cm

2 **a** A classroom is approximately 6 m long by 8 m wide. What is the approximate area?

   b A football field is approximately 100 m long and 50 m wide. What is its area in:

     i square metres?   **ii** hectares?

   c Calculate the number of square metres of paving bricks that should be bought to cover a rectangular area 6·5 m long by 2·4 m wide.

d A farmer has a rectangular field which is 620 m long and 280 m wide. What is the area of this field in: **i** square metres?   **ii** hectares?

e A painter has to paint part of a wall as shown on the right.
What is the area of the section he has to paint?

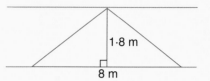

3 Find the area, to the nearest cm², of each of the following figures:
  a a rectangle with a length of 3 cm and a breadth of 5·6 cm
  b a rectangle with dimensions of 3·7 cm and 9 cm
  c a square with a side length of 2·5 cm
  d a triangle with a base of 7·7 cm and a height of 9 cm
  e a right-angled triangle whose side lengths are 2·5 m, 6 m and 6·5 m.

4 Write the dimensions (ie length and breadth) of four different rectangles that have an area of 12 cm².

5 Find the area of each composite figure by dividing it into rectangles or triangles.
All measurements are in centimetres.

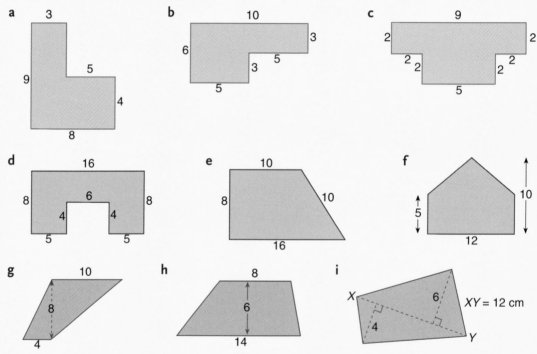

6 Under each figure the area is given. Use this to find the value of the pronumeral.

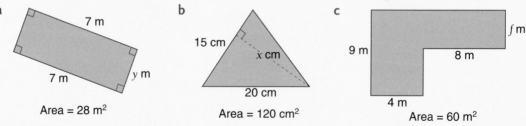

Investigation 11:01 | Area in a house

Please use the Assessment Grid on the following page to help you understand what is required for this Investigation.

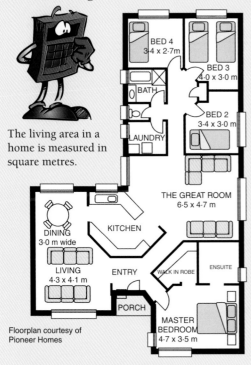

The living area in a home is measured in square metres.

Floorplan courtesy of Pioneer Homes

You have just purchased this beautiful new home. The next step is to cover the floors.

Cost of Floor Coverings, Including Laying

Carpet (Each metre length is 4 m wide.)

Bedroom:	top grade	$120/m
	2nd grade	$90/m
Kitchen:	top grade	$100/m
	2nd grade	$70/m
Living room:	top grade	$180/m
	2nd grade	$80/m
	heavy duty	$110/m
Bathroom:	top grade	$50/m
	2nd grade	$40/m

Vinyl (Each metre length is 4 m wide.)

top grade	$105/m
2nd grade	$75/m

Floor tiles (sold in m²)

top grade	$35/m²
2nd grade	$20/m²

1 Decide what type of floor covering you would choose for each part of the house.

2 Estimate the area of each type of covering needed.
   (For irregular areas, estimate a little more than otherwise.)
   Copy the grid on the right onto tracing paper.
   Each small square represents one square metre on the house plan. Check each of your estimates of area by placing your tracing paper over the plan of the house.

3 Estimate the cost if the materials were all: **a** top grade **b** second grade.

4 If you could afford top grade materials in just two rooms, which two rooms would you choose? Work out the total cost of floor coverings using this choice if a discount of 10% is given.

- Which would be worth more: a square metre of 20c coins or 1 kg of $1 coins?

Assessment Grid for Investigation 11:01 | **Area in a house**

The following is a sample assessment grid for this investigation. You should carefully read the criteria *before* beginning the investigation so that you know what is required.

			Assessment Criteria (B, C, D)		Achieved ✓
Criterion B **Investigating Patterns**	a		How the numbers are rounded to arrive at an estimate for the areas is not shown.	1	
				2	
	b		The numbers have been rounded correctly and estimates are within reasonable limits.	3	
				4	
	c		Estimates have been checked using a grid and the cost of floor covering is estimated correctly. These are compared with the exact answers and the practicality of the exact answers is discussed.	5	
				6	
	d		All methods are fully explained and a reason is given as to why the exact answer is not practical.	7	
				8	
Criterion C **Communication**	a		Estimates are given showing little working out and with no explanations.	1	
				2	
	b		Working out is complete and includes an explanation of how the estimates were obtained.	3	
				4	
	c		An explanation of how the numbers are rounded is given and an explanation of how areas are estimated is given using diagrams.	5	
				6	
Criterion D **Reflection in Mathematics**	a		An explanation is given for how areas are estimated.	1	
				2	
	b		The method of estimation is justified and the reasonableness of the findings have been checked.	3	
				4	
	c		An alternative approach has been investigated and a comparison made between the exact answer and the estimates, with a discussion of the reasonableness of each.	5	
				6	

11:02 | Areas of Special Quadrilaterals

Use ID Card 4 on page xvi to identify:

1 1   **2** 2   **3** 3   **4** 4   **5** 5   **6** 15

7 Copy the parallelogram below and draw lines to show how it can be made from a rectangle and two triangles.

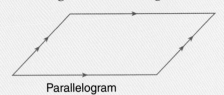

Parallelogram

8 Copy the trapezium below and add lines to show how it can be made from a rectangle and two triangles.

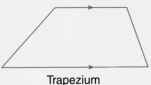

Trapezium

Divide each of the trapeziums shown into a rectangle and one triangle.

9

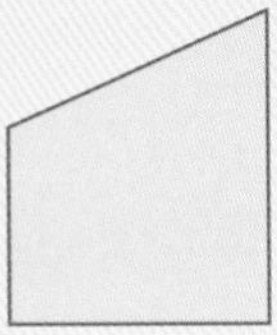

10

If you know how to find the areas of rectangles and triangles, you can calculate the areas of many other plane shapes.

Parallelogram

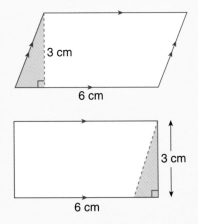

3 cm

6 cm

3 cm

6 cm

Check out these shapes!

By cutting a triangle off one end of a parallelogram and adding it to the other end, a rectangle is formed. The area of the figure has, of course, not changed.

Area of rectangle = 6 cm × 3 cm
= 18 cm²

∴ Area of parallelogram = 18 cm²

The area of a parallelogram
= base × perpendicular height
$A = bh$

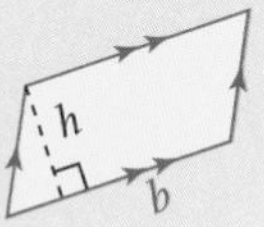

Exercise 11:02

Foundation Worksheet 11:02
FInding the area
Find the area of each figure.
1 a
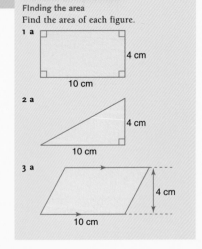

2 a

3 a

1 Find the area of each parallelogram by forming a rectangle as shown in the example above.

a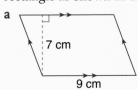
7 cm
9 cm

b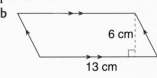
6 cm
13 cm

c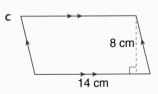
8 cm
14 cm

d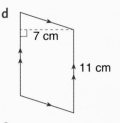
7 cm
11 cm

e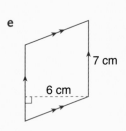
7 cm
6 cm

f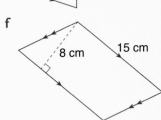
8 cm
15 cm

2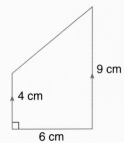
10 cm
8 cm
16 cm

This trapezium has been divided into a rectangle and a triangle.
  a What is the area of the rectangle?
  b What is the area of the triangle?
  c What is the total area of the trapezium?

3 Find the area of each right trapezium by following the steps in Question **2**.

a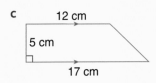
10 cm
8 cm
16 cm

b
9 cm
4 cm
6 cm

c
12 cm
5 cm
17 cm

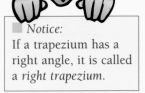

Notice:
If a trapezium has a right angle, it is called a *right trapezium*.

4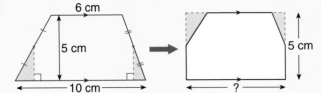

The trapezium on the left has been formed into a rectangle by moving the two triangles shown.

a What must be the length of the rectangle?

b What is the area of the rectangle?

c What is the area of the trapezium?

5 It is probably easier to see that a trapezium is divided into a rectangle, and a triangle made from the two ends.

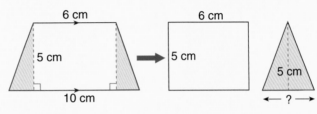

a What must be the length of the base of the triangle?

b What is the area of the triangle?

c What is the area of the rectangle?

d What is the area of the trapezium?

I thought trapeziums were in the circus!

6 Using either method above, find the area of each trapezium.

a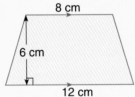

b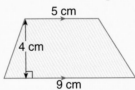

c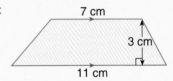

d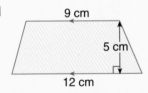

e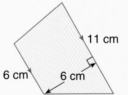

f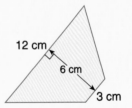

7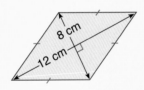

This rhombus has been split into two identical triangles.

a What is the 'height' of each triangle?

b What is the area of each triangle?

c What is the area of the rhombus?

8 The rhombus in Question **7** can also be divided and pieced together to form a rectangle.

  a What is the length of the rectangle?
  b What is the breadth of the rectangle?
  c What is the area of the rectangle?
  d What is the area of the rhombus?

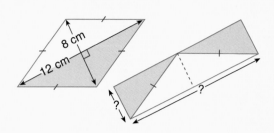

9

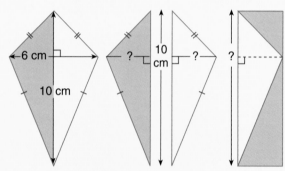

A kite can be split like a rhombus.

  a If it is split into two triangles, what is the 'height' of each triangle?
  b What is the combined area of the two triangles?
  c If a rectangle is formed, what are the dimensions of the rectangle?
  d What is the area of the rectangle?
  e What is the area of the kite?

10 Calculate the area of each kite or rhombus.

  a
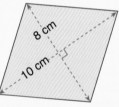

  b
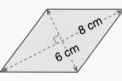

  c
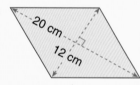

  d
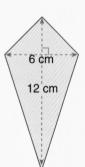

  e
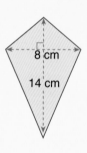

  f
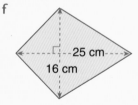

Investigation 11:02 | Car parking areas

Please use the Assessment Grid on the following page to help you understand what is required for this Investigation.

Car parking bays are based on either rectangles or parallelograms as shown.

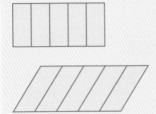

Investigate:

- What dimensions of each shape would be needed to provide a suitable size for parking a car. (Remember to allow for clearance between adjacent cars.)
- Which arrangement uses the greatest area.
- What are the advantages and disadvantages of each arrangement.

Visit at least two different types of carparks. Can you see why the parking spaces were organised the way they are? Is there a more suitable arrangement? What mathematical skills would you need to use in your investigation? What traffic characteristics needed to be considered, eg number of entrances, turning circles of vehicles, etc?

11:03 | Formulae for the Areas of Special Quadrilaterals

The previous section showed you how to find the areas of different shapes by dividing them into rectangles or triangles. Sometimes, however, it is quicker and easier to use a formula that will give the area for a particular shape.

If you are going to use a formula, **use it correctly!**

Parallelogram

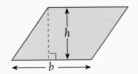

Since the **height** of the parallelogram became the **breadth** of the rectangle, then Area = $b \times h$ or $A = bh$, where b = base, h = height.

Assessment Grid for Investigation 11:02 | Car parking areas

The following is a sample assessment grid for this investigation. You should carefully read the criteria *before* beginning the investigation so that you know what is required.

			Assessment Criteria (B, C, D)		Achieved ✓
Criterion B Investigating Patterns	a		A solution has been attempted but it is disorganised and no systematic method has been used.	1	
				2	
	b		A systematic approach has been attempted with some success. Different arrangements have been investigated.	3	
				4	
	c		Different arrangements have been investigated successfully and all the points are answered to some extent.	5	
				6	
	d		The problem has been investigated fully and all the points in the investigation have been answered successfully.	7	
				8	
Criterion C Communication	a		Not much working out is shown and there are no diagrams.	1	
				2	
	b		Working out is shown and diagrams have been used but with little or no labelling and description.	3	
				4	
	c		Full working out is shown and is accompanied by diagrams which support and help explain the solution.	5	
				6	
Criterion D Reflection in Mathematics	a		Some attempt has been made to explain the solution but no comparison has been made between types of car parks.	1	
				2	
	b		An explanation of the steps taken in developing a car park is given and a satisfactory comparison has been made between arrangements.	3	
				4	
	c		A full explanation, evaluation and comparison of the different arrangements are given.	5	
				6	

Trapezium

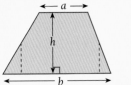 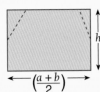

Since the length of the rectangle was the average of the two parallel sides, ie $\dfrac{a+b}{2}$, then Area $= h \times \dfrac{a+b}{2}$ or $A = \frac{1}{2}h(a+b)$, where a and b are the lengths of the parallel sides and h is the height.

Rhombus and kite

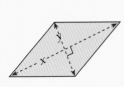 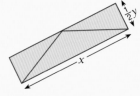

For both of these figures the length of the rectangle was the length of one diagonal, x.

The breadth was half of the other diagonal, $\frac{1}{2}y$.

So, Area $= x \times \frac{1}{2}y$ or $A = \frac{1}{2}xy$, where x and y are the lengths of the diagonals.

A summary of all the area formulae met so far would be:

Square	Rectangle	Triangle
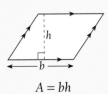 $A = s^2$	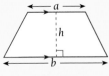 $A = lb$	$A = \frac{1}{2}bh$ or $A = \dfrac{bh}{2}$
Parallelogram	Trapezium	Rhombus and Kite
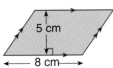 $A = bh$	$A = \frac{1}{2}h(a+b)$	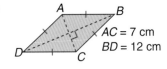 $A = \frac{1}{2}xy$

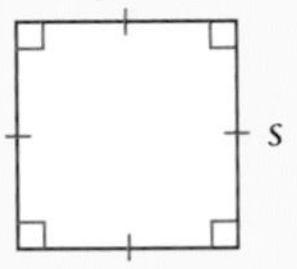

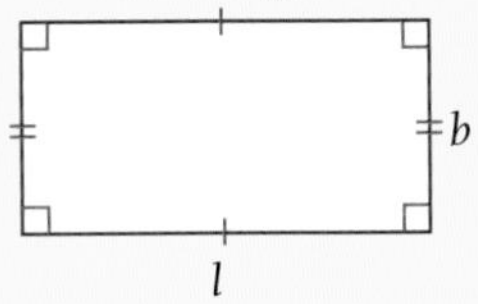

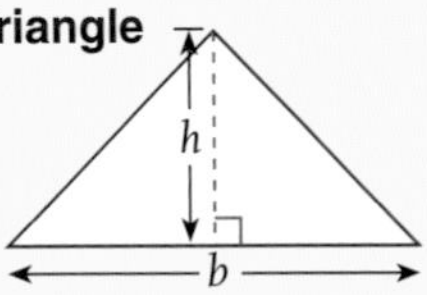

worked examples

Use the correct formula to find the area of each figure.

1

5 cm

8 cm

This is a parallelogram

so $\quad A = bh$

$\quad\quad = 8 \times 5$

$\quad\quad = 40 \text{ cm}^2$

$\therefore$ Area $= 40 \text{ cm}^2$

2

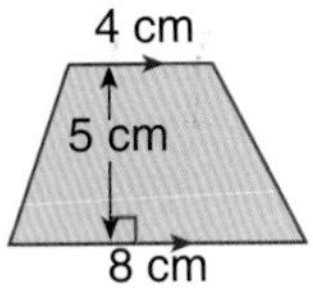

4 cm

5 cm

8 cm

This is a trapezium

so $\quad A = \frac{1}{2}h(a+b)$

$\quad\quad = \frac{1}{2} \times 5 \times (4+8)$

$\quad\quad = 30 \text{ cm}^2$

$\therefore$ Area $= 30 \text{ cm}^2$

3

A   B

D   C

$AC = 7$ cm
$BD = 12$ cm

This is a rhombus

so $\quad A = \frac{1}{2}xy$

$\quad\quad = \frac{1}{2} \times 7 \times 12$

$\quad\quad = 42 \text{ cm}^2$

$\therefore$ Area $= 42 \text{ cm}^2$

1 Use the formula $A = bh$ to find the area of each parallelogram.

a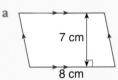
7 cm
8 cm

b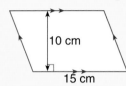
10 cm
15 cm

c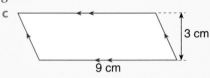
3 cm
9 cm

d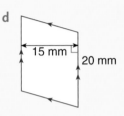
15 mm
20 mm

e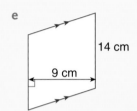
14 cm
9 cm

f
13 mm
25 mm

2 Use the formula $A = \frac{1}{2}h(a + b)$ to find the area of each trapezium.

a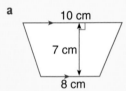
10 cm
7 cm
8 cm

b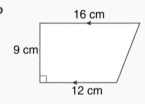
16 cm
9 cm
12 cm

c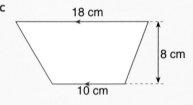
18 cm
8 cm
10 cm

d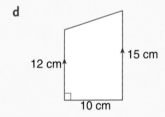
15 cm
12 cm
10 cm

e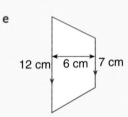
12 cm   6 cm   7 cm

f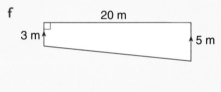
20 m
3 m
5 m

3 Use the formula $A = \frac{1}{2}xy$ to find the area of each rhombus or kite.

a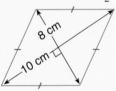
8 cm
10 cm

b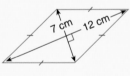
7 cm   12 cm

c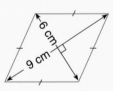
6 cm
9 cm

d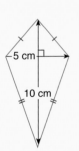
5 cm
10 cm

e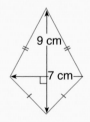
9 cm
7 cm

f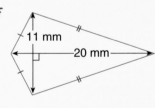
11 mm
20 mm

4 Use the correct formula to find the area of each figure.

a
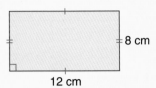
8 cm
12 cm

b
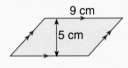
9 cm
5 cm

c
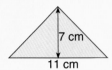
7 cm
11 cm

d
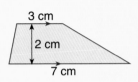
3 cm
2 cm
7 cm

e
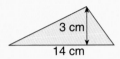
3 cm
14 cm

f
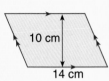
10 cm
14 cm

g
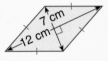
7 cm
12 cm

h
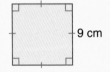
9 cm

i
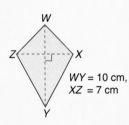
W
Z — X
Y
WY = 10 cm,
XZ = 7 cm

j
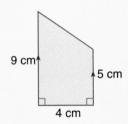
9 cm
5 cm
4 cm

k
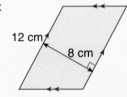
12 cm
8 cm

l
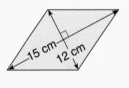
15 cm
12 cm

5 Each of the following figures has been formed from the special quadrilaterals. Calculate the area of each one.

a
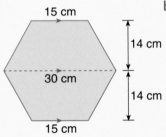
15 cm
14 cm
30 cm
14 cm
15 cm

b
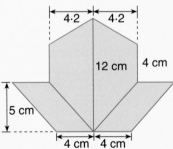
4·2   4·2
12 cm   4 cm
5 cm
4 cm 4 cm

c
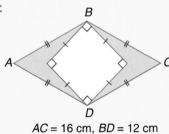
B
A — C
D
AC = 16 cm, BD = 12 cm

6 The area of a rhombus is 96 cm². The longer diagonal is 16 cm long. Find the perimeter of the rhombus.

11:04 | Volumes of Prisms

Name these solids: **1** 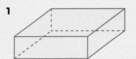   **2**   **3**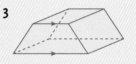

What shape is the cross-section of: **4** Figure 1?   **5** Figure 2?   **6** Figure 3?

Calculate the area of each figure:

7
7 cm

8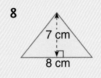
7 cm
8 cm

9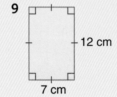
12 cm
7 cm

10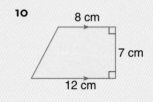
8 cm
7 cm
12 cm

- A prism has a special pair of parallel faces called **bases**. If we cut the prism parallel to its base, the cross-section formed is always the same.
- The number of cubic units in a prism is equal to the number of units in the base times the number of layers.

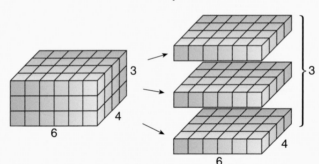
3
6
4
3
6
4

> ■ *Note!*
> The number of cubes in the base is equal to the area of the base.

Number of cubic units in the base = 6 × 4
Number of layers = 3
Volume of prism = 6 × 4 × 3
= 72 cubic units

So a formula for the volume of any prism would be:

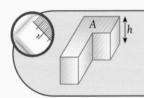
A
h

Volume of a Prism
$V = Ah$, where A is the area of the cross-section and h is the height of the prism.

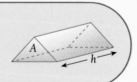
A
h

worked examples

Find the volume of each of these prisms.

1

The area of the cross-section (or one layer)
= 5 square units.

The height of the prism (or number of layers)
= 3 units
∴ Volume = 5 × 3
= 15 cubic units

2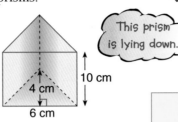

10 cm
4 cm
6 cm

Area of a triangular cross-section = $\frac{1}{2}$ × 6 × 4
= 12 cm²
Height = 10 cm
∴ Volume = 12 × 10
= 120 cm³

This prism is lying down.

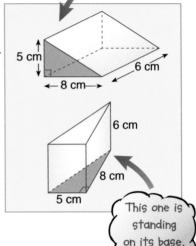

5 cm
6 cm
8 cm

6 cm
8 cm
5 cm

This one is standing on its base.

3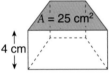

A = 25 cm²
4 cm

The cross-sectional area of this prism has been given as 25 cm²
so   V = Ah
= 25 × 4
= 100 cm³
∴ Volume of prism is 100 cm³.

4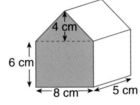

4 cm
6 cm
8 cm
5 cm

The cross-section is a triangle plus a rectangle,
so   A = $\frac{1}{2}$ × 8 × 4 + 8 × 6
= 16 + 48
= 64 cm²
∴ V = Ah
= 64 × 5
= 320 cm³
∴ Volume of prism is 320 cm³.

■ *Remember:*
Volume is measured in cubic units, such as cm³ or m³.

Exercise 11:04

Foundation Worksheet 11:04
Volumes of prisms
Find the volume of each prism.

I Calculate the volume of each prism, given the cross-sectional area *A* and the height.

a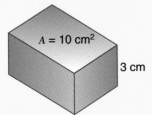

A = 10 cm²
3 cm

b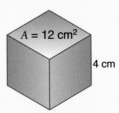

A = 12 cm²
4 cm

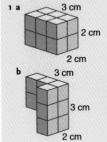

1 a
3 cm
2 cm
2 cm

b
3 cm
3 cm
2 cm

c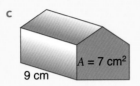
$A = 7 \text{ cm}^2$
9 cm

d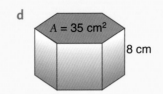
$A = 35 \text{ cm}^2$
8 cm

e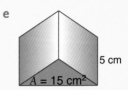
5 cm
$A = 15 \text{ cm}^2$

2 Calculate the volume of each rectangular prism.

a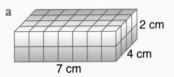
2 cm
4 cm
7 cm

b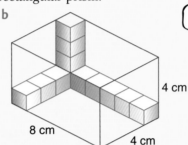
4 cm
8 cm
4 cm

Can you see why?

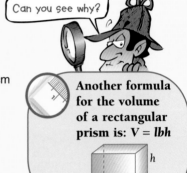

Another formula for the volume of a rectangular prism is: $V = lbh$

h
b
l

c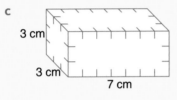
3 cm
3 cm
7 cm

d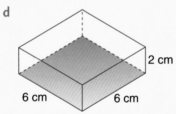
2 cm
6 cm
6 cm

e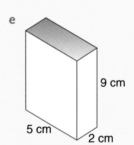
9 cm
5 cm
2 cm

f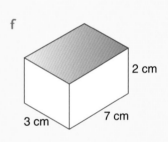
2 cm
3 cm
7 cm

3 Of course, a cube is a rectangular prism where all the dimensions are equal. Find the volumes of these cubes.

a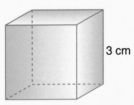
3 cm

b
5 cm

c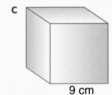
9 cm

4 **a** What volume of soil will be needed to fill a rectangular garden bed 4·2 m long by 1·8 m wide to a height of 35 cm. (*Hint:* Watch your units!) Answer correct to 1 decimal place.

b Jan's rose garden has an area of 20 m². She wishes to cover it with leaf mulch to a depth of 10 cm. What volume of mulch should she buy?

c Adam's trailer is a rectangular prism in shape. It is 1·8 m long, 1·2 m wide and 0·3 m high. What is the maximum volume of soil it can carry?

d What volume of concrete would Larry need to order for a house footing that is 450 mm wide, 300 mm deep and 10 m long. The footing is a rectangular prism in shape.

5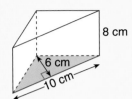

a What is the area of the triangular cross-section?

b What is the volume of the prism?

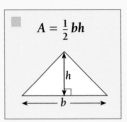

$A = \frac{1}{2}bh$

6 **a** What is the area of the cross-section of this triangular prism?

b What is the volume of the prism?

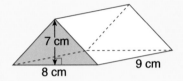

7 Calculate the volume of each of these prisms.

a

b

c

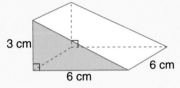
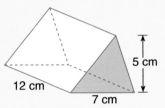

8 By first finding the area of the shaded cross-section, find the volume of each solid.

a

b

c

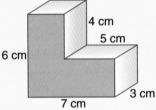
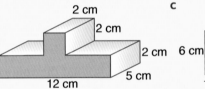
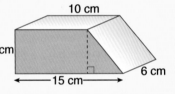

9 **a** Calculate the area of the shaded cross-section.

b Now calculate the volume of this prism. (The solid is still a prism even though it has a hole in it.)

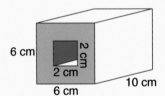

10

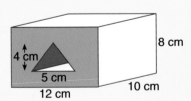

Calculate the volume of this prism which has a triangular hole cut out of it.

11 Calculate the volume of each of the following prisms, using the given information:
  a a rectangular prism with dimensions of 9 cm, 7 cm and 4 cm.
  b a rectangular prism with a length of 10 cm, a breadth of 7 cm and a height of 8 cm.
  c a cube with a side length of 6 cm.
  d a triangular prism where the triangular base has a height of 6 cm and a base length of 4 cm, and the prism has a height of 3 cm.
  e a hexagonal prism where the area of the base is 14 cm² and the height is 5 cm.
  f a pentagonal prism with a height of 12 cm and a cross-sectional area of 15 cm².

12 **a** If the volume of a prism is 36 cm³ and its height is 4 cm, what must be the area of the base?
  b If the cross-sectional area of a prism is 18 cm² and its volume is 90 cm³, what must its height be?
  c The dimensions of the base of a rectangular prism are 6 cm by 5 cm. If its volume is 180 cm³, what must be the height of the prism?

I'll have to think backwards here....

13 What is the capacity in litres of each prism?

  a

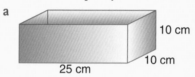

10 cm
10 cm
25 cm

  b

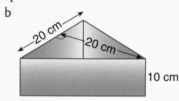

20 cm
20 cm
10 cm

█ 1 L = 1000 cm³

14 These prisms have a parallelogram, trapezium and rhombus as their cross-sections. By calculating the area of the cross-section, find the volume of each prism.

  a

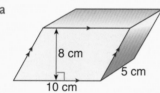

8 cm
5 cm
10 cm

  b

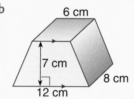

6 cm
7 cm
8 cm
12 cm

  c

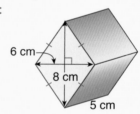

6 cm
8 cm
5 cm

15 Vince has been asked to put a path 1 m wide around a rectangular lawn which is 22 m long and 14 m wide. If the depth of the concrete is to be 10 cm, what volume of concrete does Vince need to order?

Technology
Applications

Activities

11:04 **Luggage problems**

Investigation 11:04 | **Estimating volume**

Please use the Assessment Grid on the following page to help you understand what is required for this Investigation.

Janette's family is moving to Nauru. They must take all their furniture with them as they are moving into an unfurnished house. The house has electricity and running water. One container is available to them. It measures 6 m × 3 m × 4 m.

- List each item you would take and its estimated volume. Once you have listed the necessities, fill the rest of the container with luxuries.
- Find out how furniture removalists estimate the volume of goods to be moved.

- You are looking up at these skyscrapers. If you were told the height of the building on the left, how would you find its volume?

The following is a sample assessment grid for this investigation. You should carefully read the criteria *before* beginning the investigation so that you know what is required.

			Assessment Criteria (B, C, D)		Achieved ✓
Criterion B Investigating Patterns	a		Items are given but the estimated volumes are not realistic.	1	
				2	
	b		The volumes of the items and the container are realistic and have been used to calculate how much room is left for luxury items.	3	
				4	
	c		Luxury items are listed and their estimated volumes are realistic.	5	
				6	
	d		A conclusion has been made on the method used versus the suggestion to use the dimensions of the items instead.	7	
				8	
Criterion C Communication	a		The working out is not set out in an organised way and no diagrams have been used.	1	
				2	
	b		Working out is easy to follow and the items and their estimates are easily identifiable (example in a table).	3	
				4	
	c		A clear explanation is given for the second and third bullet points.	5	
				6	
Criterion D Reflection in Mathematics	a		An attempt has been made to check the reasonableness of the estimates and to explain the steps in the solution.	1	
				2	
	b		Estimates have been checked for reasonableness and an explanation of the method is given.	3	
				4	
	c		An evaluation of the method is given and a possible alternative is discussed, and the relative advantages of using the volume and the dimensions are discussed.	5	
				6	

11:05 | Surface Area of Prisms

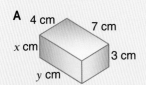

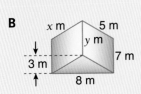

In solid **A**:

1 How many faces has the prism?
2 Do opposite faces have the same area?
3 What is the area of the top of the prism?
4 What is the value of x? 5 What is the value of y?

In solid **B**:

6 How many faces has the prism?
7 Do the two opposite ends have the same area?
8 What is the area of the front face (ie the base)?
9 What is the value of x? 10 What is the value of y?

- The surface area of a solid is equal to the sum of the areas of its faces.
- To calculate the surface area, you must know the number of faces and the shapes of the faces of the solid.
- To find the surface area of a solid:
  1 Make a sketch of the solid. Find all necessary dimensions.
  2 Calculate the area of faces. Be systematic. Do front and back, top and bottom and sides.
  3 Sum the area of the faces.
  4 Check to make sure that no face has been left out.

Open prisms have no top.

worked examples

Find the surface area of each of the following solids.

1

12 cm, 7 cm, 6 cm

Area of top and bottom
$= 2 \times (6 \times 12) = 144 \text{ cm}^2$

Area of sides
$= 2 \times (6 \times 7) = 84 \text{ cm}^2$

Area of front and back
$= 2 \times (12 \times 7) = 168 \text{ cm}^2$

∴ Total surface area
$= 144 + 84 + 168$
$= 396 \text{ cm}^2$

2

9 cm, 16 cm, 12 cm, 20 cm, 9 cm

Area of front
$= \frac{1}{2} \times (12 \times 16) = 96 \text{ cm}^2$

Area of back
$= 96 \text{ cm}^2$

Area of sides
$= (9 \times 20) + (9 \times 12) + (9 \times 16)$
$= 432 \text{ cm}^2$

∴ Total surface area
$= 96 + 96 + 432$
$= 624 \text{ cm}^2$

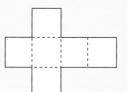 

Using a net makes finding the area easy!

- If the figure, above left, was traced on paper, cut out, and folded along the dotted lines, it would form the cube shown, above right.
- The figure, above left, is called the **net** of the solid.
- The area of the net is equal to the surface area of the solid.
- The area of a cube = 6 × (area of one face).

Exercise 11:05

Foundation Worksheet 11:05
Surface area
Find the surface area of each.
(Lengths are in centimetres.)

1   Name the solid produced when the net is folded.
    Is the solid *open* or *closed*?

a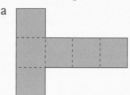

b

c

d

Make a net of your own and find its area.

2   Find the surface area of each prism. All measurements are in metres.

a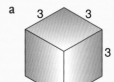

b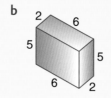

c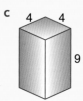

 The surface area of a rectangular prism
$$SA = 2lb + 2lh + 2bh$$

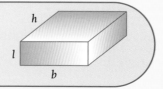

d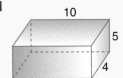

10
5
4

e

7
8
8

f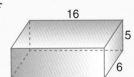

16
5
6

3 Find the surface area of each triangular prism. Measurements are in metres.

a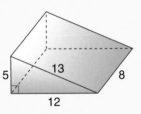

5
13
12
8

b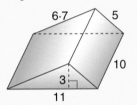

6·7
5
10
3
11

c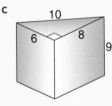

10
6
8
9

4 Find the surface area of each of these triangular prisms.

a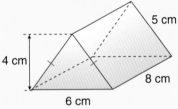

5 cm
4 cm
8 cm
6 cm

b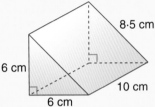

8·5 cm
6 cm
10 cm
6 cm

c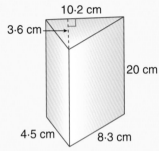

10·2 cm
3·6 cm
20 cm
4·5 cm
8·3 cm

5 In each of the following questions, use a scale drawing to calculate the unknown length, x, and then calculate the surface area.

a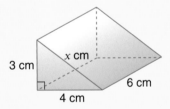

3 cm
x cm
6 cm
4 cm

b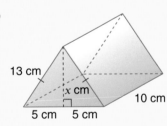

13 cm
x cm
10 cm
5 cm   5 cm

Caution: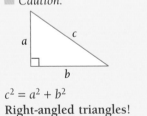

a
c
b

$c^2 = a^2 + b^2$
Right-angled triangles!

6 Measure the dimensions of the nets in Question 1 and find the area of each.

7 **a** Would prisms that have the same volume also have the same surface area?
   b Would prisms that have the same surface area also have the same volume?

Fun Spot 11:05 | Check your vision for good measure!

Often things are not what they seem. Sometimes our eyes may deceive us. Diagrams like those below are often called **optical illusions**. Answer each question, then check by measurement.

1

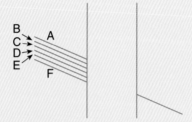

Which of the six lines on the left has been extended past the vertical lines?

2

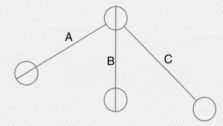

Which of the straight lines are the same length?

3

Which is the greater distance, from point A to point B, or from point B to point C?

4

Which two of the above four intervals are equal in length?

5

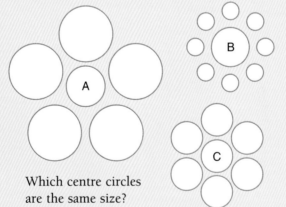

Which centre circles are the same size?

6

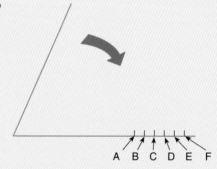

To which point would the upper arm reach if it were lowered onto the lower arm?

 Challenge worksheet 11:05 **Practical applications of surface area**

Mathematical terms 11

area

- The amount of space (square units) inside a two-dimensional shape.
- Units of area:
  square millimetre (mm²)
  square centimetre (cm²)
  square metre (m²)
  hectare (ha)
  square kilometre (km²)
- Formulae are used to calculate the area of the common plane figures.

composite figure

- A figure that is formed by joining simple figures.

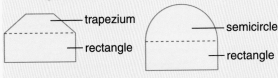

cross-section

cross-section

- The shape on the face where a solid has been sliced.

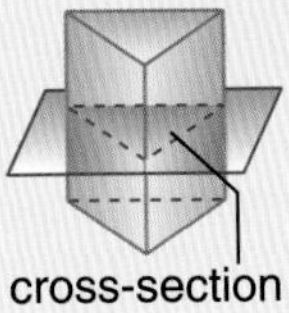

cube

- A prism that has six square faces.

dimensions

- Important measurements of shapes. eg length, breadth and height.

hectare

- An area of 10 000 m².
- The area of a square with side length 100 metres.

perimeter

- The distance around the boundary of a 2D shape.

prism

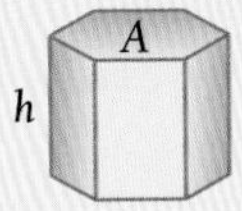

- A solid that has two identical ends joined by rectangular faces.
- Volume = area of base × height
  $$V = Ah$$

- rectangular prism
  — The ends are rectangles.
  — Volume
  = length × breadth × height
  $$V = lbh$$
  $$SA = 2lb + 2lh + 2bh$$

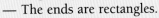

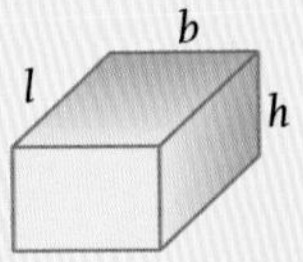

- triangular prism
  — The ends are triangles.
  — Volume
  = area of base × height
  $$= (\tfrac{1}{2} bh) \times H$$

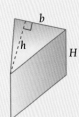

surface area

- The sum of the areas of the faces (or surfaces) of a three-dimensional figure (or solid).

volume

- The amount of space (cubic units) inside a three-dimensional shape.

Mathematical terms 11

Diagnostic Test 11: | Area and Volume

- Each section of the test has similar items that test a certain type of question.
- Errors made will indicate areas of weakness.
- Each weakness should be treated by going back to the section listed.

	Section
Calculate the area of each figure in Questions **1** to **6**.	

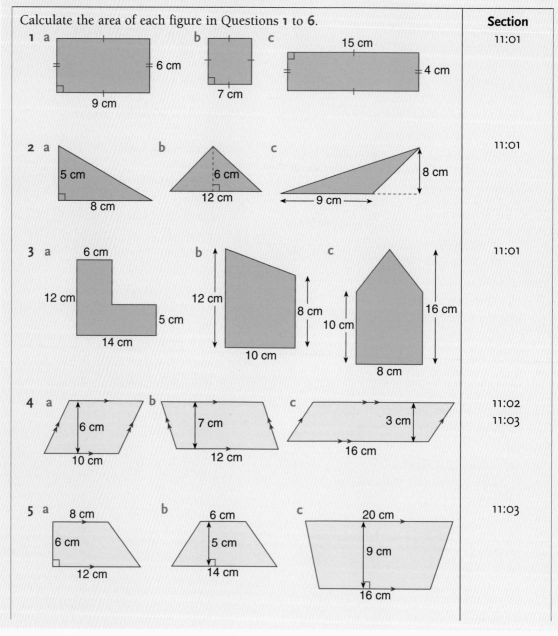

1 a — 6 cm, 9 cm   b — 7 cm   c — 15 cm, 4 cm — 11:01

2 a — 5 cm, 8 cm   b — 6 cm, 12 cm   c — 8 cm, 9 cm — 11:01

3 a — 6 cm, 12 cm, 5 cm, 14 cm   b — 12 cm, 8 cm, 10 cm   c — 16 cm, 10 cm, 8 cm — 11:01

4 a — 6 cm, 10 cm   b — 7 cm, 12 cm   c — 3 cm, 16 cm — 11:02 / 11:03

5 a — 8 cm, 6 cm, 12 cm   b — 6 cm, 5 cm, 14 cm   c — 20 cm, 9 cm, 16 cm — 11:03

6 a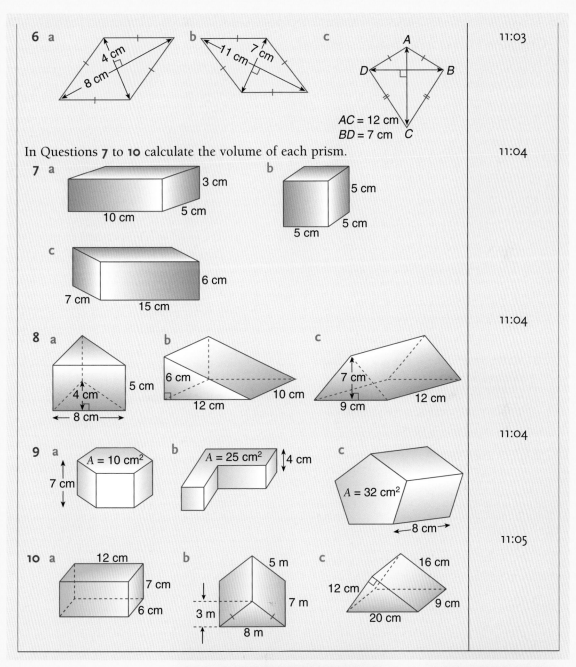

b

c

$AC = 12$ cm
$BD = 7$ cm

In Questions **7** to **10** calculate the volume of each prism.

7 a 3 cm 10 cm 5 cm

b 5 cm 5 cm 5 cm

c 6 cm 7 cm 15 cm

8 a 5 cm 4 cm 8 cm

b 6 cm 12 cm 10 cm

c 7 cm 9 cm 12 cm

9 a $A = 10$ cm² 7 cm

b $A = 25$ cm² 4 cm

c $A = 32$ cm² 8 cm

10 a 12 cm 7 cm 6 cm

b 5 m 7 m 3 m 8 m

c 16 cm 12 cm 9 cm 20 cm

- Estimate the total number of people that could stand inside the trunk of this Tasmanian tree.

Chapter 11 | Revision Assignment

1 Simplify:
  a $5a + 2a - a$ **b** $2b \times 4 + b$
  c $12a^2 \div 6a$ **d** $(4a)^2$

2 a Express 4 cm as a percentage of 2 m.
  b Increase $25 by 20%.
  c Change 0·165 to a percentage.
  d Find $16\frac{1}{2}$% of $75.

3
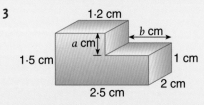

  a Find the values of a and b.
  b Draw the front view, top view and right side view of the solid.

4 Write the following numbers as basic numerals:
  a five thousand and twenty-six
  b sixty thousands, seven hundred
  c seven million, twenty thousand and six.

5 Draw a picture of:
  a a right-angled isosceles triangle
  b an obtuse-angled scalene triangle
  c an acute-angled isosceles triangle.

6
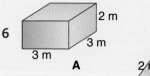
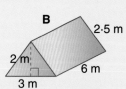

  a Do prisms **A** and **B** have the same volume?
  b Find the surface area of each prism. Are the surface areas the same?
  c Prism **B** represents a tent (with a floor) made of canvas. Find the cost of the canvas used if canvas costs $8.40 per square metre.

7 The figure shown is made from two identical overlapping rectangles which are 20 cm long and 15 cm wide. Calculate the area of the figure.

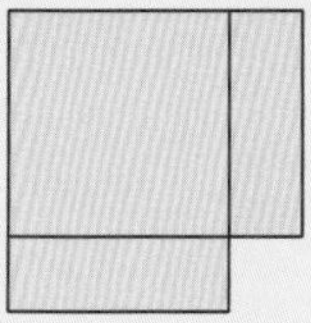

Chapter 11 | Working Mathematically

1. If each of the vowels a, e, i, o, u could be followed by any consonant (ie by letters that are not vowels), how many pairs of letters could be formed?

2. Diane and Gary married and had seven children. Six of the children married and had four children each. Assuming that no-one has died, how many people are now in this extended family altogether?

3. Five students shared a secret. Each one shared the secret with four others. Each of these shared the secret with three others. Each of these shared the secret with two others and each of these shared the secret with one other. If no one person was told the secret twice, how many people altogether now know the secret?

4. How many three-digit numbers can be formed using the digits 3, 2, 1 and 0 if each digit can be used only once in each number?

5. How many three-digit numbers can be formed using the digits 3, 2, 1 and 0 if each digit can be used as often as you like in each number?

6. Use ID Card 6 on page xviii to identify:

a 1	b 2	c 4	d 5	e 6
f 17	g 18	h 19	i 23	j 24

assignment 11B

id 11

1 Area and volume formulae
2 Recognising 3D shapes
3 Recognising plane shapes
4 Units of capacity and volume

Technology Applications — Drag and Drops

Chapter Review Questions

Teacher's Resource Practice Test

12

Circles

Chapter Contents

Learning Outcomes

Students will be able to:
- Classify, construct, and determine the properties of triangles and quadrilaterals.
- Use formulae in calculating perimeter and area of circles.

Areas of Interaction

Approaches to Learning (Knowledge Acquisition, Problem Solving, Communication Skills, Thinking Skills), Human Ingenuity

From earliest times the circle has fascinated people around the world. The sun and moon (both apparently circles) have been worshipped. From early Greek times the circle has been studied and now position on the Earth's surface is described in terms of intersecting circles. As a result of all of this interest, the parts of a circle have been carefully named.

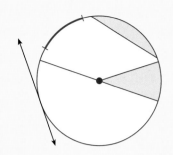

How many parts of this circle can you name?

12:01 | Parts of a Circle

It is important to know what the different parts of a circle are called. They are summarised in the table below.

Diagram	Name	Definition
1 	Circle	The set of all points that are a fixed distance from a point called the **centre** O.
2	Diameter	An interval that divides a circle in half and passes through the centre.
3	Radius	An interval drawn from the centre to the circle. It is half a diameter.
4	Arc	Part of a circle.
5	Chord	An interval joining two points on the circle.
6	Semicircle	Half of a circle.

The plural of radius is 'radii'. ie one radius two radii.

Electrical chord?

Diagram	Name	Definition
7 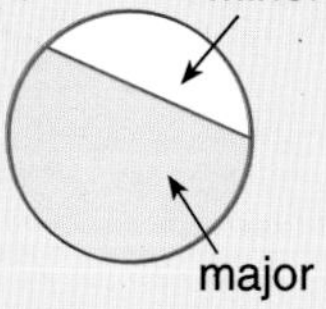 minor major	Segment	A chord cuts a circular region into two segments, a minor segment and a major segment.
8 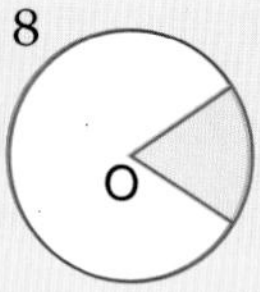 O	Sector	The section bounded by two radii and the included arc of a circle.
9 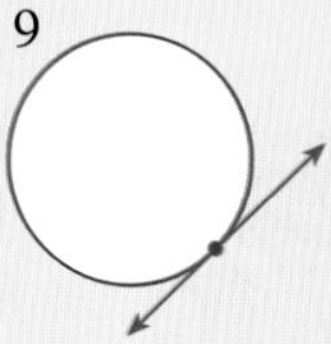	Tangent	A line that touches a circle at only one point.

The cross-section of a sphere is always a circle.

Exercise 12:01

1 Name the feature shown in red, on each circle.

a

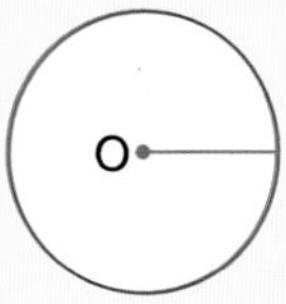

b

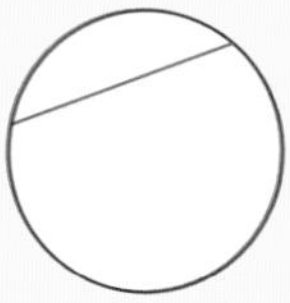

c

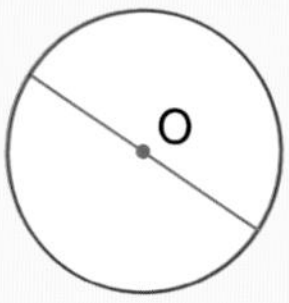

d

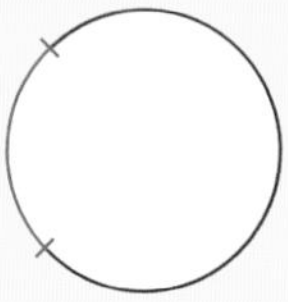

e

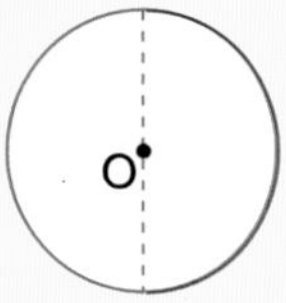

f

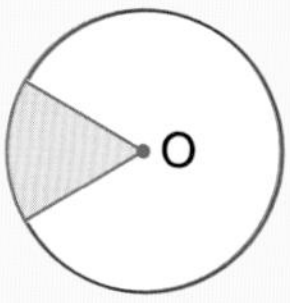

g

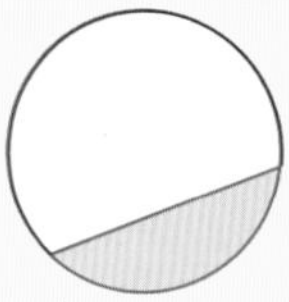

h

i

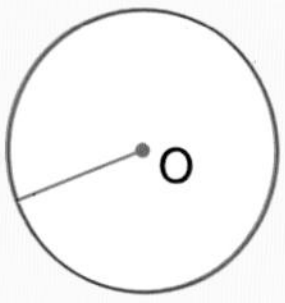

j

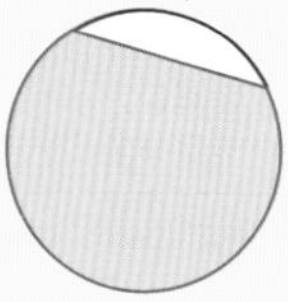

k

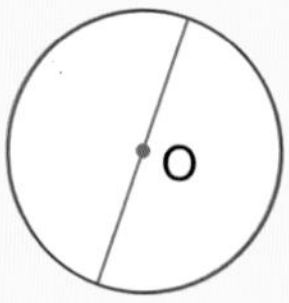

l

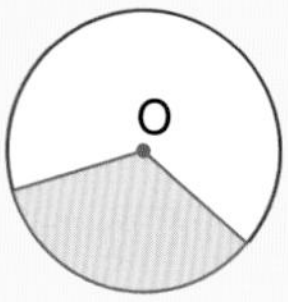

m

n

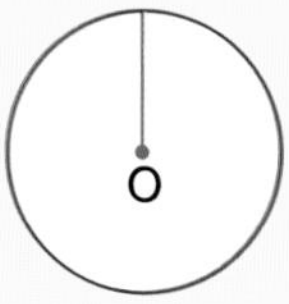

o

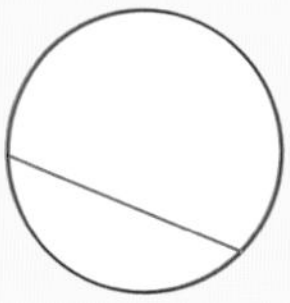

p

2 Which part of a circle is shown in these practical examples?

a A piece of pie

b Road next to a wheel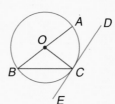

c 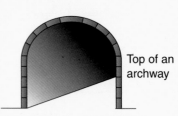 Top of an archway

3 Name the feature shown by interval:

a *AB*　　　　**b** *OC*

c *BC*　　　　**d** *DE*

4 If *O* is the centre of the circle, what type of triangle must △*AOB* be? Why?

Remember! There are 360° in a complete revolution.

5 What fraction of the area of a complete circle is each of these sectors?

a 　　**b** 120° 　　**c** 60°

Fraction = $\dfrac{\text{Angle}}{360°}$

6 If two or more circles are drawn with the same centre but different radii, they are called **concentric** circles. If radius *OX* = 5 cm and radius *OY* = 8 cm, what must be the distance *XY* between the two circles?

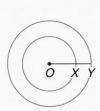

O X Y

Hey look! Concentric semicircles!

That's 'cos I only threw half a rock!

12:02 | Circumference of a Circle

 The perimeter of a circle is called the *circumference*.

It is usually easier to measure the diameter of a circle than its circumference, using either a special gauge or a method like that shown below with a ruler and set squares.

worked examples

1   Use a practical method to measure the circumference of a 20 cent coin.

We could roll that coin along a straight edge and measure the interval.

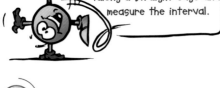

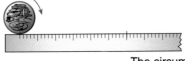

The circumference is more than 3 diameters.

Step 1
Mark a point on the circumference of a 20 cent coin.

Step 2
Place the coin beside a ruler with the mark pointing to the scale.

Step 3
Roll the coin along the ruler until the mark returns again to the scale. Make sure that the coin does not slip.

Step 4
Measure the circumference.

Circumference ≒ 8·8 cm

2   Use a practical method to measure the circumference of a can.

We could use a tape measure around that can.

Is the circumference more than three times the diameter?

Step 1
Measure the circumference with a tape measure. Also measure the diameter.

Step 2
Divide the circumference by the diameter.

The circumference > 3 × the diameter.

Obviously the larger the diameter of a circle, the greater its circumference. The following investigation will help you discover the special relationship that exists between the circumference of a circle and its diameter.

Investigation 12:02 | The circumference of a circle

Please use the Assessment Grid on the following page to help you understand what is required for this Investigation.

1 Step 1   Tie a piece of chalk to the end of a long string.

Step 2   Cut the string so that the chalk is 1 m away from the other end of the string when stretched.

Step 3   In the playground, have a friend hold one end while you stretch the string and draw a circle.

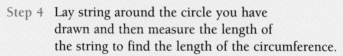

Step 4   Lay string around the circle you have drawn and then measure the length of the string to find the length of the circumference.

Step 5   How many diameters would fit around the circumference?

2 The diameter and circumference of 5 circular items were measured and the results recorded in the table below. Complete the third column of the table, giving your answers correct to 1 decimal place.

Diameter (d)	Circumference (C)	Circum. ÷ Diameter (C ÷ d)
2 cm	6·2 cm	
5 cm	15·7 cm	
3·2 cm	10 cm	
8 cm	25 cm	

You'll need me.

3 Use string or cotton to trace around each circle to measure its circumference. Also measure the diameter of each circle and complete the table given. (Give measurements to the nearest millimetre.)

a

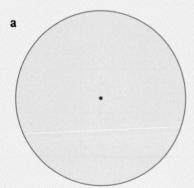

b

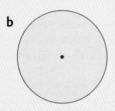

c

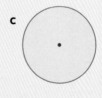

	Diameter (d)	Circumference (C)	Circum. ÷ Diameter (C ÷ d)
a			
b			
c			

4 Find some large circles in the environment (tree trunks, water tanks, etc), estimate their circumference, record these and then check by measurement.

The following is a sample assessment grid for this investigation. You should carefully read the criteria *before* beginning the investigation so that you know what is required.

		Assessment Criteria (B, C, D)		Achieved ✓
Criterion B Investigating Patterns	a	The student had some difficulties in setting up the problem as outlined in the investigation.	1	
			2	
	b	Although some difficulties were encountered, the solution has been set up reasonably well and all answers have been obtained.	3	
			4	
	c	Solutions are well organised and all answers obtained are reasonable; a pattern has been recognised as the problems were solved.	5	
			6	
	d	As well as solving the problems, a pattern has been recognised and described in words.	7	
			8	
	e	The pattern has not only been recognised but predictions have been made about the solutions to questions 2, 3 and 4.	9	
			10	
Criterion C Communication	a	The working out is hard to follow and there has been no use of diagrams or symbols to help explain the solutions.	1	
			2	
	b	Working out is good and some interpretation of the results is given. Diagrams and symbols have been used.	3	
			4	
	c	Working out is well set out and shows a good understanding of the problem. Diagrams have been used well.	5	
			6	
Criterion D Reflection in Mathematics	a	An attempt has been made to explain the steps undertaken and some comparison of answers has been made.	1	
			2	
	b	Checks have been made between answers to problems and there is some discussion of this comparison.	3	
			4	
	c	There is meaningful discussion on the comparison of results and results have been checked for reliability.	5	
			6	
	d	The implication of the results is mentioned and the possible uses of the result π have been discussed.	7	
			8	

The number π (pi)

- From **Investigation 12:02** we can conclude that for all circles:

$$\frac{\text{length of circumference } (C)}{\text{length of diameter } (d)} \doteqdot 3\cdot1$$

- Actually the value of this ratio is $3\cdot1415926\ldots$, a decimal that continues forever without repeating.

- Because this number is very special it is given the symbol π (the Greek letter pi).

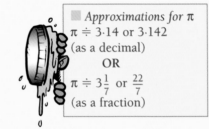

> ■ *Remember!*
> $\doteqdot$ means 'is approximately equal to'.

- Therefore $\dfrac{C}{d} = \pi$, which is more usually written as the formula $C = \pi d$.

- Sometimes the formula for the circumference is given in terms of the radius, r.
  Because $d = 2r$, this gives $C = \pi \times 2r$
  $$\text{or } C = 2\pi r.$$

- The number π is a strange number that cannot be given an exact decimal or fraction value. It is therefore called an **irrational number**. (Other examples of irrational numbers are roots, such as $\sqrt{2}$, $\sqrt{3}$, $\sqrt[3]{5}$, etc). Therefore, in calculations involving π we must use an approximation.

- There is a π button on your calculator. An eight-figure calculator will give $\pi \doteqdot 3\cdot141\,592\,6$.

> ■ *Approximations for π*
> $\pi \doteqdot 3\cdot14$ or $3\cdot142$
> (as a decimal)
> OR
> $\pi \doteqdot 3\frac{1}{7}$ or $\frac{22}{7}$
> (as a fraction)

The definition of π

The number π (pi) is the ratio of the circumference to the diameter of any circle; $\pi = \dfrac{C}{d}$.

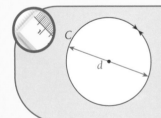

The circumference C of a circle is given by the formula:

$$C = \pi d \quad \text{or} \quad C = 2\pi r$$

where d is the diameter and r is the radius.
- The value of $\pi \doteqdot 3\cdot141\,592\,6$.

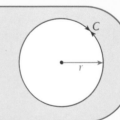

- Circles are a feature in most areas of design and technology.

1 Using the approximation $\pi = 3.14$, find the circumference of each circle.

a

10 cm

O

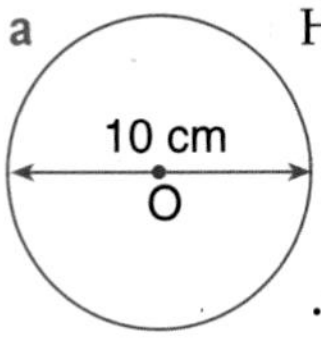

Here we are given the diameter, so $C = \pi d$

$= 3.14 \times 10$

$= 31.4$

$\therefore$ Circumference $= 31.4$ cm

b

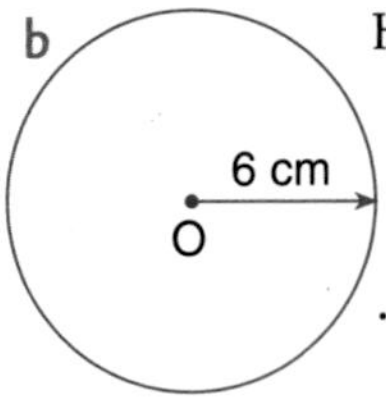

6 cm

O

Here the radius is given, so $C = 2\pi r$

$= 2 \times 3.14 \times 6$

$= 37.68$

$\therefore$ Circumference $= 37.68$ cm

2 In most cases it is much easier to use a calculator, especially one with a π button.

a

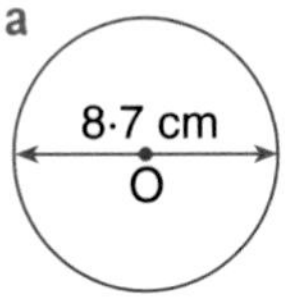

8.7 cm

O

$C = \pi d$

$= \pi \times 8.7$

Press: [π] [×] 8.7 [=]

$= 27.331856$

$= 27.3$ cm (to 1 dec. pl.)

b

4.2 cm

O

$C = 2\pi r$

$= 2 \times \pi \times 4.2$

Press: 2 [×] [π] [×] 4.2 [=]

$= 26.389378$

$= 26.4$ cm (to 1 dec. pl.)

Exercise 12:02

1 Calculate the circumference of each of these circles, using $\pi = 3.14$.

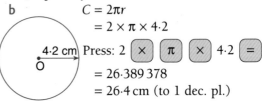

Are you given the diameter or the radius?

a

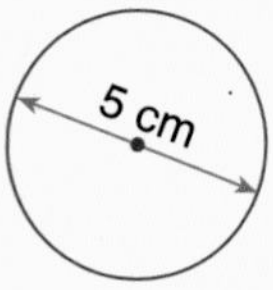

5 cm

b

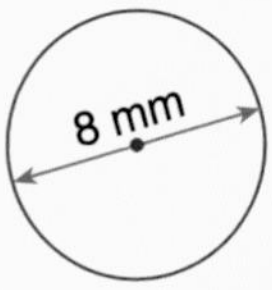

8 mm

c

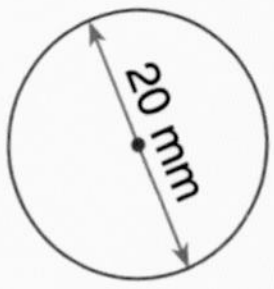

20 mm

d

6 cm

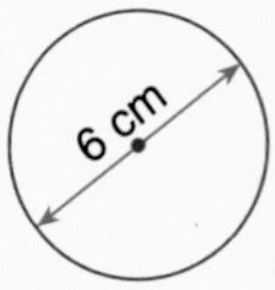

2 Calculate the circumference of each of these circles, using $\pi = 3.14$.

a

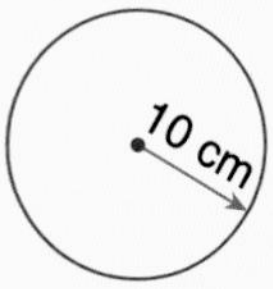

10 cm

b

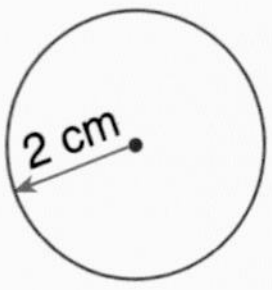

2 cm

c

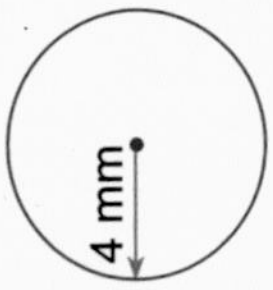

4 mm

d

9 mm

3 Using the approximation $\pi = \frac{22}{7}$, find the circumference of each circle.

a

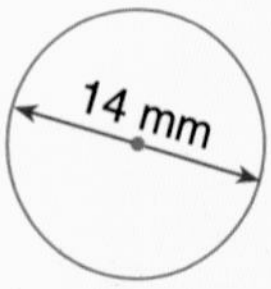

14 mm

b

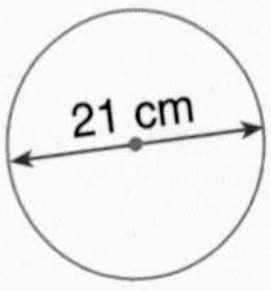

21 cm

c

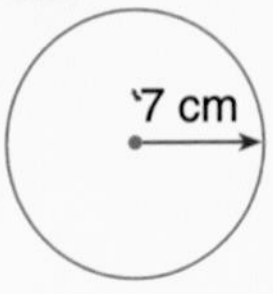

7 cm

d

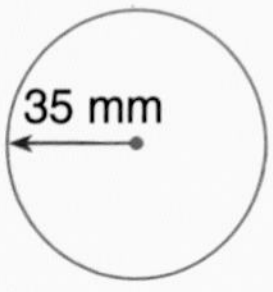

35 mm

e

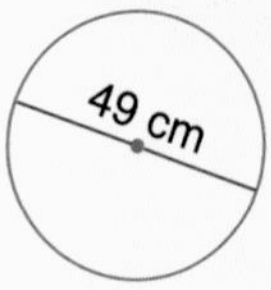

49 cm

f

42 mm

g

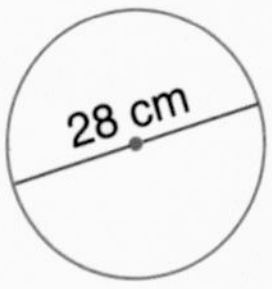

28 cm

h

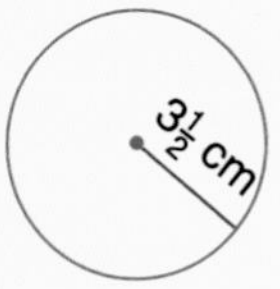

$3\frac{1}{2}$ cm

4 Using a calculator with a π button, calculate the circumference of each of these circles, correct to 1 decimal place.

a 4·5 cm   **b** 2·7 cm   **c** 12·1 mm   **d** 4·7 mm

e Diameter = 8·7 cm   **f** Diameter = 25 mm   **g** Diameter = 32·7 cm
h Radius = 1·9 cm   **i** Radius = 3·8 mm   **j** Radius = 15·6 cm

5 Measure the diameter of each of these circles and calculate the circumference to the nearest cm.

a 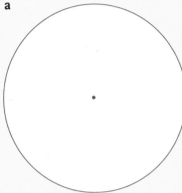   **b**    **c**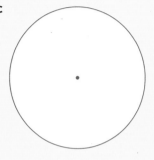

6 **a** A car tyre has a diameter of 60 cm.
How far will the wheel travel in one revolution?
b How far will it travel in 1000 revolutions (in m)?
c How many complete revolutions are needed to travel 1 km?

7 If the radius of the Earth is about 6000 km, what would its circumference be at the equator (to the nearest 1000 km)?

 **If the circumference is about 3 times the diameter,
then the diameter is about $\frac{1}{3}$ of the circumference.**

Note: **If $C = \pi d$, then $d = \dfrac{C}{\pi}$ or $C \div \pi$.**

8 Find the diameter, correct to 1 decimal place, of a circle that has a circumference of:
a 20 cm   **b** 50 mm   **c** 35 cm   **d** 15·2 mm

12:03 | Solving Problems Involving Circumference

worked examples

1 Determine the perimeters of these figures, correct to 1 dec. pl.

a Perimeter = $\frac{1}{2}$ circle + diameter

$$\therefore P = \frac{1}{2}(\pi d) + 20$$
$$= \frac{1}{2}(\pi \times 20) + 20$$
$$= 31{\cdot}415... + 20$$
$$= 51{\cdot}4 \text{ mm}$$
(to 1 dec. pl.)

←—— 20 mm ——→

b Perimeter = $\frac{1}{2}$ circle + 3 sides of rectangle

$$\therefore P = \frac{1}{2}(\pi d) + 2 + 8 + 2$$
$$= \frac{1}{2}(\pi \times 8) + 12$$
$$= 12{\cdot}566... + 12$$
$$= 24{\cdot}6 \text{ cm (to 1 dec. pl.)}$$

2 cm

←—— 8 cm ——→

2

←—— 20 cm ——→

The perimeter of this figure is made up of three semicircles, two with a diameter (d_1) of 10 cm and one with a diameter (d_2) of 20 cm.

$$\therefore P = 2(\tfrac{1}{2}\pi d_1) + \tfrac{1}{2}\pi d_2$$
$$= \pi d_1 + \tfrac{1}{2}\pi d_2$$
$$= (\pi \times 10) + (0{\cdot}5 \times \pi \times 20) \text{ cm}$$
$$= 62{\cdot}8 \text{ cm (to 1 dec. pl.)}$$

Drawing a sketch and marking what you know is very helpful.

Exercise 12:03

Foundation Worksheet 12:03

Solving circle problems

1 A 20 cent coin has a diameter of 2·8 cm. Find the length of the circumference, correct to the nearest centimetre.

2 The lid of a jam jar has a radius of 4 cm. Find the circumference of the lid correct to the nearest cm.

1 Calculate the perimeter of each of these figures correct to the nearest centimetre.

a

8 cm

b

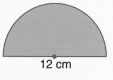

12 cm

c

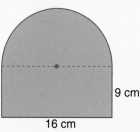

9 cm

16 cm

d

←———— 18 cm ————→

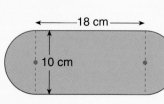

10 cm

e

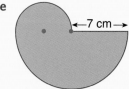

←7 cm→

Don't forget the
straight edges.

2 Cars race around a track with the measurements
shown on the diagram. Find the length of a lap and
the distance, to the nearest km, of a 20-lap race.

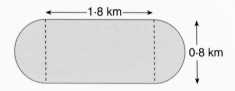

3 The minute hand of a clock is 9·5 cm long. How far will the tip of the hand travel in one day
(to the nearest m)?

4 **a** A record has a diameter of 30 cm. How far would a point on the outside rim of the record
travel in one revolution? (Answer to the nearest cm.)
   b When playing, the record revolves at a rate of 33 revolutions per minute (rpm).
   How far would the point travel in 10 minutes? (Answer to the nearest m.)

5 A trundle wheel is to have a circumference of 1 m.
What must be its diameter, to the nearest mm?

6 When athletes run around a track with circular ends, they have a 'staggered start', since the
perimeter of the outer lanes is greater. If the width of a lane is 1 metre, how much start should
a runner in lane 1 give to the runner in lane 2, if the runner in lane 1 is to complete exactly
one lap of the field?

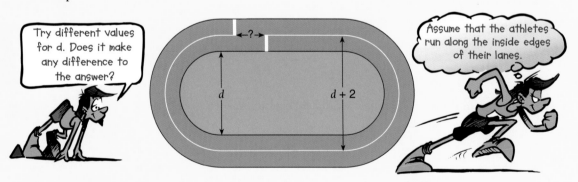

Try different values
for d. Does it make
any difference to
the answer?

Assume that the athletes
run along the inside edges
of their lanes.

Can you find out how much start the inside runner appears to give the outside runner on an
official Olympic track for a 400 m event?

Fun Spot 12:03 | Do fewer bumps mean a smoother ride?

Consider and discuss the cartoon above.
- Would three bumps per revolution give you a smoother ride than four bumps per revolution?
- Would ten bumps per revolution (wheels in the shape of decagons) give you a smoother ride than four bumps per revolution (square wheels)?

12:04 | Area of a Circle

1 If the diameter of a circle is 18 cm, what is its radius?
2 If the radius of a circle is 4·5 cm, what is its diameter?
3 What is the value of π, correct to 1 decimal place?
4 What is the formula for the circumference of a circle?

What is the area of each of these figures?

5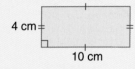
4 cm
10 cm

6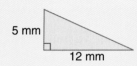
5 mm
12 mm

7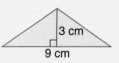
3 cm
9 cm

What fraction of the area of a circle would each of these sectors be?

8

9

10
120°

When we find the area of a figure, we divide it up into square units, such as square centimetres. This is easy for a figure like a rectangle, which has straight sides, but how can we find the area of a circle in terms of square units? By working through the following Investigation, you will discover a formula you can use to find the area of a circle.

Investigation 12:04 | The area of a circle

Please use the Assessment Grid on the following page to help you understand what is required for this Investigation.

1

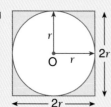

a This circle with a radius of *r* units has been drawn inside a square. Can you see that the sides of the square must be 2*r* units long? What is the area of the square?

b Which is larger, the area of the square or the area of the circle?

2

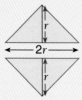

a Inside this circle with a radius of *r* units, a square has been drawn. The area of the square will be the same as two triangles that each have a base of 2*r* units and a height of *r* units. What is the area of the square?

b Which is larger, the area of the square or the area of the circle?

> From Questions 1 and 2 you should be able to see that the area of a circle lies between $4r^2$ and $2r^2$, ie
>
> $2r^2 <$ **area of a circle** $< 4r^2$
>
> So a reasonable approximation for the area of a circle might be
>
> $A \doteqdot 3r^2$ **square units.**

3 To gain an approximate value for the area inside a circle, we could 'count squares', including only those for which more than half of the square lies inside the circle.

This circle has a radius of 2 units. If we count the squares marked, what is an approximate value for the area of this circle? (How does this compare with the approximate formula $A \doteqdot 3r^2$?)

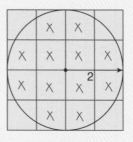

4 Of course the method in Question **3** can be made more accurate by using smaller square units.

a Carefully count the squares marked in the circle on the left. What is the approximate area of this circle in square units? How does this compare with $A \doteqdot 3r^2$?

b The number of marked squares in the circle on the right, with a radius of 10 units, is 316. If $A \doteqdot 3r^2$, what is the value of A when $r = 10$?

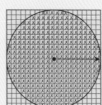

The following is a sample assessment grid for this investigation. You should carefully read the criteria *before* beginning the investigation so that you know what is required.

		Assessment Criteria (B, C, D)		Achieved ✓
Criterion B Investigating Patterns	a	There is no systematic approach to answering the problems. The student has had difficulty answering all the questions.	1	
			2	
	b	A systematic approach has been used and the student has managed to work through most of the questions successfully.	3	
			4	
	c	The student has worked successfully through the questions and has made connections between the different methods.	5	
			6	
	d	Using question 4, the student has worked towards the value of π and has made a conclusion about it.	7	
			8	
Criterion C Communication	a	Working out is not shown and no diagrams have been used to illustrate the method.	1	
			2	
	b	Most of the working out is shown and some diagrams have been used.	3	
			4	
	c	Working out is complete and diagrams have been used to help explain the solution.	5	
			6	
Criterion D Reflection in Mathematics	a	Some attempt has been made to check the reasonableness of the results obtained.	1	
			2	
	b	Results have been checked and comment has been made on the reliability of the results.	3	
			4	
	c	A comparison and evaluation of the different methods and results has been made and related to the value of π.	5	
			6	

5

Figure 1

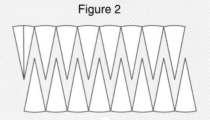

Figure 2

This way of investigating the area of a circle is to slice it into sectors (Figure 1) and then arrange them as in Figure 2.

Figure 3

By taking half of the sector on one end and placing it on the other end, we obtain a figure that looks very much like a rectangle, as in Figure 3.

a Now the length of this rectangle would be half the circumference of the circle. What is this length?

b What would be the breadth of the rectangle?

c Since the area of a rectangle is length × breadth, what would be the area of this rectangle (which, of course, would be the same as the area of the circle)?

6

Imagine the area inside a circle to be a series of rubber rings. If the rings were cut along a radius and allowed to fold out flat, the layers would form a triangle.

Here's a clever way of looking at the area.

a What is the formula for the area of a triangle?

b The height of the triangle would be r, the radius of the circle. What would be the length of the base of the triangle?

c What then would be the area of the triangle?

d What would be the area of the circle?

In **Investigation 12:04**:

- we found that the area of a circle $\doteq$ 3 × radius squared,
  or $A \doteq 3r^2$

- Questions **5** and **6** led to the discovery of the formula below.

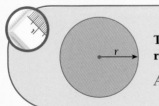

The area of a circle with a radius of r units is given by

$$A = \pi r^2$$

Pi pops up again!

1 Find the areas of these circles, using $\pi = 3.14$.

a
$$A = \pi r^2$$
$$= 3.14 \times 3^2$$
$$= 3.14 \times 9$$
$$= 28.26$$
$$\therefore \text{Area} \doteqdot 28.26 \text{ cm}^2$$

b
Here radius = 10 cm
$$A = \pi r^2$$
$$= 3.14 \times 10^2$$
$$= 3.14 \times 100$$
$$= 314$$
$$\therefore \text{Area} \doteqdot 314 \text{ cm}^2$$

2 Using a calculator, find the areas of these figures, correct to 1 decimal place.

a
$$A = \pi r^2$$
$$= \pi \times (4.7)^2$$

Press: 4.7 $\boxed{x^2}$ $\boxed{\times}$ $\boxed{\pi}$ $\boxed{=}$

Answer = 69.4 mm^2

b
7.5 cm

For a full circle,
$$A = \pi r^2$$
$$= \pi \times (7.5)^2$$
This is $\frac{1}{4}$ or a circle, so
$$A = \frac{\pi \times (7.5)^2}{4}$$

Press:

7.5 $\boxed{x^2}$ $\boxed{\times}$ $\boxed{\pi}$ $\boxed{\div}$ 4 $\boxed{=}$

Answer = 44.2 cm^2

3 Calculate the areas of these composite figures correct to 1 decimal place.

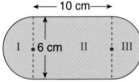
10 cm
I 6 cm II III

a Area of rectangle = lb
$$\therefore \text{Area II} = 10 \times 6$$
$$= 60 \text{ cm}^2$$
Area of I + III $= \pi r^2$
(where $r = 3$ cm)
$$\therefore \text{Area of I + III} = \pi \times 3^2$$
$$= 28.3 \text{ cm (to 1 dec. pl.)}$$
$$\therefore \text{Total area} \doteqdot 60 + 28.3$$
$$\doteqdot 88.3 \text{ cm}^2$$

b Area of I $= \frac{1}{2}\pi r^2$ (semicircle)
$$= \frac{1}{2} \times \pi \times 4^2$$
$$= 25.1 \text{ cm}^2 \text{ (to 1 dec. pl.)}$$
Area of II $= \frac{1}{2}bh$
(Can you see that $h = 7$ cm, $b = 8$ cm?)
$$= \frac{1}{2} \times 8 \times 7$$
$$= 28 \text{ cm}^2$$
$$\therefore \text{Total area} \doteqdot 25.1 + 28$$
$$\doteqdot 53.1 \text{ cm}^2$$

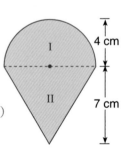
4 cm
7 cm
I
II

Units of area
1 cm^2 $= 100 \text{ mm}^2$
1 m^2 $= 1\,000\,000 \text{ mm}^2$
1 ha $= 10\,000 \text{ m}^2$
1 km^2 $= 1\,000\,000 \text{ m}^2$ $= 100 \text{ ha}$

Just for interest

Sometimes a different formula is used to find the area of a circle.

Because the radius is half the diameter, then $r = \dfrac{d}{2}$.

If we now change the formula $A = \pi r^2$ by substituting $\dfrac{d}{2}$ for r,

we now have the formula $A = \dfrac{\pi d^2}{4}$.

> Engineers prefer this formula.

 $A = \pi r^2$ and $A = \dfrac{\pi d^2}{4}$ both give the area of a circle.

Example

Calculate the area of this circle using the above formula.

4·7 cm

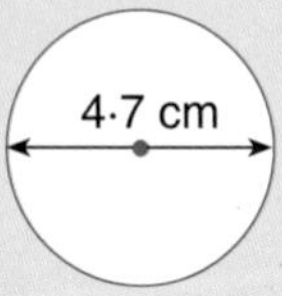

$$A = \frac{\pi d^2}{4}$$

$$= \frac{\pi \times (4\cdot7)^2}{4}$$

Press: 4·7   4 =

Answer = 17·3 cm² (to 1 dec. pl.)

Exercise 12:04

1 Using the approximation $\pi = 3\cdot14$, calculate the area of each of these circles.

a

2 cm

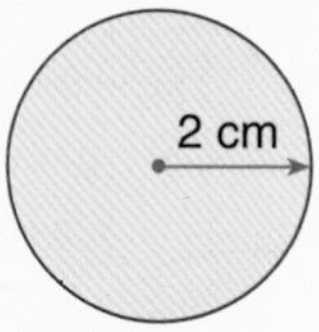

b

10 cm

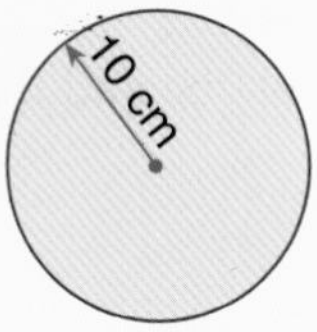

c

4 cm

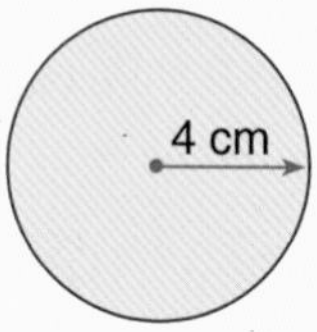

d

5 m

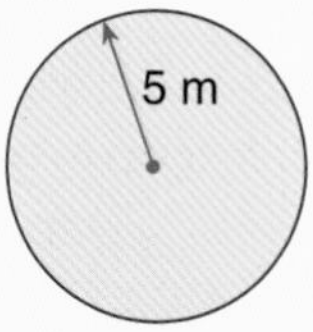

e

2 cm

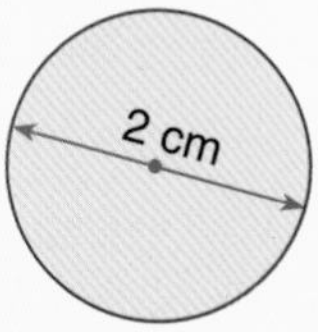

f

6 m

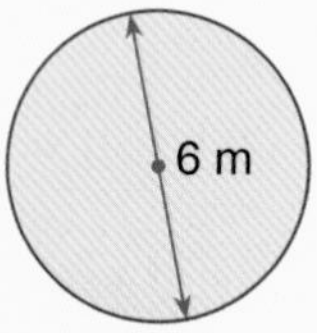

g

8 m

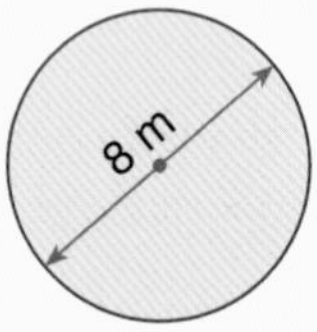

h

12 cm

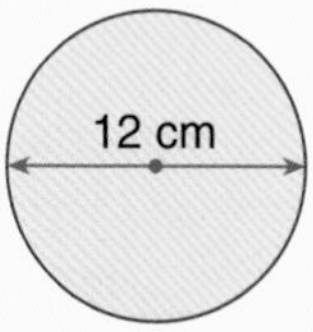

2 Calculate the area of each of these circles. Use $\pi = \dfrac{22}{7}$.

a

7 cm

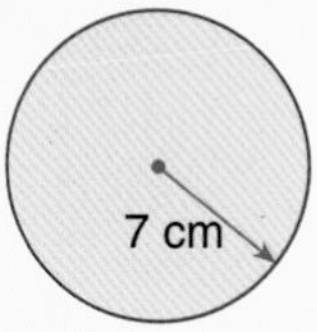

b

3 cm

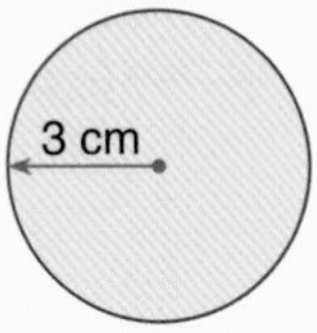

c

7 mm

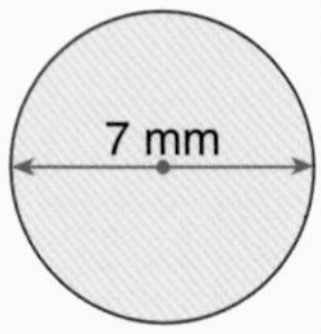

d

10 cm

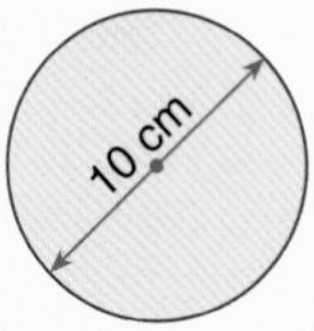

3 Use a calculator to find the area of each of these circles, correct to 1 decimal place.

a
6 cm

b
2·7 cm

c
11 cm

d
21·6 cm

e Radius = 16 cm   f Radius = 30 cm   g Radius = 7·8 mm
h Diameter = 18 cm   i Diameter = 36 cm   j Diameter = 17·6 mm

4 Use the formula $A = \dfrac{\pi d^2}{4}$ to calculate the area (to the nearest cm²) of a circle with a diameter of:

a 8 cm   b 12 cm   c 5·6 cm   d 14·8 cm

5 Measure the diameters of these circles to the nearest mm and calculate the area of each circle.
(Give your answers to the nearest mm².)

a

b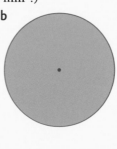

c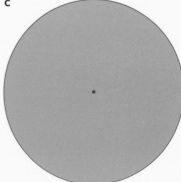

1 cm = 10 mm

6 Determine what fraction of a circle each figure must be and then calculate its area.
(Answer correct to 1 decimal place.)

a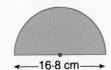
←—16·8 cm—→

b
4·2 cm

c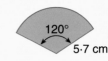
120°
5·7 cm

7 Determine the area of the shaded region between each pair of circles.
(Answer correct to 1 decimal place.)

a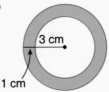
2 cm
5 cm

b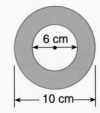
3 cm
1 cm

c
6 cm
←— 10 cm —→

The region between two circles with the same centre is called an *annulus*.

8 **a** A plate has a diameter of 30 cm. What is the area, to the nearest cm²?
b A circular rug has a radius of 2·5 m. What is its area (correct to 1 dec. pl.)?
c The lid of a can is a circle with a radius of 5·5 cm. What is its area, correct to the nearest cm²?
d The cross-section of a pipe is an annulus where the internal radius is 3 cm and the external radius is 4 cm. Find the area of the cross-section, correct to 1 decimal place.

e  The minute hand on a clock is 9·6 cm long. What area will this hand sweep out in:
  i 1 hour?
  ii 30 minutes?
  iii 40 minutes?
  (Give answers correct to 1 dec. pl.)

9 Determine the area enclosed by these composite figures. Give all your answers correct to the nearest cm².

a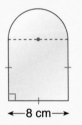
←8 cm→

b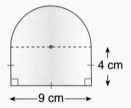
4 cm
←9 cm→

c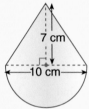
7 cm
←10 cm→

d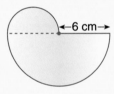
←6 cm→

e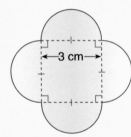
←3 cm→

f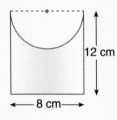
12 cm
←8 cm→

10 **a** A tablecloth is to cover a circular table that has a diameter of 1·9 m. What area of cloth is needed if the tablecloth is to hang 15 cm over the edge of the table? (Answer correct to the nearest cm²).

b A circle was cut out of the square as shown in the diagram. Using π = 3·14, the area of the circle was found to be 28·26 cm².
  i What was the side length of the square?
  ii What area of cardboard was left after the circle had been removed?

Mathematical terms 12

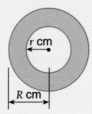

annulus
- The area bounded by two circles that have the same centre.
- The area of an annulus $= \pi R^2 - \pi r^2$

r cm

R cm

arc
- Part of a circle.

chord
- An interval joining two points on a circle.

circle
- The set of all points in a plane that are a fixed distance from a point called the *centre* (O).

O

circumference
- The perimeter of a circle.
- The length of the boundary of a circle.

concentric circles
- A group of circles that have the same centre.

diameter
- An interval that divides the circle in half. It passes through the centre of the circle.

O

pi (π)
- The ratio of the circumference to the diameter of any circle.
- An irrational number approximately equal to 3·14 (correct to 2 dec. pl.), 3·141 592 6 (correct to 7 dec. pl.) or $\frac{22}{7}$ (as a fraction).

radius (radii is the plural)
- An interval drawn from the centre of a circle to a point on the circle.
- Half of the diameter.

O

sector
- The area bounded by two radii and the included arc of a circle.

O

segment
- A section bounded by an arc and its chord.
- A chord cuts a circular region into two segments, a minor segment and a major segment.

minor

major

semicircle
- Half of a circle.

O

tangent
- A line that touches a circle at only one point.

1 Mathematical terms 12A
2 Mathematical terms 12B

- Estimate the diameter of one of the wheels and work out its circumference.

334 **INTERNATIONAL MATHEMATICS 2**

Diagnostic Test 12: | Circles

- Each section of the test has similar items that test a certain type of question.
- Errors made will indicate areas of weakness.
- Each weakness should be treated by going back to the section listed.

Section

1 Name the part of the circle shown in each diagram.   12:01

a   b   c   d   e

2 Calculate the circumference of each of these circles, correct to 1 decimal   12:02
place.

a 8 cm   b 5 cm   c 2 cm   d 9 cm

3 Find the perimeter of each of these figures to the nearest cm.   12:03

a 10 cm   b 6 cm   c 7 cm   d 8 cm   6 cm

4 Calculate the area of each of these circles, correct to the nearest cm^2.   12:04

a 5 cm   b 3 cm   c 8 cm   d 14 cm

5 Calculate the area of each shaded region to the nearest cm^2.   12:04

a 10 cm   b 3 cm 6 cm   c 3 cm 8 cm   d 6 cm

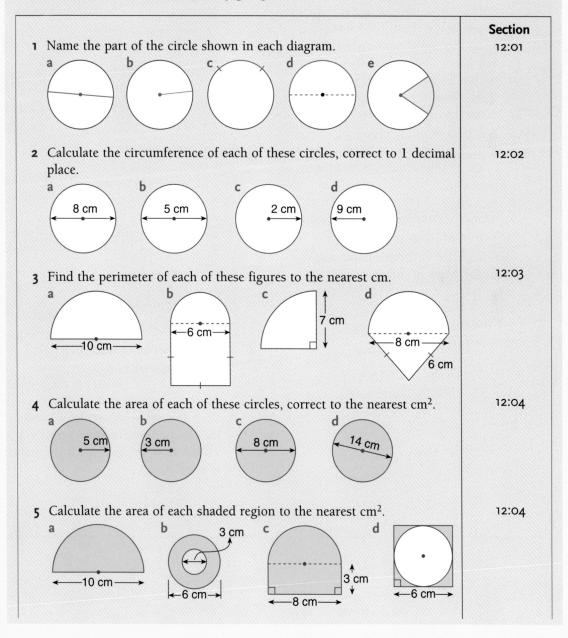

1 Simplify:
  a $5a \times 6$ b $7a^2 \times a$
  c $6 - 2(a + 2)$ d $6m \div m$

2 a Bill has three times as many stamps
     as Jeff. If they have 1260 stamps
     altogether, how many does each
     boy have?
  b Jill has \$3.50 more than Frances.
     If together they have \$19.10, how
     much does each girl have?

3 a A netball team has played 60 games.
     If the ratio of wins to losses to draws
     is $26 : 3 : 1$, how many games have
     they won?
  b In a recipe, 2 eggs are needed for
     6 cups of flour. If 3 eggs are used,
     how much flour must be used?

4 Find the value of the pronumeral in each
  of the following, giving reasons for your
  answers.
  a

  b

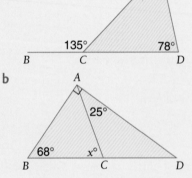

c
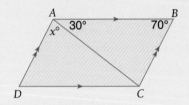

5 a Find the value of F if $m = 1.6$ and
     $a = 9.8$, given that $F = ma$.
  b If $S = \sqrt{ab}$, find S when $a = 12.5$ and
     $b = 11.52$.

6 Calculate the area of:
  a a square of side 6.5 cm
  b a rectangle 5.6 cm long and 2.4 cm wide
  c a kite with diagonals of lengths 16 cm
     and 34 cm
  d a parallelogram that has a pair of sides
     8 cm long and 5.5 cm apart.

7 Solve these equations:
  a $4(2a - 3) = 15$
  b $4x + 3(2x - 3) = 4$
  c $4(1 - x) = 3(2x + 7)$

8 a A scale drawing is made of a field
     120 m long and 50 m wide, using
     a scale of $1 : 100$. What are the
     dimensions of the scale drawing?
  b On a drawing with a scale of $1 : 1000$,
     the distance between two points is
     2.3 cm. How far apart are these points
     in real life?

Chapter 12 | Working Mathematically

assignment 12B

1 Given the rule $\square^2 + 26 = 15 \times \square$:
   a find all the positive integers between 1 and 5 which, when placed into the boxes, turn this rule into a *false* statement. (Integers are whole numbers. The same integer must go into both boxes.)
   b find all the integers which, when placed into the boxes, turn the rule into a *true* statement. (There are two such integers.)

2 Lachlan had 4 shirts, 2 ties and 3 belts. How many different combinations of a shirt, a tie and a belt can he wear?

3 There are six people in the Hollier family. Only two of them can fit in their neighbour's car. How many different pairs could be chosen to fill these two seats?

4 Fewer than 40 students are on a bus. One-quarter of them come from Kincumber while two-fifths of them come from Erina. How many students are there?

5 A length of piping is cut 15 times. How many pieces would result?

6 A pack of 52 cards contains 13 hearts, 13 diamonds, 13 clubs and 13 spades. How many cards must you take unseen and one at a time to be sure that you have at least one of each type?

1 Parts of a circle
2 Types of angles
3 Properties of 2D shapes
4 Units of area and volume

Technology Applications — Drag and Drops

Chapter Review Questions

Teacher's Resource Practice Test

Geometric Constructions and Congruent Figures

This is hard going! I was told to do all my constructions with geometrical instruments...

Chapter Contents

Learning Outcomes

Students will be able to:
- Classify, construct, and determine the properties of triangles and quadrilaterals.
- Identify congruent and similar two-dimensional figures stating the relevant conditions.

Areas of Interaction

Approaches to Learning (Knowledge Acquisition, Problem Solving, Communication Skills, Thinking Skills), Environments, Human Ingenuity

13:01 | Geometrical Constructions

- Geometrical constructions are accurate drawings.
- We will be using a ruler, a set square, a pencil, and a pair of compasses.
  The term *pair of compasses* is similar to the term *pair of trousers*.

For a more detailed treatment of the constructions in this section, go to Appendix F.

Appendix F F:01 Bisecting intervals and angles.   F:02 Constructing angles of 60°, 120°, 30° and 90°.
          F:03 Constructing perpendicular and parallel lines.   F:04 Constructing regular polygons in circles.

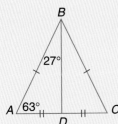

1 Which side of *ΔABC* is equal to *AB*?
2 What length is equal to *AD*?
3 Which angle is equal to ∠*BAC*?

What is the size of:

4 ∠*BCA*?   5 ∠*BDA*?   6 ∠*CBD*?

prep quiz

13:01

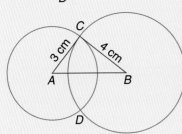

In the diagram on the left:

7 how far is *C* from *A*?
8 how far is *C* from *B*?
9 which point or points are 3 cm from *A* and 4 cm from *B*?
10 Describe how you could find a point that was 3 cm from *A* and 6 cm from *B*.

Exercise 13:01

I Bisecting an angle

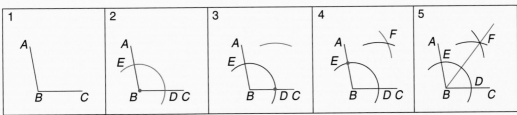

a Draw an acute angle and use the method above to bisect it.
b Draw and bisect an obtuse angle.
c Draw a large triangle and bisect each of the angles. The bisectors should meet at a point. (This point is called the *incentre*.)
d What kind of quadrilateral is *BEFD*, in Picture 5 above?

Work in pencil so you can erase easily.

2 **Bisecting an interval**

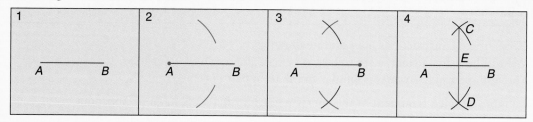

- **a** Draw a horizontal interval 4 cm in length. Bisect this interval.
- **b** Draw a vertical interval 5 cm in length. Bisect this interval.
- **c** Draw a large triangle and bisect each side. The bisectors should meet at a point. (This point is called the *circumcentre*.)
- **d** What kind of quadrilateral is *ACBD* in Picture 4 above?

3 **Constructing a perpendicular to a line from a point on the line**
(This is the same as bisecting the straight angle at *A*.)

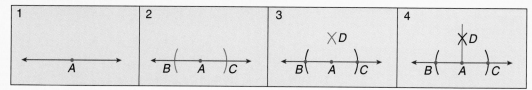

- **a** Draw a horizontal line. Choose a point on the line and construct a perpendicular to the line at that point.
- **b** Draw a vertical line. Choose a point on the line and construct a perpendicular to the line at that point.
- **c** Draw an oblique (slanting) line. Choose a point on the line and construct a perpendicular to the line at that point.
- **d** What kind of triangle is Δ*BDC* in Picture 4 above?

4 **Constructing the perpendicular to a line from a point off the line**

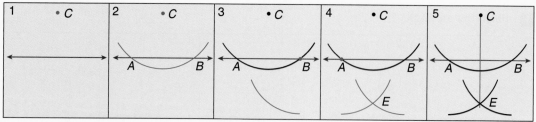

- **a** Draw a horizontal line. Choose a point above the line and construct a perpendicular to the line from that point.
- **b** Draw a horizontal line. Choose a point below the line and construct a perpendicular to the line from that point.
- **c** What kind of quadrilateral is *ACBE* in Picture 5?

5 Constructing angles of 60° and 120°

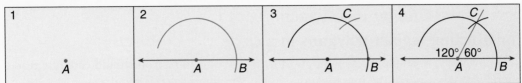

We use the same construction to draw a 60° angle as a 120° angle.

a Construct a 60° angle.

b Construct a 120° angle.

c What kind of triangle is $\triangle ACB$ in Picture 4, above?

6

a Use a pair of compasses to construct a circle.

b Choose any 4 points on the circle. Measure the distance of each point from the centre. Are these distances the same?

c Write a definition for a circle. (A definition explains clearly what it is.)

investigation 13:01

Investigation 13:01 | Constructing regular polygons in a circle

Please use the Assessment Grid on the following page to help you understand what is required for this Investigation.

- A **regular polygon** is a plane figure that has all its sides equal in length and all its angles equal in size. The equilateral triangle and the square are the simplest regular polygons.

- To construct a regular polygon in a circle, we have to space the vertices of the polygon equally around the circle. We do this by drawing equal-sized angles at the centre. The size of the angle is found by dividing 360° by the number of sides.

Example

Construct a regular hexagon in a circle of radius 2 cm.

- First draw the circle of radius 2 cm.

- Since a hexagon has six sides, we must construct six equal angles at the centre.

- The size of the angles is 360° ÷ 6 = 60°.

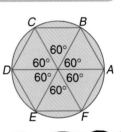

A hexagon has 6 sides.
360° ÷ 6 = 60°.
Therefore I would need six 60° angles.

Exercise

1 Construct a regular polygon that has:

a 3 sides   b 4 sides

c 8 sides   d 10 sides

Technology
Applications

Activities

13:01 Circumcentre of a triangle

Assessment Grid for Investigation 13:01 |
Constructing regular polygons in a circle

The following is a sample assessment grid for this investigation. You should carefully read the criteria *before* beginning the investigation so that you know what is required.

			Assessment Criteria (B, C, D)		Achieved ✓
Criterion B Investigating Patterns	a		Constructions have not been done in an organised way. Polygons are simply drawn.	1	
				2	
	b		Most of the constructions have been done properly showing the steps in construction.	3	
				4	
	c		All the polygons in question 1 have been drawn correctly and show how the construction was done.	5	
				6	
	d		All of the polygons in the investigation have been constructed correctly and construction is shown.	7	
				8	
Criterion C Communication	a		Although many of the polygons have been drawn, not all the construction and working out is shown.	1	
				2	
	b		The construction and most of the working out is shown.	3	
				4	
	c		All of the construction and working out is shown clearly.	5	
				6	
Criterion D Reflection in Mathematics	a		An attempt has been made to explain how the construction was done and the answers make sense.	1	
				2	
	b		The method has been explained and the answers for the polygons make sense.	3	
				4	
	c		The alternative method given in the exercise has been performed successfully and the two methods have been evaluated for their usefulness in given situations.	5	
				6	

13:02 | Congruence and Transformations

- In past years you should have encountered reflections, translations and rotations, or, to give them their more familiar names, flips, slides and turns.

Flip the shape.   Slide the shape.   Turn the shape around.

- When a figure undergoes one of these transformations it is unchanged in shape and size. The only thing that changes is its position.

 Congruent figures are the same shape and size. When one is placed on top of the other they coincide exactly.

- Congruent figures are produced by flips, slides and turns.
- When congruent figures are placed on top of each other (or superimposed) so that they coincide exactly, *the matching sides and angles are obviously equal*.

    These two figures are congruent.
Can you identify the matching sides and angles?

Exercise 13:02

1 Each diagram shows two congruent figures.
What transformations have produced the figures?

a

b

c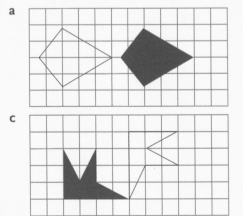

d

2 Copy the figure shown onto grid paper and make a figure which is congruent to it using:

   a a translation

   b a reflection

   c a rotation.

3 **a** In the diagram, which angle matches with:

    i ∠A?   **ii** ∠C?   **iii** ∠M?

   b In the diagram, which side matches with:

    i BC?   **ii** MN?   **iii** PO?

   c Do the shapes have the same area?

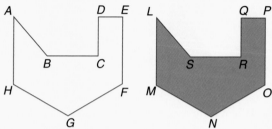

4

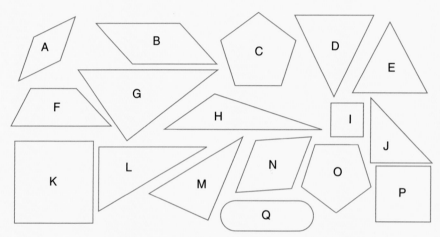

Which of the shapes above is congruent to each shape below? (Measure the shapes carefully.)

a    **b**   **c**

d    **e**    **f**

5 Show how the regular hexagon can be divided into:

   a 2 congruent figures

   b 3 congruent figures

   c 4 congruent figures

6 Copy the following figures and, by adding one line, divide each into two congruent shapes.

a 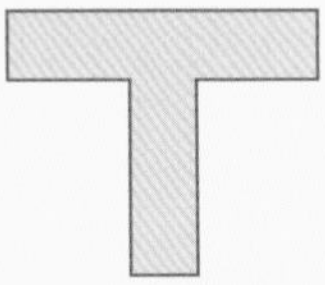 　b 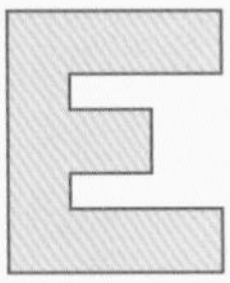 　c 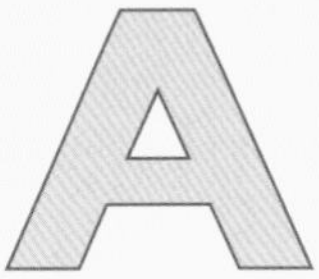 　d

e 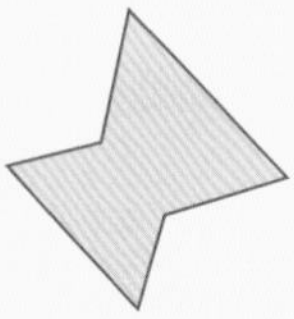 　f 　g  　h

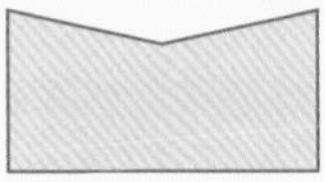

7 In each of the following, a diagonal has been drawn on a quadrilateral. State whether the two triangles obtained are congruent or not.

a 　b 　c

　　Rectangle　　　　　　　Parallelogram　　　　　　Rhombus

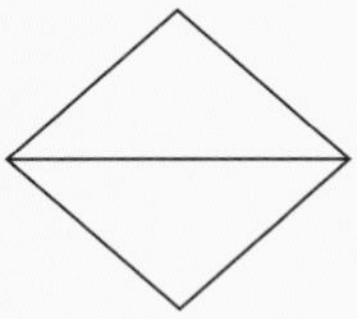

8 The figures shown are congruent.
　a What transformations have produced the figures?
　b What angle matches with:
　　i ∠C?　　ii ∠A?　　iii ∠R?
　c What side matches with:
　　i HG?　　ii DE?　　iii MN?

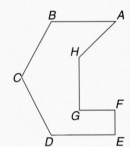
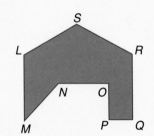

9 Tiling patterns are based on congruent figures. In the tile patterns shown, four small sections have been joined to form a 'tile'. Redraw the patterns and then colour them in using only the new 'tile' shape.

a 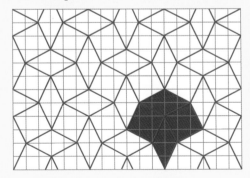　b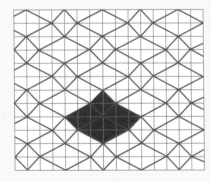

　c Do congruent shapes have the same area?

10 Show how the figure shown can be divided into:

a 2 congruent figures
b 3 congruent figures
c 4 congruent figures.

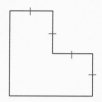

13:02

Investigation 13:02 | Congruent figures and tessellations

Please use the Assessment Grid on the following page to help you understand what is required for this Investigation.

A tiling pattern is called a **tessellation**. When you look at a tessellation which only has tiles of one shape, it is obvious that all of the tiles must be congruent, as in the example shown.

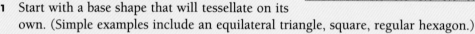

- There are different mathematical methods that can be used to produce a tile shape which will tessellate (ie form a tiling pattern or tessellation). One such method involves *translating opposite sides*. The examples below illustrate this method.

  1 Start with a base shape that will tessellate on its own. (Simple examples include an equilateral triangle, square, regular hexagon.)

  2 Construct three tessellations, one based on a triangular grid, one based on a square grid and one based on a hexagonal grid. Whatever you do to one side must be translated to the other side.

 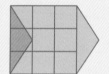 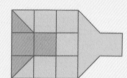

A more complicated example is shown below.

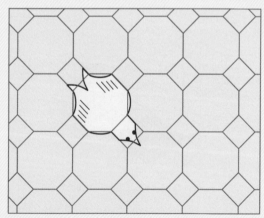

Much use is made of tessellation patterns in many art designs, and some artists use the geometry of tessellations to great effect. One such artist was a Dutchman named Maurits Escher. See if you can find out more about Escher and his designs.

Congruent figures and tessellations

The following is a sample assessment grid for this investigation. You should carefully read the criteria *before* beginning the investigation so that you know what is required.

		Assessment Criteria (B, C, D)		Achieved ✓
Criterion B Investigating Patterns	a	Constructions have not been done in an organised way. Only the base shapes are tessellated.	1	
			2	
	b	At least one tessellation has been constructed successfully using one of the base shapes.	3	
			4	
	c	Three tessellations have been constructed with some success using the base shapes given.	5	
			6	
	d	Non-regular, semi-regular tessellations have been used as a basis for at least one imaginative tessellation as in the final example.	7	
			8	
Criterion C Communication	a	Although tessellations have been attempted, construction is not clear and there is no written explanation.	1	
			2	
	b	The construction is shown and there has been some explanation of how it was accomplished.	3	
			4	
	c	All of the construction and working out is shown clearly.	5	
			6	
Criterion D Reflection in Mathematics	a	An attempt has been made to explain how the construction has been done.	1	
			2	
	b	The method is explained and there is some reference made to how the shape was formed in the tessellation.	3	
			4	
	c	All three tessellations have been drawn showing alternatives and there is some discussion on which basic pattern allows for the most interesting final tessellation.	5	
			6	

13:03 | Congruent Figures

prep quiz

13:03

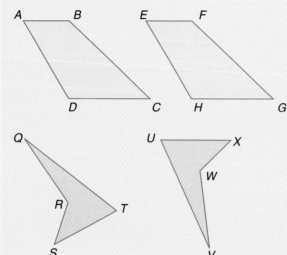

Quadrilateral *ABCD* is congruent to quadrilateral *EFGH*.
Which is the matching side to:

1 *AB*?　　　**2** *EH*?　　　**3** *DC*?

Which is the matching angle to:

4 ∠*ABC*?　　　**5** ∠*EHG*?

Quadrilateral *QRST* is congruent to quadrilateral *VWXU*.
Which side matches side:

6 *RS*?　　　**7** *UX*?　　　**8** *QT*?

Which angle matches:

9 ∠*VUX*?　　　**10** ∠*RQT*?

- **Congruent shapes have the same shape and size.**
- **△*ABC* ≡ △*EFG* means △*ABC* is congruent to △*EFG*.**
- **If two shapes are congruent, then:**
  - **matching sides are equal**
  - **matching angles are equal**
  - **the shapes have the same area.**

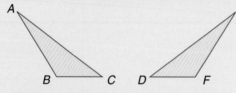

If △*ABC* ≡ △*EFD* then:

AB = *EF*	∠*ABC* = ∠*EFD*
AC = *ED*	∠*BCA* = ∠*FDE*
BC = *FD*	∠*BAC* = ∠*FED*

≡ means
is congruent to.

- **When writing a congruence statement, name the vertices in matching order, eg △*ABC* ≡ △*EFD*.**

- To construct congruent shapes we can use geometrical instruments. We simply use the same steps for both shapes or copy the original shape.

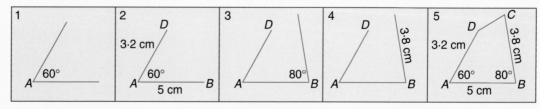

Exercise 13:03

Foundation Worksheet 13:03

Congruent figures
1 List five pairs of congruent shapes.

2 Complete:
a Shape A ≡ shape …

1

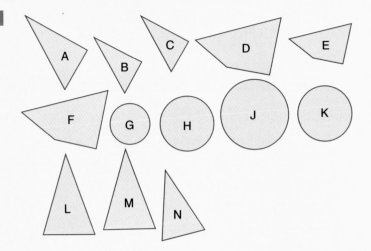

Which shape is congruent to:
a shape B?   **b** shape D?   **c** shape K?   **d** shape M?

2 Use the shapes in Question 1 to complete these congruence statements.
a ΔB ≡ …   **b** shape D ≡ …   **c** ΔM ≡ …

3

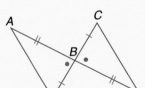

ΔABE ≡ ΔDBC.
Which side matches side:
a AB?   **b** EB?   **c** AE?
Which angle matches:
d ∠EAB?   **e** ∠ABE?   **f** ∠BEA?

4

The trapezium ACFD has been halved by the axis of symmetry BE, forming two congruent shapes.
Which side matches side:
a AB?   **b** AD?   **c** BE?
d Complete the congruence statement: ABED ≡ …
e Would these congruent shapes have the same area?
f Would all congruent shapes have the same area.

5

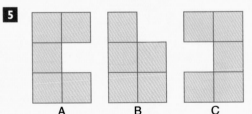

a Which two shapes are congruent?
b Do the congruent shapes have the same area?
c Do shapes B and C have the same area?
d Why aren't B and C congruent?

6 What is the condition for two circles to be congruent?

13:04 | Constructing Congruent Figures

Congruent figures have the same shape and size. A good way of checking to see if figures are congruent is by superimposing one figure on the other.

Exercise 13:04

You will need: paper, pencils, compasses, scissors

1 **a** Use either compasses or tracing paper to construct accurately, on paper, each of the triangles below.

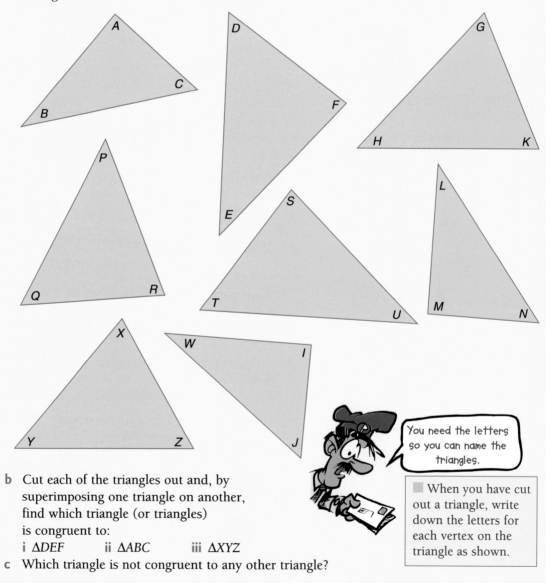

b Cut each of the triangles out and, by superimposing one triangle on another, find which triangle (or triangles) is congruent to:

    i Δ*DEF*   **ii** Δ*ABC*   **iii** Δ*XYZ*

c Which triangle is not congruent to any other triangle?

You need the letters so you can name the triangles.

■ When you have cut out a triangle, write down the letters for each vertex on the triangle as shown.

When congruent triangles are superimposed, the *matching sides and matching angles* are often called *corresponding sides* and *corresponding angles*.

2 Use the triangles you made in Question 1 to answer the following questions.

a Which triangle is congruent to ΔPQR? Write down the pairs of matching angles and matching sides in these triangles.

b Which triangle is congruent to ΔDEF? Write down the pairs of matching angles and matching sides in these triangles.

If ΔABC is congruent to ΔDEF, we write $\Delta ABC \equiv \Delta DEF$.
'$\equiv$' means 'is congruent to'.

3 Each of the following pairs of triangles is congruent. Write down the pairs of matching sides and matching angles for each part.

a

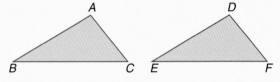

b

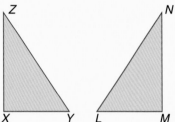

c

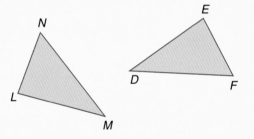

d

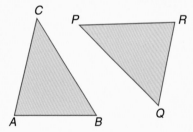

e

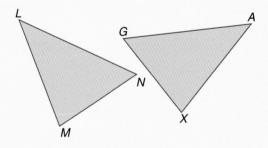

Once you know they're congruent, you can simply just match the sides according to their lengths. It's that easy!

Equal angles are opposite equal sides.

4 Use compasses to draw circles congruent to those given.

a   **b**   **c** A circle of radius 3 cm.

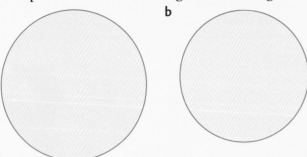

5 Construct figures congruent to the figures below.

a

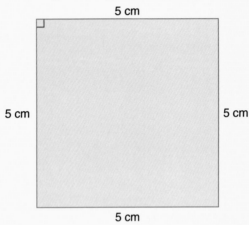

5 cm (top), 5 cm (left), 5 cm (right), 5 cm (bottom)

b

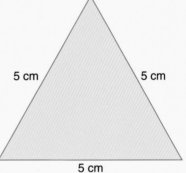

5 cm (top), 3 cm (left), 3 cm (right), 5 cm (bottom)

c

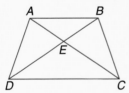

6 cm, 3·5 cm, 3·5 cm

d

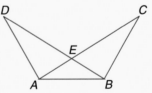

5 cm (left), 5 cm (right), 5 cm (bottom)

By drawing a straight line on each of the figures you have drawn, divide each figure into two congruent triangles.

6 In each of the following figures there are several pairs of congruent triangles. Find them.

a

A   B   E   D   C

b   D   C   E   A   B

Appendix G **G:01 The minimum conditions for congruent triangles**

Fun Spot 13:04 | What is a stupid ant?

Work out the answer to each question and put the letter for that part in the box above the correct answer.

The diagram shows a regular hexagon on which some of its diagonals have been drawn. Because of the symmetry of the hexagon, the diagonals have formed many congruent triangles.

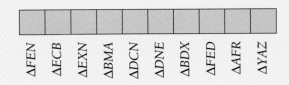

Find the triangle that is congruent to each of the following:

N ΔBFE	**G** ΔBMC	**N** ΔAFY	**A** ΔABC	**I** ΔBMY
N ΔCDN	**R** ΔBFX	**A** ΔBCP	**O** ΔAYB	**T** ΔCOP

ΔFEN ΔECB ΔEXN ΔBMA ΔDCN ΔDNE ΔBDX ΔFED ΔAFR ΔYAZ

- Explain how this playground shows congruent shapes.

Mathematical terms 13

bisect
- To cut into two equal parts.
- Bisecting an angle and bisecting an interval are covered in 13:01.

compasses (or pair of compasses)
- A geometrical instrument made from 2 arms that are joined at one end.

construct
- To draw accurately using instruments.

corresponding
- Matching.
- Corresponding sides are matching sides.
- Corresponding angles are matching angles.

interval
- The part of a straight line between two points.

parallel lines
- Straight lines in the same plane that do not meet.
  eg *AB* is parallel to *CD*,
  AB || *CD*.

perpendicular lines
- Two straight lines that are at right angles to one another.
  eg *PQ* is perpendicular to *XY*, *PQ* ⊥ *XY*.

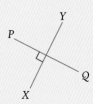

superimpose
- To place one figure on top of another so that they match.

transformations (congruence transformations)
- The movement of a shape to a new position. The shape in the new position would be congruent to the shape in the original position.
- reflection: A flip about a line.

- translation: A slide.

- rotation: A turn about a point.

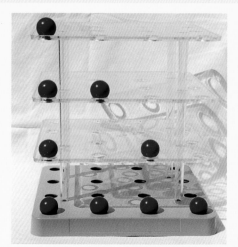

- The distance between the centres of adjacent balls on the horizontal line is 7 cm. The distance between the centres of adjacent balls on the vertical line is 8 cm. What is the distance between adjacent balls on the hypotenuse?

Diagnostic Test 13: | Geometric Constructions and Congruent Figures

- Each section of the test has similar items that test a certain type of question.
- Errors made will indicate areas of weakness.
- Each weakness should be treated by going back to the section listed.
- You will need a ruler and compasses.

Section

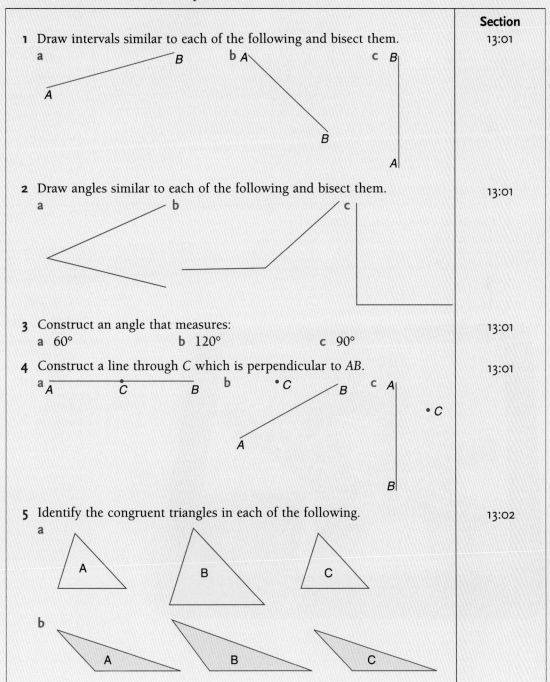

1 Draw intervals similar to each of the following and bisect them.   13:01

a   b A   c B

A   B

2 Draw angles similar to each of the following and bisect them.   13:01

a   b   c

3 Construct an angle that measures: 13:01
  a 60°   b 120°   c 90°

4 Construct a line through *C* which is perpendicular to *AB*.   13:01

a A — C — B   b • C   c A

A   B   B

• C

5 Identify the congruent triangles in each of the following.   13:02

a

A   B   C

b

A   B   C

6 $\triangle EFG \equiv \triangle MNL$

Which side matches side:

a EF? b EG? c FG?

Which angle matches:

d $\angle EFG$? e $\angle FGE$? f $\angle LMN$?

13:02
13:03

7 BD is an axis of symmetry of $\triangle ACD$.

a Complete: $\triangle ABD \equiv ...$

b Which side matches AB?

c Which side matches CD?

d Which angle matches $\angle BAD$?

e Which angle matches $\angle BDA$?

13:02
13:03

8 a Construct two congruent circles using geometrical instruments.

b Construct two congruent triangles using geometrical instruments.

c Construct two congruent quadrilaterals using geometrical instruments.

13:04

- Assuming that only one tile can be moved at a time, what is the least number of moves that would leave the empty space:
  a in the centre?
  b on the top left?
  c on the top middle?

Chapter 13 | Revision Assignment

1   Simplify the following:
    a $4x + 3y + 6 + 2x + 4y$
    b $4x^2 - 3x + 2x^2 + 8x - 6$

2   Expand and simplify:
    a $x(2x - 1) + 3x(1 - x)$
    b $4a(a - 3 + b) - b(a - 2)$

3   Solve:
    a $3p = 2p - 7$ b $1 - 6a = 3a + 8$
    c $-4 - 6b = 12 - 3b$

4   a   If $x = -3$, evaluate $3x^2 - 4x - 5$
    b   If $a = 4$, $b = -2$, evaluate $\dfrac{(a - b)^3}{a + 2b - 4}$

5   Find the value of the pronumeral in each of the following.
    a

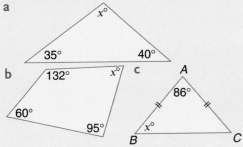

    b

    c

6   What is the equation of each line?
    a

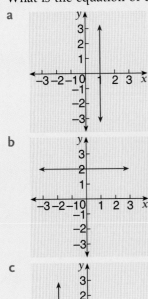

    b

    c

7   The bottom prism is made from the other two. What is its volume?

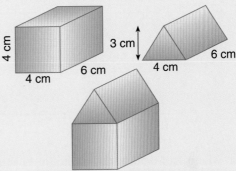

8   a   The ratio of the weights of two boxes is $3:2$. If the total weight of the boxes is $58\,\text{kg}$, find the weight of the lighter box.
    b   In making up a paint, two colours A and B are mixed in the ratio $1.5:1$. How much of each paint is needed to make $4\,\text{L}$ of paint?

9   a   A bronze alloy consists of 80% copper, 12% tin and 8% zinc. How much tin will be in $70\,\text{kg}$ of this bronze?
    b   When heated, a metal girder expands from $15\,\text{m}$ in length to $15.06\,\text{m}$. What is the percentage increase in the length of the girder?

10 Use compasses to construct a triangle with sides of $5.5\,\text{cm}$, $4.2\,\text{cm}$ and $6.2\,\text{cm}$. Measure the size of the largest angle to the nearest degree.

11 Make accurate drawings of the following and by measurement find the value of each pronumeral.
    a

    b

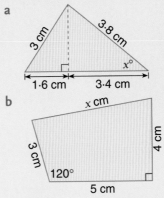

Chapter 13 | Working Mathematically

1 Complete each of the following by finding the missing digits.

a   3 8 +
    ☐ ☐
    ———
    7 4

b   9 0 4 –
    ☐ ☐
    ———
    ☐ 4 1

c   5 ☐ 4 +
    ☐ 3 ☐
    ———
    ☐ 1 0 1

d   ☐ 6 3 2 –
    9 ☐ ☐
    ———
    ☐ 0 7

2 The petrol tank of my car holds 45 litres. I drove into a petrol station and filled the tank. It cost me $11.70. If the petrol cost 97·5 cents per litre, how many litres did I buy? How much was in the tank before it was filled?

3 Rhonda bought an ice-cream or an ice-block for each of the seven people in her family. Ice-creams cost $1.90 each, while ice-blocks cost 90 cents each. if she spent $8.30 altogether, how many ice-blocks did she buy?

4 A television and a radio together cost $1440. The television is $940 dearer than the radio. How much does the television cost?

5 Everybody at a meeting shook hands once with every other person present. If there were 21 handshakes, how many people were present?

6 Four children, Sarah, Kate, Ben and Emma, sit with their parents Margaret and Peter in set positions around the meal table. Emma sits next to one of her parents. Ben, who sits opposite his father, sits between Sarah and Kate. Sarah sits between Ben and Emma. Give the name of the child who sits in each of the seats 1, 2, 3 and 4.

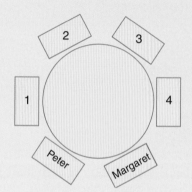

Statistics

Chapter Contents

Learning Outcomes

Students will be able to:

- Construct, read and interpret graphs, tables, charts and statistical information.
- Collect statistical data using either a census or a sample, and analyse data using measures of location and range.

Areas of Interaction

Approaches to Learning (Knowledge Acquisition, Problem Solving, Communication Skills, Thinking Skills, Information Literacy Skills, Information and Communication Technology Skills, Collaborative Skills, Reflection Skills), Health and Social Education, Environments, Community and Service, Human Ingenuity

We get bombarded by statistics every day in our society, particularly through advertising. Statistics is the branch of mathematics that is concerned with the gathering and organisation of numerical information called **data**. There are three basic steps:
- Collecting the data
- Sorting the data
- Analysing the data.

14:01 | Collecting Data

Information is collected in different ways depending upon the use that is going to be made of it and how accurate it needs to be. Two common ways are a **census** and a **sample**.

Census

A survey of a whole population is called a census. For example, if every student in the school were questioned to determine how many students catch a bush to school, this would be a **simple census**.

- I first made up some key questions.
- I refined them after a trial.
- I then applied them to my sample, and made predictions.

In many countries a **national census** is conducted every five years, collecting information on its citizens such as details of income, employment, education, housing and many other things. This, of course, is a huge task, and it takes a lot of time and effort to sort and analyse the data.

Sample

Sometimes, particularly if a population is large, a census is impractical, so only a small portion or sample of the population is surveyed. Of course, if the sample is to reflect the opinions of the whole population, the people chosen should be selected **at random**. Also, the sample must be large enough to give a fair indication of the opinions sought.

For example, if five students were selected randomly in the playground and asked if they caught a bus to school and four of them said yes, the sample would be too small to reasonably conclude that 4 out of 5, or 80%, of all students caught a bus to school. If the sample was, say, 100 students, then any data collected would have a greater chance of reflecting the total student population.

Of course, a lot of statistics does not involve either a census or a sample but merely the collecting and tabulating of numerical facts. Examples of this would be:
- sports — such as cricket: bowling and batting averages, run rates, etc.
                 tennis: first serves in, unforced errors, double faults, etc.
                 football: tackle counts, goals kicked, points for and against, etc.
- weather — temperatures, barometer readings, rainfall, tides, etc.
- stock exchange — buying and selling figures, exchange rates, etc.

Work through the following short exercise and then try some of the practical suggestions given.

Read these carefully!

1 Mr Hines suspected that Maths was the favourite subject of students in Grade 7, so he asked students in his class to conduct a survey to establish this fact.

- Matthew decided just to ask five of his friends. Since three of them liked Maths the best, he reported that 3 out of 5, or 60% of students, liked Maths best.
- Terry decided just to survey his class. Since 20 out of the class of 30 liked Maths best, he reported that $\frac{2}{3}$ out of the grade were Maths lovers.
- Caroline decided to ask 10 students from each of the four classes their opinion. From this she concluded that 70% of students liked Maths best.
- Alexis thought the only way to be really sure was to ask each student in the grade.

a Which student actually carried out a census?

b Three students surveyed a sample of the year. Which sample is likely to have been the most accurate?

c Why do you think the other two samples might have been less accurate?

d What is one problem with conducting a census, rather than surveying a sample?

2 Melody wanted to see which type of music was most popular in the community so she handed out this survey form to fellow students at school.
She discovered that Rock and Roll was by far the most popular.

a What is wrong with Melody's sample?

b How could she get a better sample of the community's opinion?

Tick Your Favourite	
Classical	[ ]
Country & Western	[ ]
Folk	[ ]
Jazz	[ ]
Rock & Roll	[ ]

3 Ben attends an international school in India. He wanted to discover the sport that was most popular in the community so he handed out this survey form to his fellow students at school. He discovered that soccer was by far the most popular.

a What is wrong with Ben's sample?

b What is wrong with his questionnaire?

c How could he get a better sample of the community's opinions?

d Design a questionnaire that would be more useful than this one.

Tick Your Favourite	
Soccer	[ ]
Rugby	[ ]
Hockey	[ ]
Basketball	[ ]
Cricket	[ ]
Tennis	[ ]
Softball	[ ]

4 Before elections, polls are carried out by different organisations which try to predict who the electors are going to vote for. Often they come up with different results. How can this happen?

5 Roland rolled a dice and got these results:
1 4 6 5 6 3 2 6
Because three times more 6s were rolled than any other number, Roland concluded that the die must be 'weighted' to give more 6s.
a Is this conclusion necessarily correct?
b What should Roland do to make sure that his conclusion is correct?
c How does this question relate to taking a sample?

6 *TV Now* magazine runs an opinion poll to see what shows and personalities are the most popular. Why might the results not be accurate?

7 What is wrong with these claims?
a 9 out of 10 dogs prefer MUNCH-O'S!
b 4 out of 5 dentists use AJAX toothpaste!
c 20% more people drink FIZ soft drink!
d ELECTRO batteries last 30% longer!

 Stratified random sampling
Where a population contains subgroups that need to be acknowledged, random sampling should be done on a sectional basis to ensure that the population is fairly represented.

1 Determine the fraction that the group is of the whole.
2 Make sure that the same fraction of the sample contains people from this group.

   eg **If our sample is to be 60 people and we know that $\frac{1}{10}$ of the whole group are Grade 7 students then we should survey $\frac{1}{10}$ of 60 (ie 6) Grade 7 students.**

8 A survey was to be held at Black Rock High School. It has been decided to use stratified random sampling to sample students from Grades 8 to 12. If 80 students are to be chosen, how many from each grade should be chosen? The number of students in each grade is shown in this table.

Grade 8	Grade 9	Grade 10	Grade 11	Grade 12	Total
160	203	245	200	202	1010

9 A survey of Germans, 15 years and over, is to be carried out to discover what percentage have seen the Brandenburg Gate. A *stratified random sample* of 1000 people is to be surveyed, with groups considered according to age. How many of each age group should be surveyed if of the 70 576 000 people 15 years and over:

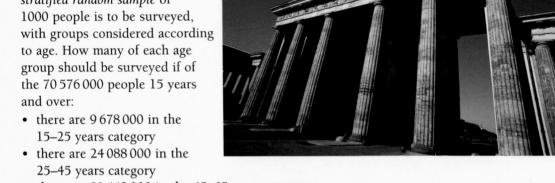

- there are 9 678 000 in the 15–25 years category
- there are 24 088 000 in the 25–45 years category
- there are 21 442 000 in the 45–65 years category
- there are 15 368 000 in the 65 years and over category.

10 If a *stratified random sample* of 100 students is to be selected from your school, how many students should be selected from each Year?

Practical Activities 14:01 | Nothing but the facts

(Data collected in these activities may be used for **Investigation 14:02.**)

1 Conduct a survey to find out how many children are in the family of each class member.

2 Go to a carpark or a point beside a fairly busy road and collect various data on the vehicles you see.
For example:
Type of vehicle: car, truck, bus, bike.
Make of vehicle: Nissan, Ford, Toyota, etc.
Colour of vehicle: red, white, etc.
Number plates: First letter or number on each plate.

3 Roll two dice a large number of times (at least 100 times!) and record the totals.

I think it might be easier if you just surveyed **parked** cars.

14:02 | Sorting Data

The frequency distribution table

When a large amount of data has been collected, it is usually fairly useless until it has been sorted in some way and presented in a form that is easily read. A common method of sorting data involves using a **frequency distribution** table. Look at the example below to see how it is done.

Now I've got this great list of data, what do I do with it?

Example

Elizabeth surveyed the 30 students in her class to determine the number of children in each family. This resulted in the following data.

```
2  3  1  2  5  4  1  2  3  3
2  4  6  4  4  2  3  1  1  3
2  1  5  3  3  2  1  2  4  2
```

If the data is organised in a frequency distribution table, it looks like this:

Outcome	Tally	Frequency
1	ЖI	6
2	ЖIIII	9
3	ЖII	7
4	Ж	5
5	II	2
6	I	1

Total: 30

Every fifth count in the tally is shown by a stroke through the other four.

Note the following features of the frequency distribution table.

- The *Outcome* column shows the possible results for the scores.
- The *Tally* column is used for recording the data, one entry at a time.
- The *Frequency* is the total tally for each outcome (the number of scores equal to the outcome).
- The *Total* of the frequencies should be the same as the number of scores.

It can easily be seen that the most common number of children per family is 2; that only one family has 6 children; that 6 students are the only children in their families; and so on.

Using graphs

Another way of showing the data in an easily read form is by drawing a graph. Two commonly used types of graphs are the frequency histogram and the frequency polygon. The data in the table on page 344 can be graphed as a frequency histogram or a frequency polygon.

The frequency histogram

This is a type of column graph where the columns are drawn next to each other. You should note the following features.

- Each axis is labelled.
- The graph has a title.
- The columns are centred on the scores.
- The first column begins one-half of a column width in from the vertical axis.

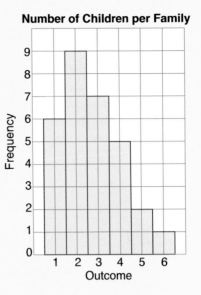

Number of Children per Family

The frequency polygon

This is a type of line graph. Note that the axes are the same as for the histogram. You should note the following features.

- Each axis is labelled.
- The graph has a title.
- The dots showing the data are joined by straight lines.
- The first and last dot are connected to the horizontal axis as shown.
- The first score is one unit in from the vertical axis.

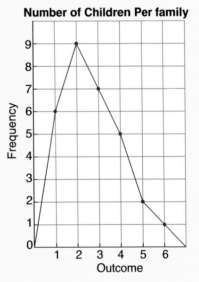

Number of Children Per family

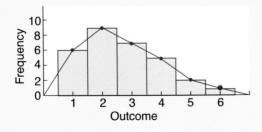

It is interesting to note that if a frequency histogram and polygon are both drawn on the same axes, the polygon joins the midpoints of the top of each column in the histogram. This is shown in the diagram on the left.

1
a Complete the frequency column of this table.
b How many scores were there altogether?
c Which outcome occurred the most?
d What was the frequency of 4?
e How many scores were 4 or more?

Outcome	Tally	Frequency
2	III	
3	IIII IIII	
4	IIII I	
5	IIII	
6	II	

Total: _____

2
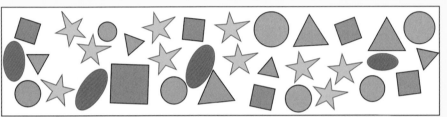

a Complete the frequency distribution table for the shapes in the rectangle above.
b How many shapes are there altogether?
c Which shape occurs most frequently?
d Of which shape are there more: triangles or squares?

Outcome	Tally	Frequency
circle		
square		
oval		
star		
triangle		

Total: _____

3 A dice was rolled 36 times and the following results were recorded:

    4 2 3 1 3 4 6 1 5 3 4 6
    6 3 4 2 1 1 4 5 6 3 4 5
    1 3 5 4 2 6 1 2 5 3 6 4

a Sort the data into a frequency distribution table.
b Which outcome had the highest frequency?
c Which outcome had the lowest frequency?
d If you rolled this dice another 36 times, would you expect to get the same results?

4 Mr Morris gave his class a spelling test of 10 Maths words. The number of words each of the 30 students spelt correctly was:

    9 7 8 6   4 7 10 9 8 7   ⟵ the scores
    6 7 5 5 10 9   8 8 7 9
    10 5 7 6   8 8   7 9 6 9

a What was the highest score?
b What was the lowest score?
c Organise the data into a frequency distribution table.
d What was the most common score?
e How many students spelt fewer than 7 words correctly?
f How many students made only 2 mistakes or fewer?

Outcome	Frequency
4	
5	
6	
7	
8	
9	
10	

Total: _____

5

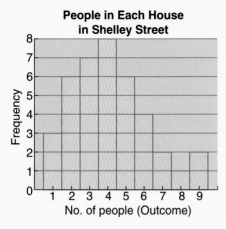

People in Each House in Shelley Street

This histogram shows the number of people living in each house in Shelley Street.

a What is the most common number of people per house?

b How many people live by themselves?

c What is the largest number of people in any one house?

d How many houses have 5 people in them?

e Work out the total number of houses in Shelley Street.

f How many people live in groups of 3?

g Calculate how many people live in Shelley Street altogether.

6

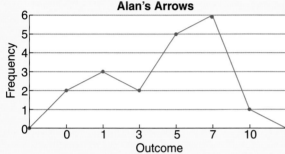

Alan's Arrows

This polygon shows the scores for the arrows Alan fired at a target.

a How many arrows hit the bullseye for a score of 10?

b How many missed the target, scoring zero points?

c How many arrows scored 7 or more?

d How many arrows were fired altogether?

7 Draw a frequency histogram for each set of data given.

a

Outcome	Frequency
1	2
2	4
3	6
4	5
5	1

b

Outcome	Frequency
7	1
8	3
9	2
10	6
11	3
12	5

8 a Fill in this frequency table by reading the frequency polygon given.
   b How many scores were there altogether?
   c How many scores were 20 or less?

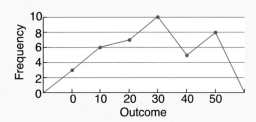

Outcome	Frequency

Total: _____

9 A bag of Goody-Gumdrops contains 30 lollies; at least, that's what it says on the packet. However, when 50 bags were surveyed for their contents, the following results were obtained:

```
31  30  29  30  30  31  32  29  28  30
30  29  30  31  33  32  31  30  28  29
27  31  30  32  30  30  31  30  32  31
30  29  28  30  31  28  30  30  27  30
33  29  32  30  30  31  30  31  32  30
```

   a Determine the highest and lowest scores in the data.
   b Organise the data into a frequency distribution table.
   c How many packets did not have at least 30 lollies in them?
   d How many packets had more than 30 lollies?
   e Graph these results by drawing a combined frequency histogram and polygon.

10 Luke was concerned about his country's gun laws. He asked 100 people to respond to the following statement:

It should be made harder for people to own a gun.
A strongly agree   B agree
C disagree   D strongly disagree

These were his results:

```
A  B  A  A  C  A  A  D  A  B  C  B  D  A  B  B  C  B  A  B
B  C  B  B  A  B  C  C  B  B  D  B  A  A  B  C  C  B  B  B
B  B  A  B  C  B  B  C  A  B  B  A  A  B  B  C  A  A  A  A
B  A  C  D  A  B  B  A  C  B  B  B  B  C  A  B  B  C  B  D
B  A  B  B  B  C  C  C  A  B  B  C  C  B  B  B  A  A  C  A
```

   a Organise these results into a frequency distribution table.
   b How many people strongly agree with the statement?
   c What percentage of the people asked strongly disagree with the statement?
   d What percentage of the people asked think that it should be made harder for people to own a gun in this country?
   e What percentage think that it should not be made harder?
   f Draw a frequency histogram of these results.

Investigation 14:02 | Sorting it out

Please use the Assessment Grid on the following page to help you understand what is required for this Investigation.

(Some of these activities refer to data collected in **Practical Activities 14:01**.)

1 Sort the data collected on the number of children in the families of each class member into a frequency distribution table. Also draw a graph showing this information. How would this information reflect the whole population of the city you live in? What differences might there be and why?

2 The data collected on motor vehicles could also be sorted into a table and graphed.

3 When two dice are rolled a large number of times the results are very interesting. What total would you expect to occur most often? Sort the results into a table to find out.

We'll examine some of this data at the end of the next exercise.

• Make a frequency polygon or histogram on some aspect of cricket or of a cricket match.

Assessment Grid for Investigation 14:02 | **Sorting it out**

The following is a sample assessment grid for this investigation. You should carefully read the criteria *before* beginning the investigation so that you know what is required.

			Assessment Criteria (B, C, D)		Achieved ✓
Criterion B Investigating Patterns	a		Data has not been collected in an organised and systematic way.	1	
				2	
	b		Data is well organised and arranged, and any recognised patterns are described.	3	
				4	
	c		Patterns in the data are discussed and conclusions and/or predictions are also discussed.	5	
				6	
	d		The results of the surveys and the rolling of dice are discussed in depth and possible expectations are also discussed.	7	
				8	
Criterion C Communication	a		Data has been collected but is not arranged in an organised way.	1	
				2	
	b		Data is arranged well in tables, illustrated in graphs and supported by some sort of description.	3	
				4	
	c		Tables and graphs are clear and any patterns are well documented and explained.	5	
				6	
Criterion D Reflection in Mathematics	a		There has been some attempt to explain how the data was collected and why that method was chosen.	1	
				2	
	b		There is a clear explanation of how the data was collected and why that method was chosen.	3	
				4	
	c		The significance of any patterns in the data is discussed in depth and other possible ways of collecting data have been evaluated.	5	
				6	

14:03 | Analysing Data

After data has been sorted, certain key numbers can be determined.

Range

- The **range** gives a rough idea of how the scores are spread.
- It is defined as the difference between the highest and lowest scores.

worked example

For the scores 5, 9, 3, 4, 7, 3, 2, the highest
score is 9 and the lowest score is 2,

so the range = 9 − 2
$$= 7$$

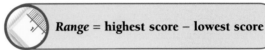

Range = **highest score − lowest score**

Measures of central tendency

The next three key numbers tell us how the scores tend to cluster.
They have the names **mode**, **median** and **mean**, and are together
called the 'measures of central tendency'.

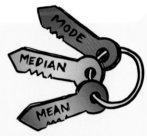

Mode

- The mode is simply the outcome that occurs the most often, ie it has the highest frequency.

worked example

For scores 2, 5, 3, 2, 5, 2, 4, the outcome 2
occurs the most often, so the mode = 2.

The *mode* is the outcome
that occurs most often.

Median

- After a set of scores has been arranged in order,
  the median is the 'middle score'. This is only
  strictly true if there is an odd number of scores.
- For an even number of scores, the median is the
  average of the middle two scores.

■ *A median strip
lies in the middle
of the road.*

worked examples

1 If the scores 5, 9, 3, 7, 4 are arranged
   in order, we get 3, 4, 5, 7, 9.
   Clearly the middle score is 5, so the median = 5.

2 If the scores 5, 9, 3, 7, 4, 6 are arranged
   in order, we get 3, 4, 5, 6, 7, 9.
   Clearly the middle two scores are 5 and 6.

   So the median = $\dfrac{5+6}{2} = 5\frac{1}{2}$ or 5·5.

The *median* is the middle score
for an odd number of scores.
The *median* is the average of
the middle two scores for an
even number of scores.

Mean

- The term 'average' usually refers to the mean.
- To calculate the mean, the sum of the scores is divided by the number of scores.

> ■ *Note:*
> The word 'average' may not always refer to the mean. In a statement like 'The average family car is a Holden' the term 'average' is really referring to the mode, ie more families own Holdens than any other make of car.

worked example

For the scores 6, 7, 8, 4, 6, 8, the sum of the score is 39, and the number of scores is 6.

$$\therefore \text{ the mean} = 39 \div 6$$
$$= 6{\cdot}5 \text{ or } 6\tfrac{1}{2}.$$

The mean is the arithmetic average.

Finding the mean from a frequency distribution table

- To calculate the mean from a frequency distribution table, another column is added: the frequency × outcome column. If x stands for outcome and f stands for frequency, then *frequency × outcome* can be abbreviated to *fx*.

Outcome (x)	Frequency (f)	fx
0	2	0
1	3	3
2	4	8
3	7	21
4	3	12
5	1	5
Totals:	20	49

- Each number in the *fx* column is obtained by multiplying the outcome and frequency together.
- The numbers in the *fx* column give the sums of all 0s, 1s, 2s, etc.

Now the sum of the *fx* column gives the sum of all the scores and the sum of the frequency column gives the number of scores.

So the mean = 49 ÷ 20
$$= 2{\cdot}45 \text{ or } 2\tfrac{9}{20}$$

> **The *mean*** $= \dfrac{\text{sum of all the scores}}{\text{total number of the scores}} = \dfrac{\text{sum of } fx \text{ column}}{\text{sum of frequency column}}$

1 For this set of scores, determine the range, mode, median and mean.

6, 9, 7, 3, 9, 4, 7, 6, 5, 7

Range = highest score − lowest score

= 9 − 3

= 6

∴ Range is 6.

Mode = outcome that occurs the most

7 occurs the most (frequency = 3)

∴ Mode is 7.

For the median the scores must be rearranged in order:

3, 4, 5, 6, 6, 7, 7, 7, 9, 9 [10 scores]

Since there is an even number of scores, median = average of two middle scores

> ■ DON'T FORGET!

$$= \frac{6 + 7}{2}$$

$$= 6\frac{1}{2} \text{ or } 6.5$$

∴ Median is 6·5.

Mean = $\dfrac{\text{sum of the scores}}{\text{total numbers of scores}}$

$$= \frac{63}{10}$$

$$= 6.3$$

∴ Mean is 6·3.

2 From this table determine the range, mode, median and mean.

Outcome	Frequency	fx
5	1	5
6	⑤	30
7	⑤	35
8	4	32
9	3	27
10	2	20
Totals:	20	149

Range = highest score − lowest score

= 10 − 5

= 5

Here there are two scores with the highest frequency, ie 6 and 7.

∴ Modes are 6 and 7.

> ■ *Note:*
> There can be more than one mode.

To work out the **median** we can use the frequency column. There are 20 scores (an even number) so we want the average of the 10th and 11th scores.

Outcome	Frequency	
5	1	→ 1
6	5	→ 6
7	5	→11
8	4	→15
9	3	
10	2	

We progressively add down the frequency column until we reach the 10th and 11th scores.

We can see that there were 6 scores of 6 or less, and 11 scores of 7 or less. This means that both the 10th and 11th scores must have been 7. Of course the average of two 7s is 7.

∴ **Median** is 7.

Mean

$$= \frac{\text{sum of } fx \text{ column}}{\text{sum of frequency column}}$$

$$= \frac{149}{20}$$

$$= 7.45$$

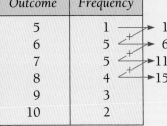

This one's a bit tricky!

Exercise 14:03

Working with data
1 a Complete the table for these scores.
7, 6, 6, 8, 8, 10, 9, 6, 7, 8, 9, 8

Outcome	Tally	*f*
6		
7		
8		
9		
10		

b Find the mode, median and mean.

1 a Determine the range of each set of scores.
   - i 2, 5, 3, 4, 5
   - ii 7, 9, 6, 9, 8, 7, 7
   - iii 10, 20, 10, 50, 40, 30
   - iv 17, 20, 19, 22, 21, 17, 20
   - v 49, 50, 48, 51, 50
   - vi 8, 10, 12, 7, 8, 10, 9, 8, 10, 8, 11
   - vii 5, 4, 6, 3, 2, 4, 6, 9, 4, 7, 3, 2
   - viii 1·1, 1·3, 1·0, 1·2, 1·1, 1·3, 1·4
   - ix 16, 17, 19, 15, 17, 19, 14, 16, 17, 20
   - x 147, 151, 148, 150, 148, 152, 151

b Determine the mode for each set of scores above.

c Find the median of each set of scores.

d Calculate the mean for each set of scores (correct to 1 dec. pl.).

I might prove handy when calculating the mean.

2 a A cricketer has scores of 63, 27, 19, 5, 47 and 21. Find his mean (average) score.

b Samantha had percentage test results of 56, 67, 81, 74 and 93. What was her mean test result?

c The mean of 5 scores is 8.
   - i What must be the total of these scores?
   - ii If four of the scores are 7, 10, 8 and 4, what must the 5th score be?

d The mean of 6 scores is 3·5. If five of the scores are 2, 4, 4, 3 and 6, what must the 6th score be?

3 Amos' and Enoch's scores for six spelling tests of 10 words were:

   Amos: 6, 9, 10, 9, 9, 10
   Enoch: 6, 7, 6, 7, 7, 10

The range of scores for both students was 10 − 6, ie 4.

a Does this mean that both boys had equally good results?

b What would be a better measure of their abilities?

4 Complete these tables and calculate the mean for each set of scores.

a

Outcome	Frequency	*fx*
1	2	
2	4	
3	5	
4	6	
5	3	

Totals: _____ __

b

Outcome	Frequency	*fx*
5	1	
6	5	
7	3	
8	8	
9	5	
10	3	

Totals: _____ __

c

Outcome	Frequency	*fx*
18	1	
19	3	
20	1	
21	4	
22	5	
23	3	
24	1	
25	2	

Totals: _____ __

5 Look at the tables in Question **4**. What is the mode for each set of scores?

6 Calculate the median for each set of scores in Question **4** by looking at the frequency column.

7 The following are the numbers of goals Mr Blackwell's soccer team scored in its matches last season:

```
1  0  2  3  0  1  4  2  3
0  1  1  5  4  3  2  1  2
```

a Sort the data into a frequency distribution table.
b What is the: **i** range?   **ii** mode?   **iii** median?   **iv** mean?
c Graph these scores on a frequency histogram.
d How can you tell the mode from this graph?

8 Six coins were tossed 64 times. The number of heads was recorded each time, with the following results:

```
3  5  3  4  2  2  3  3  5  1  0  4  3  2  3  3
2  1  3  2  3  4  2  1  4  6  3  4  2  5  4  4
3  2  4  1  2  4  3  5  2  3  4  3  1  3  6  4
4  4  3  4  2  3  2  2  3  5  1  2  3  4  1  3
```

a Sort the data into a frequency distribution table.
b Calculate the mean number of heads.
c How many throws displayed 2 heads?
d How many throws must have shown 4 tails?
e Draw a frequency polygon for these results.

9 This histogram shows the number of strike-outs pitched by Willie Chuckitt in each innings for the last baseball season.

a Complete a frequency distribution table for this set of scores.
  (*Note:* You don't need a tally column.)
b What is the mode for this data?
c Determine Willie's median score.
d Calculate the mean number of strike-outs Willie pitched per innings.
e How many more strike-outs would Willie have had to pitch to have a mean of 3 strike-outs per innings?

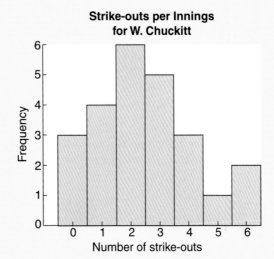

**Strike-outs per Innings
for W. Chuckitt**

10 Barbara and Rob kept a record of the number of pins knocked down with their first balls in tenpin bowling.

Barbara's results

8	7	3	10	9	8	8	7	10	9
8	8	7	9	10	6	10	5	8	7
9	3	5	9	10	8	9	7	6	8
7	9	8	10	8	7	5	8	7	9
10	6	8	9	7	6	10	5	8	9

Rob's results

9	5	3	8	10	10	10	10	4	6
8	10	7	6	10	4	5	7	9	10
9	7	6	4	10	7	6	8	5	9
10	4	8	7	6	10	9	9	8	10
7	10	6	10	9	8	10	6	10	9

a Record this information in two frequency distribution tables, one showing Barbara's results and the other showing Rob's.
b Graph the results on two frequency histograms.
c For each set of results find the:
  i range   **ii** mode   **iii** median   **iv** mean.
d Whose results were the more impressive?

---

investigation

14:03

Investigation 14:03 | Mean, mode and median

Please use the Assessment Grid on the following page to help you understand what is required for this Investigation.

(Some of these activities refer to data collected in **Practical Activities 14:01**.)

1 If you have completed a table showing the number of children in the families of your class members, determine the mode, median and mean for this data.

2 You might also determine the mean and median heights of the students in your class.

3 Look out for advertisements that use the word 'average'. Determine whether the average they are referring to is the mean, mode or perhaps even the median.

4 Choose an item of interest and survey people to discover the mean, mode or median for that item where appropriate.
  For example: • How many telephone calls do you make per week?
               • How far from school do you live?

5 When an 'average' is quoted for the cost of houses, the median is usually used. Explain why the median is the most appropriate measure.

• The height of the man in the suit is 178 cm. Estimate:
  1 the mean height of the group
  2 the median height of the group.

Technology
Applications

Activities

14:03 World temperatures

Assessment Grid for Investigation 14:03 | **Mean, mode and median**

The following is a sample assessment grid for this investigation. You should carefully read the criteria *before* beginning the investigation so that you know what is required.

		Assessment Criteria (B, C, D)		Achieved ✓
Criterion B Investigating Patterns	a	Some measures of central tendency have been found with possible difficulties.	1	
			2	
	b	Measures of central tendency have been found with minimal errors.	3	
			4	
	c	Measures have been found correctly and the examples chosen for questions 3 and 4 demonstrate an understanding of average.	5	
			6	
	d	An understanding of average with respect to mean and median is demonstrated and discussed in question 5.	7	
			8	
Criterion C Communication	a	There is little or no working out and explanations are unclear.	1	
			2	
	b	Working out is shown. An explanation of the difference between measures of central tendency and average is discussed.	3	
			4	
	c	Clear reference is made to the mean, mode and median, and how they may be used for the average is discussed. Diagrams may have been used.	5	
			6	
Criterion D Reflection in Mathematics	a	Some attempt has been made to distinguish measures of central tendency and average.	1	
			2	
	b	Examples given demonstrate some understanding of the idea of average.	3	
			4	
	c	Some examples show clearly how measures of central tendency can be used for average, and an understanding of the difference between mean and median is shown.	5	
			6	

14:04 | Grouped Data

To draw a frequency distribution table where there are many different numerical outcomes we usually group the outcomes into classes.

- If results in playing on an 18-hole golf course are to be tallied, the scores could range from 71 to 130. A table showing 61 different outcomes would be too large. A more convenient table could be constructed using class intervals of 10 marks, ie 71–80, 81–90, 91–100, 101–110, 111–120 and 121–130.
- Class groups are particularly useful if the data is **continuous** rather than **discrete**.

    eg A height of 152·3 cm would fit into the class 151–153.

    Height is *continuous* as it can assume any value in a certain range.
- The class size should be chosen so that you are using between 5 and 10 classes.

worked example

The scores of fifty-six students in a spelling test out of 50 are given below.

```
42  36  24  33  32  43  28  33  42  50  34  23  20  28
41  31  43  19  31  33  40  33  29  38  37  39  22  38
30  22  40  32  36  42  34  43  39  40  26  37  42  16
18  49  27  32  38  36  25  40  37  28  42  40  45  27
```

The frequency distribution table for this set of data could look like this:

- The *class centre (c.c.)* has been added.
- The total number of scores is shown under the *frequency* column.

Class	Class centre (c.c.)	Tally	Frequency (f)
16–20	18	|||	3
21–25	23	ⅢⅢ I	6
26–30	28	ⅢⅢ III	8
31–35	33	ⅢⅢ ⅢⅢ I	11
36–40	38	ⅢⅢ ⅢⅢ ⅢⅢ I	16
41–45	43	ⅢⅢ ⅢⅢ	10
46–50	48	||	2

Total: 56

This data is **discrete** as each score must be a whole number.

18 is halfway between 16 and 20.

This frequency histogram and frequency polygon shows the data from the previous page.

When constructing frequency diagrams for grouped data:

- The columns are indicated on the horizontal axis by the **class centres**. The class 36–40 is represented by the class centre, 38.
- The **frequency histogram** has joined columns that begin one-half of a column width in from the vertical axis.
- The **frequency polygon** can be drawn by joining the mid-points of the tops of columns. To complete the polygon, assume that the classes on either side of the columns have zero members.
- These graphs help us to interpret the findings; eg more students had a score

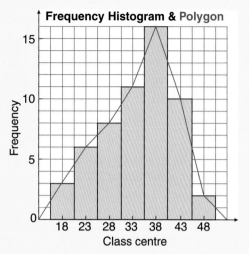

Frequency Histogram & Polygon

in the 36–40 class than in any other class, no student scored a mark that was less than 16.

Exercise 14:04

Foundation Worksheet 14:04

1 Complete the frequency table using the scores below.

51	40	63	81	73	73	35	49	55	61	31	60
44	54	87	56	97	50	37	53	60	58	84	77
63	80	60	53	42	38	52	43	50	72	80	

Class	Tally	Frequency
31–40		
41–50		
51–60		
61–70		
71–80		
81–90		
91–100		

Total:

Frequency distribution tables

1 Complete the frequency distribution table for the given scores.

1, 3, 0, 4, 3, 4, 5, 2, 3, 2, 0, 2, 2, 3, 5, 4, 3, 3, 3, 1, 3, 4, 2, 1, 3

Outcome	Tally	Frequency
0		
1		
2		
3		
4		
5		

2 Use the scores in Question 1 to complete this table.

Class	Tally	Frequency
less than 3		
3 or more		

2 Use the classes 0–2, 3–5, 6–8, 9–11, 12–14 and 15–17 to complete a frequency distribution table for the scores:

11	9	13	8	7	2	4	11	0	15	10	4
5	10	5	11	14	17	1	3	8	4	9	6
4	8	4	7	11	10	4	0	15	4	8	7
6	9	6	4	10	9	12	3	1	8	10	7

Use **class**, **tally** and **frequency** columns.

3 Complete the table for the scores below.

9	5	4	11	20	8	5	4
7	8	4	15	19	3	11	22
6	28	2	14	7	8	14	26
11	17	2	18	23	7	14	11
22	6	15	9	10	4	8	3

Class	Class centre	Tally	Frequency
1–5	3		
6–10	8		
…	…		
…	…		
…	…		
…	…		

4 Thirty people were given a driving test and each received a score out of 10. Use the scores below to complete each of the two frequency distribution tables.

5	6	2	5	7	7	8	5
4	7	6	8	10	6	4	7
6	8	7	6	4	7	5	6
7	5	9	7	8	6		

Outcome	Tally	Frequency
0		
1		
2		
3		
4		
5		
6		
7		
8		
9		
10		

Class	Tally	Frequency
2–4		
5–7		
8–10		

In which of the tables is the value of individual scores lost?

5 Use the completed frequency distribution table to complete the grouped frequency distribution table.

Outcome	0	1	2	3	4	5	6	7	8
Frequency	1	2	22	10	8	4	5	6	2

Class	Class centre	Frequency
0–2		
3–5		
6–8		

a Do you think that three classes is enough to show the spread of scores realistically?

b Normally between 5 and 10 classes are used. Why would it be difficult to use more than 5 classes in this case?

6 Draw a frequency histogram and a frequency polygon for each of these grouped frequency distribution tables.

a

Class	Class centre	Frequency
16–20	18	5
21–25	23	7
26–30	28	10
31–35	33	13
36–40	38	15
41–45	43	6
46–50	48	4

b

Class	c.c.	Frequency
3–5	4	1
6–8	7	4
9–11	10	6
12–14	13	8
15–17	16	12
18–20	19	3
21–23	22	2

(See pages 356 and 357 for an example.)

7 Draw a frequency histogram and a frequency polygon for the data in:
  a Question **1**   b Question **2**   c Question **3**

8 How would you interpret the findings for the data shown in:
  a Question **1**   b Question **2**   c Question **3**
(See the comments before this exercise on pp 356 and 357.)

- How would you use these sequins to determine the percentage of each shape produced by the manufacturer?
- What assumptions would you need to make?

14:05 | Dot Plots and Scatter Diagrams

14:05A The dot plot

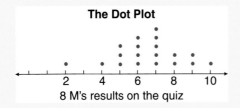

The Dot Plot

2   4   6   8   10

8 M's results on the quiz

Features

1   The dot plot uses a number line.
2   By placing one dot plot above another, comparisons can be made easily.
3   It is very similar to a column graph or simple picture graph.

Details

1   The axis should be labelled.
2   Only one axis is used.
3   When drawing the dot plot, decide what part of the number line is to be used.

▨ The scores may have been given as a list.
ie 4   6   8   7   6
    5   2   7   7   8
    9   7   5   9   5
    6   7   6   10

worked example

The length of the index fingers of 25 teachers was measured. The results are shown on this dot plot.

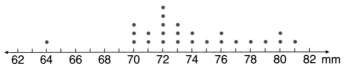

62   64   66   68   70   72   74   76   78   80   82   mm

• The mode can be seen at a glance.
  The mode is 72.
• The shape of the distribution is easily observed.
  A gap occurs between 64 and 70.
• Outliers are easily identified.
  64 is the outlier.
• The median, range and the frequency of scores are easily calculated.

▨ *Outliers* are scores that are separate from the main body of scores.

Median = middle score   Range = 81 − 64
       = 73   = 17

Score	64	70	71	72	73	74	75	76	77	78	79	80	81
Frequency	1	3	2	5	3	2	1	2	1	1	1	2	1

• The skew, which is the tendency of scores to group together on one side of the distribution, can be easily seen on the dot plot.
• The tendency of scores to form **clusters** can also be observed.
  The distribution above is skewed to the left, as the bulk of the scores are from 70 to 73 while the others trail off to the right. (Outliers are ignored when determining skewness.)

14:05B The scatter diagram

Comparison of Marks for English and Mathematics: Year 8

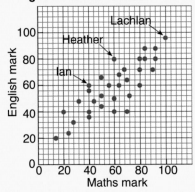

Features

1. The scatter diagram, like the dot plot, is a graph of individual cases. The points representing these cases may form a pattern.
2. The diagram is used to discover relationships between two variables such as Maths Mark and English Mark. The pattern created by the dots tell a story, eg that students tended to get similar results in Maths and English.
3. The graph is not very easy to read, so it is used only by those who know how to use it.

Details

1. The scatter diagram may have a heading.
2. Both axes must be labelled.
3. Each dot represents one person's scores in two categories. One score is given by the reading on the horizontal axis, and the other by the reading on the vertical axis, eg the point for Heather shows that she has scored 60 for Maths and 80 for English. The point for Lachlan shows that he scored 100 for Maths and 96 for English.
4. Before drawing a scatter diagram, decide on a scale for each axis.

It looks like someone has splattered paint across the diagram.

It looks more like a bug has walked across the diagram.

worked examples

1

Height/Shoe Size

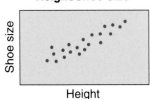

It would appear from the diagram that as height increases, shoe size tends to increase as well.

2

Alcohol/Driving Ability

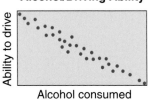

This diagram shows that as more alcohol is consumed the ability to drive decreases.

3

Street Number/Height

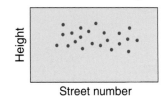

This diagram shows that there is no connection between street number and height.

Exercise 14:05

Foundation Worksheet 14:05

Dot plots and column graphs

1

1 This dot plot shows the scores of students on a driving test.

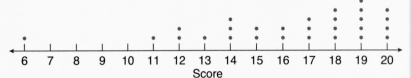

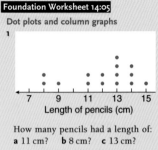

How many pencils had a length of:
a 11 cm? **b** 8 cm? **c** 13 cm?

For the scores shown on the dot plot find:
a the mode   **b** the range   **c** the median
d any outliers   **e** the frequency of the score 17
f Explain the meaning of the term *outlier*?

2 Draw a dot plot for these 30 scores.

8	11	15	10	12	9	14	10	13	11
4	7	11	19	13	10	12	11	11	9
3	8	12	14	16	12	11	6	5	7

For this set of scores, find:
a the mode   **b** the range   **c** the median
d any outliers   **e** the frequency of the score 11.

> This is discrete data as all scores are whole numbers.

3 Twenty adult smokers were chosen at random in 1986. The number of cigarettes each smoked in a day was recorded. Ten years later, in 1996, the process was repeated with the same people. The data is shown on the dot plots below.

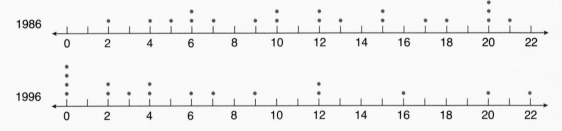

a Complete this table using the dot plots above.

	Mode	Median	Mean	Range
1986				
1996				

b How has the smoking pattern changed for these people over the 10 years? Give three factors that may have contributed to the change in pattern.

4 Represent the following data on a dot plot.

1·6 1·4 2·0 1·8 2·0 1·7 2·1 1·8 2·1 1·7 1·1 1·9
2·1 2·0 1·6 2·0 1·4 1·7 1·6 2·0 1·9 2·1 1·7 1·8

5 Thirty students entered a swimming program hoping to improve their swimming.
At the beginning and end of the program each was asked to swim as many laps as
they could in 10 minutes. The number pairs below show each student's results.

(1, 3)	(2, 6)	(5, 5)	(4, 12)	(2, 4)	(2, 11)
(10, 12)	(1, 5)	(6, 10)	(10, 10)	(3, 11)	(3, 10)
(3, 8)	(5, 8)	(7, 9)	(8, 10)	(8, 11)	(5, 8)
(1, 7)	(10, 12)	(0, 1)	(8, 12)	(8, 11)	(4, 10)
(2, 10)	(2, 7)	(5, 8)	(2, 9)	(5, 12)	(4, 9)

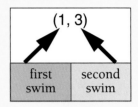

a Draw two dot plots, one above the other, to compare the ability of
the group before and after the course.
b What information is lost when the data is shown on the dot plots?
c Use the dot plots to complete the table below.

	Mode	Median	Mean	Range
Beginning				
End				

6 For each of the scatter diagrams below, state whether there is:
  i a direct relationship (ie the people involved tended to be in the same position in both
    categories)
  ii an inverse relationship (ie people who are in a high position in one category tend to be in
    a low position in the other), or
  iii no relationship (ie the position in one category does not appear to be related to the
    position in the other).

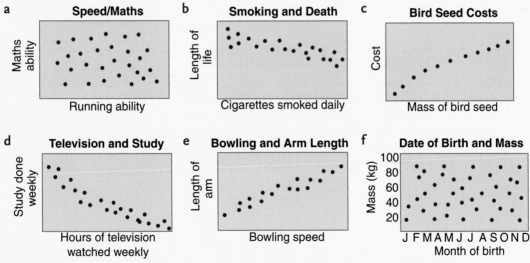

7 a Write the Maths and English marks
scored by:
  i Chris   **ii** Luke
  iii Ian   **iv** Rachel
b What was the highest:
  i Maths mark?
  ii English mark?
c What relationship is suggested by this
scatter diagram?
d What is the mode Maths mark?
e What is the median Maths mark?
f What is the mode English mark?
g What is the median English mark?

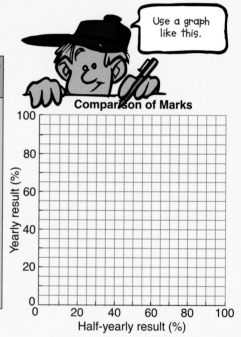

8 Mr Justins wanted to see if his students performed
in a like manner in both the mid-yearly and yearly
exams. Their results in both tests are given below:

Name	Mid-year	Year	Name	Mid-year	Year
Achnid, Rex	27	45	Madeit, Ena	48	54
Amine, Xavier	69	72	Merit, David	63	69
Bandon, Alice	45	42	Night, Unice	60	66
Beese, Owen	66	69	Press, Mark	69	63
Care, Ivy	96	90	Reason, Chris	84	69
Deals, Ian	93	90	Share, Iris	96	87
Deavour, Nell	90	78	Swerthy, Eve	87	72
Fend, Dina	54	57	Team, Sue	75	75
Hance, Nina	84	78	Tist, Ross	75	81
Honest, Ben	75	63	Vee, Tony	30	36
Ickle, Vicki	39	48	Walker, Joy	57	51
Loyal, Betty	93	84	Wander, Yin	78	72

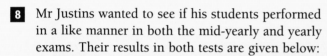

a Draw a scatter diagram to show these results.
b What relationship is there between the tests?
c What was the position of O. Beese in the yearly exam?
d What was the position of D. Merit in the mid-yearly exam?
e What was the mode in the mid-yearly exam?
f What was the median in the yearly exam?

9 Draw a scatter diagram for the following case, referring to page 383 if necessary.
Mrs Everingham wanted to see if her students performed in a like manner in English to their performance in her Maths class. Their results in both tests are given below. Use 1 mm = 2 marks as the scale on each axis.

Use graph paper for this.

Name	Maths	English
Able, Nancy	76	64
Argue, Youst	82	78
Beaudy, Ungwin	50	70
Cycle, Ivan	63	74
Deer, Ivy	46	50
Evator, Lois	38	38
Eye, Graham	68	54
Force, Neil	98	86
Hale, Xavier	60	60
Hance, Neville	78	68
Iting, Xavier	82	76
Leave, Ben	38	60
Mitt, Ona	66	50
Muse, Betty	78	78
Pand, Xavier	20	50

Name	Maths	English
Pea, Tom	58	62
Pen, Owen	48	46
Podd, Peter	80	74
Pott, Timothy	65	60
Saidit, Unice	72	78
Saw, Carol	56	62
Shooter, Petra	68	68
Side, Cicile	50	46
Snore, Irwin	60	80
Sting, Barry	46	56
Table, Theresa	84	76
Tee, Mandy	52	56
Tension, Dennis	74	82
Toteler, Tina	66	56
Tsa, Paul	70	80

10 Write a paragraph to summarise the results in Question **8**.

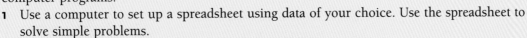

Investigation 14:05 | Using computer software

14:05

Please use the Assessment Grid on the following page to help you understand what is required for this Investigation.

> ■ Can you explain how your calculator deals with overflow?

Experimenting and exploring computer programs can be very profitable. Your library at school should have a collection of computer programs.

1 Use a computer to set up a spreadsheet using data of your choice. Use the spreadsheet to solve simple problems.

2 Use a computer package to produce graphical displays of data.

3 Use a drawing program (eg Logo) to produce designs exhibiting geometrical properties (eg symmetry).

4 Use appropriate software (eg statistical packages, spreadsheets) to provide summary statistics and plots of suitable data.

5 Use appropriate computer software to produce a scatter plot or a time series plot.

Assessment Grid for Investigation 14:05 | Using computer software

The following is a sample assessment grid for this investigation. You should carefully read the criteria *before* beginning the investigation so that you know what is required.

			Assessment Criteria (B, C, D)		Achieved ✓
Criterion B Investigating Patterns	a		The student has experienced difficulty collecting data and using software.	1	
				2	
	b		Some data has been collected and the software has been used with some success.	3	
				4	
	c		A good range of data has been collected and the spreadsheet has been used to analyse the data with some success.	5	
				6	
	d		The tables, graphs and summary of data demonstrate a very good understanding of the applicability of statistics.	7	
				8	
Criterion C Communication	a		Few or no tables and graphs have been produced to show where the answers come from.	1	
				2	
	b		Some graphs and tables have been produced to illustrate the data and the answers.	3	
				4	
	c		Complete graphs and tables illustrate the data and the solutions in a meaningful way.	5	
				6	
Criterion D Reflection in Mathematics	a		There has been an attempt to explain why particular graphs were chosen to illustrate the data.	1	
				2	
	b		Reasons for the choice of graphs are given and their use is clearly justified.	3	
				4	
	c		Different types of graphs have been used in the Investigation to demonstrate alternative approaches.	5	
				6	

14:06 | Stem-and-leaf Plots

- A stem-and-leaf plot resembles a histogram (on its side) where the data has been grouped.
- The great advantage is that the identity of individual scores is not lost.
- The back-to-back stem-and-leaf plot allows us to compare two groups of data at a glance.

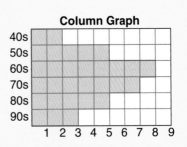

Column Graph

worked examples

1 Prepare an ordered stem-and-leaf plot for the following test marks of class 8M.

| 68 | 59 | 85 | 53 | 57 | 93 | 84 | 73 | 41 | 65 | 77 | 73 | 66 | 50 | 97 |
| 67 | 62 | 54 | 64 | 88 | 48 | 80 | 68 | 66 | 71 | 91 | 79 | 73 | 84 | 75 |

It's a bit like the graph above.

Solution

Test Results, 8M
(6/8 represents 68)

Stem	Leaf
4	18
5	93704
6	85672486
7	3731935
8	54804
9	371

Stem-and-leaf plot
- The stem-and-leaf plot needs a title.
- An example of the data could be supplied above the table.
- In this case the *stem* is the tens digit, the *leaf* is the units digit.
- The *stem* is written with the smallest stem at the top.
- At first, the *leaf* is built up by working through the data in the order it appears.

- To get an ordered plot, rewrite the table putting the *leaves* in order.
- From the display, we can find that the **range** is 97–41 (ie 56), the **mode** is 73 and the **median** is the average of 68 and 71 (ie 69·5).
- A limitation is that each leaf needs to be a single digit, so decimals may need to be rounded off.

Ordered Stem-and-leaf Plot

Stem	Leaf
4	18
5	03479
6	24566788
7	1333579
8	04458
9	137

2   Our class was given a topic test in which we performed poorly. Our teacher decided to give a similar test one week later, after a thorough revision of the topic. The results are shown on this back-to-back stem-and-leaf plot. (This is an **ordered display**.)

Test Scores (4/1 represents 41)

First Topic Test   Second Topic Test

Leaf	Stem	Leaf
9 8 6 6 0	3	
9 7 7 3 1 1 1	4	3 6 6 8
8 8 5 3 3 0	5	1 7 9 9
9 8 7 5 3	6	3 8 9
	7	0 5 5 5 8 9
	8	2 6 7 7
0	9	0 0 1 3

- The improvement in the second test is easy to see.

- The mode, median and range are easily compared.

Test 1	Test 2
mode = 41	mode = 75
median = 50	median = 75
range = 90 − 30	range = 93 − 43
= 60	= 50

- Outliers are easily identified.
  In the first test the score 90 is an *outlier*.
  In the second test there are no outliers.

Exercise 14:06

1   Complete the stem-and-leaf plot for each set of test marks.

a   26   15   62   51   47   19
    33   40   58   26   38   35
    47   41   36   29   17   16
    62   28   18   47   30   26

Test Marks (2/6 represents 26)

Stem	Leaf
1	
2	
3	
4	
5	
6	

b   53   81   74   72   91   45
    80   57   44   82   70   67
    59   80   81   60   49   77
    65   42   73   63   92   88

Test Marks (5/3 represents 53)

Stem	Leaf
4	
5	
6	
7	
8	
9	

2 Rewrite each *stem-and-leaf* plot in Question 1 as an *ordered stem-and-leaf* plot. Find the median for each case.

3 The number of runs scored by 22 players in a cricket match are recorded below as two-digit numbers. 8 runs is shown as 08.

08 15 46 62 20 18 06 04 19 36 27
33 45 26 11 29 32 40 01 09 02 43

a Complete this table for the data above.

Runs Scored
(0/8 represents 8 runs)

Stem	Leaf	Frequency (f)
0	864192	
1	5891	
2	0769	
3	632	
4	6503	
5		
6	2	

Total:

b Rewrite this as an ordered stem-and-leaf plot.
c Find the range, median and mean for this set of scores. List any outliers that are present.
d What percentage of players scored less than 20 runs? (Answer correct to 1 decimal place.)

4 Every student in Year 8 was asked to throw 3 darts at a dartboard. The score total for each student is listed below.

08 14 45 54 30 52 20 12 55 33
22 27 43 39 11 05 42 03 09 47
51 25 60 18 31 01 46 53 02 01
30 14 11 42 14 09 24 45 15 06
05 10 48 16 09 19 44 04 54 35
53 13 08 52 26 07 52 12 37 17
42 01 46 08 17 44 13 44 55 46
28 39 14 49 17 55 41 50 14 51

a Draw an ordered stem-and-leaf plot for this data.
b Find the range, mode and median of these scores.
c Describe any distinctive features in the data, such as outliers, clusters of scores and distribution shape.
d How does a score of 41 compare with the other scores?

5 This back-to-back stem-and-leaf plot shows the number of seconds taken by each member of the class 6W to complete their 3 times tables and their 6 times tables.

a Which table seems to be the better known?

b From the scores for *3× Tables*, find the mode, the median and the range.

c From the scores for *6× Tables*, find the mode, the median and the range.

d Do any outliers exist in either set of scores? Explain why or why not.

Time in seconds

3× Tables   *6× Tables*

Leaf	Stem	Leaf
9 8 8	0	
7 4 3 2 2 2 0	1	6 6 7 9
9 8 8 7 7 3 1	2	0 4 8
9 6 6 4 4	3	0 2 2 2 6 9
3 2 2	4	1 5 5 6 7 8 8 9
5	5	2 9 9 9
	6	0

6 The scores of students and parents on a sports trivia quiz are recorded below.

Students

44	15	30	35	20	24	18	40
37	34	28	39	41	19	23	30
30	41	47	20	35	28	45	22
33	26	42	25	30	21	42	19

Parents

18	32	20	24	11	35	31
42	6	38	27	16	26	16
40	23	37	31	26	30	42
21	18	41	42	22	25	32

a Prepare an ordered back-to-back stem-and-leaf plot for this data.

b For each set of scores, find the mode, the median and the range.

c Which of the measures in **b** is most useful in comparing the two groups?

d Find the mean of each set of scores correct to 2 decimal places.

Quick Scores

Students   *Parents*

Leaf	Stem	Leaf
	0	
	1	
	2	
	3	
	4	

7 The pulse rates of 24 adults and 24 children were measured and recorded below.

Adults

12	64	59	60	72	61	58	55
76	76	80	81	58	64	72	60
92	56	57	68	80	68	72	64

Students

102	86	67	85	98	77	81	85
72	62	88	92	86	82	94	78
100	94	85	95	99	86	77	99

a Use an ordered back-to-back stem-and-leaf plot to organise this data.

b What outliers are present in this data?

c Can any of these outliers be ignored? Why or why not?

d Find the median and mode of each set of scores.

e Describe each set of scores and compare them.

Challenge 14:06 | Wedding anniversaries

Are there some months or parts of a month that are more popular for weddings than others? Do many people get married on Easter Sunday or Christmas Day?

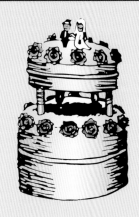

- Collect as many wedding anniversary dates as you can. (Each member of a group should collect at least 20.) You will need to ask for the day and the month. The year is not needed. The more dates you collect, the more likely it is that you will discover trends.

- Organise your results as follows.
  1 Make a list of data, eg 2 March, 10 June, 29 July.
  2 Draw an ordered stem-and-leaf display, treating each month as two halves (1 Jan to 15 Jan, 16 Jan to end of month). For example:

Wedding Anniversaries

Stem (month)	Leaf (day)											Frequency
$1^{(1)}$	1	2	4	4	8	8	9	11	11	15		10
$1^{(16)}$	16	20	27	27	28	31						6
$2^{(1)}$	4	7	7	8	12	12	14					7
$2^{(16)}$	17	20	21	21	28							5
$3^{(1)}$	3	3	8	10								4
.		.										.
.		.										.
.		.										.
$12^{(1)}$	3	8	10	10	11	11	13	13	14	14	15	11
$12^{(16)}$	16	16	17	17	18	19	20	21	21	21		10

3 Draw statistical graphs of the data collected.
4 Report on the trends and discoveries you have made. Suggest reasons for the trends present and include possible limitations to your experiment. (Could the same couple have been asked more than once by the group? Would climate cause the trends to be different for those married in Australia to those married in Europe. Should Australian weddings be considered separately? Did the length of month influence the results?)
5 Use your imagination to make an interesting project.

Mathematical terms 14

census
- A survey of a whole population.

data
- The scores or information collected.
- discrete data: Data that is a measure of something restricted to certain limited values,
  eg age in years.
- continuous data: Data that is a measure of something that can take on any value within reason,
  eg height.

dot plot
- A graph that uses one axis and a number of dots above the axis.

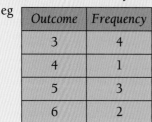

Test results out of 10

frequency
- The number of times an outcome occurs in the data.
  eg For the data 3, 6, 5, 3, 5, 5, 4, 3, 3, 6 the outcome 5 has a frequency of 3.

frequency distribution table
- A table that shows all the possible outcome and their frequencies. (It is often extended by adding other columns, such as the cumulative frequency column.)
eg

Outcome	Frequency
3	4
4	1
5	3
6	2

frequency histogram
- A type of column graph showing the outcomes and their frequencies.

eg
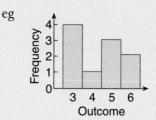

frequency polygon
- A line graph showing outcomes and their frequencies. To complete the polygon, the outcomes immediately above and below those present are used. The height of these columns is zero.

eg
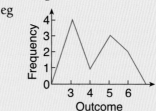

grouped data
- Data that is organised into groups or classes.
- class interval: The size of the groups into which the data is organised.
  eg 1–5 (5 scores); 11–20 (10 scores).
- class centre: The middle outcome of a class.
  eg The class 1–5 has a class centre of 3.

mean
- The number obtained by 'evening out' all the scores until they are equal.
  eg If the scores 3, 6, 5, 3, 5, 5, 4, 3, 3, 6 were 'evened out' the number obtained would be 4·3.
- The mean is the arithmetic average.

$$\text{Mean} = \frac{\text{sum of the scores}}{\text{number of scores}}$$

median
- The middle score for an odd number of scores or the mean of the middle two scores for an even number of scores.

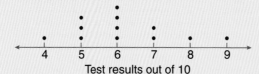

14

- **median class**
  In grouped data, the class that contains the median.

mode (modal class)
- The outcome (or class) that occurs most often.

outcome
- A possible value of the data.

outlier
- Scores that are separated from the main body of scores.

range
- The difference between the highest and lowest scores.

sample
- A part, usually a small part, of a large population.
- random sample: A sample taken so that each member of the population has the same chance of being included.

scatter diagram
- A graph that uses points on a number plane to show the relationship between two categories.

eg

Height/Shoe Size

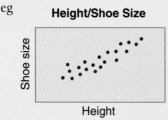

Height

statistics
- The collection, organisation and interpretation of numerical data.

stem-and-leaf plot
- A graph that shows the spread of scores without losing the identity of the data.
  eg **Test Results, 8M**
  (6/8 represents 68)

Stem	Leaf
4	18
5	93704
6	85672486
7	3731935
8	54804
9	371

- ordered stem-and-leaf plot
  The *leaves* have been placed in order.
  ie

Stem	Leaf
4	18
5	03479
6	24566788
7	1333579
8	04458
9	137

- back-to-back stem-and-leaf plot
  This can be used to compare two sets of scores, one set on each side.
  eg   **Test Scores**
                 (4/1 represents 41)

First Topic Test		Second Topic Test
Leaf	Stem	Leaf
9 8 6 6 0	3	
9 7 7 3 1 1 1	4	3 6 6 8
8 8 5 3 3 0	5	1 7 9 9
9 8 7 5 3	6	3 8 9
	7	0 5 5 5 8 9
	8	2 6 7 7
0	9	0 0 1 3

Mathematical terms 14

Diagnostic Test 14: | Statistics

- Each section of the test has similar items that test a certain type of example.
- Errors made will indicate areas of weakness.
- Each weakness should be treated by going back to the section listed.

		Section
1 Sort out each set of data into a frequency distribution table.		14:02

1 Sort out each set of data into a frequency distribution table.

a	1 2 5 4 3	b	0 2 4 4 2	c	6 7 9 10 5
	3 2 5 1 4		4 6 8 6 8		3 5 7 8 9
	4 3 2 1 2		4 6 4 2 0		7 8 6 7 9
	2 3 2 4 2		4 6 0 2 4		10 7 8 7 6
			4 6 2 4 8		4 3 5 9 6

Section 14:02

2 a Draw a frequency histogram for Question **1a**.
   b Draw a frequency polygon for Question **1b**.
   c Draw a combined frequency histogram and polygon for Question **1c**.

Section 14:02

3 State the range of each set of scores.
   a 5, 6, 9, 4, 3   b 0, 7, 3, 5, 6, 3   c 1·1, 1·3, 1·7, 1·4, 1·5, 1·0

Section 14:03

4 State the mode for each set of scores.
   a 5, 6, 7, 6, 4, 9   b 3, 5, 6, 3, 5, 3, 7   c 2, 4, 6, 5, 4, 6, 5, 2, 6

Section 14:03

5 State the mode for each set of data in Question **1**.

Section 14:03

6 State the median for each set of scores.
   a 3, 9, 4, 7, 8   b 5, 9, 4, 6, 7, 8, 6   c 5, 3, 2, 6, 4, 8

Section 14:03

7 Determine the median for each set of data in Question **1**.

Section 14:03

8 Calculate the mean for each set of scores.
   a 6, 7, 4, 8, 5   b 8, 9, 4, 3, 6, 8, 4, 2   c 8, 9, 3, 7, 7, 6, 3, 5, 9, 3

Section 14:03

9 Calculate the mean for each set of data in Question **1**.

Section 14:03

10 Complete the table for the scores below.

Section 14:04

9	11	14	20	7	3
22	12	14	8	0	7
6	10	18	13	4	8
9	7	8	15	19	9
21	16	11	17	18	11

Class	Class centre	Tally	Frequency
0–4			
5–9			
…			
…			
…			

11 The lengths of 16 fish caught were measured. The results are shown on this dot plot.

```
                        •
                        •
            •           •   •
            •   •   •   •   •   •   •
      •     •   •   •   •   •   •   •
  ┌──┬───┬───┬───┬───┬───┬───┬───┬──→
    20  22  24  26  28  30  32  34 cm
```

  a What is the:
    i mode?   **ii** median?   **iii** range?
  b Which measurement is the outlier?

12 Draw a scatter diagram to display the following information.

Performance Compared in Art and Music

Name	Art	Music	Name	Art	Music	Name	Art	Music
Alana	60	80	Adam	80	60	Shelley	90	50
Rachel	50	90	Bronwyn	85	55	Kylie	68	72
Naomi	55	85	John	40	50	Allyson	65	75
Luke	70	70	Richard	56	58	Jane	50	50
Heather	75	65	Tina	52	59	Damian	80	40
Sandy	56	52	Michelle	73	70	Amber	70	50
Ian	60	60	Daniel	45	49	Ruth	65	60

Is there a positive relationship between Art marks and Music marks?

13 Grade 3 and Grade 4 students were tested on their knowledge of multiplication tables. The results are shown in this back-to-back stem-and-leaf display.

Test Scores
(5/1 represents 51)

Grade 3 Results   Grade 4 Results

Leaf	Stem	Leaf
9 8 3 0	3	5
8 8 7 4 2 2 2	4	
8 7 7 4 0	5	1 4 6 6 9
7 6 3	6	0 2 2 5 8
1	7	3 6 8 8 9 9 9
	8	0 0

  a List any outliers in these results.
  b Find the mode, median and range for Grade 3.
  c Find the mode, median and range for Grade 4.

Chapter 14 | Revision Assignment

14A

1

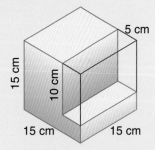

5 cm

15 cm

10 cm

15 cm   15 cm

The diagram shows a cube with a part of it removed. The removed piece has the shape of a rectangular prism. Calculate:
a the volume of the cube
b the volume of the rectangular prism that has been removed
c the volume of the remaining shape.

2 Find the values of the pronumerals, giving reasons for your answers.

a

75°
←a°

b

30°
b°
20°

c

x°
110° 130°

3 A map has a scale of 1 : 5000. What distance is represented by a length of 1 mm on the map? If the distance between two points in real life is 350 m, how far apart would they be on the map?

4 A man walks 1 km in 8 minutes. At this rate how long would it take him to walk 400 m? How far could he walk in 30 seconds?

5 A woman athlete runs 100 m in 12 seconds. How fast is this in km/h?

6 a A property is 20 m wide and 150 m long. Assuming that it is a rectangular shape, find its area in hectares.
b A cube has a volume of 250 cm³. What is its side length, to the nearest whole number?

7 Find the rule connecting y and x in each case.

a

x	4	5	6	7
y	8	10	12	14

b

x	2	3	4	5
y	7	10	13	16

c

x	1	2	3	4
y	1	4	9	16

8 a What percentage of 1 kg is 6 g?
b What percentage of 2·4 m is 60 cm?

9 Simplify:
a $-3 - 4 \times 2$
b $12 - 6 \times 5$
c $-4 - 3 + 6 - 2 + 8$
d $\dfrac{12 - 4}{4 - 8}$

10 a Draw a frequency histogram for the data given.
b Calculate the range, mode and mean of the data.

Outcome	Frequency
1	5
2	7
3	6
4	12
5	5
6	4

398 INTERNATIONAL MATHEMATICS 2

Chapter 14 | Working Mathematically

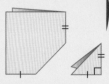

1 Plastic figures are needed for the doors on the 3rd floor of a large hotel. If all of the numbers 301 to 346 are needed, how many of each of the digits 0, 1, 2, 3, 4, 5, 6, 7, 8 and 9 will be needed?

2 The second digit of a four-digit number is twice as big as the first digit. The third digit is twice as big as the second digit and the fourth digit is twice as big as the third digit. What is the four-digit number?

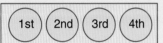

Keep trying!

3 A rectangular piece of paper 8 cm long and 4 cm wide was folded. This was then cut (as shown) from midpoint to midpoint of the sides shown. The smaller part was then unfolded and laid flat. What was the area of this triangle?

4 Peter was tracing his family tree. How many great-great-grandparents would he have? (The order goes: parents, grandparents, great-grandparents, then great-great-grandparents.)

5 If I use only 5c, 10c and 20c coins, how many different ways can I make up 40 cents?

6 Use ID Card 7 on page xix to identify:
  a 5   b 6   c 7   d 8
  e 9   f 10   g 11   h 12
  i 13   j 14   k 15   l 16

id

14

Technology Applications

Chapter Review Questions

1 Types of graphs and tables

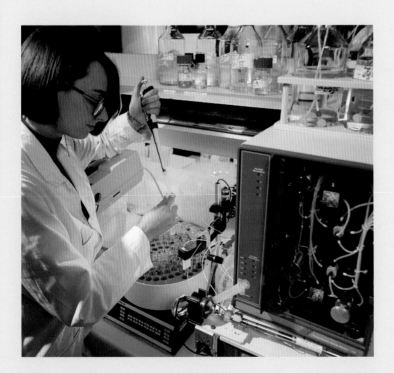

• The careful handling of statistics is essential in any research laboratory.

Probability

Chapter Contents

Learning Outcomes

Students will be able to solve probability problems involving simple events.

Areas of Interaction

Approaches to Learning (Knowledge Acquisition, Problem Solving, Communication Skills, Thinking Skills), Health and Social Education, Human Ingenuity

15:01 | The Language of Probability

In Grade 6 we considered the words commonly used to describe the chance of something happening.

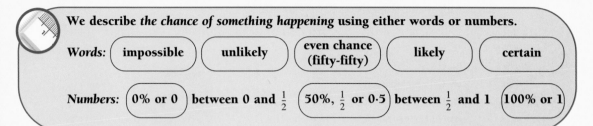

We describe *the chance of something happening* using either words or numbers.

Words: impossible — unlikely — even chance (fifty-fifty) — likely — certain

Numbers: 0% or 0 — between 0 and $\frac{1}{2}$ — 50%, $\frac{1}{2}$ or 0·5 — between $\frac{1}{2}$ and 1 — 100% or 1

For each of these events, estimate its chance to be:
A an even chance, B less than an even chance or C more than an even chance. Give a reason for each answer.

1   If you toss a coin it will come down *tails*.
2   When next you catch a bus, it will break down.
3   On your next birthday you will be given a present.
4   You will score 100 runs when next you play cricket.
5   The next child born in the nearest hospital will be a girl.

prep quiz

15:01

worked example

Order the following events from *least likely* to *most likely*.

A   A dice is thrown. The result will be either a 1, a 2 or a 3.
B   The next person to walk into our classroom will have their birthday in December.
C   If I pick a counter at random from this group it will be red.

'At random' means 'without looking'.

Solution
The least likely would be **B** as December is 1 of 12 possible months in which the person could be born.
For the person to be born in December is unlikely.

The next is **A** since half of the possible numbers will give success.
Throwing a 1, a 2 or a 3 would have a *fifty-fifty* (or *even*) chance.

The most likely is **C** as 4 out of 6 counters are red.
It is likely that a red counter would be chosen.

Exercise 15:01

1. a What does it mean for something to be impossible?
   b What does it mean for something to be certain?

2. For each event choose one of the categories: impossible, unlikely, even chance, likely or certain.

   a A dice is to be thrown.
   Event 1:   A 6 will be thrown.
   Event 2:   A number less than 4 will be thrown.
   Event 3:   A number greater than 3 will be thrown.
   Event 4:   A zero will be thrown.
   Event 5:   A number less than 7 will be thrown.

   b A ball is to be drawn at random from the jar shown.
   Event 1:   The ball will be green.
   Event 2:   The ball will be brown.
   Event 3:   The ball will be red.
   Event 4:   The ball will be coloured.
   Event 5:   The ball will be either green or blue.

   c One card is to be chosen at random from these five.
   Event 1:   The card will be a *heart*.
   Event 2:   The card will be less than 8.
   Event 3:   The card will be a *diamond*.
   Event 4:   The card will be a 2.
   Event 5:   The card will not be a 3.

3. Order the following events from *least likely* to *most likely*.
   a A dice is to be thrown.
   A The number showing will be even.
   B The number showing will be larger than 4.
   C The number showing will be less than 6.

   b A ball is to be drawn at random from the jar shown.
   A The ball will be brown.
   B The ball will be green.
   C The ball will be blue or pink.

   c One card is to be chosen at random from these five.
   A The card will be a 2.
   B The card will be a 7.
   C The card will be greater than 3.

15:02 | The Probability of Simple Events

prep quiz

15:02

Write *true* or *false* for each statement, and give a reason for each answer.

1 On my last three attempts to jump 1·5 metres, I failed. I am likely to succeed the next time I try.

2 If I throw 2 dice, their total must be 12 or less.

3 If I choose at random a number between 1 and 10, it will have 1 digit.

4 Even if I have thrown 4 heads in a row, the chance of throwing a head with the next toss of a coin is an even chance.

5 If I choose at random a counter from a jar that contains 999 red counters and 1 yellow counter, it is sure to be red.

- A *simple event* is an event in which each possible outcome is equally likely.
- The term *sample space* is used to refer to all of the possible outcomes. eg For tossing a fair dice, the sample space is: 1, 2, 3, 4, 5, 6.
- All probabilities must be in the range 0 to 1 (ie 0% to 100%).

> A likely outcome has better than a 50% chance of occurring.

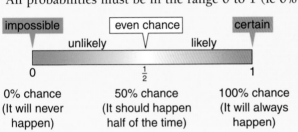

| impossible | even chance | certain |
| unlikely | likely | |

| | | |
| 0 | $\frac{1}{2}$ | 1 |

0% chance
(It will never happen)

50% chance
(It should happen half of the time)

100% chance
(It will always happen)

If all outcomes are equally likely:

$$\text{Probability} = \frac{\text{number of favourable outcomes}}{\text{total number of outcomes}}$$

ie Probability of an event, $P(E) = \dfrac{n(E)}{n(S)}$

where **n(E) = number of ways the event can occur**
n(S) = number of possible outcomes.

worked example

From these pictures, one will be chosen at random.
What is the probability that the picture chosen is of:

a   a woman?   b   a man?

c   a man or woman?   d   someone wearing a hat?

Solution

a   P(a woman) = $\frac{3}{4}$ or 75%

b   P(a man) = $\frac{1}{4}$ or 25%

c   P(a man or woman) = $\frac{4}{4}$ or 100%

d   P(wearing a hat) = $\frac{3}{4}$ or 75%

Exercise 15:02

Foundation Worksheet 15:02

Probability

1 One of these balls is chosen at random. What is the probability of choosing:
a a green ball?
b a yellow ball?
c a red ball?
d a purple ball?

1 List all possible outcomes of each event.
That is, list the sample space.

   a A dice is thrown.   **b** A coin is tossed.
   c This spinner is spun.   **d** A coloured ball is chosen.

Note: If there were two green balls, we would name them *green 1* and *green 2*.

2 How many outcomes are in each sample space?

   a A number between 4 and 7 is chosen at random.
   b A ticket is chosen from tickets numbered 1 to 99.
   c A ticket is chosen from tickets numbered 0 to 100.
   d Ten cards are placed in a hat and one is chosen at random.

3 Liam throws a dice. Write, as a fraction, the probability that he will throw:

   a a 2   **b** a zero
   c an even number   **d** an odd number
   e either a 1 or a 6   **f** a number less than 4
   g a number less than 7.

4 A coin is tossed.

   a Write, as a fraction, the probability of tossing:
     i a head   **ii** a tail.
   b Write as a percentage, the probability of tossing:
     i a head   **ii** a tail.

5 The spinner to the right, marked 1 to 5 is spun.
Write, as a fraction, the probability of spinning:

   a a 3   **b** an odd number
   c an even number   **d** a zero.

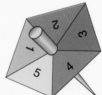

6 A 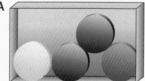   B 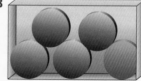   C

Counters have been slid into these narrow containers. One counter will be chosen at random from each container. For each container, find the probability of choosing:

   a a red counter   **b** a blue counter
   c a yellow counter   **d** a counter that is either red or blue.

7 The *five* on a dice is covered by a sticker showing a red *one*.
When I throw this dice, what is the probability that I will throw:

   a a *one*?   **b** a *three*?   **c** *three* or less?
   d a *five*?   **e** a number greater than *one*?

8 Naomi approaches a roundabout from the west.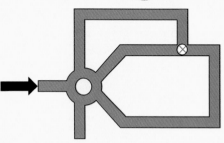
She chooses one of the other exit roads at random
when leaving the roundabout.

   a What is the probability that she chooses the
   dead end?
   b What is the probability that she chooses a
   road that leads to ⊗?

9 Of 100 tickets sold in a raffle, Luke bought 10, Heather bought 5 and Alan bought 1.
A ticket was chosen at random to determine who won the prize. What is the probability that
the prize was won by:

   a Alan?   **b** Luke?   **c** Heather?   **d** none of these three people?

   How many of the 100 tickets would I need to buy for the probability of my winning to be:

   e 0? Explain why.   **f** 1? Explain why.

10   A 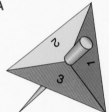   B 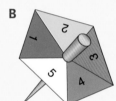   C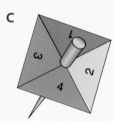

   For which of these spinners is the probability of spinning a 3 equal to:

   a 20%   **b** 25%   **c** $\frac{1}{3}$

A standard pack of cards has 4 suits: hearts (♥), diamonds (♦), clubs (♣) and spades (♠).
There are 13 cards in each suit and 52 cards altogether.

The first of these cards is called an **Ace**. The last three cards are the *picture* or *court* cards:
the **Jack**, the **Queen** and the **King**.

---

11 From the 13 cards shown above, one card is to be chosen at random. What is the probability
that the card chosen will be:

   a the 7?   **b** the Ace?   **c** a picture card?
   d a heart?   **e** a spade?   **f** either a 9 or a 10?

12 From a standard pack of 52 cards, a card is chosen at random. What is the probability that the
card will be:

   a a diamond?   **b** a red card?   **c** a black card?
   d a 3?   **e** a picture card?   **f** either an Ace or a King?

Fun Spot 15:02 | What chance of success?

- Luke is running his mouse through a variety of mazes. When the mouse comes to a point where there is more than one path to choose from, it is just as likely to choose any one of them. The mouse never turns back of its own accord.
- In each case below, the mouse begins with a number of 'success chances'. We will work out the mouse's probability of reaching cheese without doubling back, by working out what fraction of the success chances lead to cheese. (This fraction can then be expressed as a percentage.)

Example

Starting with 12 success chances, work out the probability of the mouse reaching the cheese without retracing its steps. At each fork in the maze, the success chances must be shared equally among the new paths.

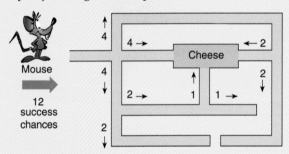

From the diagram, we can see that 7 out of 12 success chances reach the cheese.

$$\therefore \text{P (reaching cheese)} = \frac{7}{12}$$

$$= \frac{7}{12} \times \frac{100}{1}\%$$

$$= 58\frac{1}{3}\%$$

$\therefore$ The mouse has $58\frac{1}{3}\%$ chance of reaching the cheese without having to turn back.

Questions

In these questions find the probability (as a fraction and as a percentage) that the mouse will find the cheese without having to turn back.

1 Start with 100 chances.

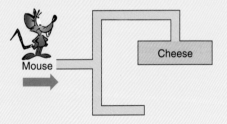

2 Start with 100 chances.

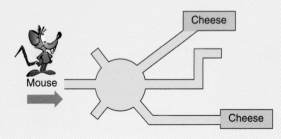

3 Start with 100 chances.

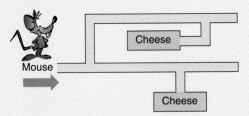

4 Start with 100 chances.

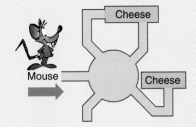

5 Start with 100 chances.

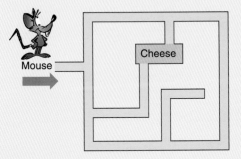

6 Start with 12 chances.

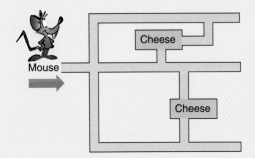

7 Start with 24 chances.

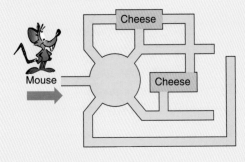

8 Start with 30 chances.

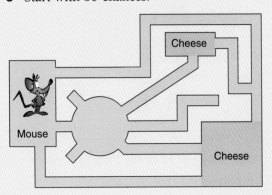

• You might like to make up some mazes of your own.

• Estimate the probability that a green tee would be chosen at random.

• Find the probability of selecting each colour at random.
• What is the sum of all of these probabilities?

15:02 Two dice

From these 10 counters, one is to be chosen at random. What is the probability that the counter chosen will be:

1   purple?   2   not purple?
3   red?   4   not red?
5   green?   6   not green?
7   orange?   8   not orange?
9   yellow?   10   not yellow?

11   If P(red) means the probability of choosing a red counter, find:
     P(red) + P(orange) + P(purple) + P(green).

• Question **11** of the Prep Quiz shows us that the sum of the probabilities of all possible outcomes of an event is always 1 or 100%.

Event: tossing a coin

$P(head) = \frac{1}{2}$

$P(tail) = \frac{1}{2}$

$P(head) + P(tail) = 1$

Event: throwing a dice

$P(1) = \frac{1}{6}$ $P(3) = \frac{1}{6}$ $P(5) = \frac{1}{6}$

$P(2) = \frac{1}{6}$ $P(4) = \frac{1}{6}$ $P(6) = \frac{1}{6}$

$P(1) + P(2) + P(3) + P(4) + P(5) + P(6) = 1$
The sum of the probabilities of the possible outcomes is 1 or 100%.

• Questions **1** to **10** of the Prep Quiz show us that:

$P(purple) + P(not\ purple) = \frac{1}{10} + \frac{9}{10} = 1$ $\therefore$ P(not purple) = 1 − P(purple)

$P(orange) + P(not\ orange) = \frac{4}{10} + \frac{6}{10} = 1$ $\therefore$ P(not orange) = 1 − P(orange)

$P(yellow) + P(not\ yellow) = \frac{0}{10} + \frac{10}{10} = 1$ $\therefore$ P(not yellow) = 1 − P(yellow)

These pairs of events, P(E) and P(not E), are called *complementary*.
The sum of their probabilities is 1 or 100%.

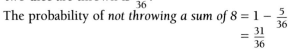
worked examples

1   Luke's chance of clearing the high jump is $\frac{7}{10}$.
    Luke's chance of *not doing this* = $1 - \frac{7}{10}$
    $\qquad\qquad\qquad\qquad\qquad = \frac{3}{10}$

2   The probability of throwing a sum of 8 when two dice are thrown is $\frac{5}{36}$.
    The probability of *not throwing a sum of 8* = $1 - \frac{5}{36}$
    $\qquad\qquad\qquad\qquad\qquad\qquad\qquad = \frac{31}{36}$

- The sum of the probabilities of all possible outcomes to a simple event is 1 or 100%. eg If there is a 97% chance that something will happen, then there is a 3% chance that it will not happen.

$$P(E') = 1 - P(E)$$

where P(E') is the probability of E not occurring.

- E' is set notation for the complement of E.
  The complement of E is the set of possible outcomes outside of E.
  eg The complement of *catching less than 3 balls out of 5* would be to *catch 3 or more* of the 5.

Exercise 15:03

1 Match each event below with its complementary event from the list on the right.
  a It will rain tomorrow.
  b I will win the race.
  c A *six* will be rolled.
  d I will not catch a cold next year.
  e That team won't beat us.
  f Alice will be school captain.

Choose one of these.
- A *six* will not be rolled.
- I will catch a cold next year.
- Alice will not be school captain.
- It won't rain tomorrow.
- That team will beat us.
- I won't win the race.

2 Write the complement of each event.
  a The egg will break.
  b The plate will not break.
  c We will score 200 runs.
  d We will toss at least one head.
  e I will win the raffle.
  f We will win the soccer match.

3 In each case the probability of an event P(E) is given. You are asked to find the probability of its complementary event P(E').
  a P(I will get a flat tyre) = 2%
     P(I won't get a flat tyre) = ☐
  b P(I will throw a 4 or less) = $\frac{2}{3}$
     P(I will throw higher than 4) = ☐
  c P(Dad will raise my allowance) = 40%
     P(Dad won't raise my allowance) = ☐
  d P(I will be given a present) = 0·99
     P(I will not be given a present) = ☐
  e P(You will select a yellow ball) = 1
     P(You won't select a yellow ball) = ☐
  f P(Lisa will learn to swim) = $\frac{7}{10}$
     P(Lisa won't learn to swim) = ☐

4 In a standard pack of cards there are two red suits (hearts and diamonds) and two black suits (clubs and spades). When a card is chosen at random, the probability of selecting a red card is $\frac{1}{2}$. What is the probability of selecting:
  a a black card?
  b a card that is not red?
  c either a black card or a red card?
  d neither a black card nor a red card?

5 A stamp is to be selected at random from this collection. We know some probabilities already.

P(Australian) = $\frac{3}{10}$, P(Polish) = $\frac{1}{17}$, P(French) = $\frac{37}{170}$.
Find the probability that the stamp selected is:
  a not Polish
  b not Australian
  c not French.

6 From this coin collection, a coin is to be chosen at random. We know some probabilities already.

$P(\text{Australian}) = \frac{1}{4}$, $P(\text{Chinese}) = \frac{3}{800}$, $P(\text{British}) = \frac{1}{8}$,

$P(\text{Singaporean}) = 2\%$, $P(\text{African}) = \frac{3}{20}$, $P(\text{American}) = 21\%$.

Find the probability that the coin chosen is:

a not Australian   **b** not British

c not African   **d** not Singaporean

e not American   **f** not Chinese.

7

In a cardboard box I have 37 red pens, 120 black pens and 43 blue pens. If one pen is chosen at random, find the probability that the pen is:

a red   **b** not red   **c** blue

d not blue   **e** black   **f** not black

g either red, black or blue.

8

From these five paper clips, one is chosen at random. Find the probability that the one chosen would be:

a yellow   **b** not yellow

c either yellow or red   **d** either yellow, green or red.

9 This pasta has pieces of different colour. 20% of the pieces are black, 23% are yellow and 49% are red. Some pieces are of another colour. One piece is to be taken at random. Find the probability that the piece will be:

a either black or yellow   **b** either yellow or red

c not black   **d** not red

e neither black nor yellow   **f** neither yellow nor red.

> **Probabilities can be written as fractions, percentages or decimals.**

10 In a raffle, the probabilities of the winning ticket being certain colours are given here: $P(\text{red}) = 0.375$, $P(\text{green}) = 0.125$, and $P(\text{blue}) = 0.25$.

a Are there tickets of any other colour? How do you know?

Find as a decimal, the probability that the winning ticket:

b is not red   **c** is not green   **d** is not blue

e is neither red, green nor blue.

11 From a standard pack of 52 cards, one card is taken at random. Find the probability that the card will be:

a a diamond   **b** not a diamond   **c** a 4

d not a 4   **e** a picture card   **f** not a picture card

g between 3 and 7   **h** not between 3 and 7   **i** either red or black.

12 The pack of cards we are using is a standard pack plus a Joker. When a card is selected at random, the probability of selecting a red card is $\frac{26}{53}$.

   a What is the probability of selecting a card that is not red?
   b What is the probability of selecting the Joker?

13 Using the probabilities given in Question **5**, find the probability that the stamp chosen will be:
   a either Polish or Australian   **b** neither Polish nor Australian
   c either Australian or French   **d** neither Australian nor French.
   e Give two possible answers for the total number of stamps in this collection.
       Give a reason for your answer.

14 Using the probabilities given in Question **6**, find the probability that the coin chosen will be:
   a either Chinese, British or African   **b** neither Chinese, British nor African
   c either Australian or American   **d** neither Australian nor American.
   e Give two possible answers for the total number of coins in this collection.
       Give a reason for your answer.

fun spot

15:03

Fun Spot 15:03 | Probability in games

Game 1: Snakes and Ladders

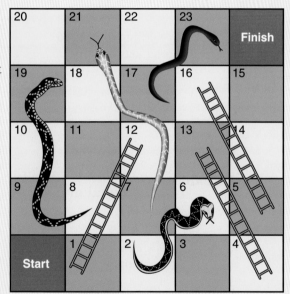

In this game, if you land on the head of a snake, you must move down to its tail. If you land on the foot of a ladder, you must move up to its top.

   Your counter is at the start.
   You must throw one dice and move forward following the rules above.

1 Find the probability that after one turn your counter will be on square number:

   a 3   **b** 20   **c** 13   **d** 2

2 Find the probability that after one throw your counter will be on:

   a an odd number   **b** an even number

Game 2: Spiral

   Your counter is at the start. You must throw one dice and move forward following the directions.

3 Find the probability that after one turn your counter will be on square number:

   a 4   **b** 2   **c** 5   **d** 6

15:04 | Using Probability

Write the sample space (all possible outcomes) for:
1 throwing a dice   2 tossing a coin   3 trying to clear a high jump.
In a standard pack of cards:
4 how many cards are there?   5 how many suits are there?
6 how many cards are in each suit?   7 what are the suits called?
A dice is thrown. What is the probability that the result will be:
8 a six?   9 even?   10 a zero?

We use probability within our community to predict the most likely outcomes of future events.

• Every person should try to calculate the chance of success before beginning a new venture so that failure can be avoided or plans changed so that the chance of success can be increased.

• The captains of sporting teams (eg hockey) will assess the probabilities of each possible action when making decisions.
eg *Should we attack or defend? What strategy is likely to give us our best chance of winning?*

• Insurance companies work out the likelihood of death or accident to calculate the cost of policies and to decide on the wording to be used.
eg *Should the policy cover acts of terror?*

Remember:
• **If all outcomes are equally likely:**

$$\text{Probability} = \frac{\text{number of favourable outcomes}}{\text{total number of outcomes}}$$

$$P(E) = \frac{n(E)}{n(S)}$$

where: **n(E) = number of ways the event can occur**
n(S) = number of possible outcomes.

• **If the probability of an event occurring is P(E), then the probability that it will not occur is 1 − P(E).**

$$P(E') = 1 - P(E)$$

where: **P(E) is the probability of the original event and P(E') is the probability of the complementary event.**

We met these in 15:02 and 15:03.

Exercise 15:04

Foundation Worksheet 15:04

Using probability

1 Six runners are to run in a race. If one is chosen at random, what is the probability that the one chosen would:
  a win?   b not win?
2 More questions relating to the probability of simple events.

1 Use one of the terms *impossible*, *very unlikely*, *unlikely*, *even chance*, *likely*, *very likely* and *certain* to rewrite each statement.
  a Manchester United is *expected* to continue its winning way this Saturday.
  b We *predict* early showers today.
  c The drought has been severe and we are *hoping* it might rain tomorrow.
  d We *believe* that our company is *on the rocks*.
  e The school council president election is a cliff-hanger between Hyun Jun and Danielle.
  f Everybody overboard! The ship is *doomed*!

2 7 women and 4 men *draw straws* to decide who will buy morning tea. (*Drawing straws* is a way of making a random choice.) What is the probability that the person chosen will:
  a be a man?   b be a woman?   c not be a woman?
  d not be a man?   e be either a man or a woman?

3 I have 3 pairs of shoes in a box. I chose one shoe and I am to choose a second at random. What is the probability that:
  a the second shoe will match the first?
  b the second shoe will not match the first?

4 If there is a probability of 0·03 of losing luggage while travelling, what is the probability that luggage will not be lost?

5 Our basketball team's last ten scores have been 0, 33, 14, 87, 15, 8, 2, 10, 49 and 50. If one of these scores is selected at random, what is the probability that it will be:
  a 0?   b greater than 40?   c greater than 100?
  d less than 50?   e between 5 and 30?   f less than 100?

6 The probability that I can avoid being absent from school for one month is 0·65, for two months is 0·41 and for three months is 0·34. What is the probability that I will not be able to avoid being absent for:
  a one month?   b two months?   c three months?

7 In our next game of soccer the probability that we will win is 0·45 and that we will play a draw is 0·23. What is the probability that we will lose?

8 The doctor told me that there is a 5% chance that I will have a bad reaction to this medicine. What is the chance that my reaction will not be bad?

9 If I toss a coin three times and record the results in order, there are eight possible outcomes: (head, head, head), (head, head, tail), (head, tail, head), (head, tail, tail), (tail, head, head), (tail, head, tail), (tail, tail, head) and (tail, tail, tail). If I toss a coin three times what is the probability of getting:
  a three heads?   b two heads?   c one head?
  d no heads?   e at least one head?

10 300 tickets are to be sold in a raffle. How many tickets must I buy to have:

    a a 10% chance of winning?   **b** a 30% chance of winning?

    c a probability of $\frac{1}{4}$ of winning?   **d** a probability of 1 of winning?

Challenge worksheet **15:04 Probability: An unusual case**

Mathematical terms 15

at random
- A way of choosing so that each outcome is equally likely to be chosen.

certain
- Sure, inevitable.
- A probability of 1 (ie 100%).

complementary events
- The complement of an event is all possible outcomes outside of that event.
  eg The complementary event to *throwing a six* is *not throwing a six.*
- The probabilities of the event and its complement add up to 1. If P(E) is the probability that E will occur, then the probability that E won't occur, P(E′), is 1 − P(E).
  ie P(E′) = 1 − P(E).

even chance (fifty-fifty chance)
- Equal chance of happening or not happening, eg tossing a *head* in a coin toss.
- 50% chance of happening and 50% chance of not happening.

heads and tails
- Each coin has two sides, a 'head' and a 'tail'.

—heads

tails

impossible
- Cannot happen, not possible.
- Having a probability of 0 (ie 0%).

probability
- The chance of an event happening.
- Must be in the range 0 to 1 (ie 0% to 100%).

$$\text{Probability} = \frac{\text{number of favourable outcomes}}{\text{total number of outcomes}}$$

- $P(E) = \dfrac{n(E)}{n(S)}$ where

  n(E) = number of ways it can occur

  n(S) = number of possible outcomes
      (the number in the sample space)

sample space (S)
- All of the possible outcomes.
  eg The sample space for tossing a coin is *head*, *tail*.

simple event
- An event where each outcome is equally likely.

standard pack of cards
- 4 suits:

  ♥   ♦   ♣   ♠

  hearts   diamonds   clubs   spades
- 52 cards (13 each of the four suits), Ace, 2, 3, 4, 5, 6, 7, 8, 9, 10, Jack, Queen and King in each suit.
- Picture cards (or court cards): Jacks, Queens and Kings (12 in total).

Mathematical terms 15

Diagnostic Test 15: | Probability

- Each section of the test has similar items that test a certain type of question.
- Failure in more than one item will identify an area of weakness.
- Each weakness should be treated by going back to the section listed.

	Section

1 Order the following events from least likely to most likely.
  a **A** A dice will be thrown. The result will either be a 1, a 2 or a 3.
    B The next person to walk into our classroom will have their birthday in December.
    C If I pick a counter at random from a group containing four red, one green and one yellow, it will be red.
  b When I toss a dice:
    A I will throw a zero
    B I will throw a number less than 3
    C I will throw a number greater than 3.
	15:01

2 List all possible outcomes. **a** A coin is tossed. **b** A dice is thrown.	15:02

3 How many outcomes are in each sample space below?
  a A dice is thrown.
  b A card is selected from a standard pack of cards.
	15:02

4 From these pictures, one will be chosen at random. What is the probability that the one chosen is of:
  a a woman?   **b** a man?
  c someone wearing a hat? 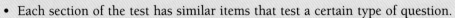
	15:02

5 A letter is chosen at random from the vowels, *a*, *e*, *i*, *o* and *u*. What is the probability of choosing:
  a either the *a* or the *e*?   **b** a vowel?
  c the letter *t*?   **d** a letter that is not the *u*?
	15:02

6 a Luke's chance of clearing the high jump is $\frac{7}{10}$. What is Luke's chance of not clearing the high jump?
  b The probability of throwing a sum of 8 when two dice are thrown is $\frac{5}{36}$. What is the probability of not throwing a sum of 8?
  c The chance of choosing a picture card from a standard pack is $\frac{3}{13}$. What is the complement of choosing a picture card and what is its probability?
  d Our team's chance of winning our next hockey game is $\frac{7}{10}$. What is the complement of the event *winning the game*? What is the probability of this complementary event?
	15:03

Chapter 15 | Revision Assignment

Please use scale drawings to answer questions 1–5.

1 Which of these triangles would be right-angled?

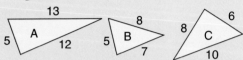

2 Find the value of the pronumeral correct to 2 decimal places.

a

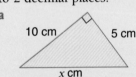

b

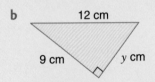

3 a Is ΔOAB a right-angled triangle?

  b Find the length of AB.

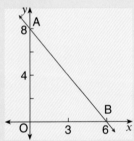

4 Would a triangle that had sides of length 10 cm, 24 cm and 26 cm be a right-angled triangle? If so, then would {10, 24, 26} be a Pythagorean triad?

5 The radius of this cone is 3 cm and its slant height is 7 cm. Find the height, h of the cone.

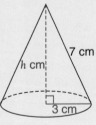

6 Change to a percentage:

  a 0·375   b $\frac{7}{8}$

7 Convert to a decimal:

  a 4·5%   b $12\frac{1}{2}\%$

8 a Find 7% of 1400 g.

  b What fraction is 24 seconds of 3 minutes?

  c A sandwich contains 10 g of meat, 50 g of bread and 4 g of cheese. Find the percentage, by mass, of cheese.

  d Increase $12 by 15%.

  e Decrease $12 by 15%.

9 Declan sells books for a living. He is given a commission of 6% on the first $15 000 of sales made and 4% on sales in excess of $15 000. How much commission would he make on sales of $45 000?

10 Use the rule $y = 4x + 11$ to complete this table.

x	0	1	2	15
y				

11 What rule connecting x and y is shown in this table?

x	0	1	2	3
y	1	11	21	31

12 Simplify:

  a $7m - 5m$ b $8x - x$

  c $ab + 3ab$ d $6x^2 + 2x^2 - 3x^2$

  e $2a + b + 7a$ f $6a - 13a$

  g $-3 \times 6y$ h $7a \times 4b$

  i $24m \div 3m$ j $6a^2 \div 2a$

  k $8a \div 8 \times a$ l $2ma \times 3a \div m$

13 Evaluate each expression if $a = 10$, $b = 7$ and $c = 4$.

  a $ab - 4$ b $a^2 + b^2$

  c $c - 2a + b$ d $bc - a^2$

14 Simplify:

  a $m \times m \times m \times m$ b $5 \times a \times a \times a$

  c $4(3x + 1) + 8$ d $2(9m - 5) - 3$

  e $\dfrac{9x}{10} - \dfrac{6x}{10}$ f $\dfrac{m}{3} + \dfrac{m}{2}$

  g $\dfrac{a}{5} \times \dfrac{2a}{3}$ h $\dfrac{5x}{6} \div \dfrac{2}{3}$

15 Factorise:

  a $2x + 14$ b $m^2 - 3m$

  c $22 - 33y$ d $9ab + 12a^2$

Chapter 15 | Working Mathematically

1 Use ID Card 6 on page xviii to identify:

a	1	b	2	c	4	d	5
e	6	f	7	g	8	h	9
i	10	j	11	k	12	l	16

2 How many triangles can you find in this figure?

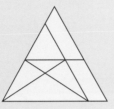

3 The Eiffel Tower in Paris is 312 m high. 500 sheets of paper make a pile 55 mm high. How many sheets of paper would form a pile as high as the Eiffel Tower? (Answer correct to the nearest 1000.)

4 If *24H in a D* stands for *24 Hours in a Day*, what might the following cryptic statements mean?

a 365 D in a Y
b 9 L of a C
c 52 C in a S P
d 26 L in the A
e 66 B of the B
f 12 M in a Y
g 1000 Y in a M
h 64 S on a C B

5  I calculated the cost of buying a number of sound systems by multiplying the marked price by the number of systems I wanted. This calculator shows the answer ($5683.89).

15B

a How many sound systems are involved? (Try *guess and check*.)
b What is the cost of one system?

6

a Explain how the turning of one wheel can affect other wheels.
b Estimate the number of cogs (teeth) that are on the whole wheel at the top left of the photograph.

7 Causes of disability
Young men

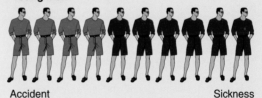

Accident   Sickness

Young women

Accident   Sickness

Compare the results for young men and young women shown above.

a What information is communicated by this graph?
b What could account for the differences in the results for men and women?

1 Probability of simple events
2 Probability of spinners

16
Graph theory

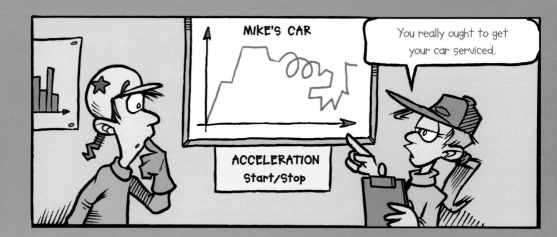

MIKE'S CAR

You really ought to get your car serviced.

ACCELERATION
Start/Stop

Chapter Contents

Learning Outcomes

Students will be able to:

- Read and interpret graphs used for transport networks.
- Recognise subgraphs and trees.
- Represent given information graphically.
- Use graphs and networks to solve problems.

Areas of Interaction

Human Ingenuity, Environments, Community and Service

16:01 | What is a Graph?

We are used to graphs like bar charts, line graphs and sector graphs. In this chapter we look at different sorts of graphs but no graph paper is needed.

A **graph** is a collection of dots that may or may not be connected to each other by lines. Here are some examples of graphs that you may have seen before:

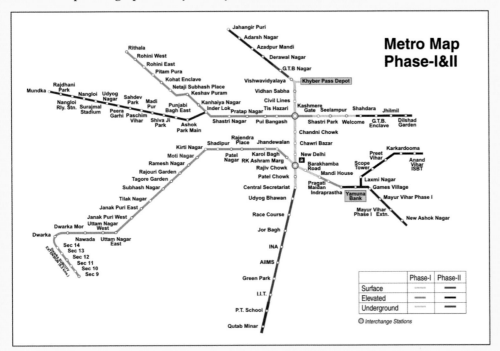

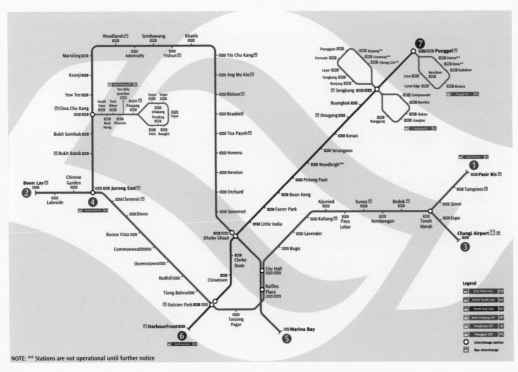

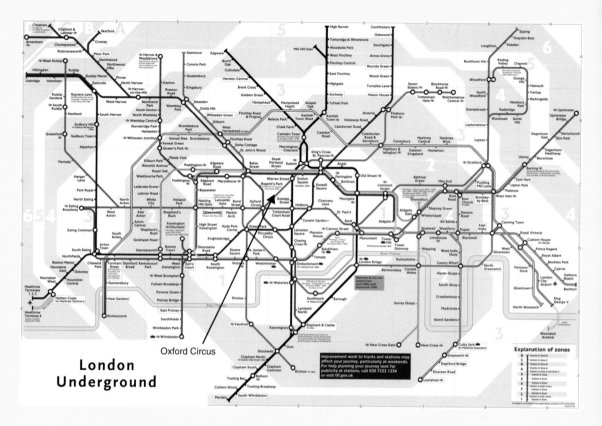

London
Underground

These three graphs represent train networks. The first is the Delhi Metro, the second the Singapore MRT and the third the London Underground (the Tube). The London Underground was the first train network to be drawn in this way. The man who first used a graph for this purpose was Harry Beck in 1933. Now all train networks use the same idea.

Each of these graphs is made up of a collection of dots joined together by lines. Each dot is called a **vertex** (if there is more than one, they are called **vertices**) and each line is called an **edge**.

The **degree** of a vertex is found by counting the number of edges which join it to other vertices.

The graph shown here is a very simple one but it still has vertices and edges. It represents the rail network on the Island of 'Beck'.

Vertex A has degree 1
Vertex B has degree 3
Vertex C has degree 2
Vertex D has degree 2

Exercise 16:01

1 In the graphs on the previous pages, what does each vertex and edge represent?

2 What advantage does the London Underground have over the Singapore MRT, and what advantage does the MRT have over the Delhi Metro?

3 Here is a map of Singapore which also shows the rail network.

Give two reasons why the graph version of the Singapore rail network shown on the previous page is preferable.

4 A graph of the Dragonair network based in Hong Kong is shown.

  a What do the vertices and edges represent on this graph?

  b What is the main difference between this graph and the Singapore MRT and London Underground graphs?

5 Using the graphs that have been given, find the degree of the following vertices:

  a Kashmere Gate (Delhi Metro)

  b Jurong East (Singapore MRT)

  c Oxford Circus (London Underground).

6 What can be said about all the vertices on the Dragonair graph, except for Hong Kong?

7 The railway system for the town of Kruskal is shown on the right. The engineer used his friends' names for the stations on the Metro.

  a Do you think this graph is drawn to scale? Why, or why not?

  b An interchange is where you can change from one line to another. How many interchanges are there on the Kruskal Metro? What are their degrees?

  c How many vertices have an even degree?

  d If you were to give one suggestion on how to improve this Metro, what would it be?

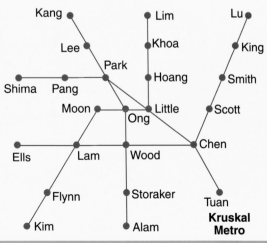

16:02 | Subgraphs, Connectivity and Trees

A **subgraph** is part of another graph. Below is an example of a subgraph of the London Underground graph. It represents one railway line — the Victoria line — within the London network.

Although this section is not the same shape as it appears on the original graph, it has all the vertices and edges that appear on the original, so it is a subgraph.

In a **connected** graph you can travel from any vertex to any other vertex using the edges.

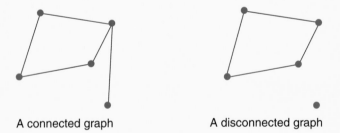

A connected graph   A disconnected graph

A **tree** is a connected graph which has only one way of getting from one vertex to another.

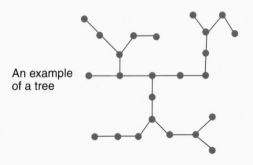

An example of a tree

Exercise 16:02

1 Which of the graphs shown so far in this chapter are examples of trees?

2 Draw all the trees which show all the possible ways to get from Lam station to Little station on the Kruskal Metro.

3 Draw six examples of trees and complete the following table — the first four are from the examples given.

Tree	Number of Vertices	Number of Edges
Deli Metro	97	96
Dragonair	31	30
Victoria Line Subgraph	16	15
Tree Example	24	23
Tree 1		
Tree 2		
Tree 3		
Tree 4		
Tree 5		
Tree 6		

4 From the table you completed, finish the following statement:

If a tree has n vertices then it has _____ edges.

5 Give a reason why most airline route graphs are trees but subway graphs usually contain loops.

6 From the graph shown, draw a subgraph:
  a that is a tree
  b that is not a tree
  c that has 3 edges and is not a tree
  d that has 4 edges and is not a tree
  e that is a disconnected graph.

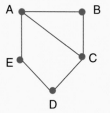

7 A **spanning tree** is a tree which joins all of the vertices of a graph.
Draw all the spanning trees of the graph shown on the right.

Fun Spot 16:02 | The Königsberg Bridge problem

Königsberg, a town in East
Prussia in the eighteenth
century, had a river running
through it. In the middle of the
river were two islands. These
islands were joined together
with seven bridges as shown
in the map.

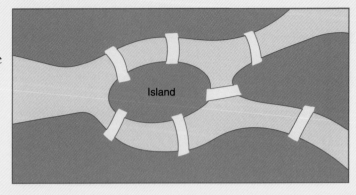

Island

The people of this town
wondered if there was a way
to cross all the bridges exactly
once. Can you draw a trail that
crosses every bridge once, without taking your pencil off the page?

We can simplify the problem by making each bridge an edge in a graph and land masses
vertices.

Is it possible to do the task?

16:03 | Drawing Graphs and Isomorphisms

worked examples

1   A graph has 5 vertices labelled *A*, *B*, *C*, *D*, *E* with edges joining the following:
    A and *B*
    B and *C*
    C and *E*
    A and *C*
    B and *E*.

2   The graph on the right shows the
    railway system for the small island
    of Trai.

    The railway system on Trai winds
    around the island, connecting the
    main towns. The president wants a
    simpler graph to show the system.

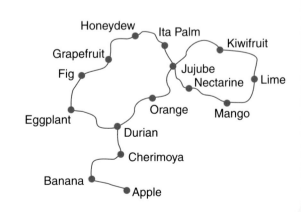

Solutions

1 There are a number of possible solutions. Here are three:

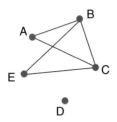 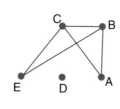 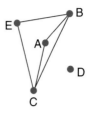

Can you draw a different one?

Although these graphs look different, they represent the same information. Graphs which do this are called **isomorphisms**.

2 There are many possibilities. Here are two which are isomorphisms:

Trai Trains 1

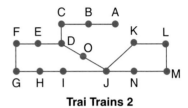

Trai Trains 2

Exercise 16:03

1 Discuss the relative advantages or disadvantages of the graphs of the train system on Trai.

2 Draw another graph to represent the trains system on Trai.

3 This map shows the proposed bus routes in a new suburban area. There is a red bus and a blue bus, both of which have 10 stops numbered 1 to 10 indicated by coloured dots. The green dots indicate places where both buses stop. Draw a simple graph to represent this information using only straight edges.

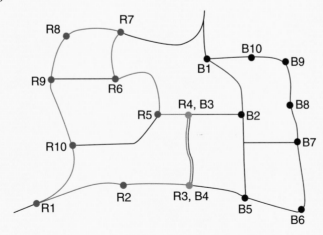

4 Anita has drawn a map of the layout of her school and the paths that join the buildings. Represent this information in a simple graph.

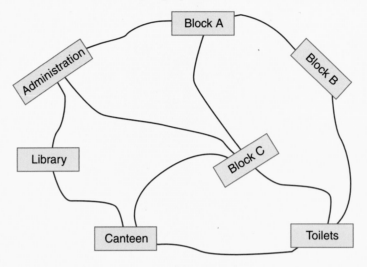

Investigation 16:03 | Eulerian trails

Please use the Assessment Grid on page 428 to help you understand what is required for this Investigation.

A graph has an **Eulerian trail** if a route can be found through the graph that visits every edge exactly once. In other words, you must be able to draw the graph without lifting your pencil off the page, or drawing any edge more than once.

This is an example of a graph with an Eulerian trail:

It can be drawn by this Eulerian trail:

- Complete the table for the given graphs and indicate which ones have eulerian trails.

Graph	Vertices with even degree	Vertices with odd degree	Eulerian trail?
Example above			

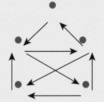			

Graph	Vertices with even degree	Vertices with odd degree	Eulerian trail?
Example above			
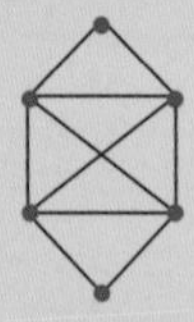			

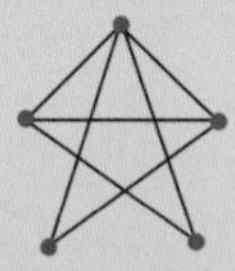			
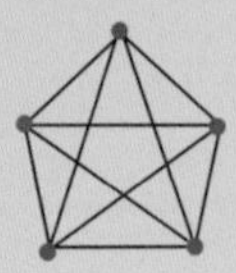			

- In addition to these graphs, draw three or four of your own, some of which have eulerian trails and some that do not.
- Is there a pattern in the degree of the vertices in the graphs, and whether or not it has an eulerian trail?

These graphs are named after a famous mathematician Leonhard Euler who lived in the eighteenth century.

- Find out more about him and his connection with graph theory.
- Look back at Fun Spot 16:02 and comment on the possibility of the task.

Assessment Grid for Investigation 16:03 | Eulerian trails

The following is a sample assessment grid for this investigation. You should carefully read the criteria *before* beginning the investigation so that you know what is required.

			Assessment Criteria (B, C, D)		Achieved ✓
Criterion B Investigating Patterns	a		The student had some difficulty in applying skills to this task — particularly inventing new graphs.	1	
				2	
	b		A systematic approach has been attempted and an effort made to describe patterns in the table.	3	
				4	
	c		A systematic approach has been used and the pattern in the table has been described in words or symbols, with some success.	5	
				6	
	d		In describing the patterns, predictions have been made and proven by drawing further graphs and a reason has been given why the pattern given works.	7	
				8	
Criterion C Communication	a		Little working out is shown, and no further graphs have been drawn.	1	
				2	
	b		Working out is shown and extra graphs have been drawn to illustrate the conclusion made.	3	
				4	
	c		Descriptions are well written using correct mathematical terminology and/or diagrams.	5	
				6	
Criterion D Reflection in Mathematics	a		Some attempt has been made to check the reliability of the findings.	1	
				2	
	b		The reliability of findings has been checked with some success.	3	
				4	
	c		The reliability of findings has been thoroughly checked using many examples.	5	
				6	

16:04 | Using Graphs to Solve Problems

1 Five people are invited to a dinner party and all say hello to each other exactly once. How many hellos will there be?

2 Bron's school has 7 buildings, all joined by walkways as shown in the graph. Each vertex represents a building and each edge a walkway.

Parents have asked the principal of the school to cover the walkways so that the students don't get wet when moving from one building to another in the rain.

What is the minimum length of walkway to be covered so that all the buildings are joined by covered walkways?

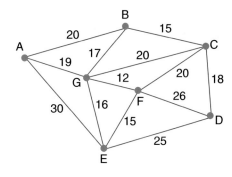

Solutions

1 Draw a graph with 5 vertices — each one represents a person.

Let each edge in the graph be a hello — everyone says hello to everyone else exactly once, so each vertex is joined to each other vertex exactly once.

If each edge is a hello, then there must be 10 hellos as there are 10 edges.

Since all the vertices are joined to all the other vertices, this is called a **complete** graph.

2 This is a little different to the other graphs we have done because all the edges have numbers which represent the distance between the buildings.

Graphs with numbers like this one are called **networks**.

Redraw the network with no edges.

Choose any vertex, say G, and join it to the nearest vertex, F.

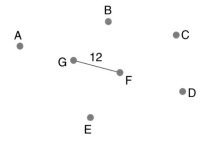

Now join GF to the next nearest vertex, E, and then the next, B (or C as it is the same distance).

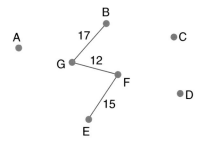

As you can see, a **tree** is forming. Continue to build the tree by joining the next nearest vertex to the tree, vertex C.

Do the same for vertices D and A and the tree is connected.

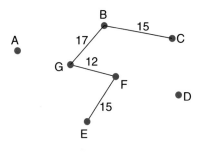

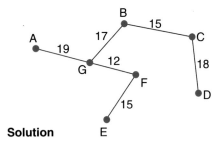

Solution

The final solution is a tree showing all the minimum connections between the vertices. This is called the **minimum spanning tree** for this network.

For this problem *the minimum length of walkway to be covered is 96 metres.*

Exercise 16:04

1 Four couples attend a dinner party. Every person says hello exactly once to everybody except his/her partner.
   a Draw a graph with vertices to represent the people and edges to represent the hellos.
   b How many hellos are there?

2 Deb wants to try and find out the minimum number of colours she could use to colour a map of South America so that no two colours are joined.

Deb constructs a graph in which all the countries are represented by vertices.

She then joins together those countries which border one another and figures that vertices that are joined must be different colours.

   a What is the minimum number of colours needed if the ocean is not included?
   b If the ocean is to be a different colour from the countries it borders, what is the minimum number of colours now needed?

3 The network on the right shows the layout of campsites at a National Park camping area.

Management has decided to install power at all the sites and wants to know the minimum length of wire needed to join all the sites so they all have electricity. What is the minimum length of wire needed?

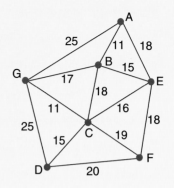

4 A company wishes to set up business in South Korea. The company plans to have outlets in the cities shown on the map of mainland South Korea below. To have a dedicated communication network, the company must pay according to the distance between its offices.

Use your ruler to create a minimum spanning tree for the company.

Practical Activities 16:04 | Making connections

A company has offices in all the ASEAN capital cities. The company wants to have its own dedicated computer network and must pay for connections between its offices. To minimise costs, the manager needs to know the minimum distance required to connect all the offices.

The table shows the distances between capitals in kilometres.

	Bandar Seri Begawan	Bangkok	Ha Noi	Jakarta	Kuala Lumpur	Manila	Phnom Penh	Singapore	Vientiane	Yangon
Bandar Seri Begawan	—	1909	1913	1697	1623	1099	1374	1453	1976	2476
Bangkok	1909	—	900	2322	1184	2206	535	1434	522	576
Ha Noi	1913	900	—	2916	1929	1713	945	2096	408	1083
Jakarta	1697	2322	2916	—	1185	2788	1986	893	2725	2809
Kuala Lumpur	1623	1184	1929	1185	—	2467	1001	318	1651	1630
Manila	1099	2206	1713	2788	2467	—	1770	2395	1991	2664
Phnom Penh	1374	535	945	1986	1001	1770	—	1151	753	1106
Singapore	1453	1434	2096	893	318	2395	1151	—	1862	1918
Vientiane	1976	522	408	2725	1651	1991	753	1862	—	699
Yangon	2476	576	1083	2809	1630	2664	1106	1918	699	—

a Create a network to represent this information. You may use the vertices on the map on the right or make up your own arrangement.

b Find the minimum spanning tree for this network and the minimum distance of dedicated lines the company will need to buy.

Don't forget to explain the steps you used along the way to your answer and use correct terminology.

Mathematical terms 16

Graph
- A collection of points that may or may not be connected to each other by lines.
- Graphs are usually used to represent information of some sort.

Network
- A graph in which the edges have numbers associated with them.

Vertex
- The points in a graph — usually where two or more lines meet.
- If there is more than one vertex, they are collectively known as vertices.

Edge
- The line in a graph that joins vertices.

Degree of a vertex
- The degree of a vertex is the number of edges that join it to other vertices.

Trail
- A trip through part, or all of a graph, without lifting the pencil off the page.

Eulerian trail
- A trail through a graph that travels along each edge exactly once.

Subgraph
- Part of another graph.

Connected graph
- A graph in which all vertices are connected by at least one edge.

Tree
- A connected graph in which there is only one way to travel from one vertex to another.

Spanning tree
- A tree which connects all the vertices of a graph.

Isomorphism
- Graphs which look different but represent the same information.

Diagnostic Test 16: | Graphs and Networks

- Each section of the test has similar items that test a certain type of question.
- Errors made will indicate an area of weakness.
- Each weakness should be treated by going back to the section listed.

Section
16:01

1 For each of the following graphs, complete the table indicating the degree of each vertex.

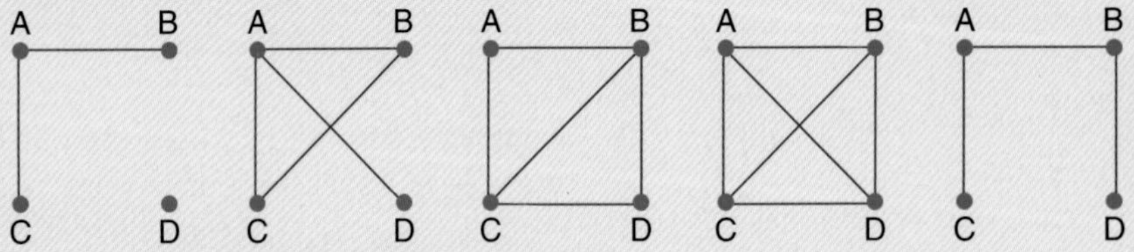

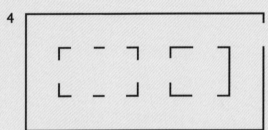

16:02

16:03

16:04

	Graph 1	Graph 2	Graph 3	Graph 4	Graph 5
Degree of vertex A					
Degree of vertex B					
Degree of vertex C					
Degree of vertex D					

2 Draw the subgraph of the railway system on Trai (see page 424) which represents the loop through Lime.

3 Draw an isomorphism to your answer to question 2.

4

The floorplan of a museum is shown above.
a Is it possible to enter the museum and go through every door without using one twice?
b Is it possible to enter the museum, go through every door without using one twice and then exit?

16A

1 Change to a fraction:
   a 0·625   b 13.$\dot{3}$ %

2 a Find 12·5% of $6400.
   b What fraction of an hour is 40 minutes?

3 Simplify:
   a $2a - 5a$
   b $12b + 7d - d + 9b$
   c $3x^2 - 6y - x^2 + 4y$
   d $8m \times 4mn \div 2m$

4 Find the value of a in the following:
   a
   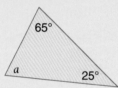
   b

   c
   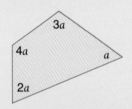

5 a The ratio of chickens to ducks in a farmyard is 4:5. If there are 20 ducks, how many chickens are there?
   b For two-stroke engines, oil is mixed with petrol in the ratio 1:50. How much oil would there be in 25 litres of two-stroke petrol?

6 Calculate the area of:
   a a rectangle 2·3 cm wide and 4·2 cm long
   b a triangle with base 6 m and height 8 m
   c a parallelogram with parallel sides 5.4 mm that are 3 mm apart.

7 Determine the mean of the following sets of scores:
   a 2, 3, 4, 3, 2, 2, 2, 3, 3, 4, 5
   b
   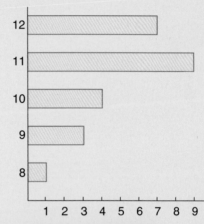
   c

Score	Frequency
51	5
52	6
53	9
54	3
55	1
56	2

8 A jar contains 35 jelly beans. All the jelly beans are black, blue or red. If a jelly bean is chosen at random, the probability of choosing a red one is $\frac{2}{7}$ and a black one $\frac{3}{5}$.
   a How many red jelly beans are in the jar?
   b What is the probability of choosing a blue jelly bean at random?

Chapter 16 | Working Mathematically

1 Felix, Fiona and Philip are triplets. In how many different orders could they have been born if it is known that a boy was born first?

2 Six people can survive in a life raft for 24 days with the given supplies. For how long would 8 people survive with the same supplies, given that they all use the same amount?

3 In a barnyard there are only chickens and goats. If there are 80 legs altogether and it is known there are 25 animals, how many chickens and goats are there?

4 In a class of 24 people, 16 study music, 9 study art and 3 do not study either music or art.
   a How many study both music and art?
   b How many study music but not art?

5 A plane leaves Hong Kong at 2:15 pm (Hong Kong time) and arrives in Dubai at 10:00 pm (Dubai time). If it is midnight in Dubai when it is 4:00 am in Hong Kong,
   a What is the time in Hong Kong when the plane lands in Dubai?
   b How long is the flight?

6 Right now, Sam's father is 30 years older than Sam. In three years' time he will be 3 times Sam's age. How old is Sam?

Answers

Chapter 1: Review of last year's work

Exercise 1:01
1 a 60 **b** 40 **c** 34 **d** 118 **e** 1788 **f** 1988 **g** 5321 **h** 1615
2 a DCXXX **b** DCCCXLVII **c** MCCCVIII **d** MMMCCXL
  e CCCXC **f** CXCIX **g** $\overline{\text{X}}$ **h** MDCCLXXIII
3 a 6 090 000 **b** 140 600 **c** 84 705 **d** 74 398
4 a 5×5; 25 **b** $10 \times 10 \times 10 \times 10$; 10 000 **c** $2 \times 2 \times 2$; 8
  d $2 \times 2 \times 2 \times 2 \times 2$; 32 **5** 6^4
6 a 80 000 **b** 6000 **c** 900 000 **d** 200
7 a 1100 **b** 20 000 **c** 30 000 **d** 500 **e** 800 **f** 20 000

Exercise 1:02
1 a 32 **b** 0 **c** 8 **d** 60 **e** 30 **f** 47
2 a 347 **b** 0 **c** 36 **d** 3842 **e** 30 406 **f** 0
3 a true **b** true **c** true **d** true **e** true **f** true **g** true **h** true
4 a $\{1, 2, 3, 4\}$ **b** $\{0, 2, 4, 6\}$ **c** $\{16, 17, 19, 20, 22, 23\}$ **d** $\{6\cdot5, 7\cdot5, 8\cdot5\}$
  e $\{0\cdot1, 0\cdot3, 0\cdot4, 0\cdot5, 0\cdot8\}$ **f** $\{\frac{1}{4}, \frac{3}{4}, 1\frac{1}{4}, 1\frac{3}{4}\}$
5 a true **b** true **c** true **d** true **e** true **f** false **g** true **h** true
6 a 0, 3, 4, 6, 11, 16, 19, 20 **b** 3, 4, 6, 11, 16, 19, 20 **c** 4, 6, 16, 20
  d 3, 11, 19 **e** 4, 16 **f** 3, 6
7 a $\{1, 12, 2, 6, 3, 4\}$ **b** $\{1, 102, 2, 51, 3, 34, 6, 17\}$ **c** $\{1, 64, 2, 32, 4, 16, 8\}$
  d $\{1, 140, 2, 70, 4, 35, 5, 28, 7, 20, 10, 14\}$
8 a $\{7, 14, 21, 28\}$ **b** $\{5, 10, 15, 20\}$ **c** $\{12, 24, 36, 48\}$ **d** $\{13, 26, 39, 52\}$
9 a 5 **b** 51 **c** 16 **d** 42
10 a 24 **b** 45 **c** 100 **d** 72
11 a $\{2, 3, 5, 7, 11, 13, 17, 19, 23, 29\}$ **b** $\{32, 33, 34, 35, 36, 38, 39\}$

12 a

```
          2 5 2
         /      \
        4        6 3
       / \      /   \
      2   2    7     9
      |   |    |    / \
      2   2    7   3   3
```

  b $2 \times 2 \times 2 \times 2 \times 5 \times 5$
  c $2 \times 2 \times 2 \times 3 \times 3 \times 3 \times 5$
  d 40
  e 10 800

13 a 2002 **b** 2001 **c** 2004 **d** 2005 **e** 2004 **f** 2008 **g** 2007 **h** 2010
  i 2002 **j** 2025 **k** 2100 **l** 2004
14 a 15 **b** 8 **c** 13 **d** 4

Exercise 1:03
1 a 5 **b** $2\frac{1}{4}$ **c** $8\frac{7}{10}$ **d** $1\frac{3}{8}$ **2 a** $\frac{7}{2}$ **b** $\frac{53}{10}$ **c** $\frac{7}{4}$ **d** $\frac{22}{7}$
3 a $\frac{4}{5}$ **b** $\frac{2}{5}$ **c** $\frac{3}{20}$ **d** $\frac{3}{4}$ **4 a** $\frac{\boxed{4}}{10}$ **b** $\frac{\boxed{75}}{100}$ **c** $\frac{\boxed{40}}{10}$ **d** $\frac{\boxed{40}}{120}$
5 a $\frac{7}{10}$ **b** $\frac{13}{100}$ **c** $1\frac{2}{8}$ or $1\frac{1}{4}$ **d** $\frac{4}{12}$ or $\frac{1}{3}$ **6 a** $\frac{9}{10}$ **b** $\frac{3}{20}$ **c** $1\frac{3}{20}$ **d** $\frac{11}{100}$
7 a $\frac{6}{10}$ **b** $\frac{2}{5}$ **c** $\{\frac{3}{4}, \frac{8}{10}, \frac{17}{20}\}$ **d** $\{\frac{2}{3}, \frac{3}{5}, \frac{1}{2}, \frac{1}{4}\}$
8 a $5\frac{3}{20}$ **b** $7\frac{3}{8}$ **c** $2\frac{2}{5}$ **d** $8\frac{7}{10}$ **9 a** $\frac{3}{10}$ **b** $\frac{21}{100}$ **c** $\frac{2}{5}$ **d** $\frac{27}{32}$
10 a $2\frac{2}{5}$ **b** $5\frac{5}{8}$ **c** 5 **d** $4\frac{1}{2}$ **11 a** $1\frac{4}{5}$ **b** $\frac{5}{8}$ **c** $6\frac{2}{3}$ **d** $\frac{2}{5}$
12 a 1200 m or $1\frac{1}{5}$ km **b** $\frac{1}{5}$

Exercise 1:04

1 **a** 17·537 **b** 684·02

2 **a** $\frac{7}{10}$ **b** $2\frac{13}{100}$ **c** $\frac{9}{1000}$ **d** $5\frac{3}{10}$ **e** $\frac{17}{20}$ **f** $\frac{1}{40}$ **g** $1\frac{4}{5}$ **h** $9\frac{1}{25}$

3 **a** 0·9 **b** 0·13 **c** 1·5 **d** 2·99 **e** 0·6 **f** 0·165 **g** 0·625 **h** $0·2\dot{7}$

4 **a** {0·3, 0·303, 0·33} **b** {0·5, 2, 3·1} **c** {0·055, 0·505, 5·5}

5 **a** 5·22 **b** 61·35 **c** 9·625 **d** 6·375 **6 a** 0·003 **b** 4·202 **c** 0·0025 **d** 24·83

7 **a** 60 **b** 0·75 **c** 0·816 **d** 0·0045

8 **a** 16·3 **b** 0·3 **c** 1·038 **d** 0·030 7 5 **e** 19 **f** 20·34 **g** 17 500 **h** 3·01

9 **a** $365.42 **b** $58.37 **c** $66.96 **d** $11.25

10 **a** 97 000 000 **b** 0·09 **c** 86·1 **d** 0·67

Exercise 1:05

1 **a** $\frac{9}{100}$ **b** $\frac{16}{25}$ **c** $1\frac{1}{4}$ **d** $\frac{29}{200}$ **2 a** 75% **b** $137\frac{1}{2}$% **c** $12\frac{1}{3}$% **d** 460%

3 **a** 0·47 **b** 0·04 **c** 3·25 **d** 3 **e** 0·5 **f** 1·04 **g** 0·127 **h** 0·003

4 **a** 87% **b** 130% **c** 500% **d** 82·5%

5 **a** 44·8 L **b** 476 g **c** $40 **d** 1·79 m **e** 75% **f** 25%

Exercise 1:06

1 **a** ∠ABC **b** ∠SBE, ∠DBT **c** ∠MPN, ∠PNQ **d** reflex ∠BAD

2 **a** 15° **b** 148°

3 **a** revolution **b** acute angle **c** straight angle **d** reflex angle **e** right angle **f** obtuse angle
  g reflex angle **h** acute angle

4 **a** **b** **c** **d**

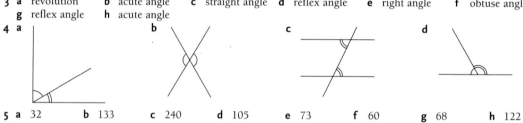

5 **a** 32 **b** 133 **c** 240 **d** 105 **e** 73 **f** 60 **g** 68 **h** 122

Exercise 1:07

1 **a** regular hexagon **b** 6 **c** 6 **d** 6 **e** 9

2 **a** equilateral, acute-angled; $a = 60$ **b** isosceles, acute-angled; $b = 40$ **c** scalene, obtuse-angled; $c = 30$
  d scalene, right-angled; $d = 35$ **e** isosceles, right-angled; $e = 45$ **f** isosceles, obtuse-angled; $f = 40$
  g scalene, acute-angled; $g = 65$ **h** isosceles, acute-angled; $h = 50$

3 **a** $a = 90$ **b** $b = 90$ **c** $c = 120$ **d** $d = 60$

4 **a** A: rectangle, B: square, C: rhombus, D: trapezium **b i** A, B, C **ii** B, C **iii** A, B, C **iv** D **v** B, C

Exercise 1:08

1 **a** A: rectangular prism, B: triangular prism, C: cylinder, D: cone, E: square pyramid
  b C, D **c i** $F = 5$ **ii** $V = 6$ **iii** $E = 9$ **iv** $E + 2 = 11$ **v** $F + V = 11$

2 **a** square pyramid **b** cone **c** pentagonal prism

3 **a** **b** **c**

Exercise 1:09

1 **a** 0·8 cm **b** 2·2 cm **c** 4·5 cm **d** 8 cm **e** 11·8 cm

2 **a** 300 cm **b** 2·5 L **c** 0·63 g **d** 7000 m **e** 7800 g **f** 250 cm

3 7 mm

4 **a** 32 m **b** 32·8 m **c** 20 cm

5 **a** 25 minutes past 1; 1:25 **b** Half past 10; 10:30 **c** 10 minutes to 7; 6:50 **d** A quarter to 5; 4:45

6 **a** 05:20 **b** 17:30 **c** 12:00 **d** 23:57

7 **a** 100 m **b** 3 m/s **c** 4 hours

8 **a** 13·5 cm^2 **b** 4500 cm^2 **c** 49 mm^2 **d** 24 m^2 **e** 17·5 cm^2 **f** 30 cm^2

9 **a** 15 cm^3 **b** 42 cm^3 **c** 30 cm^3 **d** 1980 m^3

10 **a** B, 5 mL **b** C, 1 L **c** B, 1 cm^2 **d** B, 50 g **e** A, 20 kg

11 **a** 100 g **b** 970 g

Exercise 1:10

1 −3, 4, 0, −10

2 a 4   **b** 12   **c** −7   **d** −20   **e** −11   **f** −3   **g** −12   **h** −13
   i 16   **j** 15   **k** 10   **l** 16   **m** 16   **n** 18   **o** 7   **p** 24

3 a 12   **b** 16   **c** 0·6   **d** 1·5   **e** −56   **f** −40   **g** −7·7   **h** −72
   i 7   **j** 4   **k** −10   **l** −2   **m** 7   **n** 6   **o** −8   **p** −0·9

4 a 9   **b** −20   **c** −10   **d** −10   **e** −26   **f** 0   **g** −6   **h** 10
   i −$11.50   **j** −15°

Exercise 1:11

1 $A(2, 1)$, $B(1, 3)$, $C(3, 0)$, $D(0, 2)$, $E(3, −2)$, $F(0, −3)$, $G(−3, 2)$, $H(−1, 0)$, $I(−3, −1)$, $J(−2, −3)$

2

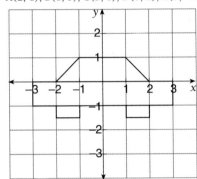

Exercise 1:12

1 a $m = 4s$

s	1	2	3	4	10	20	30	100
m	4	8	12	16	40	80	120	400

b $m = 3s + 1$

s	1	2	3	4	10	20	30	100
m	4	7	10	13	31	61	91	301

2 a $5h + 2$ **b** $a + 3y$ **c** $6(a + 7)$ **d** $\dfrac{5a}{7}$

3 a $3 \times a + 8$ **b** $5 \times p − 6 \times q$ **c** $4 \times (x + 2)$ **d** $(a + 7) \div 3$

4 a 18   **b** 16   **c** 45   **d** 1   **5 a** 41   **b** 4   **c** 24   **d** 29

6 201   **7 a** $y = 3x + 4$ **b** $y = 4x + 7$

8 a m **b** a **c** $4y$ **d** $4y$ **e** $5f$ **f** ab **g** $5k$ **h** $5ab$ **i** 0   **j** 0
   k $6m$ **l** $3a$ **m** $12a$ **n** $11a$ **o** $6b$ **p** $50a$ **q** $−2m$ **r** $−2b$ **s** $7x^2$ **t** ab

9 a $15a$ **b** $60b$ **c** $21mp$ **d** $32xy$ **e** $4ab$ **f** $30m$ **g** $15k$ **h** $−18y$ **i** $4t$ **j** $10t$
   k $\dfrac{3m}{a}$ **l** $\dfrac{2a}{b}$ **m** $\dfrac{3r}{2}$ **n** $\dfrac{4m}{3}$ **o** $21a^2b$ **p** $20ab^2$

10 a $2m$ **b** x **c** $5x + 9y$ **d** $10a + 3b$ **e** $10p + 3q$ **f** $8r + 5A$ **g** $4a + 12b$ **h** $2m + 4$
   i $6m − 6a$ **j** $9a^2 − 4a$ **k** $2x^2 + 5x$ **l** $2x^2 + 5x + 3$

11 a $3a + 27$ **b** $5x + 10$ **c** $10m − 40$ **d** $18a − 27$
   e $24t + 18$ **f** $10 + 20x$ **g** $m^2 + 7m$ **h** $a^2 − 3a$ **i** $6a + a^2$

12 a $x = 4$ **b** $x = 24$ **c** $a = 7$ **d** $a = 7$
   e $m = 7$ **f** $m = 20$ **g** $m = −5$ **h** $m = −4$

13 45, 46

14

1A Working Mathematically

1 a hectare **b** net of a cube **c** cross-section **d** coordinates **e** tally
f picture graph **g** column graph **h** line graph **i** sector (or pie) graph **j** bar graph
2 a 273, 274, 275 **b** 665, 666, 667 **c** 8283, 8284, 8285 **d** 6, 7, 8
e 12, 13, 14 **f** 24, 25, 26
3 a 14 **b** 56 **c** 2
4 a 241 days **b** 0·5 tons/hour **c** 1 442 335·9 tonnes
5 a i $121.92 **ii** $168.96 **iii** $78.72 **iv** $61.44 **b** Answers will vary
c The top 3 reasons given were: holiday (23%), retirement 14%, home deposit 10%

Chapter 2: Working mathematically

Exercise 2:01

1 a Answers will vary. **b** Answers will vary.
c i 64 000 (*Note:* There are 5 people on the assembly line.)
ii Estimates should be about 1·5 km. *Method:* Since 0·6 cm on the picture represents 20 cm, the scale is $1:33\frac{1}{3}$.
To fill 5 boxes the belt moves $8.5 \times 33\frac{1}{3}$ cm (ie $283\frac{1}{3}$ cm). The average belt movement for one box is $283\frac{1}{3} \div 5$ cm
(ie $56\frac{2}{3}$ cm). So to fill 2560 boxes, the belt moves $2560 \times 56\frac{2}{3}$ cm (ie $145\,066\frac{2}{3}$ cm). This is about 1·45 km.
d i Your answer might include the efficient working of the machinery, the speed of the packing at the end of the line,
ensuring that there are sufficient chocolates to pack in boxes, ensuring sufficient workers etc.
ii Your answer might include maintenance of machinery, sufficient supply of boxes, replacement of sick/weary
workers, what to do with large cartons when packed etc.
e Answers will vary.
2 a Answers will vary but note that everything is done to ensure the sheep are in the right place ready to be drenched
when the drencher is ready.
b Answers will vary but might include how the sheep were brought to this place.
c i 360 **ii** 13, 787 **iii** $260, $216\frac{2}{3}$ % **iv** 3 truckloads, $44 574
d Answers will vary; however, using this equipment you can only drench one sheep at a time so not much time can
be saved.
e Answers will vary; however, the person drenching sheep and those herding the sheep should stand so their shadows
don't fall on the path of the sheep. Answers will vary. A different way could be: instead of using the machine at the
end of the process to feed one sheep at a time past the drencher, the sheep could be crowded into the last stall and
the drencher could move from sheep to sheep. Answers will vary in terms of *costs*.

Exercise 2:02

1 a 12 **b** C **c** F1 **d i** 10 **ii** 24 **e** 13 (if we include the driver)
f 308 **g** 3 **h** 28
2 a $1152 **b** 89 cm **c** at least 45 cm **d** Collison, Foster, Bills **e** 5 lions, 5 tigers *or* 8 lions, 3 tigers
f 7 **g** Mr French — Craft, Mr English — French, Mr Kraft — Music, Mr Musik — English
h 5 horses **i** 18

Exercise 2:03

1 a 2 **b** 10 **c** 12 **2 a** 5 **b** 57 **c** 60
3 a 17 **b** 48 **c** 20
4 a Some people played both sports. **b** 18 **c** 22
5 23
6 a 1 **b** 3 **c** 6 **d** 7 **e** 17 **f** 6 **g** 21 **h** 22
7 a 10 **b** 12 **c** 12 **d** 5 **e** 7 **f** 2 **g** 2 **h** 4 **i** 7 **j** 5
k 5 **l** 3
8 a 3 **b** 5 **c** 2
9 a 17 **b** 3 **c** 27 **d** 6 **e** 23 **f** 5 **g** 36 **h** 20 **i** 65
10 a 13 **b** 25 **c** 11 **d** 21 **e** 0 **f** 22 **g** 119

2A Revision Assignment

1 a 34 **b** 1640 **c** 2413 **d** 1992
2 $3 \times 3 \times 3 \times 3 = 81$ **3** 900 000
4 a 3 **b** $2\frac{1}{2}$ **c** 44 **5**
6 a F **b** T **c** T **7** 1, 2, 3, 4, 6, 8, 12, 24
8 a $\frac{2}{5}$ **b** 8 **c** $2\frac{1}{4}$ **d** $\frac{2}{5}$ **e** $\frac{21}{100}$ **f** 4
9 a T **b** T **c** T **10 a** 0·09 **b** $\frac{3}{5}$ **c** 75% **d** 44·8 km

2B Working Mathematically

1 1293   2 9 with 3 legs, 15 with 4 legs   3 31   4 15   5 $28, $44

6   1 $6 - 2 = 4$ 2 $6 + 2 = 8$ 3 $6 \div 2 = 3$ 4 $6 - 2 = 4$ 5 $6 \div 2 = 3$ 6 2

    7 6   8 $6 \times 2 = 12$ 9 $6 - 2 = 4$ 10 $6 \times 2 = 12$ 11 $2 + 6 = 8$ 12 $6 - 2 = 4$

   13 $6^2 = 36$ 14 $\sqrt{36} = 6$ 15 $6 - 2 = 4$ 16 $6 \times 2 = 12$ 17 $(6 + 2) \div 2 = 4$ 18 $6 + 2 = 8$

   19 $6^2 = 36$ 20 $6 - 2 = 4$ 21 $6 - 2 = 4$ 22 $6 + 2 = 8$ 23 $6 \div 2 = 3$ 24 $6 + 2 = 8$

Chapter 3: Percentages

Exercise 3:01

1 a $\frac{1}{100}$ b $\frac{9}{100}$ c $\frac{3}{100}$ d $\frac{57}{100}$ 2 a $\frac{1}{5}$ b $\frac{1}{2}$ c $\frac{3}{5}$ d $\frac{1}{20}$

3 a 1   b $1\frac{3}{20}$ c $3\frac{1}{2}$ d 4   4 a 1%   b 3%   c 7%   d 10%

5 a 30%   b 14%   c 55%   d 40%   e 36%   f 307%   g 150%   h 210%   i 380%   j 200%

6 a $17\frac{1}{2}$%   b $37\frac{1}{2}$%   c 80%   d $33\frac{1}{3}$%   e $83\frac{1}{3}$%

7 a $112\frac{1}{2}$%   b $314\frac{2}{7}$%   c $408\frac{1}{3}$%   d 225%   e 1060%

8 a 0·14   b 0·63   c 0·85   d 0·32   e 0·11   f 0·03   g 0·09   h 0·01

   i 0·02   j 0·06   k 0·10   l 0·30   m 0·50   n 0·90   o 0·70

9 a 5%   b 1%   c 8%   d 66%   e 17%   f 50%   g 40%   h 10%   i 30%   j 80%

10 a $\frac{1}{4}$, 0·5, 100%   b 1%, $\frac{1}{10}$, $\frac{1}{2}$ c 9%, $\frac{13}{100}$, $\frac{3}{4}$ d 5%, $\frac{99}{100}$, 1

11 a 2   b 6   c 1   d 3   e 5   f 1·2   g 2·09   h 1·97   i 2·5   j 3·9

12 a 145%   b 365%   c 125%   d 235%   e 185%   f 290%   g 110%   h 360%   i 34%   j 70%

13 a 1·46   b 1·13   c 1·24   d 0·68   e 0·35   f 0·43   g 0·09   h 0·06   i 0·04   j 2·48

   k 0·02   l 0·18   m 0·136   n 0·092   o 0·163   p 0·1225   q 0·1075   r 0·836 25

14 a 15%, 0·51, $\frac{3}{5}$ b 18%, $1\frac{1}{8}$, 1·8   c $1\frac{1}{2}$, 152%, 15·2   d 60%, 0·65, $\frac{2}{3}$

Exercise 3:02

1 a 40%   b 80%   c 90%   d 30%   e 20%   f 80%   g 10%   h 80%

   i 50%   j 60%   k 70%   l 60%   m 10%   n 50%   o 60%   p 20%

2 a 150%   b 130%   c 190%   d 230%

3 30%, 80%, 50%

4 a 26%   b 36%   c 3%   d 27%   e 8%

Prep Quiz 3:03

1 12·5   2 6·25   3 11·75   4 109·5   5 62·5   6 33·$\dot{3}$ 7 33·3   8 16·$\dot{6}$ 9 1%, $\frac{1}{100}$ 10 10%, $\frac{1}{10}$

Exercise 3:03

1 a 37·5%   b 8·6%   c 17·4%   d 124·5%   e 612·5%   f 237·5%

   g 230%   h 1·5%   i 0·5%

2 a 0·145   b 0·279   c 0·954   d 0·021   e 0·096   f 0·2385

   g 0·8735   h 1·125   i 2·875

3 a 0·125   b 0·875   c 0·135   d 0·0725   e 0·1075   f 0·1525

   g 1·0675   h 2·545   i 1·3125

4 a 28·57%   b 83·33%   c 87·5%   d 93·75%   e 66·67%   f 7·5%

   g 116·67%   h 283·33%

Prep Quiz 3:04

1 62%   2 $66\frac{2}{3}$%   3 25%   4 $12\frac{1}{2}$%   5 $6\frac{1}{4}$%   6 $\frac{1}{4}$ 7 $\frac{1}{5}$ 8 0·24   9 0·06   10 0·145

Exercise 3:04

1 a 80 g   b 225 m   c $51   d 160 L   e $33\frac{1}{5}$ cm or 33·2 cm

   f 287 mL   g 34 min   h 13 400 t   i $51   j $8.76

2 a $1.20   b 45 L   c $4.80   d 144 g   e 60 t   f 9 min

   g 24 km   h 4 min   i 350 L   j 840 m   k $2300   l 10 200 km

   m 168 kL   n 613·98 km   o 1022 days

3 a 28·35 L   b 145·5 m   c 8·4 t   d 6·08 km   e 3·36 m   f 3·36 g

   g 2·205 t   h 10·08 mm   i 6·8 s   j 2·1 mL   k 1050   l 6·4 g

   m 0·15 km   n 0·42 L   o $4.50   p 40 g   q 734·25 kg   r $87.50

Prep Quiz 3:05

1 0·5 **2** 0·03 **3** 0·72 **4** 0·035 **5** 1·25 **6** $3 **7** $87 **8** $6.70 **9** 1000 **10** 1000

Exercise 3:05

1 £352.50 **2** 2 280 000 000 **3** €105 000 **4** 160 **5** 1.68 million **6** $119 000
7 215 280 **8** 18 **9** 48 s **10** 375 **11** 1750
12 a $342 **b** $220.80 **c** $365.20 **d** $608

Prep Quiz 3:06

1 $\frac{1}{2}$ **2** $\frac{1}{4}$ **3** $\frac{3}{4}$ **4** $\frac{1}{10}$ **5** 50% **6** 25% **7** 75% **8** 10% **9** 87·5% **10** $\frac{1}{10}$

Exercise 3:06

1 a 60% **b** 75% **c** 25% **d** $62\frac{1}{2}$%
2 a 10% **b** 25% **c** 1% **d** 25% **e** 20% **f** 62% **g** $7\frac{1}{2}$% **h** $17\frac{1}{2}$%
  i $77\frac{1}{2}$% **j** $33\frac{1}{3}$% **k** $5\frac{2}{5}$% or 5·4% **l** $66\frac{2}{3}$% **m** 300% **n** 125% **o** 110%
3 a 70% **b** 5% **c** 75% **d** $112\frac{1}{2}$% **e** 7% **f** $81\frac{1}{4}$% **g** 25% **h** 750%
  i 200% **j** 30% **k** 350% **l** 875% **m** 90% **n** 2% **o** 1·25%
4 a seasoning = 6%, cornflour = 4% **b i** 1·14 g **ii** 30·4 g **iii** 1·9 g **c** 1%
  d i 4·25% **ii** 2·59% **iii** 0·05% **e** team members = 4%, female spectators = 53·5%, male spectators = 42·5%
  f i 17·5% **ii** 82·5% **g** 14% **h** 3·5%
  i typing = 37·5%, filing = 18·75%, sorting mail = 6·25%, telephone = 3·125%, meetings = 9·375%, other activities = 25%
  j Mining 93 700, 1·4%; Food Beverages 175 300, 2·6%; Metal Products 203 200, 3·1%; Other 758 400, 11·5%;
  Electricity, gas and water 133 000, 2·0%; Construction 485 000, 7·3%; Wholesale 1 318 500, 19·9%;
  Transport 365 800, 5·5%; Communication 146 800, 2·2%; Finance 652 200, 9·8%; Public Administration
  323 900, 4·9%; Community Services 1 140 900, 17·2%; Recreation 441 800, 6·7%.

Prep Quiz 3:07

1 60% **2** 87% **3** 118% **4** 400% **5** 80% **6** 225% **7** 106% **8** 96% **9** 170 **10** 230

Exercise 3:07

1 a 125% **b** 115% **c** 110% **d** 109% **e** 200% **f** 400% **g** 255% **h** 232%
2 a 75% **b** 85% **c** 90% **d** 91% **e** 99% **f** 5% **g** 63% **h** 70%
3 a $880 **b** $360 **c** 5·8 m **d** 4·48 L **e** 111 g **f** 99·4 t **g** 10·4 kg **h** 31·8 ha
  i 112 h **j** 243 s or 4 min 3 s
4 a $48 **b** $72 **c** 6·88 m **d** 1·89 m **e** 1·95 m **f** 6·65 L **g** 19 kg **h** 768 mm
  i 3·08 t **j** 58·8 L
5 a $130.50 **b** $11.60 **c** £43.50 **d** $17.40 **e** $290 **f** €82.65
6 a $416 **b** $374.40 **c** $2195.44 **d** $316.38 **e** $890.47 **f** $1083.47
7 a $332.50 **b** $602 **c** $416.50 **8** $27 528
9 314·64 m **10** 34 450 t **11** 178 024 **12** 6560 m **13** $7084.80 **14** $73.50 **15** $1152
16 a $457.42 **b** €1647.52 **c** ¥128.81 **d** $1149.41 **e** €100.07 **f** £1120.13 **g** $5.54
  h ¥13.96 **i** £0.61 **j** $44.47 **k** €184.98 **l** ¥313.50
17 $4455 **18** $321

Prep Quiz 3:08

1 48% **2** true **3** 82 cents **4** $a = 7$ **5** $x = 4$ **6** 0·32 **7** $60 **8** $0 **9** $\frac{1}{100}$ **10** 1%

Exercise 3:08

1 We can't know which shop is cheaper because we don't know the original price at each store.
2 4, no **3** $7
4 a £96 **b** £100 **c** Honest Anne's, £4
5 $295.50, no **6** The one with a 35% discount is cheaper by $0.96
7 a 6% **b** 90% **c** They would not impress people.
8 a $196 **b** 30%
9 a $184.80 **b** $368 **c** $2.43 **d** $30 000 **e** $37.80 **f** $10 560 **g** $3120 profit
10 a 5% **b** 20% **c** 35% **d** $16\frac{2}{3}$%
11 d 20% **e** 10% **f** 32% **g** 65% **12 a** $5 **b** 100% **c** 50%
13 a $240 **b** 37·5% **c** 60% **14 a** ¥800 000 **b** ¥4 800 000 **c** $16\frac{2}{3}$%
15 a 12 rabbits **b** 200% **c** $66\frac{2}{3}$%
16 a 7800 books **b** 205·26% **c** 67·24%

Exercise 3:09

1 a $28.80 **b** $272 **c** $336 **d** $92.80

2 a $900 **b** $2400 **c** $3300   **3 a** $236 **b** $345.50 **c** $543.95

4 a ¥88 **b** €264 **c** $40.50 **d** £202.50 **e** €3750 **f** 30 000 **g** $945 **h** ¥3780

i $148 **j** £2664

5 a $11 200 **b** $33 600 **c** $89 600   **6 a** $364 **b** $1092 **c** $2912

7 a 8% p.a. **b** 12% p.a. **c** 16% p.a.

Exercise 3:10

1 a 500 m **b** 27 100 ha **c** 90 kg **d** 3500 t **e** $104 **f** $600 **g** 700 mm **h** $103

2 $3900   **3** 200 runs   **4** 1200   **5** $1835

Diagnostic Test 3: Percentages

1 a $\frac{9}{100}$ **b** $\frac{12}{25}$ **c** $3\frac{1}{2}$ **2 a** 173% **b** 44% **c** 314%

3 a 0·17 **b** 0·04 **c** 1·06   **4 a** 22% **b** 90% **c** 370%

5 a 20% **b** 160%   **6 a** 0·138 **b** 0·0625 **c** 0·875

7 a $12\frac{1}{2}$% **b** $162\frac{1}{2}$% **c** $16\frac{2}{3}$%   **8 a** 128 g **b** 0·21 km **c** 14·4 L

9 a 16% **b** 42·5% **c** 51%   **10 a** $5.75 **b** $4.25 **c** $99.40

11 a $6.80 **b** $6\frac{1}{4}$%   **12 a** $39 **b** $288

3A Revision Assignment

1 a 7500 mL **b** 400 000 mL **c** 14 L **d** 2·1 kL

2 a −6 **b** 1 **c** −10 **d** 2 **e** −20

3

4 a $3 \times a$ **b** $4 \times m + 2 \times n$ **c** $5 \times (x + y)$

d $a \div 5$ **e** $3 \times m \div 2$ or $(3 \times m) \div 2$

5 a 20 **b** 18 **c** 4 **d** 34

6 a 15·12 **b** 151·2 **c** 1·512

7 a a^5 **b** 10^3 **c** a^3b^2 **d** $12p^3$

8 a $5a + 20$ **b** $4a + 6$ **c** $4m - 20$ **d** $2ab - 3a$

9 a 1, 36, 2, 18, 3, 12, 4, 9, 6

b 1, 54, 2, 27, 3, 18, 6, 9

c 18 **d** 36, 72, 108, 144; 54, 108, 162, 216; 108

3B Problem Solving

1 6 **2** 24 **3** 35 **4** 63 min **5** 8 **6** Third largest number is 7 654 231; third smallest number is 1 234 657.

Chapter 4: Ratio, rates and scale drawing

Exercise 4:01

1 a i 4:1 **ii** 1:4 **b** no   **2 a** no **b i** 2:1 **ii** 1:2

3 a $\frac{1}{5}$ **b** $\frac{4}{5}$ **4 a** $\frac{2}{5}$ **b** 3:2

5 a 5:3 **b** 5:2 **c** 3:2 **d** 2:5 **e** 3:2:5

6 a 14:16 **b** 16:14 **c** 14:30 **d** $\frac{14}{30}$ **e** 16:30 **f** $\frac{16}{30}$

7 a yellow **b** We can't tell. It would be one of the other colours. **c** $\frac{1}{2}$ **d** $\frac{3}{10}$ **e** 3:10

8 a $\frac{1}{7}$ **b** $\frac{4}{7}$ **c** 1:4 **d** 1:2 **e** 4 kg

9 a 10:1 **b** 100:1 **c** 1000:1 **d** 1000:1 **e** 60:1

10 a 1:10 **b** 1:4 **c** 10:1 **d** 3:4 **e** 3:10

11 a $\frac{2}{3}$ **b** 2:1 **c** 1:2   **12 a** 6:9 **b** 4:6 **c** 24:54

13 a no **b** sweeter   **14 a** lighter **b** weaker

Exercise 4:02

1 a 3 **b** 2 **c** 80 **d** 9 **e** 27 **f** 12 **g** 9 **h** 24

i 2 **j** 1 **k** 2 **l** 3 **m** 2 **n** 2 **o** 9·6 **p** 7

2 a 3:1 **b** 1:3 **c** 3:2 **d** 8:15 **e** 1:3 **f** 15:1 **g** 10:1 **h** 1:10

i 6:1 **j** 1:6 **k** 2:5 **l** 20:3 **m** 1:12 **n** 2:7 **o** 5:7 **p** 3:40

q 3:2 **r** 5:9 **s** $\frac{1}{3}$ **t** $\frac{4}{1}$ **u** $\frac{2}{5}$ **v** $\frac{20}{9}$ **w** $\frac{2}{3}$ **x** $\frac{7}{2}$

3 a 30:1 **b** 5:2 **c** 2:1 **d** 1:40 **e** 15:2 **f** 7:1 **g** 3:1 **h** 1:5
i 5:1 **j** 8:1 **k** 10:1:11
4 a 6:5 **b** 3:1 **c** 3:4 **d** 25:4 **e** 1:5 **f** 5:1 **g** 1:2 **h** 2:3
i 4:3 **j** 2:7:5 **k** 2:1:3 **l** 11:3:4 **m** 20:13:7
5 a i 8:7 **ii** 7:8 **iii** 8:15 **iv** 8:7:15 **b i** 1:2 **ii** 3:2 **iii** 1:3 **iv** 2:1:3
c 1:100 **d i** 1:5 **ii** 5:1:4 **e** 9:5 **f** 9:7:5 **g i** 5:3 **ii** 3:4 **iii** 5:4
iv 5:12 **v** 5:3:4 **h** 3:1 000 000
6 a 3·2:1 **b** 1·5:1 **c** 0·75:1 **d** 1·$\dot{3}$:1 **e** 0·25:1
7 a 1:0·6 **b** 1:0·5 **c** 1:1·875 **d** 1:4 **e** 1:3·5

Challenge 4:02
c d e and **g** are the only correct reasons given.

Prep Quiz 4:03
1 30 cm **2** 90 cm **3** 3 m **4** 10 cm **5** 0·4 m **6** 15 **7** 45 **8** 48 **9** 10 **10** $6\frac{2}{3}$

Exercise 4:03
1 a $x = 8\frac{3}{4}$ **b** $x = 10\frac{1}{2}$ **c** $x = 3\frac{1}{8}$ **d** $x = 7.47$ (2 dec. pl.) **e** $y = 14$ **f** $m = 3\frac{1}{3}$ **g** $a = 4\frac{2}{3}$
h $b = 3\frac{3}{4}$
2 a 16 **b** $340 **c** 40 **d** $8.10, $13.50 **e** 3 parts **f** 5 L
3 a 72 kg **b i** 3·6 kg **ii** 427·5 g **c** 68 m **d** 4 teachers **e** $54.10
4 a 875 m **b** 12·5 parts of gravel and 10 parts of sand. **c** 33·6 kg of tin and 25·2 kg of zinc.
d $1200 and $1920; total divided = $3840
5 a 3:5 **b** 40 g **c** 36 g

Investigation 4:03
1 a 450 tiles **b** 200 **c** 220 black, 275 white **d** $1067

Exercise 4:04
1 a 10, 6 **b** 40, 160 **c** 245, 175 **d** 906, 604 **e** 65, 195:325 **f** 16 560, 11 040, 13 800
2 a 16 kg tin, 4 kg lead **b** 6000 **c** 150 mL **d** 900 mL
e 12·5 kg nitrates, 18·75 kg each of potash and phosphates **f** 14 000, 3500, 10 500
g 36 kg gravel, 24 kg sand, 6 kg cement **h** 7·1 cm, 14·2 cm, 21·3 cm
3 a i J **ii** H **iii** D **iv** I **v** C
b

10 cm	A 2 cm

c

5 cm	3 cm
A	

d

1·2 cm	4·8 cm
A	

4 a 20 cm **b** town A: 18 030; town B: 48 080; town C: 19 232 **c** 2 mL

Exercise 4:05
1 a 4 km/h **b** 2 kg/$ **c** 0·25 km/min **d** 30 L/h **e** 25c/g **f** $45/day
g 30 children/teacher **h** 4 degrees/min **i** 20 sheep/h **j** 5 kg/m^2
k 7 g/cm^3 **l** 40 km/h **m** 100 L/h **n** 4 min/km
2 a 120 km/h **b** 240 kg/h **c** 200 kg/ha **d** 120 L/day **e** $5000/kg **f** 300 mL/h
g 4000 m/h **h** 2000 mL/h **i** 1200 kg/d **j** $0.20/min **k** 245c/kg **l** 0·015 L/min
m 10·8 km/h **n** 90 L/h **o** 360 t/day **p** 200 kg/ha **q** 10 m/mL **r** 7 t/m^3
3 a 15 km **b** 200 km **c** 250 km **d** 81 km **e** $2\frac{1}{2}$ h **f** 56 min
g 12 h **h** 140 h (5 days 20 h) **i** 95 km/h **j** 20 000 km/h; $3333\frac{1}{3}$ km **k** 17·46 km/h
4 a $92 **b** 85 **c** 120 **d** 3750 g **e** 5400 **f** $120
g 201 600 t **h** £335.50 **i** 1000 m^2 **j** 120 L
5 a 4·35 kg (correct to 2 dec. pl.) **b** 25 **c** $26\frac{2}{3}$ h **d** 160 min
e 22 trucks (21 full loads, 1 load of 18 t) **f** 33·25 **g** $8\frac{1}{3}$ min **h** 2·5
i 7 **j** 15 hours
6 a i 18 000 000 km **ii** 496 s = 8 min 16 s **b** 150 kg **c** 36 km/h **d** 2 s
e i $742.50 **ii** $11 000
7 a $3\frac{1}{3}$ min **b** 500 revs/min **c i** 10 km/h **ii** 18·75 km

Prep Quiz 4:06
1 100   **2** 10   **3** 1000   **4** 20   **5** 250   **6** 1:100   **7** 1:1000   **8** 500   **9** 6800   **10** 5 m

Exercise 4:06
1 a 1 m   **b** 10 m   **c** 1 km
2 a 1:100   **b** 1:1000   **c** 1:10 000   **d** 1:5000   **e** 1:50   **f** 1:200
   g 1:20   **h** 1:20 000
3 a 5000 cm = 50 m   **b** 3500 cm = 35 m   **c** 10 600 cm = 106 m   **d** 8100 cm = 81 m
   e 1000 mm = 1 m   **f** 8000 mm = 8 m   **g** 26 000 mm = 26 m   **h** 500 mm
4 a 2 m   **b i** 2 m   **ii** 4 m   **iii** 18 m   **iv** 6·4 m   **c** 10 m^2 **d** 148 m^2
   e 24 m^2 **f** \$924
5 a 10 m   **b** 25 m   **c** 32 m   **d** 21 m   **e** 0·5 m   **f** 21 m   **g** 13·5 m   **h** 29·5 m
6 a 1 cm   **b** 3 cm   **c** 7·5 cm   **d** 0·043 m = 4·3 cm   **e** 0·63 m = 63 cm
   f 0·42 m = 42 cm   **g** 0·156 m = 15·6 cm   **h** 0·024 m = 2·4 cm
7 a 2 cm   **b** 3 cm   **c** 10 cm   **d** 1·5 cm   **e** 0·4 cm = 4 mm   **f** 1·25 cm
   g 0·55 cm   **h** 15·75 cm
8 a 3·6 m by 4·2 m   **b** 2160 cm = 21·6 m   **c i** 250 m   **ii** 8750 m   **iii** 2500 m
   iv 13 000 m = 13 km   **d i** 5 cm:10 m = 1:200   **ii** 6·0 m   **iii** 30 m^2
9 a i 8·5 cm by 5·8 cm   **ii** 17 cm by 11·6 cm   **iii** 42·5 cm by 29 cm
   b 233 mm by 122 mm   **c** 0·5 m = 50 cm   **d** 1:25
   e 52 mm by 38 mm; refrigerator 6 mm square; sink 12 mm by 5 mm
10 a 80 km   **b** 130 km   **c** 270 km   **d** 130 km

Challenge 4:06
The ratio length : width alternates between 3 : 2 and 3 : 4.
   a The ratio length : width alternates between 1 : 1 and 1 : 2
   b The ratio length : width alternates between 3 : 1 and 3 : 2

Fun Spot 4:06
No idea
Still no idea

Diagnostic test 4: Ratio, Rates and Scale Drawing
1 a 1:2   **b** 1:4   **c** 1:2:4   **d** 4:1:2   **2 a** 5:2   **b** 4:1   **c** 1:4   **d** 2:3
3 a 4   **b** 6   **c** 24   **d** 8   **4 a** 1·875   **b** 16·6   **c** 1·44   **d** 1·6
5 a 18   **b** 10·5   **c** \$2·70   **d** 15 kg   **6 a** 10:5   **b** 10:35   **c** 220:200   **d** 12:24:84
7 a 25 km/h   **b** 150 t/h   **c** 12·5 g/cm^3 **d** 0·4 kg/m^2 **8 a** 3600 m/h   **b** 4·8 t/d   **c** \$15 000/kg   **d** 100 mL/min
9 a 2800 t   **b** 350 km   **c** $5\frac{1}{2}$ h   **d** 20·8 L (to 1 dec. pl.)
10 a 300 cm = 3 m   **b** 520 cm = 5·2 m   **c** 100 mm = 0·1 m   **d** 4200 mm = 4·2 m
11 a 15 m   **b** 26 m   **c** 0·5 m   **d** 21 m
12 a 0·05 m = 5 cm   **b** 0·43 m = 43 cm   **c** 0·75 cm   **d** 0·048 m = 4·8 cm
13 a 2·5 cm   **b** 21·5 cm   **c** 0·375 cm   **d** 2·4 cm

4A Revision Assignment
1 a 13 m   **b** 6 cm
2 a $6m + 5n + 8$ **b** $6a + 22$ **c** $a + b$ **3 a** 1·125%   **b** 99·1%
4 a \$108   **b** \$187.50   **5 a** 1·25   **b** 3
6 16·56   **7 a** 97·5 m^2 **b** 20·52 m^2 **c** 76·98 m^2
8 199·5 cm^2 **9 a** $a = 3·2$ **b** $m = 6\frac{2}{3}$ **c** $p = -10$

4B Working Mathematically
1 a interval *AB*   **b** line *AB*   **c** ray *AB*   **d** collinear points
   e diagonals   **f** $(a + b)°$ **g** 360°
2 5 and 7   **3** 6   **4** C   **5** 12   **6** 64
7 Many schools, especially in lower years, will decide not to have textbooks at all, because they can't afford to subsidise those students who can't or won't pay. They would defend this action when questioned by parents who want to give their children the best education possible. Because teachers are employed by the state government, they would probably not lay the blame on government policy. Some parents, in their frustration, would move their children to private schools.

Chapter 5:   The calculator and using spreadsheets

Exercise 5:01

1 a 8586 **b** 2891 **c** 32 745 **d** 13 **e** 4 **f** 500 **g** 28 **h** 220 **i** 2300 **j** 42
  k 1·2 **l** 20 **m** 10 **n** 180 **o** 10 **p** 30 **q** 160 **r** 4 **s** 20 **t** 20
  u 392

2 a 936 **b** 16 164 239 **c** 0·0941 **d** 371·615 **e** −2 705 814 **f** 836·426
  g 639 790 **h** 505 818 **i** 41 081·04 **j** 1 084 375 **k** 1·166 97 **l** 0·014 85
  m 243·572 94 **n** 354·2 **o** 0·281 52 **p** 1 023 895 **q** 100 **r** 143·71
  s 41·16 **t** 0·026 **u** 74·0148

3 a 2·4 **b** 3·1 **c** −20

4 a 86·36 tonnes **b** 540·27 miles **c** 17 088 600 **d** 12 960 **e** 116 100 **f** 44 900
  g $54 750 **h** $1779.05

Prep Quiz 5:02

1 800 **2** 70 **3** 8 **4** 17 000 **5** 0·69 **6** 0·35 **7** 0·33 **8** 0·10 **9** 7 million **10** 0·2

Exercise 5:02

1

	Rounding off	Estimate	Calculator display
a	700 + 200 + 90	990	989·87
b	200 000 − 90 000 − 40 000	70 000	62 700
c	40 × 10 × 30	12 000	12 807·977
d	3000 ÷ 50 − 40	20	26·15
e	7 million × 7 × 10	490 million	486·864 million

2 a 14 713·38 **b** 56·74 **c** 728·45
  d 294 929·45 **e** 5138·62 **f** 4633·07
  g 6704·80 **h** 69·81 **i** 75 614·91
  j 1140·00 **k** 9·24 **l** 830·12

Exercise 5:03

1 a 3·142 **b** 0·143 **c** 0·833 **d** 0·091 **e** 55·639 **f** 20·000

2 a −11·300 **b** 4·768 **c** −7·600 **d** −0·900 **e** 18·170 **f** 6·715 **g** −15·082 **h** −2·215
  i 179·560 **j** −14·678 **k** 34·081 **l** −13·5 **m** −3·9 **n** −10·511 **o** 6·14
  p −1·048 **q** 9·360

3 a 81 **b** 100 000 **c** 64 **d** 27 **e** 1024 **f** −16 807 **g** 625 **h** −512

4 a 17·32 **b** −286·29 **c** 0·117 **d** 1·77 **e** 2·30 **f** 218·33 **g** 4·44 **h** 16·57
  i 1·09 **j** 1·12 **k** 1211·74 **l** −205·38

5 a $31.12 **b** $73.91 **c** $283.97 **d** $2279.54 **e** $31 769.63

Exercise 5:04

1 a −8·73 **b** 6·859 **c** 306 **d** −2·1 **e** 63 **f** $21.98 **g** 84·78
  h 0·34375 **i** 5·95 m **j** $113.88

2 a −3·28 **b** 3·375 **c** 478 **d** −1·8 **e** 58 **f** $19.56 **g** 51·287
  h 0·59375 **i** 2·775 m **j** $116.79

3 a −3·54 **b** 4·913 **c** 198 **d** −2·4 **e** 88 **f** $35.82 **g** 66·987
  h 0·65625 **i** 3·5 m **j** $143.07

4 a −0·44 **b** 4·096 **c** 345 **d** −6·9 **e** 62 **f** $29.19 **g** 37·68
  h 0·40625 **i** 3·75 m **j** $104.16

5 a −1·38 **b** 9·261 **c** 299 **d** −4·7 **e** 70 **f** $31.35 **g** 26·167
  h 0·84375 **i** 2·925 m **j** $104.76

Prep Quiz 5:05

1 25 **2** 16 **3** 196 **4** 8 **5** 27 **6** 64 **7** 6 **8** 10 **9** 42 **10** 100

Exercise 5:05

1 a 26 **b** 125 **c** 3·4 **d** 0·19 **e** 5 **f** 14 **g** 1·2 **h** 0·7

2 a 3·1 **b** 13·2 **c** 2·7 **d** −7·3 **e** 93·4 **f** 28·4 **g** 3·0 **h** 0·7

3 a $1\frac{7}{20}$ **b** $\frac{5}{24}$ **c** $2\frac{5}{6}$ **d** $6\frac{7}{40}$ **e** $\frac{35}{48}$ **f** $\frac{12}{35}$ **g** $2\frac{4}{5}$ **h** $37\frac{1}{8}$
  i $2\frac{1}{4}$ **j** $\frac{23}{25}$ **k** $2\frac{10}{11}$ **l** $5\frac{7}{8}$

4 a 0·185 **b** 0·345 **c** −0·196 **d** 0·084 **e** 0·143 **f** 0·095 **g** 0·083 **h** 0·421

Prep Quiz 5:06

1 1010 **2** 14·1 **3** 405 **4** 5·48 **5** 8·64 **6** 22·70 **7** $\frac{9}{20}$ **8** 0·35 **9** −3·35 **10** 10·50

Exercise 5:06

1 a 15, 30, 45, 60, 75, 90, 105   **b** 27, 54, 81, 108, 135, 162, 189
  c 153, 306, 459, 612, 765, 918, 1071   **d** 617, 1234, 1851, 2468, 3085, 3702, 4319
  e 333, 666, 999, 1332, 1665, 1998, 2331
2 a 7, 17   **b** 3, 11, 17   **c** 2, 19, 23, 31   **d** 13, 17, 19, 23   **e** 3, 5, 7, 11, 13, 23, 29
3 a 13, 337·9, 18 857·2, 1 074 457·3, 61 243 663
  b 0·272727, 0·27272727, 0·2727272727, 0·272727272727, 0·27272727272727
  c 3626, 3224·2, 2942·94, 2746·058, 2608·2406   **d** −4096, −4608, −4672, −4680, −4681
4 a No   **b** Yes   **5 a** 0·9375   **b** 0·625   **c** 0·1̇6̇   **d** 0·6̇
6 a 0·33   **b** 0·71   **c** 0·83   **d** 0·55
7 a 175 463·2   **b** 887 964·54   **c** 96·175   **d** 1923·5   **e** 115·3   **f** 5385·8
  g 692 620   **h** 153·88   **i** 147 994·09   **j** 1538·8   **k** 171 090   **l** 64
8 a $80.46, $32.40, $25.79, $59.67, $204.75, $28.80, Net total $431.87
  b i 50·8 mm   **ii** 76·2 mm   **iii** 12·7 mm   **iv** 19·05 mm   **v** 914·4 mm   **vi** 1828·8 mm

Exercise 5:07

1 a 2   **b** 6   **c** yes   **d i** 120   **ii** 40 320   **iii** 39 916 800
2 7   **3** 10, decagon
4 a 1, 3, 7, 11, 19   **b** 1, 4389, 3, 1463, 7, 627, 11, 399, 19, 231, 21, 209, 33, 133, 57, 77
5 187, 67, 314, 183, 249   **6 a** 23, 56   **b** 67, 78   **c** 634, 566
7 a 1·35 cents   **b** $1.35   **c** 9·15 cents   **d** $9.15
8 a $68 305   **b** $6082.74   **c** $2456.10   **d** $7.09   **e** $15.67   **f** $0.27
9 a $235.72   **b** $6.51   **c** $61.55   **d** $699 300.70   **e** $569.58   **f** $0.61
10 83

Fun Spot 5:07

5:08 Spreadsheets

Spreadsheet 1
  1 a B2   **b** C2   **c** A12
Spreadsheet 3
  2 a 1, 100, 2, 50, 4, 25, 5, 20, 10   **b** 1, 21, 3, 7
  3 a 1, 36, 2, 18, 3, 12, 4, 9, 6   **b i** 1, 15, 3, 5   **ii** 1, 28, 2, 14, 4, 7   **iii** 1, 35, 5, 7
    iv 1, 99, 3, 33, 9, 11   **v** 1, 29

Diagnostic Test 5: The Calculator

1	**a** 128	**b** 226·5			**2**	**a** 963·633	**b** 184 897	
3	**a** 958·5	**b** 10			**4**	**a** 735·75	**b** 1·8	
5	**a** 374	**b** 2·3			**6**	**a** 396	**b** 8·000 625	
7	**a** B	**b** C			**8**	**a** −18	**b** −79·883	**c** 258·125
9	**a** 81	**b** −18·895 68	**c** 70·728 1		**10**	**a** 53·14	**b** 20·000	**c** 270·107 0
11	**a** 13·4	**b** 13	**c** 5·2		**12**	**a** 16	**b** 18	**c** 20
13	**a** $\frac{15}{32}$	**b** $8\frac{3}{8}$	**c** $\frac{23}{25}$		**14**	**a** 0·156 25	**b** 0·3125	**c** 0·08

5 Working Mathematically

1 about 5·6 cm (assuming that a real soldier has a height of about 180 cm)

2 a

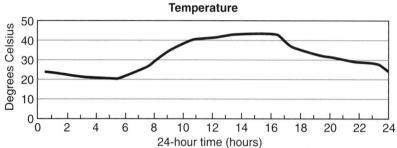

b

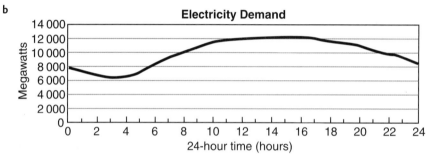

c Answers will vary.

3 14 times

Chapter 6: Patterns and algebra

Prep Quiz 6:01

1 12 **2** 12 **3** 12 **4** 12 **5** 43, 54 **6** 3, 0 **7** 12, 15 **8** $4^2 + 1, 5^2 + 1$

9

n	0	1	2	3
M	1	3	5	7

10

x	4	5	6	7
y	6	5	4	3

Exercise 6:01

1 a $f = 3p - 3$ **b** 33 **c** 320 m

2 a

P	1	2	3	4
F	0	1	2	3

b

P	1	2	3	4
F	0	2	4	6

c

P	1	2	3	4
F	0	4	8	12

d

x	1	2	3	4
y	4	5	6	7

e

x	1	2	3	4
y	3	6	9	12

f

x	1	2	3	4
y	3	5	7	9

3 a $y = 7 - x$ **b** $m = 24 \div d$ **c** $p = 10w + 7$ **d** $y = 3x - 5$ **e** $b = a^2 + 7$ **f** $p = 50 - 8n$

4 a $y = 7x$ **b** $b = d - 5$ **c** $M = 2v + 1$ **d** $M = a^2$ **e** $e = 13 - d$ **f** $x \times y = 12$

5 a

S	3	4	5	6	7	8
P	5	30	55	80	105	130

b $P = -70$ **c** 3

6 a $P = L + 2 + 2 + (L - 1) = 2L + 3$ **b i** 11 **ii** 13 **iii** 23 **iv** 203 **v** 139
c No, because the basic shape cannot be made with a base length of zero.

Investigation 6:01

1 a $2x + 1$ **b** $3 + 3x$ **c** $y + x + 1$ **d** $(x + 2) + (x + 2) = 2x + 4$
e $1 + x + 1 + x + 1 = 2x + 3$ **f** $y + 1 + y + 3 = 2y + 4$ **g** $(3x + 3) + (2x + 4) = 5x + 7$
2 A a 21 **b** 33 **c** 27 **d** 24 **e** 23 **f** 36 **g** 57
B a 15 **b** 24 **c** 19 **d** 18 **e** 17 **f** 26 **g** 42

Prep Quiz 6:02

1 $7x$ **2** $3a$ **3** $12p$ **4** $10m$ **5** $5m$ **6** $8a^2$ **7** $8mn$ **8** $11ab$ **9** $9x$ **10** p

Exercise 6:02A

1 a $8x$ **b** $9y$ **c** $7a$ **d** $8b$ **e** $5m$ **f** $5n$ **g** $9a$ **h** 0
i $13l^2$ **j** $30x^2$ **k** $12xy$ **l** $14pq$

1 a

+	a	$2a$	$5a$	$6a$	$10a$
$3a$	$4a$	$5a$	$8a$	$9a$	$13a$
$5a$	$6a$	$7a$	$10a$	$11a$	$15a$
a	$2a$	$3a$	$6a$	$7a$	$11a$
$6a$	$7a$	$8a$	$11a$	$12a$	$16a$
$10a$	$11a$	$12a$	$15a$	$16a$	$20a$

b

−	$3a$	a	$2a$	$5a$	$4a$
$5a$	$2a$	$4a$	$3a$	0	a
$7a$	$4a$	$6a$	$5a$	$2a$	$3a$
$12a$	$9a$	$11a$	$10a$	$7a$	$8a$
$8a$	$5a$	$7a$	$6a$	$3a$	$4a$
$10a$	$7a$	$9a$	$8a$	$5a$	$6a$

3 a $10a$ **b** $9y$ **c** $11m^2$ **d** $5x^2$ **e** $4pq$ **f** p **g** $18a$ **h** $8k$
i $3q^2$
4 a $7a, 21$ **b** $5a, 15$ **c** $6a, 18$ **d** $2a, 6$ **e** $a, 3$ **f** $5a, 15$ **g** $5a^2, 45$ **h** $8a^2, 72$
i $2a^2, 18$
5 a $6x + 3y$ **b** $9m + 2n$ **c** $10a$ **d** $3x + 4y$ **e** $6p + 4m$ **f** $t + 3w$ **g** $7a + 4b$ **h** $2t + 6w$
i $2p + 5q$
6 a $5x + y, 20$ **b** $7y + 10, 45$ **c** $5x + 4y - 35, 0$ **d** $5x + 3y, 30$
e $3x + 4y, 29$ **f** $2x + 2y, 16$

Exercise 6:02B

1 a $7a$ **b** $-7a$ **c** $-a$ **d** $2x$ **e** $-p$ **f** $5y$ **g** $-3m$ **h** $-4a$ **i** $-10y$ **j** $-5x$
k $-7y$ **l** $-10p$ **m** $11x$ **n** $8y$ **o** $7t$ **p** $2ab$ **q** $-6xy$ **r** $-12x^2$ **s** $-x$ **t** $3x$
u 0

2 a

+	$-4x$	$-x$	$3x$	$-5x$	$7x$
$3x$	$-x$	$2x$	$6x$	$-2x$	$10x$
$5x$	x	$4x$	$8x$	0	$12x$
x	$-3x$	0	$4x$	$-4x$	$8x$
$-2x$	$-6x$	$-3x$	x	$-7x$	$5x$
$-7x$	$-11x$	$-8x$	$-4x$	$-12x$	0

b

−	$-4x$	$-x$	$3x$	$-5x$	$7x$
$3x$	$7x$	$4x$	0	$8x$	$-4x$
$5x$	$9x$	$6x$	$2x$	$10x$	$-2x$
x	$5x$	$2x$	$-2x$	$6x$	$-6x$
$-2x$	$2x$	$-x$	$-5x$	$3x$	$-9x$
$-7x$	$-3x$	$-6x$	$-10x$	$-2x$	$-14x$

3 a $x + 2y$ **b** $9m - n$ **c** $3q - p$ **d** $2x - 7$ **e** $10 - 2p$ **f** $9q + 4p$
g $-3b$ **h** $2n - 2m$ **i** $4n + 2q$ **j** $-x - 5y$ **k** $-7t + 3w$ **l** $-6m - 2n$
m $-6a - 2b$ **n** $8xy - 3x$ **o** $-2ab + 6$ **p** $9x - x^2$ **q** $7pq - 10p$ **r** $5 - x^2$
4 a $8a + 6b$ **b** $4x + 7y$ **c** $11m + 5n$ **d** $15p - 12$ **e** $3a + 12$ **f** $15 - 11q$
g $2k + 2l$ **h** $2l - 2m$ **i** $3x + 2y$ **j** $5ab + 7a$ **k** $2xy - 3$ **l** $10x^2 + x$
m $6a + 7$ **n** $10 + 8a$ **o** $6y + 4x$ **p** $4a - 2b$ **q** $3l + 2q$ **r** $-t - 4w$
s $7ab - bc$ **t** $10mn - 9m$ **u** $-3 - 7kl$ **v** $x^2 - 3x$ **w** $2q - q^2$ **x** $-9 - 6h$
5 a $3xy$ **b** $-6ab + a$ **c** $6mn + 6$ **d** $10 - 6ab$ **e** $3m^2 + 2m + 3$ **f** $11a^2 - a - 1$
g $5xy - 12yz$ **h** $3a^2 + ab$ **i** $1 + 5mn + m$ **j** $9k^2 + 7t^2$ **k** $ab + 9a - 4b$ **l** $8m^2 + 6n^2 - 11n$

Prep Quiz 6:03

1 $5a$ **2** pq **3** $3ab$ **4** $15xy$ **5** $2x^2$ **6** 12 **7** 9 **8** 22 **9** 16 **10** $m \times v \times v$

Exercise 6:03

1 a $10a$ b $21x$ c $16m$ d $60y$ e $56p$ f $30n$ g $21q$ h $44k$
  i $15b$ j $12a$ k $18y$ l $48a$ m $3a$ n $3b$ o $5m$ p y

2 a $6mn$ b $12xy$ c $25tw$ d $21ab$ e $7ab$ f $5pq$ g $12kl$ h $3ab$
  i $40mn$ j $18x^2$ k $36ay$ l $5x^2$ m $15y^2$ n $42m^2$ o $7k^2$ p $2y^2$

3 a $20ab$ b $6xy$ c $18mn$ d $42a$ e $24b$ f $4ab$ g $5ab$ h $6bc$
  i $5mn$ j $24ab$ k $30abc$ l $12xy$

4 a a^2b b m^2n c $3ax^2$ d $6a^2b$ e $12pq^2$ f $15k^2l$ g $12abc$ h $90ab^2c$
  i $20x^2yz$ j $24abc$ k $m^2n^2p^2$ l $6a^2b^2$

5 a

×	6	a	$2b$	$9m$	$3ab$
$2a$	$12a$	$2a^2$	$4ab$	$18am$	$6a^2b$
$3b$	$18b$	$3ab$	$6b^2$	$27bm$	$9ab^2$
7	42	$7a$	$14b$	$63m$	$21ab$
a	$6a$	a^2	$2ab$	$9am$	$3a^2b$
ab	$6ab$	a^2b	$2ab^2$	$9abm$	$3a^2b^2$

b

×	x	$2y$	xy	$5x$	$2xz$
$4x$	$4x^2$	$8xy$	$4x^2y$	$20x^2$	$8x^2z$
y	xy	$2y^2$	xy^2	$5xy$	$2xyz$
$5y$	$5xy$	$10y^2$	$5xy^2$	$25xy$	$10xyz$
$2xy$	$2x^2y$	$4xy^2$	$2x^2y^2$	$10x^2y$	$4x^2yz$
yz	xyz	$2y^2z$	xy^2z	$5xyz$	$2xyz^2$

6 a $-15x$ b $-14m$ c $12a$ d $-27m$ e $30k$ f $14a$ g $-2ab$ h pq
  i $-10mn$ j $6tw$ k $-56xy$ l $-30m^2$ m $36y^2$ n $-12a^2$ o $3x^2$ p $-60a$
  q $30y$ r $-24a^2$ s $-54mn$ t $-32k^2$ u $24p^2$ v $-10x^2y$ w $24a^2b$ x $-5m^2np$

7 a

×	-3	5	$2x$	$-4x$	$-y$
7	-21	35	$14x$	$-28x$	$-7y$
-2	6	-10	$-4x$	$8x$	$2y$
$-x$	$3x$	$-5x$	$-2x^2$	$4x^2$	xy
$4x$	$-12x$	$20x$	$8x^2$	$-16x^2$	$-4xy$
$-3y$	$9y$	$-15y$	$-6xy$	$12xy$	$3y^2$

b

×	$2a$	$3b$	$-a$	$-4b$	$-ab$
$6a$	$12a^2$	$18ab$	$-6a^2$	$-24ab$	$-6a^2b$
$-3b$	$-6ab$	$-9b^2$	$3ab$	$12b^2$	$3ab^2$
$-b$	$-2ab$	$-3b^2$	ab	$4b^2$	ab^2
$3a$	$6a^2$	$9ab$	$-3a^2$	$-12ab$	$-3a^2b$
$2ab$	$4a^2b$	$6ab^2$	$-2a^2b$	$-8ab^2$	$-2a^2b^2$

8

	A	B	C	D
a	$15xy$	$-8m$	$-18x^2$	$2y^2$
b	$30ab$	abc	$6ab$	m^2n
c	$8ab$	$-12pq$	$6xy^2$	$30a^2$
d	$16m^2$	$5ab$	$30m^2n^2$	$4ab^2$
e	$6x^2y$	$15tw$	$-3a^2$	$24mn^2$
f	$-18k^2$	$6l^2$	$100abc$	$35xy$
g	0	$-x^2$	$-8hk$	$-54a^2$
h	$18x^2$	$-8a^2b$	$28m^2np$	$-24xy$

Prep Quiz 6:04

1 $2x$ 2 $4y$ 3 $5a$ 4 $20m$ 5 $2x$ 6 $4y$ 7 $5a$ 8 $20m$ 9 4 10 4

Exercise 6:04

1 a $2a$ b $2m$ c $4p$ d 3 e 3 f 2 g $3n$ h $6b$
  i $4p$ j $\frac{x}{2}$ k $\frac{3a}{5}$ l $\frac{m}{5}$ m $\frac{n}{3}$ n $\frac{1}{2}$ o $\frac{1}{2}$ p $\frac{1}{3}$
  q $\frac{3}{4}$ r $2n$ s $2a$ t $2x$ u $3a$

2 a $2m$ b $5x$ c $5p$ d $2a$ e $3n$ f $2p$ g $3l$ h $5k$
  i 2 j 2 k 6 l 6 m 3 n 5 o 4 p 2
  q $5b$ r $3n$ s 8 t $2w$ u m v x w 12 x $2a$

3 a $-2a$ b $-3m$ c $2q$ d $3p$ e -2 f -3 g 2 h 3
  i $-2y$ j $-4m$ k $3k$ l $4mn$ m $-4x$ n $-3m$ o $-2t$ p $3n$
  q -2 r -7 s 3 t 2 u $-2a$ v $-2mn$ w $4b$ x b

4

	A	B	C	D
a	5	$10q$	$-m$	$-2p$
b	$3t$	-1	3	5
c	$2a$	$\frac{3}{2}$	$\frac{7b}{3}$	$2x$
d	2	$-3a$	$-m$	$2p$

Prep Quiz 6:05
1 $18m$ **2** $2m$ **3** $16a^2$ **4** 4 **5** $50pq$ **6** $8a^2b$ **7** 12 **8** 2 **9** m **10** $3x$

Exercise 6:05
1 a $30xy$ **b** $40abc$ **c** 3
   d $3m$ **e** $15pq$ **f** $15a$
   g 1 **h** 2 **i** $4m$
   j $3a^2$ **k** $21a^2b^2$ **l** $8t^2$

3 a $2ab$ **b** $4n^2$

2

	A	B	C
a	$10m^2$	2	$2p$
b	$2a$	$6p^2q$	1
c	$-6pq$	$-4m$	$3x^2y$
d	$9m^2$	$25a^2$	$16x^2$
e	$6mn$	$4l$	$3a^2$
f	$12p^2q$	$-10x^2y$	$4n$
g	$9p^2q^2$	$49m^2n^2$	$4t^2w^2$
h	$24pq$	$24abc$	$18mp$
i	0	$6a^2x$	$-30t^2$
j	$-5y$	-1	$2x$
k	$6a^2$	$6p$	$8x$
l	2	$2x$	$2q$
m	1	x	$2a$

Prep Quiz 6:06
1 $10x$ **2** $8a + 7b$ **3** $-3m$ **4** $2x^2 - x$ **5** $21x$ **6** 2 **7** $-30x^2$ **8** $15a^2b$ **9** $2x$ **10** $4a$

Exercise 6:06
1 a $(a + 27)$ cm   **b** $(2y + 14)$ cm   **c** $(8 + 4x)$ cm   **d** $4b$ m   **e** $16a$ cm
2 a $6a$ cm^2 **b** $7y$ cm^2 **c** $8x$ cm^2 **d** b^2 m^2 **e** $12a$ cm^2
3 a $4x$ mm   **b** 2 L $+ 2$B mm   **c** $2p + 6q$ mm   **d** $20k$ mm   **e** $6x$ mm
   f $10n + 3m$ mm   **g** $9x + 5$ mm   **h** $3m + 2n - 1$ mm   **i** $4a + 3b$ mm
4 a $4m^2$ cm^2 **b** $30a$ cm^2 **c** $14xy$ cm^2 **d** $3p^2$ cm^2 **e** $20b$ cm^2 **f** $30h^2$ cm^2
5 a $3p + 4q$ **b** $14a$ **c** $40x$ cents   **d** $9m + 8n$

Prep Quiz 6:07
1 4 **2** 25 **3** $10\,000$ **4** 8 **5** 27 **6** 3^3 **7** a^5 **8** 10^4 **9** x^6 **10** y^7

Exercise 6:07
1 a m^2 **b** a^6 **c** x^4 **d** $5n^3$ **e** $21a^2$ **f** $16y^3$ **g** p^2q **h** $56xy^2$ **i** $4m^3n^2$
2 a $x \times x \times x$ **b** $8 \times b \times b$ **c** $7 \times m \times m \times m \times m \times m$ **d** $y \times y \times y \times y \times y$
   e $3 \times a \times a \times a \times a$ **f** $x \times x \times x \times y \times y$ **g** $a \times m \times m \times m \times m$
   h $x \times x \times x \times x \times y \times y \times y$ **i** $a \times a \times a \times b$ **j** $a \times p \times p \times p$
   k $2 \times a \times p \times p$ **l** $4 \times a \times p \times p \times p$ **m** $6 \times x \times x \times x \times y \times y$
   n $5 \times a \times a \times a \times a \times a \times b$ **o** $10 \times m \times m \times m \times n \times n \times n \times n$
3 a 16 **b** 25 **c** 16 **d** $1\,000\,000$ **e** 27 **f** 300
   g 16 **h** 36 **i** 162 **j** 5000 **k** 400 **l** -240
   m 432 **n** 800 **o** -375

Prep Quiz 6:08
1 20 **2** 20 **3** 6 **4** 6 **5** -14 **6** -14 **7** $5a + 10$ **8** $6x + 15y$ **9** $6x^2 + 10x$ **10** $12a^2 - 6ab$

Exercise 6:08A
1 a $3a + 6$ **b** $4x + 12$ **c** $2x + 14$ **d** $5v + 5$ **e** $6m - 30$ **f** $5n - 10$
   g $4b - 12$ **h** $6l - 6$ **i** $6 + 2a$ **j** $12 + 3x$ **k** $36 + 6t$ **l** $14 + 7w$
   m $7 - 7x$ **n** $10 - 5y$ **o** $12 - 4p$ **p** $72 - 9y$ **q** $3a + 3b$ **r** $2x + 2y$
   s $6p + 6q$ **t** $7m + 7n$ **u** $4p - 4q$ **v** $5a - 5b$ **w** $10t - 10w$ **x** $8x - 8y$
2 a $4a + 6$ **b** $15x + 5$ **c** $8m + 12$ **d** $18n + 12$ **e** $10m - 5$ **f** $16n - 20$
   g $10p - 4$ **h** $35t - 21$ **i** $12 + 18m$ **j** $7 + 28x$ **k** $9 + 12n$ **l** $8 + 20t$
   m $20 - 30x$ **n** $4 - 12p$ **o** $6 - 15w$ **p** $8 - 16x$ **q** $6a + 4b$ **r** $12m + 3n$
   s $20x + 15y$ **t** $10x + 30y$ **u** $10x - 5y$ **v** $8a - 12b$ **w** $14m - 4n$ **x** $18t - 6w$
3 a $x^2 + 2x$ **b** $y^2 + 3y$ **c** $a^2 + 5a$ **d** $m^2 + 10m$ **e** $a^2 - a$ **f** $m^2 - 5m$
   g $n^2 - 3n$ **h** $y^2 - 8y$ **i** $xy + 2x$ **j** $ab + 2a$ **k** $mt - 3m$ **l** $nx - 6n$
   m $ax + a^2$ **n** $x^2 + xy$ **o** $m^2 + mn$ **p** $tw + t^2$ **q** $k^2 + kl$ **r** $pq - p^2$
   s $tw + ty$ **t** $ab - ac$
4 a $2a^2 + 4a$ **b** $3x^2 + 15x$ **c** $5n^2 + 10n$ **d** $4m^2 + 16m$ **e** $3p^2 - 12p$ **f** $4q^2 - 4q$
   g $10m^2 - 70m$ **h** $8a^2 - 40a$ **i** $24x - 6x^2$ **j** $2m + 2m^2$ **k** $9t^2 + 18t$ **l** $25n - 5n^2$
   m $2a^2 + 2ab$ **n** $4p^2 + 4pq$ **o** $3x^2 + 3xy$ **p** $7mn + 7m^2$ **q** $6y^2 + 12y$ **r** $3ab + 6a^2$
   s $6m^2 + 15mn$ **t** $12pq - 8p^2$

5 a $6x + 6$ **b** $7m + 6$ **c** $2a + 25$ **d** $7n - 8$ **e** $3a - 20$ **f** $7m - 3$
  g $8a + 16$ **h** $5x + 2$ **i** $2y + 17$ **j** $9x + 12$ **k** $8a - 6$ **l** $12m - 8$
6 a $5x + 12$ **b** $6x + 14$ **c** $8a + 13$ **d** $7m + 8$ **e** $9y$ **f** $7m + 3$
  g $22 + 9a$ **h** $5m + 25$ **i** $24 + 3y$ **j** $12x$ **k** $11p + 14$ **l** $2a + 29$
  m $4m + 4n$ **n** $10x$ **o** $5p + q$

Exercise 6:08B

1 a $-2x - 6$ **b** $-3a - 15$ **c** $-5y - 5$ **d** $-9k - 18$ **e** $-4a + 8$ **f** $-2p + 6$
  g $-7t + 42$ **h** $-5x + 5$ **i** $-18 - 3x$ **j** $-63 + 9q$ **k** $-20 - 2y$ **l** $-48 + 6h$
2 a $-a - 2$ **b** $-x - 3$ **c** $-p - 7$ **d** $-q - 1$ **e** $-x + 3$ **f** $-t + 2$
  g $-w + 6$ **h** $-y + 1$ **i** $-2x - 7$ **j** $-3x + 2$ **k** $-4x - 5$ **l** $-7y + 3$
3 a $-x^2 - 2x$ **b** $-a^2 - 3a$ **c** $-m^2 + 4m$ **d** $-n^2 + n$ **e** $-ab - 3a$ **f** $-pq - 5p$
  g $-tx + 3t$ **h** $-mn + 10m$ **i** $-2m^2 - 8m$ **j** $-10a^2 - 25a$ **k** $-6x^2 + 42x$ **l** $-20t^2 - 12t$
4 a $8 - 2a$ **b** $6p - 5$ **c** $-a - 5$ **d** $3 - a$ **e** $6 - 2x$ **f** $6a - 2$
  g $-2 - 4a$ **h** $3x - 6$ **i** $4m + 2$ **j** $9x - 3$ **k** $11 - x$ **l** $2y - 2$
  m $3m - 1$ **n** $5a - 2$ **o** $10 + 2a$
5 a x **b** $2a + 2$ **c** $y + 19$ **d** $a + 24$ **e** $4m + 34$ **f** $2t + 48$
  g $-m - 10$ **h** $-y - 34$ **i** $p - 22$ **j** $2p - 7$ **k** $2t + 2$ **l** $2q - 18$
  m $2p + 28$ **n** $5q + 9$ **o** $3m - 14$
6 a $2x + 18$ **b** $-2m - 8$ **c** $11a + 12$ **d** $15a - 68$ **e** $x^2 + 37$ **f** $2a^2 + 6ab - 2b^2$
  g $3y^2 - 34y + 2xy - 8x$ **h** $6a^2 + 3bc - 9ac$

Prep Quiz 6:09

1 $2x + 6$ **2** $5a - 35$ **3** $p^2 + 4p$ **4** $2m^2 - 2mn$ **5** $1, 2, 3, 6$ **6** $1, 2, 3, 4, 6, 12$ **7** $1, 2, 4, 5, 10, 20$ **8** 3 **9** 4 **10** 5

Exercise 6:09

1 a 2 **b** 5 **c** 3 **d** 5 **e** 2 **f** 2 **g** a **h** x **i** p **j** a
2 a $m + 5$ **b** $x + 2$ **c** $a + 1$ **d** $y - 3$ **e** $k - 2$ **f** $m - 1$
  g $2x + 3$ **h** $2n + 3$ **i** $4k + 3$ **j** $3y - 2$ **k** $2x - 5$ **l** $2a - 3$
  m $x + 3$ **n** $m + 5$ **o** $4 + x$ **p** $a - c$ **q** $x - 1$ **r** $1 - q$
  s $x + 3$ **t** $5 + a$ **u** $1 - 2x$
3 a $2(y + 3)$ **b** $3(x + 2)$ **c** $5(m + 4)$ **d** $6(k + 2)$ **e** $9(n - 2)$ **f** $3(2a - 1)$
  g $4(y - 3)$ **h** $7(2p - 1)$ **i** $5(2 + a)$ **j** $2(3 + 2p)$ **k** $2(5 + 3q)$ **l** $8(1 + y)$
  m $10(2 - m)$ **n** $4(3 - a)$ **o** $3(5 - q)$ **p** $7(1 - p)$ **q** $6(m + n)$ **r** $5(x + 2y)$
  s $6(n - 2m)$ **t** $8(p - q)$ **u** $2(2p - 3)$ **v** $3(3a + 4)$ **w** $2(4 + 7x)$ **x** $2(5 - 4k)$
4 a $x(a + 2)$ **b** $y(x + 5)$ **c** $b(a + 3)$ **d** $x(9 + y)$ **e** $m(5 - n)$ **f** $q(p - 3)$
  g $x(10 - a)$ **h** $w(t - 1)$ **i** $x(a + b)$ **j** $q(p + r)$ **k** $n(m - p)$ **l** $b(a - c)$
  m $x(x + 3)$ **n** $y(y + 2)$ **o** $m(m + 1)$ **p** $t(t + x)$ **q** $p(p - 5)$ **r** $m(6 - m)$
  s $x(2x - 3)$ **t** $l(9 - 7l)$ **u** $m(5 + 2n)$ **v** $x(7y - 3)$ **w** $b(3a + 5c)$ **x** $p(8q - 7r)$
5 a $5x(1 + 2y)$ **b** $4m(1 + 2n)$ **c** $2p(3 + 2q)$ **d** $5t(2 + 3w)$ **e** $3m(3n - 1)$ **f** $6q(p - 2)$
  g $4t(2 - w)$ **h** $3a(2 - b)$ **i** $2x(x + 2)$ **j** $3m(3m - 2)$ **k** $5n(2 + n)$ **l** $4q(2p - q)$
  m $3n(m + 2r)$ **n** $4p(q + 2r)$ **o** $3b(2a + c)$ **p** $2x(4y + z)$ **q** $3x(3y - z)$ **r** $6a(b - 2c)$
  s $5m(n - 3p)$ **t** $4w(2t - x)$ **u** $ab(a - 1)$ **v** $5x(x - 2y)$ **w** $3m(3n + 2m)$ **x** $4q(p - 5q)$
6 a $3(x + y + z)$ **b** $6(a + b - c)$ **c** $5(m + n + 1)$ **d** $5(a + 2b - 3c)$
  e $3(2p - q + 3r)$ **f** $3(4x + 2y - 3)$ **g** $3(a^2 + a + 1)$ **h** $5(m^2 + 2m + 3)$
  i $2(2p^2 - p + 4)$ **j** $a(x + y + z)$ **k** $x(p + q + r)$ **l** $t(5 + w - x)$
  m $5x(x - 2 + 3y)$ **n** $3m(2 + 5n + 3p)$ **o** $5a(2a + 3b - 1)$
7 a $-2(x + 2)$ **b** $-6(m + 2)$ **c** $-3(p + 3)$ **d** $-5(p - 2)$ **e** $-3(q - 1)$ **f** $-7(n - 3)$
  g $-10(2 + a)$ **h** $-4(3 + p)$ **i** $-3(3 - 2q)$ **j** $-6(a + 2b)$ **k** $-5(m - 3n)$ **l** $-2(5a - b)$
  m $-x(x - 3)$ **n** $-a(x + 5)$ **o** $-3x(2a - b)$

Prep Quiz 6:10

1 1 **2** $\frac{2}{5}$ **3** $\frac{5}{6}$ **4** $\frac{17}{20}$ **5** $\frac{1}{2}$ **6** $\frac{4}{5}$ **7** $6x$ **8** m **9** $2x + 3y$ **10** $6xy$

Exercise 6:10A

1 a $\dfrac{2x}{5}$ **b** $\dfrac{5m}{7}$ **c** $\dfrac{7n}{4}$ **d** $\dfrac{x}{5}$ **e** $\dfrac{5t}{8}$ **f** $\dfrac{2m}{7}$ **g** a **h** $\dfrac{3p}{5}$ **i** $\dfrac{t}{2}$ **j** $\dfrac{5w}{6}$
  k $\dfrac{5a}{8}$ **l** $\dfrac{3x}{5}$ **m** $\dfrac{m}{2}$ **n** $\dfrac{4y}{9}$ **o** n **p** $\dfrac{x}{2}$ **q** $\dfrac{t}{2}$ **r** $\dfrac{7x}{6}$ **s** $\dfrac{7m}{8}$ **t** $\dfrac{y}{2}$
  u $\dfrac{x}{4}$

2 a $\dfrac{11a}{12}$ **b** $\dfrac{9m}{10}$ **c** $\dfrac{5x}{6}$ **d** $\dfrac{7t}{6}$ **e** $\dfrac{m}{6}$ **f** $\dfrac{4w}{15}$ **g** $\dfrac{a}{6}$ **h** $\dfrac{9n}{10}$ **i** $\dfrac{3x}{4}$ **j** $\dfrac{5a}{6}$

k $\dfrac{m}{2}$ **l** $\dfrac{7y}{3}$ **m** $\dfrac{3t}{10}$ **n** $\dfrac{y}{4}$ **o** $\dfrac{m}{2}$ **p** $\dfrac{n}{9}$ **q** $\dfrac{19x}{20}$ **r** $\dfrac{5m}{18}$ **s** $\dfrac{11a}{12}$ **t** $\dfrac{13n}{24}$

u $\dfrac{5y}{24}$ **v** $\dfrac{9x}{20}$ **w** $\dfrac{7m}{12}$ **x** $\dfrac{p}{9}$

Exercise 6:10B

1 a $\dfrac{xy}{6}$ **b** $\dfrac{ab}{30}$ **c** $\dfrac{mn}{12}$ **d** $\dfrac{2a}{3x}$ **e** $\dfrac{5n}{3m}$ **f** $\dfrac{10p}{3q}$ **g** $\dfrac{m^2}{6}$ **h** $\dfrac{xy}{4}$ **i** $\dfrac{a}{12}$ **j** $\dfrac{3t}{2w}$

k 6 **l** $\dfrac{2mn}{3}$ **m** $\dfrac{1}{4}$ **n** $\dfrac{2x}{5}$ **o** 1 **p** 6 **q** $\dfrac{a^2}{5}$ **r** $\dfrac{x}{6}$

2 a $\dfrac{2}{3}$ **b** $\dfrac{3}{4}$ **c** $\dfrac{5}{6}$ **d** $\dfrac{5}{2}$ **e** $\dfrac{10}{x^2}$ **f** $\dfrac{a^2}{6}$ **g** $\dfrac{mn}{12}$ **h** $\dfrac{15}{tw}$ **i** $\dfrac{10}{3}$ **j** $\dfrac{5m^2}{12}$

k $\dfrac{a^2}{6}$ **l** $\dfrac{3}{2}$ **m** $\dfrac{ay}{bx}$ **n** $\dfrac{m^2}{n^2}$ **o** $\dfrac{3}{2}$ **p** $\dfrac{2c}{3b}$ **q** $\dfrac{b^2}{3}$ **r** $\dfrac{5}{9}$ **s** $\dfrac{2b}{3c}$ **t** $6y$

Challenge 6:10

1 a a^2+6a+8 **b** $x^2+7x+10$ **c** y^2+3y+2 **d** $p^2+9p+14$ **e** x^2+2x-3 **f** q^2+2q-8
g a^2-a-12 **h** $m^2+3m-10$ **i** y^2-y-6 **j** x^2+2x-3 **k** n^2-n-20 **l** a^2-9
m x^2-3x+2 **n** $a^2-8a+16$ **o** $t^2-11t+28$ **p** $x^2-11x+30$

2 a a^2+4a+4 **b** $m^2+10m+25$ **c** $x^2+14x+49$ **d** $m^2+20m+100$ **e** x^2-2x+1
f a^2-6a+9 **g** $n^2-8n+16$ **h** $y^2-16y+64$

3 a $ab+ay+bx+xy$ **b** $px+py+qx+qy$ **c** $ac-ad+bc-bd$ **d** $mx-my-nx+ny$ **e** $15+3y+5x+xy$
f $ab+5a+4b+20$ **g** $xy-3x+7y-21$ **h** $tw-3t-5w+15$

4 a $2x^2+15x+7$ **b** $3a^2+8a+5$ **c** $3y^2+23y+14$ **d** $3m^2+4m+1$ **e** $6y^2+19y+10$
f $8n^2+10n+3$ **g** $6p^2+23p+20$ **h** $10y^2-11y-6$ **i** $4m^2+4m+1$ **j** $25x^2+30x+9$
k $4m^2-12m+9$ **l** $25-20a+4a^2$

Diagnostic Test 6: Further Algebra

1 a

S	0	2	4	6
P	4	8	12	16

b

P	1	2	3	4
F	0	3	6	9

2 a $y=4x$ **b** $b=2a+2$

3 a $8x$ **b** $9xy$ **c** $9x^2$ **4 a** $8m$ **b** $2ab$ **c** a^2

5 a $9x$ **b** $9a$ **c** $5m$ **6 a** $-3a$ **b** m **c** $-5x$

7 a $8x+2y$ **b** $4m+2n$ **c** $10a+b$ **8 a** $7m-3n$ **b** $-a+3b$ **c** $2m-2n$

9 a $18m$ **b** $15x$ **c** $28k$ **10 a** $3mn$ **b** $18ab$ **c** $35xy$

11 a $-14x$ **b** $-15m$ **c** $6xy$ **12 a** $2x$ **b** 3 **c** $3x$

13 a a **b** $2p$ **c** $3y$ **14 a** a^5 **b** x^3y **c** $8m^4$

15 a $x\times x\times x\times x\times x\times x$ **b** $x\times x\times x\times x\times y\times y\times y\times y\times y\times y$

c $6\times a\times a\times a\times a\times a\times a\times b$

16 a $3x+6$ **b** $5a-35$ **c** a^2+3a **17 a** $m+9$ **b** $7x-3$ **c** $5x+5$

18 a $-3x-9$ **b** $-2a+10$ **c** $-x^2-7x$ **19 a** $3x+13$ **b** $2a+14$ **c** $x-14$

20 a $2(x+4)$ **b** $5(y-1)$ **c** $6(1+2m)$ **21 a** $x(a+3)$ **b** $m(6-n)$ **c** $y(y+3)$

22 a $\dfrac{4a}{5}$ **b** $\dfrac{2m}{7}$ **c** $\dfrac{x}{2}$ **23 a** $\dfrac{7a}{12}$ **b** $\dfrac{m}{15}$ **c** $\dfrac{5x}{4}$

24 a $\dfrac{xy}{12}$ **b** $\dfrac{a^2}{10}$ **c** 4 **25 a** $\dfrac{4}{3}$ **b** $\dfrac{a^2}{10}$ **c** $\dfrac{3}{2}$

6A Revision Assignment

1 a $\dfrac{1}{5}$ **b** $\dfrac{1}{4}$ **c** $\dfrac{3}{5}$ **d** $\dfrac{18}{25}$ **2 a** 5% **b** 27% **c** 100% **d** 110%

3 a 30% **b** 36% **c** 35% **d** $27\tfrac{1}{2}\%$ **4 a** 0.15 **b** 0.07 **c** 1.08 **d** 0.74

5 a 37.5% **b** 2.5% **c** 93.75% **d** 0.1075 **6 a** $\$4.20$ **b** $27.6\,\text{L}$ **c** $15\,750$ **d** $\$967.50$

7 a $33\tfrac{1}{3}\%$ **b** 156 **c** $\div 8.9\%$ **d** 17.5% **8 a** 14 **b** 58 **c** Monday **d** Tuesday

6B Working Mathematically

1 98 mm   **2** More than one answer is possible. One solution is:

Round 1 1 v 2, 3 v 4
Round 2 1 v 3, 2 v 4
Round 3 1 v 4, 2 v 3
Round 4 2 v 1, 4 v 3
Round 5 3 v 1, 4 v 2
Round 6 4 v 1, 3 v 2

3 a 30 cm; 4 **b** 70 cm   **4 a** 5 **b** 11   **5 a** 26 **b** 155

Chapter 7: Equations, formulae and inequations

Prep Quiz 7:01

1 $x + 5$ **2** $3a$ **3** $\dfrac{y}{8}$ **4** $p - 2$ **5** $3x + 2$ **6** $7(y - 2)$ **7** subtracting 8
8 adding 5   **9** dividing by 4   **10** multiplying by 3

Exercise 7:01

1 a $\times 9$ **b** $+ 2$ **c** $- 7$ **d** $\times 5, - 1$ **e** $\div 10$ **f** $+ 6, \div 5$
   g $\div 3, + 9$ **h** $- 8, \div 7$ **i** $\div (-5), + 3$ **j** $+ 3, \times 2$ **k** $\times (-3), + 5$

2 a $\div 3$ **b** $\times 2$ **c** $- 5$ **d** $+ 7$ **e** $\div 10$ **f** $\times 3$
   g $- 8$ **h** $+ 5$ **i** $- 1, \div 2$ **j** $+ 2, \div 5$ **k** $- 3, \div 7$ **l** $+ 4, \div 9$
   m $- 6, \div 3$ **n** $- 7, \times 2$ **o** $+ 2, \times 5$ **p** $\times 3, - 7$ **q** $\times 5, + 2$ **r** $- 5, \div (-3)$
   s $- 8, \div (-2)$ **t** $- 5, \times (-3)$

3 a $m \xrightarrow{\times 8} 8m$ **b** $p \xrightarrow{\div 7} \dfrac{p}{7}$ **c** $x \xrightarrow{+5} 5 + x$ **d** $q \xrightarrow{-10} q - 10$

   e $x \xrightarrow{\times 3} 3x \xrightarrow{+2} 3x + 2$ **f** $n \xrightarrow{\times 5} 5n \xrightarrow{-3} 5n - 3$ **g** $p \xrightarrow{\times 6} 6p \xrightarrow{+7} 6p + 7$ **h** $a \xrightarrow{\times 9} 9a \xrightarrow{-1} 9a - 1$

   i $x \xrightarrow{\div 3} \dfrac{x}{3} \xrightarrow{+5} \dfrac{x}{3} + 5$ **j** $a \xrightarrow{+4} \dfrac{a}{4} \xrightarrow{+7} 7 + \dfrac{a}{4}$ **k** $y \xrightarrow{+3} y + 3 \xrightarrow{\div 4} \dfrac{y + 3}{4}$ **l** $n \xrightarrow{-1} n - 1 \xrightarrow{\div 5} \dfrac{n - 1}{5}$

   m $m \xrightarrow{+2} m + 2 \xrightarrow{\times 7} 7(m + 2)$ **n** $x \xrightarrow{-3} x - 3 \xrightarrow{\times 9} 9(x - 3)$ **o** $x \xrightarrow{+2} 2 + x \xrightarrow{\times 5} 5(2 + x)$

   p $q \xrightarrow{-4} q - 4 \xrightarrow{\times 3} 3(q - 4)$ **q** $x \xrightarrow{\times(-2)} -2x \xrightarrow{+3} 3 - 2x$ **r** $a \xrightarrow{\times(-5)} -5a \xrightarrow{+7} -5a + 7$

   s $x \xrightarrow{\div(-3)} -\dfrac{x}{3} \xrightarrow{+6} 6 - \dfrac{x}{3}$ **t** $p \xrightarrow{\times(-9)} -9p \xrightarrow{+10} 10 - 9p$

4 a $a - 2$ **b** $4x$ **c** $\dfrac{m}{3}$ **d** $t + 9$ **e** $5p, 5p + 2$ **f** $6x, 6x - 4$
   g $y + 1, 7(y + 1)$ **h** $\dfrac{b}{4}, \dfrac{b}{4} + 2$ **i** $q - 3, \dfrac{q - 3}{3}$ **j** $-2n, -2n + 6$ **k** b **l** a
   m m **n** n **o** $2x, x$ **p** $5p, p$ **q** $7t, t$ **r** $m + 5, m$
   s $\dfrac{a}{3}, a$ **t** $-2x, x$

5 a $- 6$ **b** $\div 3$ **c** $+ 5$ **d** $\times 7$ **e** $\times 2, + 3$ **f** $\times 5, - 2$
   g $\times 3, + 6$ **h** $\times 7, - 1$ **i** $+ 7, \div 5$ **j** $- 4, \div 3$ **k** $\div 8, + 5$ **l** $\div 3, - 4$
   m $+ 3, \times 2$ **n** $- 9, \times 5$ **o** $\times (-6), + 8$ **p** $\times (-3), + 10$

6 a $+ 7$ **b** $\div 5$ **c** $- 6$ **d** $\times 3$ **e** $\div (-4)$ **f** $- 5, \div 2$
   g $+ 1, \div 3$ **h** $- 5, \div 7$ **i** $+ 6, \div 5$ **j** $- 8, \div (-3)$ **k** $\times 7, - 3$ **l** $- 3, \times 7$
   m $\div 5, - 2$ **n** $\div 3, + 1$ **o** $\times 5, + 9$

7 a $\times 5, - 3, \div 2$ **b** $\div 6, - 7, \div 3$ **c** $\times 6, - 7, \div (-3)$ **d** $- 9, \times 3, \div 2$ **e** $\div 5, - 2, \div (-3)$
   f $\times 7, - 5, \div (-1)$ **g** $- 6, \times 3, \div (-5)$ **h** $\times 5, \div 7, - 4, \div 3$

Prep Quiz 7:02

1 x **2** x **3** a **4** m **5** dividing by 3   **6** subtracting 7   **7** adding 1   **8** multiplying by 5   **9** $- 3, \div 5$ **10** $+ 2, \div 8$

Exercise 7:02

1 a $x = 8$ **b** $p = 2$ **c** $y = 14$ **d** $n = 3$ **e** $q = 8$ **f** $k = 9$ **g** $y = 8$ **h** $m = 9$
   i $x = 13$ **j** $x = 3$ **k** $x = 6$ **l** $p = 12$ **m** $y = 4$ **n** $y = 2$ **o** $x = 3$ **p** $n = 6$
   q $x = 15$ **r** $m = 16$

2 a $x = -1$ **b** $m = -4$ **c** $n = -2$ **d** $p = -8$ **e** $q = -6$ **f** $y = -12$ **g** $a = 5$ **h** $x = 7$
   i $p = 5$ **j** $q = 1$ **k** $y = 0$ **l** $t = 4$ **m** $m = -2$ **n** $p = -2$ **o** $w = -1$ **p** $n = -6$
   q $q = -9$ **r** $m = 2$ **s** $x = -6$ **t** $m = -80$ **u** $n = -196$ **v** $x = 3$ **w** $y = -8$ **x** $x = -3$

3 a correct   **b** incorrect   **c** correct   **d** correct   **e** correct   **f** incorrect   **g** correct   **h** incorrect
   i incorrect   **j** correct   **k** incorrect   **l** incorrect

4 a $x = 2$ **b** $a = 2$ **c** $m = 3$ **d** $n = 3$ **e** $k = 5$ **f** $t = 2$ **g** $a = 4$ **h** $w = 1$
   i $q = 1$ **j** $x = 3$ **k** $m = 2$ **l** $q = 4$ **m** $x = 9$ **n** $y = 2$ **o** $a = -2$ **p** $x = 11$
   q $x = -1$ **r** $x = 2$

5 a $x = 2$ **b** $x = 10$ **c** $m = 8$ **d** $x = 11$ **e** $a = 1$ **f** $n = 13$ **g** $m = 14$ **h** $n = 19$
   i $a = 42$ **j** $y = 6$ **k** $x = -4$ **l** $m = 25$ **m** $a = 10$ **n** $x = 18$ **o** $m = 4$

6 a $x = \dfrac{3}{2}$ **b** $a = \dfrac{5}{2}$ **c** $m = \dfrac{1}{3}$ **d** $n = \dfrac{6}{5}$ **e** $p = \dfrac{5}{2}$ **f** $q = \dfrac{3}{4}$ **g** $n = \dfrac{9}{5}$ **h** $y = \dfrac{2}{3}$
   i $k = \dfrac{7}{2}$ **j** $x = \dfrac{2}{3}$ **k** $a = \dfrac{2}{3}$ **l** $a = \dfrac{3}{2}$ **m** $m = -\dfrac{3}{2}$ **n** $p = -\dfrac{6}{5}$ **o** $a = -\dfrac{3}{2}$ **p** $a = \dfrac{4}{3}$

7 a $x = 7$ **b** $m = 4$ **c** $x = 1$ **d** $n = 5$ **e** $a = 3$ **f** $a = -1$ **g** $y = -2$ **h** $m = 2$
   i $x = -4$ **j** $n = \dfrac{5}{3}$ **k** $x = \dfrac{2}{3}$ **l** $q = -4$ **m** $x = 50$ **n** $p = 4$ **o** $x = 3$ **p** $a = 18$
   q $a = 6$ **r** $a = -3$ **s** $m = 46$ **t** $m = \dfrac{6}{5}$ **u** $a = -1$ **v** $p = -1$ **w** $q = -4$ **x** $n = -7$

Prep Quiz 7:03

1 x **2** $6a$ **3** 0 **4** 0 **5** -5 **6** $+4$ **7** $\times 5$ **8** 5 **9** 1 **10** 5

Exercise 7:03

1 a $a=2$ **b** $x=7$ **c** $p=3$ **d** $q=8$ **e** $n=5$ **f** $x=-3$ **g** $m=-3$ **h** $a=-2$
   i $x=3$ **j** $m=3$ **k** $y=4$ **l** $x=-3$ **m** $x=6$ **n** $m=-4$ **o** $x=2$ **p** $x=1$
   q $m=2$ **r** $p=0$

2 a correct   **b** correct   **c** incorrect   **d** incorrect   **e** correct   **f** incorrect   **g** incorrect   **h** correct
   i correct   **j** correct   **k** incorrect   **l** incorrect   **m** incorrect   **n** incorrect   **o** correct

3 a $x=\frac{1}{2}$ **b** $m=1\frac{1}{2}$ **c** $p=\frac{2}{3}$ **d** $m=\frac{1}{3}$ **e** $a=-\frac{1}{2}$ **f** $n=1\frac{1}{5}$ **g** $a=2\frac{1}{2}$ **h** $n=3\frac{1}{3}$
   i $q=2\frac{2}{3}$ **j** $n=-\frac{1}{2}$ **k** $a=\frac{2}{3}$ **l** $k=-1\frac{1}{3}$ **m** $a=1\frac{1}{2}$ **n** $x=1\frac{1}{3}$ **o** $q=2\frac{1}{4}$ **p** $t=2\frac{2}{3}$
   q $m=\frac{2}{3}$ **r** $x=\frac{5}{8}$ **s** $a=-1\frac{1}{3}$ **t** $w=-1\frac{1}{3}$ **u** $m=-1\frac{1}{3}$ **v** $y=\frac{2}{3}$ **w** $x=-\frac{1}{8}$ **x** $p=4\frac{1}{3}$

Prep Quiz 7:04

1 $2x+6$ **2** $3a-15$ **3** $8a+12$ **4** $10p-5$ **5** $21-14q$ **6** $x=5$ **7** $x=-5$ **8** $p=2$ **9** $p=\frac{1}{2}$ **10** $x=11$

Exercise 7:04

1 a $x=-1$ **b** $a=2$ **c** $n=0$ **d** $p=2$ **e** $a=4$ **f** $m=7$ **g** $x=3$ **h** $q=4$
   i $a=\frac{1}{2}$ **j** $x=\frac{5}{8}$ **k** $x=\frac{5}{2}$ **l** $t=1\frac{2}{5}$ **m** $a=1$ **n** $x=4$

2 a $x=1$ **b** $a=2$ **c** $m=2$ **d** $a=1$ **e** $p=2$ **f** $q=2$ **g** $x=1$ **h** $a=3$
   i $m=1$ **j** $m=2$ **k** $n=6$ **l** $a=2$ **m** $m=8$ **n** $x=1$ **o** $x=4$

3 a $x=1\frac{1}{2}$ **b** $a=-6\frac{1}{3}$ **c** $p=-2\frac{3}{5}$ **d** $a=2$ **e** $q=\frac{2}{5}$ **f** $t=2\frac{5}{7}$ **g** $x=\frac{1}{2}$ **h** $p=\frac{1}{2}$
   i $w=-3\frac{1}{2}$ **j** $x=2\frac{1}{2}$ **k** $q=1\frac{1}{2}$ **l** $k=\frac{1}{3}$ **m** $m=3\frac{1}{2}$ **n** $x=1\frac{2}{3}$ **o** $n=\frac{5}{9}$

4 a $a=-4$ **b** $x=13$ **c** $p=18$ **d** $q=4$ **e** $m=4$ **f** $x=6$ **g** $a=2$ **h** $t=2$
   i $a=7$ **j** $p=4\frac{1}{2}$ **k** $t=3$ **l** $a=2\frac{2}{7}$ **m** $m=2$ **n** $p=-5$

5 a $a=1$ **b** $m=1$ **c** $m=1$ **d** $x=2$ **e** $p=1$ **f** $t=2$ **g** $a=2$ **h** $m=2$
   i $a=2$ **j** $a=-46$

6 a $a=2$ **b** $m=3$ **c** $n=2$ **d** $a=2$ **e** $a=1$ **f** $p=2$ **g** $a=-1\frac{3}{8}$ **h** $x=3\frac{1}{3}$

Prep Quiz 7:05

1 2 **2** -2 **3** 19 **4** 9 **5** 34 **6** 2 **7** -1 **8** -8 **9** 12 **10** -2

Exercise 7:05A

1 a 15 **b** 12 **c** 135 **d** 40 **e** 75 **f** 28

2 a 16 **b** 16 **c** 48 **d** 44 **e** 40 **f** 22

3 a 8 **b** 15 **c** $7\frac{1}{2}$ **d** $1 \cdot 9$ **e** $2 \cdot 4$ **f** $3 \cdot 8$

4 a 11 **b** 37 **c** 21 **d** 11 **e** 26 **f** 13

5 a 17 **b** 2 **c** 1 **d** 4 **e** 4 **f** 1

6 a 30 **b** $7 \cdot 536$ **c** $1 \cdot 17$ **d** 55 **e** 30 **f** 19 **g** 480 **h** 12

7 a $21\,\text{cm}^2$ **b** $130\,\text{m}^2$ **c** $2250\,\text{m}^2$ **d** $27\,\text{mm}^2$

8 a $6\,\text{mL}$ **b** $12\,\text{mL}$ **c** $15\,\text{mL}$

9 a 8 joules   **b** 45 joules   **c** 100 joules   **d** $20 \cdot 8$ joules   **e** $4 \cdot 32$ joules   **f** 1 joule

Exercise 7:05B

1 a 4 **b** 16 **c** 4 **d** $15 \cdot 5$ **2 a** $u=2$ **b** $u=9$ **c** $u=18$ **d** $a=2$

3 a 8 **b** 32 **c** $10 \cdot 9$ **4 a** $6\,\text{m}$ **b** $10\,\text{cm}$ **c** $2 \cdot 1\,\text{km}$ **d** $0 \cdot 3\,\text{m}$

5 a 0 **b** 8 **c** -6

6 a $a=2$ **b** $y=2$ **c** $n=8$ **d** $C=30$ **e** $a=8$ (or -8)   **f** $B=3$ **g** $m=2$

7 a $\$80$ **b** $\$680$ **c** 7

8 a $\$110$ **b** $\$220$ **c** They need at least 20 students to make a worthwhile profit.   **d** 26 students

9 a 7 closets   **b** 2 closets   **c** $-\$200$. This is a loss of $200. It costs $400 a day in wages, rent etc. just to run the factory.

Prep Quiz 7:06

1 $x=8$ **2** $a=-3$ **3** $m=18$ **4** $n=-2$ **5** $x=-4$ **6** $a+b$ **7** $5y$ **8** $x+5$ **9** $m-6$ **10** $n+2$

Exercise 7:06

1 a 12   **b** 22   **c** 7   **d** 12   **e** −8   **f** 17

2 a 4   **b** 5   **c** 6   **d** 13   **e** 15   **f** 11, 12   **g** 16, 17, 18

3 a 4   **b** 6   **c** 6   **d** 2

4 a 16   **b** 7   **c** 5   **d** 4   **e** 7   **f** 11

5 a $x = 11$ **b** $a = 7, b = 13$ **c** $y = 6$ **d** $x = 7$ **e** $p = 6, q = 5$ **f** $n = 5, k = 3$

6 a 14   **b** 18   **c** 30   **d** 22   **e** 50   **f** 54

7 a 12, 36   **b** \$7, \$28   **c** pen = 55c; pencil = 30c   **d** $5{\cdot}5\,\text{cm} \times 16{\cdot}5\,\text{cm}$; area $= 90{\cdot}75\,\text{cm}^2$
   e 100 units $\times$ 15 units, area $= 1500$ units^2 **f** Vinh = \$16, Tuan = \$10, Jakob = \$3
   g father = 48, Juan = 24

8 Each log is 5 m long.

Prep Quiz 7:07

1 True   **2** True   **3** True   **4** True   **5** {0, 1, 2, 3}

6 {2, 3, 4, 5, 6}   **7** {−3, −2, −1}   **8**

9   **10**

Exercise 7:07

1 a $x > 3$ **b** $x < 3$ **c** $x = 3$ **d** $x \le 3$

2 a $x > 3$ **b** $x \le 7$ **c** $a \le 0$ **d** $a > -1$ **e** $m < 28$ **f** $m < 26$ **g** $x \ge -6$ **h** $x \ge -2$

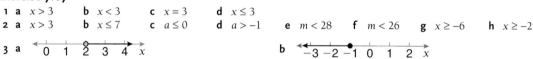

Prep Quiz 7:08

1 yes   **2** yes   **3** yes   **4** yes   **5** yes   **6** yes   **7** yes   **8** yes   **9** $<$ **10** $>$

Exercise 7:08

1 a −8, −6, −4   **b** 8   **c** −8, −6, −4, −2, 0, 2

2 a $a \le 2$ **b** $x > 2$

   c $y \ge 5$ **d** $x < 9$

   e $m > 15$ **f** $x \le 110$

   g $x < 32$ **h** $x \ge 42$

   i $m > 7$ **j** $y \le 12$

   k $x \ge 1$ **l** $x < 0$

   m $x \le 8$ **n** $y > 4$

   o $x < 27$ **p** $x \ge 32$

3 a $a > 3\frac{2}{3}$ **b** $y \le 2\frac{4}{5}$ **c** $x \ge 1\frac{3}{10}$ **d** $m < 1.1$ **e** $x \le 1\frac{1}{4}$ **f** $x > \frac{1}{4}$ **g** $y < 0$ **h** $x \ge \frac{4}{11}$
i $x < 11$ **j** $x \ge 1\frac{1}{2}$ **k** $m \le \frac{2}{5}$ **l** $x > 68.6$ **m** $a \ge 7.5$ **n** $y < \frac{1}{4}$ **o** $x > 2.2$ **p** $x \le 1\frac{1}{4}$
q $x > 1\frac{2}{5}$ **r** $m \le 2.4$ **s** $x \ge 2$ **t** $y = 10.1$

4 a $x < -2$ **b** $x \ge 6$ **c** $x > -2$ **d** $m \ge -\frac{1}{8}$ **e** $y < -3$ **f** $x \le 16$ **g** $y \le -7$ **h** $a > 0$
i $x < -1\frac{1}{6}$ **j** $x > -24$ **k** $m \le 3\frac{1}{2}$ **l** $x \ge -3$

5 a $x > -2$ **b** $m < -10$ **c** $x \le -9$ **d** $m \le 4$ **e** $x \ge 8$ **f** $x > -8$ **g** $x < -8$ **h** $m > -35$
i $x \ge 24$

6 a $x > 2$ Check: Substitute $x = 3$, $4 \times (3) + 3$, $15 > 11$, true.
b $m \le 8$ Check: Substitute $m = 7$, $7 \times (7) - 4$, $45 \le 52$, true.
c $x < 11$ Check: Substitute $x = 10$, $15 + 3(10)$, $45 < 48$, true.
d $x \le 8$ Check: Substitute $x = 7$, $6 + 2(7)$, $20 \le 22$, true.
e $x \ge 4$ Check: Substitute $x = 5$, $5(5) + 21$, $46 \ge 41$, true.
f $x > 3$ Check: Substitute $x = 4$, $40 + 7(4)$, $68 > 61$, true.
g $x < 40$ Check: Substitute $x = 39$, $\frac{(39)}{2} - 4$, $15.5 < 16$, true.
h $x > 4$ Check: Substitute $x = 5$, $\frac{5}{4} + 3$, $4\frac{1}{4} > 4$, true.
i $x \le -9$ Check: Substitute $x = -10$, $\frac{-10}{3} - 1$, $-4\frac{1}{3} \le -4$, true.

7 a $x \ge 2$ Check: Substitute $x = 3$, $8 - (2 \times 3)$, $2 \le 4$, true.

b $x < -2\frac{2}{3}$ Check: Substitute $x = -3$, $9 - 6(-3)$, $27 > 25$, true.

c $x \ge -3$ Check: Substitute $x = -2$, $-6(-2) + 3$, $15 \le 21$, true.

d $x < -6\frac{1}{3}$ Check: Substitute $x = -7$, $-3(-7) - 8$, $13 > 11$, true.

e $x > -19$ Check: Substitute $x = -18$, $-(-18) - 5$, $13 < 14$, true.

f $x \le 3$ Check: Substitute $x = 2$, $8(4 - 2)$, $16 \ge 8$, true.

Diagnostic Test 7: Equations, Formulae and Inequations

1 a $x = 16$ **b** $p = 7$ **c** $a = -2$ **d** $y = 5$ **2 a** $m = 9$ **b** $x = \frac{5}{3}$ **c** $n = 32$ **d** $a = -6$
3 a $x = 2$ **b** $m = 3$ **c** $y = 4$ **d** $a = -1$ **4 a** $x = 2\frac{1}{2}$ **b** $y = 1\frac{3}{4}$ **c** $k = -\frac{4}{5}$ **d** $t = 1\frac{1}{2}$
5 a $m = 8$ **b** $m = 10$ **c** $x = 4$ **d** $w = 12$ **6 a** $a = 6$ **b** $m = -4$ **c** $k = 1$ **d** $x = 4\frac{1}{2}$
7 a $a = 0$ **b** $m = 5$ **c** $y = 1$ **d** $m = 2$ **8 a** $n = 1$ **b** $p = 10$ **c** $x = 9$ **d** $x = \frac{1}{6}$
9 a 42 **b** 13 **c** 52 **d** 28 **10 a** 3 **b** 12 **c** 13 **d** 3
11 a 9 **b** -3 **c** 4 **d** 9 **12 a** 4 **b** 5 **c** 65

13 a   **b**   **c**

14 a $x \le 4\frac{2}{3}$ **b** $x > -6$ **c** $x < 40$

7A Revision Assignment

1 a 50% **b** $33\frac{1}{3}\%$ **2 a** 2.5 **b** 48
3 0.65   **4 a** $20.4\,cm^2$ **b** $21\,cm^2$ **c** $56.25\,cm^2$
5 a $6x - 18$ **b** $4(3a - 5)$ **c** $4a^2 - 8a$ **d** $6b(a + 2)$ **6 a** $17\,000\,000\,kg$ **b** $7.8\,km$ **c** 13 h 20 min
7 a -9 **b** -2 **c** 24 **d** -4 **8 a** 400 kg **b** \$5625
9 a $2160\ m^3$ **b** $720\ m^3$

7B Working Mathematically

1 C **2** C **3** 6118.7 m **4** 200 701 votes **5** 68
6 a decimetres **b** millimetres **c** kilometres **d** square centimetres
e hectares **f** cubic centimetres **g** seconds **h** tonnes
i millilitres **j** degrees Celsius

Chapter 8: The number plane

Prep Quiz 8:01

1 Turnham Green **2** Yes **3** Heathfield Terrace, Town Hall **4** Ivy Cres
5 Barrowgate Rd **6** Belmont Rd **7** C2 or C3 **8** E2 **9** G3 **10** B6 or C6

Exercise 8:01

1 a Hanover St **b** Manchester Victoria Railway Station **c** D8, D9, D10 **d** H14
 e They are green and yellow **f** Black and white striped lines **g** Angel St
2 a rectangle **b** oval **c** hexagon **d** circle **e** E15 **f** D10 **g** B08 **h** A01
3 a 036 012 **b** 033 033 **c** 023 021 **d** school **e** station **f** church **g** bridge **h** PO
4 a Philippa's campsite **b** junction of two rivers **c** 295 505 **d** 325 510 **e** 350 492
5 a D **b** H **c** J **d** F **e** E **f** B **g** C **h** G
 i A **j** I
6 a 15°N 91°W **b** 12°N 86°W **c** 8°N 79°W **d** 17°N 89°W
 e 14°N 89°W **f** 14°N 87°W **g** 12°N 81°W **h** 7°N 82°W
 i 12°N 83°W **j** 18°N 88°W

Prep Quiz 8:02

1 x-axis **2** y-axis **3** $(0, 0)$ origin **4** $(3, 1)$ **5** $(-2, 0)$ **6** $(-3, -2)$ **7** $(0, -3)$ **8** F **9** E **10** 3 units

Exercise 8:02

1 a C **b** B **c** N **d** D **e** S **f** P **g** H **h** I
 i Q **j** J **k** L **l** M
2 a $(1, 2)$ **b** $(-1, 4)$ **c** $(-3, 3)$ **d** $(3, -1)$ **e** $(0, 0)$ **f** $(2, 1)$ **g** $(-2, -3)$ **h** $(2, -4)$
 i $(1, 0)$ **j** $(0, 4)$ **k** $(-2, 0)$ **l** $(0, -3)$ **m** $(4, -2)$ **n** $(-1, -1)$ **o** $(1, -2)$
3 a 1st **b** 2nd **c** 3rd **d** 4th **e** 2nd **f** 4th **g** 1st **h** 3rd
 i 3rd **j** 4th **k** 2nd **l** 1st
4 a

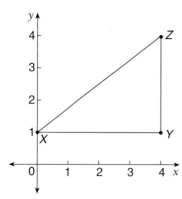

 b rectangle
 c 4 units, 2 units
 d 12 units
 e 8 units^2

5

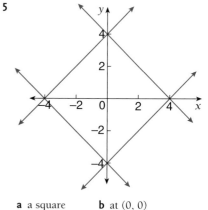

 a a square **b** at $(0, 0)$
 b right-angled
 c i 4 units **ii** 3 units
7 a 10 **b** 13 **c** $\sqrt{32}$ **d** $\sqrt{41}$
 e $\sqrt{50}$ **f** $\sqrt{61}$
8 a 4 units **b** 3 units **c** 6 units^2
9 a 10 units^2 **b** 10·5 units^2
 c 12 units^2 **d** 4·5 units^2

6 a

Fun Spot 8:02

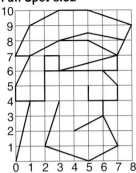

Prep Quiz 8:03

1 $(-2, 1)$ **2** $(1, 2)$ **3** $(-1, -2)$ **4** $(2, -1)$ **5** 12 **6** 7 **7** -2 **8** -1 **9** -3 **10** $y = 5$

Exercise 8:03

1 a $x + y = 4$

x	0	1	2	3	4
y	4	3	2	1	0

b $y = 2x$

x	0	1	2	3	4
y	0	2	4	6	8

c $y = 3x - 2$

x	0	1	2	3	4
y	-2	1	4	7	10

d $y = 10x + 36$

x	0	1	2	3	4
y	36	46	56	66	76

e $y = 8 - x$

x	0	1	2	3	4
y	8	7	6	5	4

f $2x + y = 16$

x	0	1	2	3	4
y	16	14	12	10	8

2 a true **b** false **c** true **d** true **e** true **f** false **g** true **h** true **i** false
3 a $y = 3x$ **b** $y = x + 2$ **c** $y = x - 5$ **d** $y = 8 - x$ or $y = -x + 8$ **e** $y = 10x + 1$ **f** $y = 4x + 8$

Exercise 8:04

1 a $y = x + 3$

x	-1	0	1	2
y	2	3	4	5

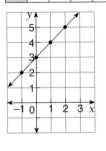

b $y = x - 1$

x	-1	0	1	2
y	-2	-1	0	1

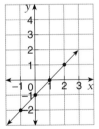

c $y = \frac{1}{2}x$

x	-2	0	2	4
y	-1	0	1	2

d $y = -x$

x	-1	0	1	2
y	1	0	-1	-2

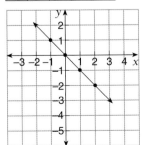

e $y = 5 - x$

x	-1	0	1	2
y	6	5	4	3

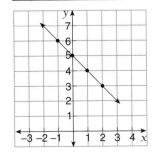

f $y = 4 - 2x$

x	-1	0	1	2
y	6	4	2	0

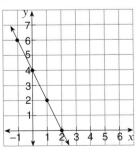

2 a 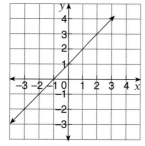 **b** 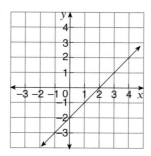 **c**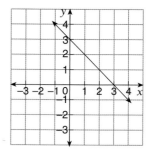

d 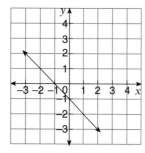 **e** 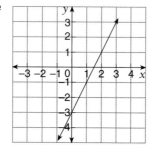 **f**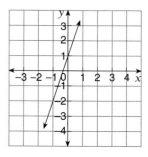

g 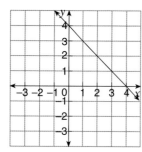 **h**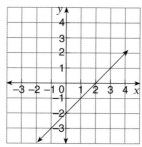

3 a $y = x + 1$

x	−1	0	1	2
y	0	1	2	3

b $y = 2 − x$

x	−1	0	1	2
y	3	2	1	0

c $y = 2x$

x	−1	0	1	2
y	−2	0	2	4

d $y = x$

x	−1	0	1	2
y	−1	0	1	2

e $y = 3x − 1$

x	−1	0	1	2
y	−4	−1	2	5

f $y = -\frac{1}{2}x$

x	−1	0	1	2
y	$\frac{1}{2}$	0	$-\frac{1}{2}$	−1

4 a no **b** no **c** yes **d** no **e** yes **f** no **g** no **h** no **i** no **j** no
 k yes **l** no
5 a C **b** B **c** A **d** D

Exercise 8:05
1 a $x = 1$ **b** $y = −1$ **c** $x = −2$ **d** $y = 1\frac{1}{2}$
2 a A: $y = 3$, B: $y = 1$, C: $x = 3$, D: $y = −4$, E: $x = −1$, F: $x = −4$
 b A: $x = 2$, B: $x = 4$, C: $y = 4$, D: $y = 2$, E: $y = −2$, F: $x = −3$
3 a $x = 0$ **b** $y = 0$

4 a

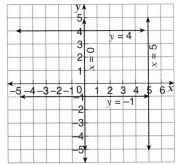

b

c

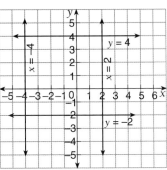

d

e

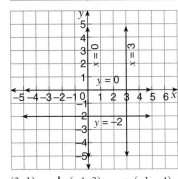

The lines in **a** and **c** enclose a square region.

5 a (3, 1)　　b (−4, 3)　　c (−1, −4)　　d (2, −2)　　e (−3, 2)　　f (4, 4)　　g (0, 3)　　h (2, 0)　　i (0, 0)

Fun Spot 8:06

Because corn has ears and beans talk

Exercise 8:06

1 a (3, 2)　　b (3, 2)　　c (−1, 2)　　d (3, −3)　　e (−2, −3)　　f (1, 0)　　g (0, 1)　　h (−2, −3)
　i (1, 0)　　j (3, 2)

2 a (−1, 1)　　b (2, 3)　　c (−3, −3)　　d (−4, −3)　　e (0, 0)　　f (2, 0)　　g (2, 3)　　h (2, 2)

3 a

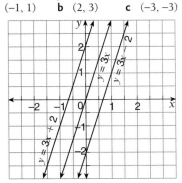

Parallel lines. *y*-values increase as *x* gets bigger.

b

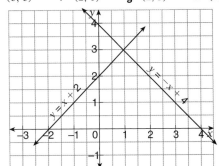

Perpendicular lines

c

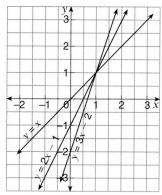

These lines are concurrent.
They all pass through the same point, (1, 1).

d

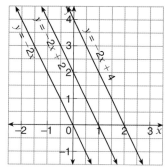

Parallel lines.
Values of y decrease as x gets larger.

4 $y = x^2$

x	-3	-2	-1	0	1	2	3
y	9	4	1	0	1	4	9

5 $y = x^3$

x	-2	$-1\frac{1}{2}$	-1	$-\frac{1}{2}$	0	$\frac{1}{2}$	1	$1\frac{1}{2}$	2
y	-8	$-3\frac{3}{8}$	-1	$-\frac{1}{8}$	0	$\frac{1}{8}$	1	$3\frac{3}{8}$	8

6 $y = \frac{1}{x}$

x	-4	-3	-2	-1	$-\frac{1}{2}$	$-\frac{1}{4}$	0	$\frac{1}{4}$	$\frac{1}{2}$	1	2	3	4
y	$-\frac{1}{4}$	$-\frac{1}{3}$	$-\frac{1}{2}$	-1	-2	-4	$-$	4	2	1	$\frac{1}{2}$	$\frac{1}{3}$	$\frac{1}{4}$

Investigation 8:06

1 a The red lines are parallel. They have the same gradient. (This is equal to 2 as they go up 2 for every 1 across.)
  b The red equations all have 2 as the coefficient of x in the equation.
2 a The blue lines are parallel. They have the same gradient. (This is equal to $-\frac{1}{2}$ as they drop 1 for every 2 across.)
  b The blue equations all have $-\frac{1}{2}$ as the coefficient of x in the equation.
3 a $y = 2x$, $y = 1x$ and $y = -\frac{1}{2}x$ are the lines that intersect at the origin.
  b These equations are alike in that none of them has a constant term
     (or the constant has value 0).
4 a The lines parallel to $y = -\frac{1}{2}x + 4$ are $y = -\frac{1}{2}x + 1$, $y = -\frac{1}{2}x$,
     $y = -\frac{1}{2}x - 1$ and $y = -\frac{1}{2}x - 3$.
  b The lines parallel to $y = 2x + 1$ are $y = 2x + 4$, $y = 2x$ and $y = 2x - 4$.

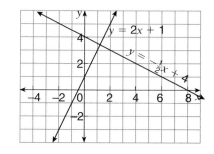

5 a Lines with a negative *x* term decrease as *x* increases in value. They slope down.
  b All lines with a positive *x* term increase as *x* increases in value. They slope up.
  c The constant *b* in the equation determines the *y*-intercept (0, *b*). It shows where the line crosses the *y*-axis.

Diagnostic Test 8: The Number Plane

1 a (3, 1)   **b** (−1, 1)   **c** (−1, −3)   **d** (0, −2)   **2 a** A   **b** C   **c** E   **d** H
3 a 2nd   **b** 4th   **c** 1st   **d** 3rd   **4 a** 2 units   **b** 4 units   **c** 4 units   **d** 6 units
5 a $y = 2$ **b** $x = -2$
6 a rectangle   **b** square   **c** parallelogram   **d** trapezium

7 a

x	−1	0	1	2
y	1	2	3	4

b

x	−1	0	1	2
y	5	4	3	2

c

x	1	2	3	4
y	−1	1	3	5

8 a 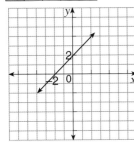   **b** 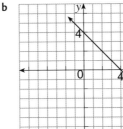   **c**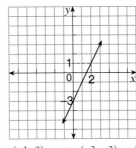

9 a $y = x + 4$ **b** $x + y = 5$ **c** $y = \frac{1}{2}x$ **10 a** (−4, 3)   **b** (−1, 0)   **c** (−2, −2)   **d** (0, −1)

8A Revision Assignment

1 6.4 m   **2 a** $2584   **b** $19.20   **3 a** 30°, 60°, 90°   **b** 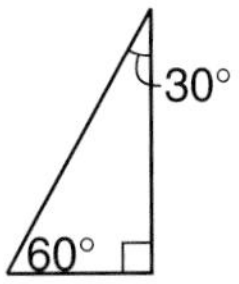
4 $\frac{103}{108}$ **5 a** $6a + 5b$ **b** $24x^2$ **c** $42 - 24b$ **d** $-18x$
6 a 5   **b** 1   **c** 9   **d** 5   **7 a** 11·25 cm   **b** 8 cm
8 a 25%   **b** 20·83%   **c** 25 ha
9 a 90%, 88%   **b** 80%, 60%   **c** 24%, 24%   **d** The students tended to perform as well in
    Maths as in English, especially in terms of their position in class. A person poor
    in Maths tended to be poor in English.
10 a divided bar graph   **b** 43%   **c** 6 teachers

8B Working Mathematically

1 a *obtuse* angle   **b** *reflex* angle   **c** *revolution*   **d** *adjacent* angles
  e *supplementary* angles   **f** *vertically opposite* angles   **g** 360°
2 437·5 mm   **3** 32   **4** 8   **5** 6 m   **6** 28

Chapter 9:   Graphs and tables

Exercise 9:01

1 a A divided bar graph is a graph where a bar is divided into parts to show the relative sizes of the categories.
  b A sector graph is a circle divided into sectors that show the relative size of the categories.
  c A line graph is drawn by joining a number of points in order and shows the relationship between two things,
    such as time and mass.
  d A conversion graph is a straight line graph showing the relationship between two types of measurements, allowing
    us to convert from one to another.
  e A step graph is a graph made up of several horizontal steps or intervals.
  f A discontinuous graph has gaps in the graph.
2 a line graph **b** pie graph **c** travel graph, conversion graph, step graph, etc.
3 a Religion in Liberia (Ivory Coast)   **b** 455 000   **c** 14%   **d** 0·7 cm
4 a R.O. Plants Production   **b** No. The amount of water is not given, only the percentages.
  c 59·76°. Yes, as accurate as can be expected.   **d** 95·04°
5 a 5900 g   **b** 2 weeks   **c** 5th   **d** over 6000 g, perhaps 6200 g
6 a 5 miles   **b** 8 km   **c i** 12 km   **ii** 3 km   **iii** 9 km   **d i** 1 mile   **ii** 3 miles   **iii** 7 miles
  e 16 km
7 a hours
  b First you would assess the longest time that you might stay in the parking spot, then work out the cost for this
    period of time and finally use the parking meters to pay this amount.
  c i €1.80   **ii** €5.40   **iii** €7.20   **d i** 1 hour   **ii** 4 hours   **iii** 2 hours

Exercise 9:02A

1 a 50 t   **b** 25 t   **c** 150 t   **d** 75 t   **2 a** C   **b** C   **c** B   **d** A

3

Climbing the Eiffel Tower

4 a A   **b** C   **c** B

5 a sector graph   **b** $\frac{1}{4}$

   c 150   **d** 270°

6 a 11%   **b** 38%   **c** 11%   **d** South Korea

7 a i 21%   **ii** 16%   **iii** 12%   **iv** 8%   **v** 35%   **vi** 3%   **b** airports, motels, sporting events etc.
   c 43%   **d** $\frac{1}{4}$ **e** Sunday   **f** Clever way to show sector graphs, reminding reader of cars.
   g i 18   **ii** 12   **iii** 2   **iv** 8   **v** 12   **vi** 18   **h** no

8 a 32°F   **b** 212°F   **c** 77°F   **d** 122°F   **e** 59°F   **f** 230°F   **g** 0°C   **h** 80°C
   i 71°C   **j** 40°C   **k** −9°C   **l** −18°C

9 Answers are given correct to 2 sig. figs. in **a** to **h** and 1 sig. fig. in **i** to **p**.
   a Rs900   **b** Rs450   **c** Rs270   **d** Rs590   **e** Rs2700   **f** Rs590
   g Rs27 000   **h** 68 000   **i** $2   **j** $8   **k** $10   **l** $1
   m $7   **n** $20   **o** $30   **p** $300

10 a i €6   **ii** €6   **b** 3 hours   **c** €32

11 a April, KRW12 000 000   **b** March   **c** loss of KRW11 000 000
   d Word spread that his Korean food was delicious.   **e** February   **f** $20 000

12 a i 96 mm   **ii** 48 mm   **iii** 45 mm   **b** 1   **c** 16 times   **d** 16
   e 15 times   **f i** 50%   **ii** $3\frac{1}{8}$%   **iii** $46\frac{7}{8}$%

13 a sector graph   **b** expansion   **c** 109°   **d** $21\frac{17}{18}$% or 21·94%

14 a $17   **b** $9   **c** $24   **d** 5 kg   **e** 30 kg   **f** 40 kg   **g** $37.20

15 a line graphs   **b** 2%   **c** 80%   **d** 18%
   e unskilled, 65%; mid-level, 29%; professional, 6%   **f** unskilled, 20%; mid-level, 62%; professional, 18%
   g No. You would not expect the lines joining the points for 1900 and 1980 to be perfectly straight.
   h 0%, no.   **i** Yes; at schools, colleges of advanced education, and universities, to name a few.

16 a There are gaps because you can only purchase a whole number of T-shirts, ie 4 shirts or 5 shirts but not $4\frac{1}{2}$ shirts. (Strictly speaking, each of the intervals should be a series of dots, for the same reason. Intervals are used here because in each interval the rate is constant.)   **b** No
   c The graph should be made up of a series of discrete points, each point corresponding to an integral value on the horizontal axis.
   d An advantage is that it is easier to see the trends in the graph because the solid line gives a better indication than a series of points.   **e i** 4   **ii** 12   **iii** 28

Exercise 9:02B

1 a 9:01 am   **b** 2 cm   **c** 9:03 am   **d** 6 cm   **e** 9:04 am
   f It would drop. The line would begin to drop.

2 a 20 cm   **b** 28 cm   **c** 3 min   **d** Because the barrel is full and running over.
   e after 10 minutes   **f** 40 cm

3 a column graph   **b** June/July   **c** 32   **d** 16   **e** 38, August/September
   f Some workers may have been on holidays.   **g** 133

4 a 5 pm, 5   **b** 30 min   **c** 11   **d** 6 pm, 15   **e** 9 pm, 5   **f** 1 am   **g** answers vary

5 a 1980/81   **b i** 450 million tonnes   **ii** 500 million tonnes   **iii** 600 million tonnes   **iv** 700 million tonnes
   c 1986/87, US$112

6 a divided bar graph   **b** coal   **c** 37%   **d** 18%
   e coal, oil, gas, water   **f** No; other forms of energy have been developed, eg solar.
   g solar and nuclear

7 a 100 cm   **b** 70 cm   **c** 10 cm   **d** 90 cm   **e** about 65 cm   **f** about 44 cm

8 a 96   **b** 124   **c** 3   **d** 5   **e** 8   **f** 284   **g** 278
   h W Indies   **i** equal   **j** 0 runs   **k** 43rd   **l** 47th

Exercise 9:03

1 a divided bar graph   **b** The picture catches our interest and tells us that coffee is involved.
   c 6·4%   **d** 19·6%   **e** Exports of coffee from the Philippines

2 a $24   **b** 3 hours   **c** $48   **d** $12   **e** It looks like steps.

3 a i 4 years old   **ii** 12 years old   **b** line graph   **c i** 90°   **ii** 15°   **d** 10°C, 22°C
   e i 18°C   **ii** 13°C   **iii** 20°C   **f** 8 am, 10 pm   **g** 13°C, 21°C

4 a line graph **b** number   **c** no   **d** It's meant to create an impression.   **e** #100   **f** about #45
5 a You can see what the figures mean.   **b** A horizontal column graph in which the time taken is the length of each column and the left-hand side of the graph has been cut off.
  c Jim Hines   **d** 0·09 seconds   **e** 6   **f** 0·46 s   **g** 0·02 s   **h** Research
6 a i 0–4 years   **ii** 15–64 years   **b i** 1200   **ii** 2700   **iii** 10 300   **iv** 1700
  c 15 900   **d** 65 and over. Females tend to live longer than males.
7 a a sector graph   **b** yes   **c** yes   **d** 15%   **e** 15%
  f 0%   **g** 42%   **h** 15%

Exercise 9:04

1 a

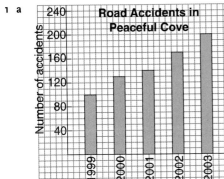

b

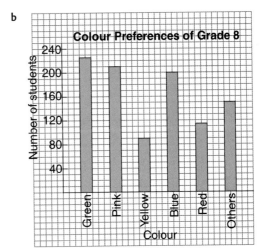

2 a

Favourite Pet

b

Subject Choice of Grade 8 Students

| Music | Art | Computing |

— Photography

3 a i 10°
  b i $\frac{1}{2}$ **ii** $\frac{1}{4}$ **iii** $\frac{1}{4}$
  c i 180°   **ii** 90°   **iii** 90°
  d

4 a Rhonda's expenses in Sydney   **b** Composition of concrete mix

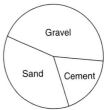

  c Method of travel to school   **d** Favourite swimming stroke

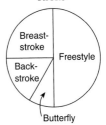

5 a

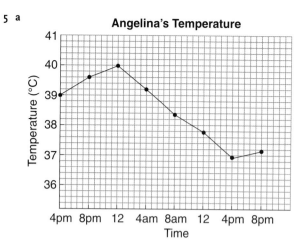

Angelina's Temperature

b

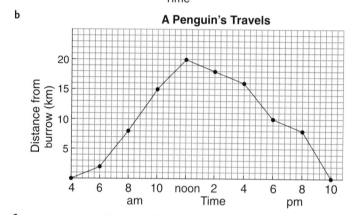

A Penguin's Travels

c

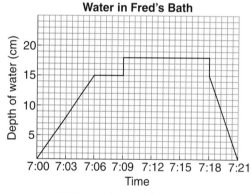

Water in Fred's Bath

6

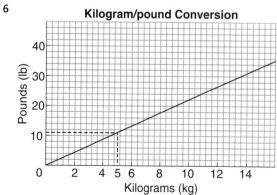

Kilogram/pound Conversion

7

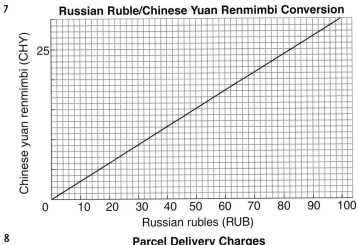

Russian Ruble/Chinese Yuan Renmimbi Conversion

8

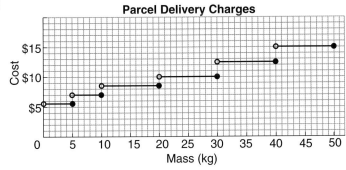

Parcel Delivery Charges

9

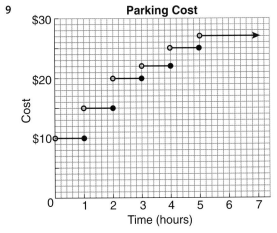

Parking Cost

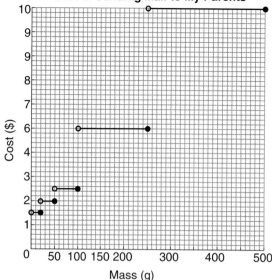

10

Cost of Sending Mail to My Parents

Exercise 9:05

1 **a** 10 km **b** 5 km **c** 5 km **d** 0 km. Luke is at home at 11 am. **e** 5 km
   f 0 km. Luke is at home. **g** 5 km **h** 7·5 km **i** Luke was resting from 9 am to 10:30 am and from
   j From 8 am to 9 am, and from 10:30 am to 11 am. 11 am to 11:30 am.
2 **a** Rajiv **b** Indu
3 **a** 5 km **b** 20 km **c** 10 km **d** 5 km **e** Between 5 am and 6 am **f** 6 am **g** 15 km
4 **a** 4 cm **b** 4 cm **c** 2 cm **d** 0 cm. The snail had returned to the starting position.
   e $1\frac{1}{2}$ minutes after starting and 5 minutes after starting.
   f The snail was 4 cm from where it started from the 2nd to the 4th minute.
   g The snail was not moving from 2 minutes after starting until 4 minutes after starting.
   h 2 cm **i** 8 cm **j** 3 cm
5 **a** 20 km, 10 km/h
   b 10 km, 5 km/h
   c 3 hours after the start.
      1 hour to fix his bicycle. 2 km/h
   d Eun Sung, 1 hour
   e $7\frac{1}{2}$ hours

6
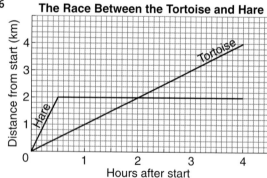

a 1 km/h. The tortoise passed the hare after 2 hours.
b i 4 km/h **ii** 0·5 km/h

Exercise 9:06

1 Religion: categorical; Amount of water used: continuous, quantitative; Mass: continuous quantitative;
   Time: continuous quantitative; Distance: continuous quantitative; Cost: discrete quantitative;
   Test mark: discrete quantitative; Country of birth: categorical; Number of shirts made: discrete quantitative;
   Depth of water: continuous quantitative.
2 **a** 6 to 6:29 pm **b** Earlier; it may be colder temperature that causes this.
   c Retired people, they don't have to come home from work first. Older people have more routine.
   d 2% **e** 73% **f** 47%
   g One effect would be to reduce conversation in the home. This would harm relationships.
   h Overall, students. **i** Answers here will vary. **j** categorical
3 **a i** 93°C **ii** 72°C **iii** 23°C **iv** 2°C **b i** 32°F **ii** 212°F **iii** 99°F **iv** 72°F
   c i quantitative **ii** continuous

4 a runs **b** R T Ponting **c** Answers will vary but many consider Garfield Sobers to be a better batsman than the ten listed in the table because he has a higher average.

d 35% (Include his 100s as well.) **e** R T Ponting, S R Tendulkar, B C Lara. **f** 23 174 **e** 27 500

5 a Rounded **b** 42 400 **c** Alajuela and Heredia. **d** San Jose. It is the capital.
f The data is quantitative and discrete.

6 a St Louis Cardinals, Chicago Cubs, Cincinatti Reds and Pittsburgh Pirates **b** St Louis Cardinals
c 1900 **d** Houston Astros **e** Chicago Cubs **f** 29 years
g 10; not played because of Word Wars I and II

7 a 2617 km **b** €39.50 **c** i 2300 km **ii** 969 km **iii** 1562 km **iv** 354 km
d €30.50 **e** €35.50 **f** €27.00 **g** €42.00

8 a i 39.7% **ii** 30.1% **iii** 38.3% **iv** 87·5% **b** i Filipino **ii** Filipino **iii** East Indian **iv** Lebanon
c i Manitoba **ii** Quebec **iii** Nova Scotia **iv** Prince Edward Is **v** Quebec **vi** Prince Edward Is
vii Quebec **viii** Ontario
d People from other Asian countries.

Exercise 9:07

1 a 2 times **b** 4 times **c** 8 times **2 a** $\frac{2}{3}$ **b** $\frac{2}{3}$ **c** Yes
d 3 times **e** 9 times **f** 27 times **d**
g

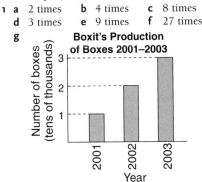

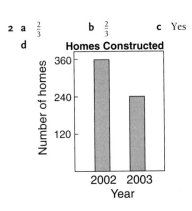

3 a $5 **b** yes **c** yes, 6 kg **d** They have different scales on at least one axis.
4 a 100 **b** 0 **c** 1 person **d** 5 people **e** graph A **f** yes
5 a July, Sept., Oct., Nov. are left off the horizontal axis and space is not left for them.
b The vertical axis is broken between 40 and 300. **c** Angles are wrong at the centre.
d The vehicle symbols are not the same size. **e** The vertical axis does not begin at zero.
f Solid objects (volume) are used when only the heights should be compared.
6 a Most people who answer the telephones would own them. The telephone should not have been used if a random sample was to be used.
b This is not a random sample either. Those coming out of Zac's Discount are more likely to be using Zac's Toothpaste.
c Not enough people were interviewed to get an idea of community trends.
d Not enough types of answers were allowed or the question was misleading.

Fun Spot 9:07

Lady	Husband	Town	Hair
Izabel	Maureo	Campinas	Red
Morela	Justino	Rio de Janeiro	Black
Yelena	Humberto	Brasilia	Grey
Mirari	Duarte	Recife	Blonde
Aitana	Mateus	Belo Horizonte	Brown
Fia	Ramiro	Sao Paulo	White

Diagnostic Test 9: Graphs and Tables

1

Eastern US Stock of Adult and Juvenile Steller Sea Lions

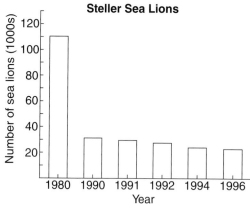

2

Choice of Breakfast Cereal

Vita Brits	Corn Flakes	Weet Bix

3

Choice of Flavours

4

Temperature over 24 Hours

5

Centimetres/Inches Conversion Graph

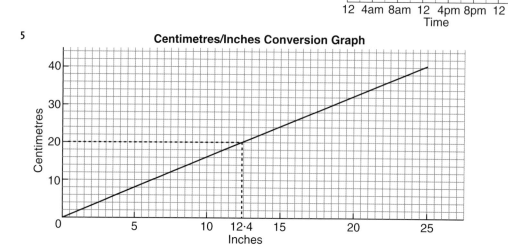

6

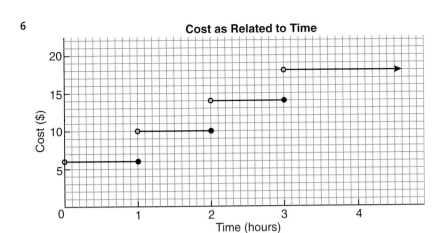

Cost as Related to Time

7

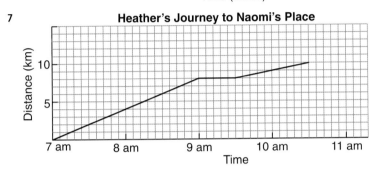

Heather's Journey to Naomi's Place

9A Revision Assignment

1

```
+--+--+--+--●--+--●--+--●--+--+--+
0     1     2     3     4     5     6     7
```

2 a 123   **b** 44   **c** 1609   **d** 1988

3 a 94   **b** 0   **c** −2   **d** 5   **e** 72 185

4 a $1\frac{6}{10}$ or $1\frac{3}{5}$ **b** $\frac{31}{40}$ **c** $\frac{13}{20}$ **d** $\frac{9}{20}$ **e** $\frac{17}{200}$ **f** $1\frac{1}{2}$ **g** $1\frac{1}{5}$ **h** $\frac{3}{20}$

5 a 23·05   **b** 6·85   **c** 0·415   **d** 0·65   **e** 1·5   **f** 1·0325   **g** 230   **h** 0·0025   **i** 0·67

6 a 75%   **b** 140%   **c** 14·5%   **d** 205%

7 a $3440   **b** 104 km   **c** $1680   **d** $1596   **e** $650

8 a 6·3   **b** 5·3

9 a 11x   **b** a   **c** $8x^2$ **d** 5m   **e** 40y   **f** 10b   **g** 4a   **h** 14ab

i $\frac{2x}{5}$ **j** $\frac{13m}{20}$ **k** $\frac{2xy}{35}$ **l** $\frac{5}{4}$ **10 a i** $\frac{1}{20}$ **ii** $\frac{1}{25}$ **iii** $\frac{1}{100}$ **b** $\frac{17}{20}$

c i m = 128, corresponding angles and parallel lines   **ii** x = 60, angle sum of a triangle
iii y = 135, exterior angle of a triangle

9B Working Mathematically

1 31

2 a B   **b** G   **c** J

3 ($1, $1, $1, 20c, 10c, 10c) or ($1, $1, 50c, 50c, 20c, 20c) or ($2, $1, 20c, 10c, 5c, 5c) or ($2, 50c, 50c, 20c, 10c, 10c)

4 a 11   **b** 7   **c** (70 × 3) + 2 = 212   **d** 302   **5** 4 horses

6 a regular hexagon   **b** kite   **c** isosceles triangle   **d** equilateral triangle
e square pyramid   **f** rectangular pyramid   **g** triangular pyramid   **h** cylinder
i cone   **j** sphere

Chapter 10: Reasoning in geometry

ID 10:01

See answers for ID Card 6 on page 497.

Prep Quiz 10:01

1 90°   **2** m = 60   **3** x = 48   **4** 180°   **5** a = 130   **6** b = 45
7 They add up to 180°.   **8** They add up to 180°.   **9** They add up to 90°.
10 They add up to 90°.

Exercise 10:01

1 **a** $x = 35$ **b** $a = 50$ **c** $x = 45$ **d** $x = 15$ **e** $x = 25$ **f** $a = 40$ **g** $a = 130$ **h** $y = 120$
i $p = 125$ **j** $a = 55$ **k** $a = 80$ **l** $a = 20$

2 All are adjacent complementary angles. **a** $x = 70$ **b** $a = 80$ **c** $b = 40$ **d** $e = 40$ **e** $\alpha = 68°$
f $\beta = 65°$ **g** $x = 67$ **h** $a = 18$ **i** $x = 65$ **j** $x = 56$ **k** $b = 25$ **l** $a = 28$ **m** $x = 65$
n $x = 30$

3 All are adjacent supplementary angles. **a** $a = 60$ **b** $b = 155$ **c** $x = 150$ **d** $y = 110$ **e** $e = 52$
f $p = 135$ **g** $x = 75$ **h** $c = 20$ **i** $a = 50$ **j** $\alpha = 15°$ **k** $m = 50$ **l** $x = 48$ **m** $p = 120$
n $x = 125$

4 **a** $\alpha + 30° = 90°$ **b** $2\beta + 80° = 180°$ **c** $4\alpha + 2\alpha = 180°$
  $\alpha = 60°$ $\beta = 50°$ $6\alpha = 180°$
          $\alpha = 30°$

 d $\alpha + \alpha + 20° = 90°$ **e** $\alpha + 100° + \alpha = 180°$ **f** $3\beta + 75° = 90°$
  $2\alpha = 70°$ $2\alpha = 80°$ $3\beta = 15°$
  $\alpha = 35°$ $\alpha = 40°$ $\beta = 5°$

Exercise 10:02

1 All are angles at a point. **a** $x = 100$ **b** $a = 30$ **c** $y = 70$ **d** $x = 80$
2 All are vertically opposite angles. **a** $a = 130$ **b** $b = 25$ **c** $c = 100$ **d** $a = 70$
 e $x = 135$ **f** $y = 85$

3 **a** $4\alpha + 40° + 70° + 90° = 360°$ **b** $b + b + 160 + 100 = 360$ **c** $a = 70$
  (angles at a point)   (angles at a point)   (vert. opp. $\angle$s)
  $4\alpha = 160°$ $2b = 100$ $a + b + 30 = 180$
  $\alpha = 40°$ $b = 50$ (adj. supp. $\angle$s)
          $70 + b + 30 = 180$
          $b = 80$

 d $a = 60$ **e** $x = 260$ **f** $\beta = 45°$ **g** $2a = 100$
  (vert. opp. $\angle$s) (angles at a point) (vert. opp. $\angle$s) (vert. opp. $\angle$s)
  $c + 60 = 180$ $a = 50$
  (adj. supp. $\angle$s)
  $c = 120$
  $b + 60 + 90 = 180$
  (adj. supp. $\angle$s)
  $b = 30$

 h $b = 155$ **i** $m = 120$ **j** $a + 50 = 30 + 40$ **k** $a = 115$
  (vert. opp. $\angle$s) (adj. supp. $\angle$s) (vert. opp. $\angle$s) (vert. opp. $\angle$s)
  $a = 25$ $120 + p + 28 = 180$ $a = 20$ $b = 65$
  (adj. supp. $\angle$s) (adj. supp. $\angle$s)   (adj. supp. $\angle$s)
    $p = 32$

4 **a** $b = 45$ **b** $\alpha = 100°$ **c** $6\alpha = 360°$
  (vert. opp. $\angle$s) (vert. opp. $\angle$s) (angles at a point)
  $a = 135$ $\beta = 80°$ $\alpha = 60°$
  (adj. supp. $\angle$s) (adj. supp. $\angle$s)
 d $\alpha + 70° + 40° = 180°$ **e** $\alpha + 70° = 90°$ **f** $\alpha + 70° = 180°$
  (adj. supp. $\angle$s) (adj. comp. $\angle$s) (adj. supp. $\angle$s)
  $\alpha = 70°$ $\alpha = 20°$ $\alpha = 110°$
    $\beta + 60° = 90°$ $\beta + 20° = 90°$
    (adj. comp. $\angle$s) (adj. comp. $\angle$s)
    $\beta = 30°$ $\beta = 70°$

Exercise 10:03

1 **a**
b
c

2 a

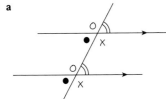

b

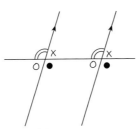

c

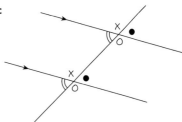

3 All reasons are: corresponding angles and parallel lines.

  a $a = 38$ **b** $b = 140$ **c** $c = 80$ **d** $d = 120$ **e** $f = 85$ **f** $a = 100, b = 110$

4 a

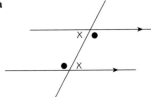

b

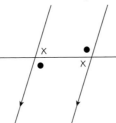

c

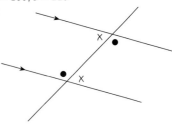

5 All reasons are: alternate angles and parallel lines.

  a $a = 30$ **b** $e = 140$ **c** $c = 80$ **d** $f = 132$ **e** $a = 83, b = 42$ **f** $x = 65, y = 72$

6 a

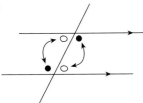

b

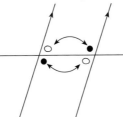

c

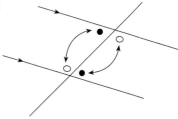

The pairs are shown by arrows.

7 All answers are: cointerior angles and parallel lines.

  a $a = 120$ **b** $b = 60$ **c** $c = 145$ **d** $x = 50, y = 92$ **e** $a = 98, b = 115$

8 a $a = 42$ (altern. angles, // lines)   **b** $b = 138$ (coint. angles, // lines)   **c** $c = 135$ (corresp. angles, // lines)

  d $d = 105$ (corresp. angles, // lines)   **e** $e = 68$ (altern. angles, // lines)   **f** $f = 122$ (coint. angles, // lines)

  g $a = 55$ (corresp. angles, // lines)   **h** $b = 70$ (coint. angles, // lines)   **i** $a = 30$ (altern. angles, // lines)

9 a $a = 145$ (coint. angles, // lines), $b = 35$ (altern. angles, // lines)

  b $\alpha = 125°$ (corresp. angles, // lines), $\beta = 125°$ (vert. opp. angles)

  c $a = 50$ (coint. angles, // lines, $b = 50$ (coint. angles, // lines)

  d $m = 60$ (altern. angles, // lines), $n = 120$ (coint. angles, // lines)

  e $a = 120$ (opp. angles of a parallelogram equal), $b = 60$ (coint. angles, // lines), $d = 60$ (coint. angles, // lines)

10 a Alternate angles are equal.   **b** Corresponding angles are equal.   **c** Cointerior angles are supplementary.

  d Alternate angles are equal.   **e** Cointerior angles are supplementary.

Exercise 10:04

1 a $a = 110$ ($\angle$ sum of a triangle)   **b** $b = 50$ ($\angle$ sum of Δ)   **c** $c = 60$ ($\angle$ sum of Δ)

  d $x = 90$ ($\angle$ sum of Δ)   **e** $y = 101$ ($\angle$ sum of Δ)   **f** $x = 40$ ($\angle$ sum of Δ)

  g $g = 94$ (exterior $\angle$ of Δ)   **h** $h = 116$ (exterior $\angle$ of Δ)   **i** $i = 150$ (exterior $\angle$ of Δ)

2 a $2a + 60 + 50 = 180$ **b** $2\alpha + 2\alpha + 90° = 180°$ **c** $3a + 2a + 4a = 180$

$$2a = 70$$
$$a = 35$$

$$3\alpha = 90°$$
$$\alpha = 30°$$

$$9a = 180$$
$$a = 20$$

  d $d + 51 = 103$ **e** $40 + 2e = 120$ **f** $2f + f = 130$

$$d = 52$$

$$2e = 80$$
$$e = 40$$

$$3f = 130$$
$$f = 43\tfrac{1}{3}$$

3 a $a = 80$ ($\angle$ sum of ΔLMN)   **b** $a = 70$ ($\angle$ sum of ΔADE)   **c** $a = 43$ ($\angle$ sum of ΔLMZ)

4 a $a = 84; b = 67$ **b** $a = 67$ **c** $a = 40; b = 40$

5 a $x + 50 + 105 = 180$ **b** $x = 36$ **c** $x = 40$

($\angle$ sum of ΔABC)

$$x = 25$$
$$25 + 92 + y = 180$$

(vert. opp. $\angle$s)
$$y + 36 + 90 = 180$$

($\angle$ sum of ΔABD)
$$40 + y = 90$$

($\angle$ sum of ΔEDC)

($\angle$ sum of ΔPNR)

(comp. $\angle$s)

$$y = 63$$

$$y = 54$$

$$y = 50$$

6 a $c = 50$ ($\angle$ sum of $\triangle ADE$); $a = 70$ (corresp. $\angle$s, // lines); $b = 60$ (corresp. $\angle$s, // lines)
  b $b = 50$ (vert. opp. $\angle$s); $a = 66$ ($\angle$ sum of $\triangle ABC$); $c = 60$ ($\angle$ sum of $\triangle CDE$)
  c $a = 95$ (vert. opp. $\angle$s); $b = 33$ (alt. $\angle$s, // lines); $c = 52$ ($\angle$ sum of $\triangle ABT$)

Exercise 10:05

1 The reason for all is: angle sum of a quadrilateral.
  a $a = 50$ **b** $b = 120$ **c** $c = 32$ **d** $g = 275$ **e** $x = 123$

2 a $5x + 84 + 85 + 116 = 360$ **b** $2x + 67 + 78 + 105 = 360$ **c** $3\alpha + 140° + \alpha + 28° = 360°$
            $5x + 285 = 360$ $2x + 250 = 360$ $4\alpha + 168° = 360°$
                   $5x = 75$ $2x = 110$ $4\alpha = 192°$
                      $x = 15$ $x = 55$ $\alpha = 48°$

  d $3\beta + 50° + \beta + 40° = 360°$
            $4\beta + 90° = 360°$
                $4\beta = 270°$
                $\beta = 67\frac{1}{2}°$

3 a $x = 75$; $y = 87$ **b** $x = 70$; $y = 20$ **c** $x = 142$; $y = 38$

4 a $x = 230$ (angles at a point); $y = 70$ ($\angle$ sum of quad.)   **b** $x = 102$ (adj. supp. $\angle$s); $y = 75$ ($\angle$ sum of quad.)
  c $x = 55$ ($\angle$ sum of $\triangle$); $y = 74$ ($\angle$ sum of quad.)   **d** $x = 75$ ($\angle$ sum of quad.); $y = 45$ ($\angle$ sum of $\triangle$)
  e $x = 120$ (coint. $\angle$s, // lines); $y = 70$ ($\angle$ sum of quad. $ABCE$)

Prep Quiz 10:06

1 all of them   **2** $\triangle XYZ$ **3** $\angle CAB$ and $\angle CBA$ **4** DE and EF **5** two angles equal
6 two sides equal   **7** equal   **8** all equal   **9** all equal   **10** $60°$

Exercise 10:06

1 a $b = 33$ (base $\angle$s of isos. $\triangle$)   **b** $c = 28$ (base $\angle$s of isos. $\triangle$)
  c $y = 5·8$ (equal sides of isos. $\triangle$)   **d** $x = 120$ ($\angle$ sum of $\triangle$); $y = 4$ (equal sides of isos. $\triangle$)
  e $x = 5$ (equal sides of isos. $\triangle$); $a = 45$ ($\angle$ sum of $\triangle$)   **f** $a = 7$ (equal sides of isos. $\triangle$); $b = 30$ ($\angle$ sum of $\triangle$)
  g $a = 60$ (equilateral $\triangle$)   **h** $x = 60$ (equilateral $\triangle$)
  i $y = 20$; $z = 20$ (equilateral $\triangle$)

2 a $a = 70$ (base $\angle$s of isos. $\triangle$); $b = 40$ ($\angle$ sum of $\triangle$)   **b** $a = 25$ (base $\angle$s of isos. $\triangle$); $b = 130$ ($\angle$ sum of $\triangle$)
  c $a = 50$ (base $\angle$s of isos. $\triangle$); $b = 80$ ($\angle$ sum of $\triangle$)

3 a $a = 60$ (angle of equil. $\triangle$); $b = 120$ (adj. supp. $\angle$s)
  b $a = 60$ (angle of equil. $\triangle$); $b + 40 = 60$ (angle of equil. $\triangle$), $\therefore b = 20$
  c $a = 58$ (adj. supp. $\angle$s); $b = 58$ (equal $\angle$s of isos. $\triangle$)   **d** $a = 20$ (equal $\angle$s of isos. $\triangle$); $b = 140$ ($\angle$ sum of $\triangle$)
  e $a = 65$ (equal $\angle$s of isos. $\triangle$); $b = 25$ ($\angle$ sum of $\triangle ABD$)   **f** $a = 33$ (alt. $\angle$s, // lines); $b = 33$ (equal $\angle$s of isos. $\triangle$)

Exercise 10:07

1 a $\angle EBC = 85°$ (adj. supp. $\angle$s)   **b** $\angle ACB + 48° + 44° = 180°$ ($\angle$ sum of $\triangle$)
       $\angle ECB = 45°$ (adj. supp. $\angle$s) $\angle ACB = 88°$
       $\therefore a = 50$ (angle sum of $\triangle$) $y = 88$ (vert. opp. $\angle$s)
  c $\angle AED = 95°$ (corresp. $\angle$s, // lines)   **d** $\angle ECD = 140°$ (coint. $\angle$s, // lines)
       $\therefore a + 95 + 30 = 180$ ($\angle$ sum of $\triangle AED$) $\therefore a + 140 + 25 = 180$ ($\angle$ sum of $\triangle$)
               $\therefore a = 55$ $\therefore a = 15$
  e $\angle FEC = 130°$ (vert. opp. $\angle$s)   **f** $\angle ADY = 140°$ (corresp. $\angle$s, // lines)
       $\therefore a + 130 = 180°$ (coint. $\angle$s, // lines) $\therefore y + 140 = 180$ (adj. supp. $\angle$s)
           $\therefore a = 50$ $\therefore y = 40$
  g $\angle DBC = 79°$ (corresp. $\angle$s, // lines)   **h** $\angle ABC = 95°$ ($\angle$s at a point)
       $\therefore x + 58 + 79 = 180$ ($\angle$ sum of $\triangle$) $\therefore x + 115 + 95 + 95 = 360$ ($\angle$ sum of a quad.)
           $\therefore x = 43$ $\therefore x = 55$
  i $\angle ABC = 78°$ (alt. $\angle$s, // lines)
       $\therefore y = 78$ (equal $\angle$s of isos. $\triangle$)

2 a $\angle ACB = 70°$ (equal $\angle$s of isos. $\triangle$)   **b** $\angle ABC = a°$ (equal $\angle$s of isos. $\triangle$)
       $\therefore m + 70 + 70 = 180$ ($\angle$ sum of $\triangle$) $a + a + 130 = 180$ ($\angle$ sum of $\triangle$)
           $\therefore m = 40$ $\therefore a = 25$
  c $\angle AEC + 75° + 100° + 70° = 360°$ ($\angle$ sum of quad. $ABCE$)   **d** $\angle ADC = 60°$ (angle of equil. $\triangle$)
                $\angle AEC = 115°$ $\therefore \angle CDB = 60° + 70°$ ($\angle CDB = \angle ADC + \angle ADB$)
       $\therefore a + 115 = 180$ (adj. supp. $\angle$s) $= 130°$
           $\therefore a = 65$ $\therefore m + 130 = 180$ (coint. $\angle$s, // lines)
  e $\angle DAE + 60° + 45° = 180°$ ($\angle$ sum of $\triangle ADE$)   **f** $\therefore m = 50$
           $\angle DAE = 75°$ $\angle ACD = 145°$ (coint. $\angle$s, AB // CD)
       $\therefore 50 + 75 + x = 180$ ($\angle$ sum of $\triangle ABC$) $\angle ECD = 135°$ (coint. $\angle$s, EF // CD)
           $\therefore x = 55$ $\therefore b + 145 + 135 = 360$ ($\angle$s at a point)
                                           $\therefore b = 80$

g $\angle CDB = 70°$ (coint. $\angle$s and $AB \parallel CD$)

         $\angle CED = 80°$ (adj. supp. $\angle$s)

$\therefore \angle ECD + 70° + 80° = 180°$ ($\angle$ sum of ΔECD)

            $\angle ECD = 30°$

              $\therefore m = 150$ (adj. supp. $\angle$s)

i $\angle ACD = 110°$ (coint. $\angle$s, $AB \parallel CD$)

     $\therefore 2x = 110$ ($\angle ACE + \angle ECD = \angle ACD$)

        $x = 55$

$\therefore y + 55 = 180$ (coint. $\angle$s, $CD \parallel EF$)

      $\therefore y = 125$

3 a $\angle BDC + 150° + 90° = 360°$ ($\angle$s at a pt)

          $\angle BDC = 120°$

          $\angle BCD = a°$ (equal $\angle$s of isos. Δ)

   $\therefore a + a + 120 = 180$ ($\angle$ sum of ΔBDC)

          $\therefore a = 30$

c $\angle HAC = 90°$ (coint. $\angle$s, $HA \parallel GC$)

$\therefore x + 68 = 90$ ($\angle CAD + \angle DAH = \angle CAH$)

      $\therefore x = 22$

h $\angle FEB = 60°$ (corresp. $\angle$s, $BE \parallel CD$)

         $\angle ABE = 120°$ (coint. $\angle$s, $AB \parallel FE$)

$\therefore p + 40 = 120$ ($\angle EBF + \angle FBA = \angle ABE$)

        $\therefore p = 80$

b $\angle PTS = 60°$ (coint. $\angle$s, $PX \parallel TS$)

     $\angle PTY + 55° = 180°$ (coint. $\angle$s, $AD \parallel BC$)

       $\therefore \angle PTY = 125°$

   $\therefore 125 = x + 60$ ($\angle PTY = \angle PTS + \angle STY$)

       $\therefore x = 65$

Diagnostic Test 10: Reasoning in Geometry

1 a 140   **b** 60   **c** 20

2 a $x = 30$ (adj. comp. $\angle$s)   **b** $x = 37$ (adj. comp. $\angle$s)   **c** $x = 80$ (adj. supp. $\angle$s)

3 a $x = 140$ ($\angle$s at a point)   **b** $x = 135$ (vert. opp. $\angle$s)   **c** $x = 80$ ($\angle$s at a point)

4 a $x = 55$ (alt. $\angle$s, // lines)   **b** $x = 110$ (coint. $\angle$s, // lines)   **c** $x = 130$ (corresp. $\angle$s, // lines)

5 All reasons: $\angle$ sum of a triangle.   **a** $x = 70$ **b** $x = 60$ **c** $x = 35$

6 a $a = 50$ (ext. $\angle$ of Δ)   **b** $b = 78$ (ext. $\angle$ of Δ)   **c** $c = 52$ (ext. $\angle$ of Δ)

7 All reasons: $\angle$ sum of a quad.   **a** $x = 65$ **b** $x = 95$ **c** $\alpha = 20°$

8 a $x = 35$ (equal $\angle$s of isos. Δ)   **b** $x = 7$ (equal sides of isos. Δ)   **c** $a = 60$ ($\angle$ of equil. Δ)

9 a $\angle EFB = 115°$ (corresp. $\angle$s, $AB \parallel CD$)

     $x + 115 = 180$ (adj. supp. $\angle$s)

        $\therefore x = 65$

b $\angle BCA = a°$ (equal $\angle$s of isos. Δ)

     $a + a + 110 = 180$ ($\angle$ sum of Δ)

       $\therefore a = 35$

c $\angle AFE = 40°$ (vert. opp. $\angle$s)

     $\angle CEF = 140°$ (coint. $\angle$s, $AB \parallel CD$)

$\therefore x + 100 = 140$

      $\therefore x = 40$

10A Revision Assignment

1 a $a = 70$ (equal $\angle$s of isos. Δ)

b $\angle BCA = a°$ (equal $\angle$s of isos. Δ)

     $2a + 90 = 180$ ($\angle$ sum of Δ)

       $\therefore a = 45$

c $\angle ABC = 40°$ (equal $\angle$s of isos. Δ)

    $a + 40 + 40 = 180$ ($\angle$ sum of Δ)

       $\therefore a = 100$

2 a 90°   **b** 130°   **c** It's impossible to draw a triangle where the combined length of the two smaller sides is not as long as the largest side. 3 cm + 6 cm is less than 10 cm. Once the longest side is drawn, the other sides cannot be drawn so that they meet.

3 a $x = 130$ (ext. $\angle$ of a Δ)

b $a + 30 + 100 + 28 = 180$ ($\angle$ sum of ΔLMN)

           $\therefore a = 22$

     $a + b + 28 = 180$ ($\angle$ sum of ΔMNP)

      $22 + b + 28 = 180$

          $\therefore b = 130$

4 a $6x^2$ **b** $12a^2b^2$ **c** 3   **d** $2b$ **5 a** $4(a - 4)$ **b** $a(a - 6)$ **c** $2m(m - 6)$ **d** $6a(2b - 1)$

6 a $\dfrac{5p}{4}$ **b** $\dfrac{m}{10}$ **c** $\dfrac{3a^2}{8}$ **d** 48   **7 a** 23·3   **b** 33   **c** 80   **d** 80

8 a 4·5%   **b** 7·5%   **9** $\dfrac{1094}{1105}$

10 a $\dfrac{1}{15}$ **b** $\dfrac{1}{3}$ **c** $\dfrac{17}{30}$ **d** 0   **e** 1   **11 a** 150°   **b** 150°   **12** 15°

10B Working Mathematically

1 89   **2** 38   **3** 10   **4** 18   **5** 32

6 $3^1 = 3$, $3^2 = 9$, $3^3 = 27$, $3^4 = 81$, $3^5 = 243$, $3^6 = 729$; last digit of 3^{2000} is 1.

Chapter 11: Area and volume

Prep Quiz 11:01
1 $36\,cm^2$ **2** $16\,cm^2$ **3** $35\,cm^2$ **4** $18\,cm^2$ **5** $48\,cm^2$ **6** $18\,cm^2$ **7** $20\,cm^2$ **8** $40\,cm^2$ **9** $21\,units^2$ **10** $20\,units^2$

Exercise 11:01
1 a $1\cdot26\,cm^2$ **b** $1\cdot21\,cm^2$ **c** $25\,m^2$ **d** $10\cdot8\,cm^2$ **e** $28\,cm^2$ **f** $24\,cm^2$ **g** $4\cdot4\,cm^2$ **h** $12\,m^2$
i $45\,cm^2$
2 a $48\,m^2$ **b i** $5000\,m^2$ **ii** $0\cdot5\,ha$ **c** $15\cdot6\,m^2$ **d i** $173\,600\,m^2$ **ii** $17\cdot36\,ha$ **e** $7\cdot2\,m^2$
3 a $17\,cm^2$ **b** $33\,cm^2$ **c** $6\,cm^2$ **d** $35\,cm^2$ **e** $8\,m^2$
4 There are an infinite number of answers but the obvious ones are rectangles with dimensions:
$1\,cm \times 12\,cm$, $2\,cm \times 6\,cm$, $3\,cm \times 4\,cm$, $\frac{1}{2}\,cm \times 24\,cm$.
5 a $47\,cm^2$ **b** $45\,cm^2$ **c** $28\,cm^2$ **d** $104\,cm^2$ **e** $104\,cm^2$ **f** $90\,cm^2$ **g** $56\,cm^2$ **h** $66\,cm^2$
i $60\,cm^2$
6 a 4 **b** 16 **c** 3

Prep Quiz 11:02
1 square **2** rectangle **3** parallelogram **4** rhombus (or diamond) **5** trapezium **6** cube

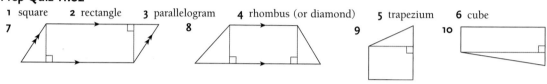

7   **8**   **9**   **10**

Exercise 11:02
1 a $63\,cm^2$ **b** $78\,cm^2$ **c** $112\,cm^2$ **d** $77\,cm^2$ **e** $42\,cm^2$ **f** $120\,cm^2$
2 a $80\,cm^2$ **b** $24\,cm^2$ **c** $104\,cm^2$ **3 a** $104\,cm^2$ **b** $39\,cm^2$ **c** $72\cdot5\,cm^2$
4 a $8\,cm$ **b** $40\,cm^2$ **c** $40\,cm^2$ **5 a** $4\,cm$ **b** $10\,cm^2$ **c** $30\,cm^2$ **d** $40\,cm^2$
6 a $60\,cm^2$ **b** $28\,cm^2$ **c** $27\,cm^2$ **d** $52\cdot5\,cm^2$ **e** $51\,cm^2$ **f** $45\,cm^2$
7 a $4\,cm$ **b** $24\,cm^2$ **c** $48\,cm^2$ **8 a** $12\,cm$ **b** $4\,cm$ **c** $48\,cm^2$ **d** $48\,cm^2$
9 a $3\,cm$ **b** $30\,cm^2$ **c** $3\,cm \times 10\,cm$ **d** $30\,cm^2$ **e** $30\,cm^2$
10 a $40\,cm^2$ **b** $24\,cm^2$ **c** $120\,cm^2$ **d** $36\,cm^2$ **e** $56\,cm^2$ **f** $200\,cm^2$

Exercise 11:03
1 a $56\,cm^2$ **b** $150\,cm^2$ **c** $27\,cm^2$ **d** $300\,mm^2$ **e** $126\,cm^2$ **f** $325\,mm^2$
2 a $63\,cm^2$ **b** $126\,cm^2$ **c** $112\,cm^2$ **d** $135\,cm^2$ **e** $57\,cm^2$ **f** $80\,m^2$
3 a $40\,cm^2$ **b** $42\,cm^2$ **c** $27\,cm^2$ **d** $25\,cm^2$ **e** $31\cdot5\,cm^2$ **f** $110\,mm^2$
4 a $96\,cm^2$ **b** $45\,cm^2$ **c** $38\cdot5\,cm^2$ **d** $10\,cm^2$ **e** $21\,cm^2$ **f** $140\,cm^2$
g $42\,cm^2$ **h** $81\,cm^2$ **i** $35\,cm^2$ **j** $28\,cm^2$ **k** $96\,cm^2$ **l** $90\,cm^2$
5 a $630\,cm^2$ **b** $107\cdot2\,cm^2$ **c** $24\,cm^2$
6 $40\,cm$

Prep Quiz 11:04
1 rectangular prism **2** triangular prism **3** trapezoidal prism **4** rectangle **5** triangle **6** trapezium
7 $49\,cm^2$ **8** $28\,cm^2$ **9** $84\,cm^2$ **10** $70\,cm^2$

Exercise 11:04
1 a $30\,cm^3$ **b** $48\,cm^3$ **c** $63\,cm^3$ **d** $280\,cm^3$ **e** $75\,cm^3$
2 a $56\,cm^3$ **b** $128\,cm^3$ **c** $63\,cm^3$ **d** $72\,cm^3$ **e** $90\,cm^3$ **f** $42\,cm^3$
3 a $27\,cm^3$ **b** $125\,cm^3$ **c** $729\,cm^3$ **4 a** $2\cdot6\,m^3$ **b** $2\,m^3$ **c** $0\cdot648\,m^3$ **d** $1\cdot35\,m^3$
5 a $30\,cm^3$ **b** $240\,cm^3$ **6 a** $28\,cm^2$ **b** $252\,cm^3$
7 a $54\,cm^3$ **b** $210\,cm^3$ **c** $200\,cm^3$ **8 a** $66\,cm^3$ **b** $140\,cm^3$ **c** $450\,cm^3$
9 a $32\,cm^2$ **b** $320\,cm^3$ **10** $860\,cm^3$
11 a $252\,cm^3$ **b** $560\,cm^3$ **c** $216\,cm^3$ **d** $36\,cm^3$ **e** $70\,cm^3$ **f** $180\,cm^3$
12 a $9\,cm^2$ **b** $5\,cm$ **c** $6\,cm$ **13 a** $2\cdot5\,L$ **b** $2\,L$
14 a $400\,cm^3$ **b** $504\,cm^3$ **c** $120\,cm^3$ **15** $7\cdot6\,cm^3$

Prep Quiz 11:05
1 6 **2** yes **3** $28\,cm^2$ **4** 3 **5** 7 **6** 5 **7** yes **8** $12\,m^2$ **9** 5 **10** 7

Exercise 11:05
1 a cube, closed **b** rectangular prism, open **c** triangular prism, closed **d** rectangular prism, closed
2 a $54\,m^2$ **b** $104\,m^2$ **c** $176\,m^2$ **d** $220\,m^2$ **e** $352\,m^2$ **f** $412\,m^2$

3 a $300\,\text{m}^2$ b $260\,\text{m}^2$ c $264\,\text{m}^2$ 4 a $152\,\text{cm}^2$ b $241\,\text{cm}^2$ c $496{\cdot}72\,\text{cm}^2$
5 a $x = 5$, $84\,\text{cm}^2$ b $x = 12$ cm, $480\,\text{cm}^2$
6 These answers are approximate.   a $3{\cdot}6\,\text{cm}^2$ b $5{\cdot}3\,\text{cm}^2$ c $6{\cdot}9\,\text{cm}^2$ d $7{\cdot}9\,\text{cm}^2$
7 a No. A cube with volume $8\,\text{cm}^3$ (surface area $24\,\text{cm}^2$) would have less surface area than a prism of volume $8\,\text{cm}^3$
       with dimensions $1\,\text{cm} \times 2\,\text{cm} \times 4\,\text{cm}$ (surface area $28\,\text{cm}^2$).
   b No. A cube with surface area $24\,\text{cm}^2$ and volume $8\,\text{cm}^3$ as above has the same surface area as a rectangular prism
       with dimensions $1\,\text{cm} \times 2\,\text{cm} \times 3\frac{1}{3}$ cm. However, the volume of the prism is $6\frac{2}{3}\,\text{cm}^3$.

Fun Spot 11:05
1 D 2 A, B and C 3 B to C 4 A and D 5 A and B 6 C

Diagnostic Test 11: Area and Volume
1 a $54\,\text{cm}^2$ b $49\,\text{cm}^2$ c $60\,\text{cm}^2$ 2 a $20\,\text{cm}^2$ b $36\,\text{cm}^2$ c $36\,\text{cm}^2$
3 a $112\,\text{cm}^2$ b $100\,\text{cm}^2$ c $104\,\text{cm}^2$ 4 a $60\,\text{cm}^2$ b $84\,\text{cm}^2$ c $48\,\text{cm}^2$
5 a $60\,\text{cm}^2$ b $50\,\text{cm}^2$ c $162\,\text{cm}^2$ 6 a $16\,\text{cm}^2$ b $38{\cdot}5\,\text{cm}^2$ c $42\,\text{cm}^2$
7 a $150\,\text{cm}^3$ b $125\,\text{cm}^3$ c $630\,\text{cm}^3$ 8 a $80\,\text{cm}^3$ b $360\,\text{cm}^3$ c $378\,\text{cm}^3$
9 a $70\,\text{cm}^3$ b $100\,\text{cm}^3$ c $256\,\text{cm}^3$ 10 a $504\,\text{cm}^3$ b $84\,\text{m}^3$ c $864\,\text{cm}^3$

11A Revision Assignment
1 a $6a$ b $9b$ c $2a$ d $16a^2$ 2 a 2% b $\$30$ c $16{\cdot}5\%$ d $\$12.38$
3 a $a = 0{\cdot}5$, $b = 1{\cdot}3$ b
4 a 5026 b $60\,700$ c $7\,020\,006$

front   top   side

5 a

b

c

6 a yes ($18\,\text{m}^3$)   b A: $42\,\text{m}^2$, B: $54\,\text{m}^2$, no   c $\$453.60$
7 $375\,\text{cm}^2$

11B Working Mathematically
1 105 2 39 3 325 4 18 5 58
6 a *parallel* lines   b *perpendicular* lines   c *concurrent* lines   d *angle ABC or CBA*
   e *acute* angle   f *transversal*   g *corresponding* angles   h *alternate* angles
   i $\angle CAD = 60°$ j *CD is perpendicular to AB*

Chapter 12:   Circles

Exercise 12:01
1 a radius   b chord   c diameter   d arc   e semicircle
   f sector   g minor segment   h tangent   i radius   j major segment
   k diameter   l sector   m arc   n radius   o chord
   p tangent
2 a sector   b tangent   c semicircle   d tangent   e semicircle
3 a diameter   b radius   c chord   d tangent
4 isosceles. Two sides are equal radii.
5 a $\frac{1}{4}$ b $\frac{1}{3}$ c $\frac{1}{6}$ 6 3 cm

Exercise 12:02
1 a $15{\cdot}7$ cm   b $25{\cdot}12$ mm   c $62{\cdot}8$ mm   d $18{\cdot}84$ cm
2 a $62{\cdot}8$ cm   b $12{\cdot}56$ cm   c $25{\cdot}12$ mm   d $56{\cdot}52$ mm
3 a 44 cm   b 66 cm   c 44 cm   d 220 mm   e 154 cm   f 264 mm   g 88 cm   h 22 cm
4 a $14{\cdot}1$ cm   b $17{\cdot}0$ cm   c $38{\cdot}0$ mm   d $29{\cdot}5$ mm   e $27{\cdot}3$ cm   f $78{\cdot}5$ cm   g $102{\cdot}7$ cm   h $11{\cdot}9$ cm
   i $23{\cdot}9$ mm   j $98{\cdot}0$ cm
5 a 16 cm   b 9 cm   c 12 cm
6 a $188{\cdot}5$ cm (to 1 dec. pl.)   b 1885 m (to nearest m)   c 531 revolutions (to nearest rev.)
7 $38\,000$ km
8 a $6{\cdot}4$ cm   b $15{\cdot}9$ mm   c $11{\cdot}1$ cm   d $4{\cdot}8$ cm

Exercise 12:03

1 a 29 cm   **b** 31 cm   **c** 59 cm   **d** 67 cm   **e** 40 cm
2 ≐ 6·1 km; 122 km   **3** 14 m   **4 a** 94 cm   **b** 310 m
5 318 mm   **6** 2π metres, ie ≐ 6·3 m

Prep Quiz 12:04

1 9 cm   **2** 9·0 cm   **3** 3·1   **4** $C = \pi d$ or $C = 2\pi r$ **5** 40 cm²   **6** 30 cm²   **7** 13·5 cm²   **8** $\frac{1}{4}$ **9** $\frac{3}{4}$ **10** $\frac{1}{3}$

Investigation 12:04

1 a $4r^2$ square units   **b** square   **2 a** $2r^2$ square units   **b** circle
3 12 units²   **4 a** 52 units²   **b** 300
5 a πr **b** r **c** πr^2 square units   **6 a** $A = \frac{1}{2}bh$ **b** $2\pi r$ **c** πr^2 **d** πr^2

Exercise 12:04

1 a 12·56 cm² **b** 314 cm² **c** 50·24 cm² **d** 78·5 m² **e** 3·14 cm² **f** 28·26 m² **g** 50·24 m² **h** 113·04 cm²
2 a 154 cm² **b** $28\frac{2}{7}$ cm² **c** $38\frac{1}{2}$ mm² **d** $78\frac{4}{7}$ cm²
3 a 113·1 cm²   **b** 22·9 cm²   **c** 95·0 cm²   **d** 366·4 cm²   **e** 804·2 cm²   **f** 2827·4 cm²
　g 191·1 mm²   **h** 254·5 cm²   **i** 1017·9 cm²   **j** 243·3 mm²
4 a 50 cm² **b** 113 cm² **c** 25 cm² **d** 172 cm²   **5 a** 1257 mm² **b** 707 mm² **c** 1886 mm²
6 a 110·8 cm² **b** 13·9 cm² **c** 34·0 cm²   **7 a** 66·0 cm² **b** 22·0 cm² **c** 50·3 cm²
8 a 707 cm² **b** 19·6 m² **c** 95 cm² **d** 22·0 cm² **e i** 289·5 cm² **ii** 144·8 cm² **iii** 193·0 cm²
9 a 89 cm² **b** 68 cm² **c** 74 cm² **d** 71 cm² **e** 23 cm² **f** 71 cm²
10 a 3·8013 m² **b i** 6 cm **ii** 7·74 cm²

Diagnostic Test 12: Circles

1 a diameter **b** radius   **c** arc   **d** semicircle **e** sector
2 a 25·1 cm **b** 15·7 cm **c** 12·6 cm **d** 56·5 cm   **3 a** 26 cm   **b** 27 cm   **c** 25 cm   **d** 25 cm
4 a 79 cm² **b** 28 cm² **c** 50 cm² **d** 154 cm²   **5 a** 39 cm² **b** 21 cm² **c** 49 cm² **d** 8 cm²

12A Revision Assignment

1 a 30a   **b** $7a^3$ **c** $2 - 2a$ **d** 6
2 a Bill = 945 stamps, Jeff = 315 stamps   **b** Frances = $7·80, Jill = $11·30
3 a 52   **b** 9 cups
4 a $x = 57$ (ext. ∠ of a Δ)   **b** ∠BAC = 65° (∠s in a right ∠);   **c** ∠ACD = 30° (alt. ∠s, AB // CD)
　　　　　　　　　　　　　　$x = 47$ (∠ sum of Δ)   　　　　　∴ $x = 80$ (∠ sum of Δ)
5 a 15·68   **b** 12   **6 a** 42·25 cm² **b** 13·44 cm² **c** 272 cm² **d** 44 cm²
7 a $a = 3·375$ or $3\frac{3}{8}$ **b** $x = 1·3$ **c** $x = -1·7$ **8 a** 1·2 m by 0·5 m   **b** 23 m

12B Working Mathematically

1 a 3, 4   **b** 2, 13   **2** 24   **3** 15   **4** 20   **5** 16   **6** 40

Chapter 13:   Geometric constructions and congruent figures

Prep Quiz 13:01

1 BC   **2** DC   **3** ∠BCA   **4** 63°   **5** 90°   **6** 27°   **7** 3 cm   **8** 4 cm   **9** C and D
10 Draw a circle of radius 3 cm and centre A, and a circle of radius 6 cm and centre B. The points where the circles cross will be 3 cm from A and 6 cm from B.

Exercise 13:01

1 a 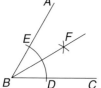   **b**   **c** 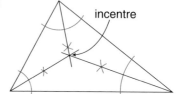   **d** kite

2 a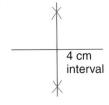

4 cm interval

b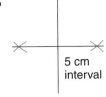

5 cm interval

c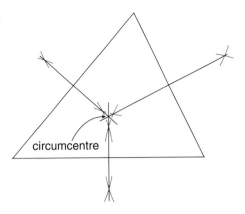

circumcentre

d rhombus

3 a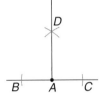

b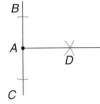

c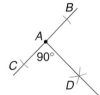

d isosceles triangle

4 a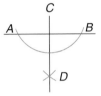

b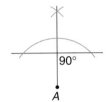

c *rhombus* (if the radii of all arcs are the same) or *kite* (if the arc drawn from *C* has a different radius to those drawn from *A* and *B*)

5 a

b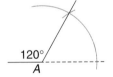

c equilateral triangle

6 a

b

The distances from all points on the circle to the centre are the same.

c A circle is the set of all points that are a fixed distance from a point called the centre.

Investigation 13:01

1 a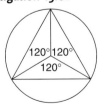

b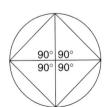

c

d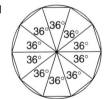

Exercise 13:02

1 a translation **b** reflection **c** rotation **d** rotation and translation

2 a 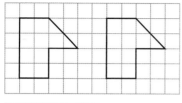 **b**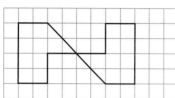

c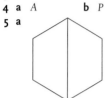

3 a **i** ∠*L* **ii** ∠*R* **iii** ∠*H* **b** **i** *SR* **ii** *HG* **iii** *EF* **c** Yes

4 a *A* **b** *P* **c** *F* **d** *O* **e** *H* **f** *G*

5 a **b** **c**

6 a **b** **c** **d**

e **f** **g** **h**

7 a yes **b** yes **c** yes

8 a The figure has been produced by a combination of rotation, reflection and translation.

b **i** ∠*S* **ii** ∠*M* **iii** ∠*D* **c** **i** *NO* **ii** *RQ* **iii** *AH*

9 a 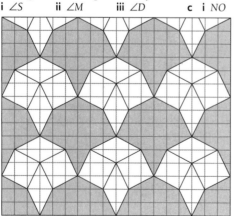 **b** 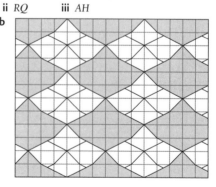 **c** yes

10 a **b** **c**

Prep Quiz 13:03

1 *EF* **2** *AD* **3** *HG* **4** ∠*EFG* **5** ∠*ADC* **6** *WX* **7** *TS* **8** *VU* **9** ∠*QTS* **10** ∠*WVU*

Exercise 13:03

1 a shape C **b** shape F **c** shape H **d** shape L
2 a Δ*B* ≡ Δ*C* **b** shape D ≡ shape F **c** Δ*M* ≡ Δ*L*
3 a *DB* **b** *CB* **c** *DC* **d** ∠*CDB* **e** ∠*DBC* **f** ∠*BCD*
4 a *CB* **b** *CF* **c** *BE* **d** *ABED* ≡ *CBEF* **e** yes **f** yes
5 a *A* and *C* **b** yes **c** yes **d** Shapes B and C are not congruent because sides do not match. They are not the same shape.

6 Two circles will be congruent if they have the same radius.

Exercise 13:04

1 b i Δ*TUS* **ii** Δ*MLN* and Δ*IWJ* **iii** Δ*RPQ* **c** Δ*GHK*
2 a Δ*YZX*; corresponding angles are ∠*P* and ∠*Y*, ∠*Q* and ∠*Z*, ∠*R* and ∠*X*; corresponding sides are *PQ* and *YZ*, *PR* and *YX*, *QR* and *ZX*.
  b Δ*TUS*; corresponding angles are ∠*S* and ∠*F*, ∠*T* and ∠*D*, ∠*U* and ∠*E*; corresponding sides are *ST* and *FD*, *TU* and *DE*, *US* and *EF*.
3 a angles: ∠*A* and ∠*D*, ∠*B* and ∠*E*, ∠*C* and ∠*F* sides: *AB* and *DE*, *BC* and *EF*, *AC* and *DF*
  b angles ∠*X* and ∠*M*, ∠*Y* and ∠*L*, ∠*Z* and ∠*N* sides: *XY* and *ML*, *XZ* and *MN*, *YZ* and *LN*
  c angles: ∠*L* and ∠*E*, ∠*M* and ∠*D*, ∠*N* and ∠*F* sides: *LM* and *ED*, *LN* and *EF*, *MN* and *DF*
  d angles: ∠*A* and ∠*R*, ∠*B* and ∠*Q*, ∠*C* and ∠*P* sides: *AB* and *RQ*, *AC* and *RP*, *BC* and *OP*
  e angles: ∠*M* and ∠*X*, ∠*N* and ∠*G*, ∠*L* and ∠*A* sides: *LM* and *AX*, *LN* and *AG*, *MN* and *XG*
4 a The circle drawn will be identical to the one shown.
  b The circle drawn will be identical to the one shown.
  c

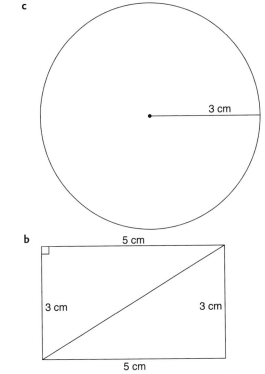

5 a

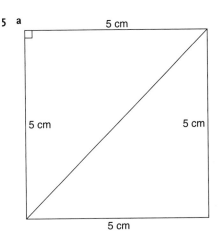

  b

c

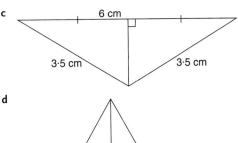

  d

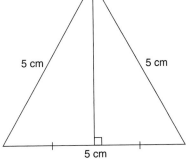

6 a Δ*ABC* and Δ*BAD*; Δ*ADC* and Δ*BCD*; Δ*AED* and Δ*BEC*
  b Δ*ABD* and Δ*BAD*; Δ*AED* and Δ*BEC*

Diagnostic Test 13: Geometric Constructions and Congruent Figures

1 a   **b**   **c**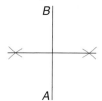

2 a   **b**    **c**

3 a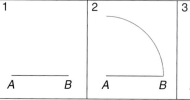

b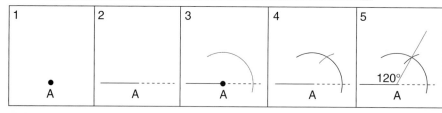

c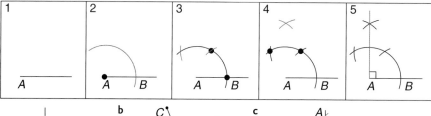

4 a 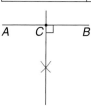   **b** 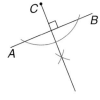   **c**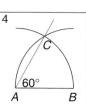

5 a *A* and *C*   **b** *A* and *C*

6 a *MN*   **b** *ML*   **c** *NL*   **d** $\angle MNL$ **e** $\angle NLM$ **f** $\angle GEF$

7 a $\triangle ABD \equiv \triangle CBD$ **b** *CB*   **c** *AD*   **d** $\angle BCD$ **e** $\angle BDC$

8 a   **b**    Answers will vary, but the identical process would be used to construct each triangle.

   c Answers will vary but the identical process would be used to construct each quadrilateral. (See Appendix A:07E.)

13A Revision Assignment

1 a $6x + 7y + 6$ **b** $6x^2 + 5x - 6$ **2 a** $-x^2 + 2x$ **b** $4a^2 - 12a + 3ab + 2b$

3 a $p = -7$ **b** $a = -\frac{7}{9}$ **c** $b = -5\frac{1}{3}$ **4 a** 34   **b** -54

5 a 105   **b** 73   **c** 47   **6 a** $x = 1$ **b** $y = 2$ **c** $x = -2$

7 132 cm³   **8 a** 23·2 kg   **b** 2·4 L of A and 1·6 L of B   **9 a** 8·4 kg   **b** 0·4%

10

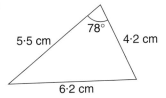

5·5 cm   78°   4·2 cm

6·2 cm

11 a $x = 27$ **b** $x = 6.6$ (to nearest mm)

13B Working Mathematically

1 a $\begin{array}{r} 38 + \\ 36 \\ \hline 74 \end{array}$ **b** $\begin{array}{r} 904 - \\ 63 \\ \hline 841 \end{array}$ **c** $\begin{array}{r} 564 + \\ 537 \\ \hline 1101 \end{array}$ **d** $\begin{array}{r} 1632 - \\ 925 \\ \hline 707 \end{array}$ **2** 12 L, 33 L

3 5   **4** $1190   **5** 7   **6** (1, Emma); (2, Sarah); (3, Ben); (4, Kate)

Chapter 14:   Statistics

Exercise 14:01

1 a Alexis   **b** Caroline's   **c** not a representative sample   **d** more time-consuming

2 a Fellow students are all in a particular age group.   **b** Survey people in the street.

3 a His sample is limited to students of his own school, who would all have a similar range of ages and experiences.

   b He has not listed all sports. The order of sports could also influence the result.

   c He could use stratified random sampling.

   d Student response. (Each person could be asked to write down their favourite sport.)

4 They survey different samples of people.

5 a no   **b** Roll the dice a large number of times.

   c The number of times a person rolls a dice is limited by the time available. We would get closer to the real probability if we threw the dice millions of times. In this sense, it is like a sample.

6 The accuracy of the survey would depend on the size of the sample and the sample is limited to the readers of the magazine.

7 a To what is MUNCH–O's preferred?   **b** Which 5 dentists?   **c** 20% more than what?   **d** Longer than what?

8 Grade 8, 13; Grade 9, 16; Grade 10, 19; Grade 11, 16; Grade 12, 16

9 15–25 years, 137; 25–45 years, 341; 45–65 years, 304; 65 years and over, 218.   **10** Student research.

Exercise 14:02

1 a

Outcome	Frequency
2	3
3	9
4	6
5	4
6	2
Total	24

b 24   **c** 3   **d** 6   **e** 12

2 a

Shape	Tally	Frequency
circle	ЖНТ II	7
square	ЖНТ I	6
oval	IIII	4
star	ЖНТ ЖНТ	10
triangle	ЖНТ II	7
	Total	34

b 34   **c** star   **d** triangles

3 a

Outcome	Tally	Frequency
1	ЖНТ I	6
2	IIII	4
3	ЖНТ II	7
4	ЖНТ III	8
5	ЖНТ	5
6	ЖНТ I	6
	Total	36

b 4   **c** 2   **d** No

4 a 10   **b** 4   **c**

Outcome	Tally	Frequency
4	I	1
5	III	3
6	IIII	4
7	ЖНТ II	7
8	ЖНТ I	6
9	ЖНТ I	6
10	III	3
	Total	30

d 7   **e** 8   **f** 15

5 a 4   **b** 3   **c** 9   **d** 6   **e** 39   **f** 21   **g** 162

6 a 1   **b** 2   **c** 7   **d** 19

7 a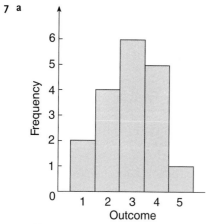

b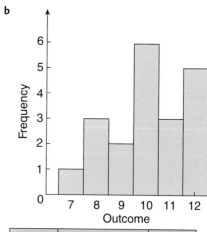

8 a

Outcome	Freq.
0	3
10	6
20	7
30	10
40	5
50	8
Total	39

b 39
c 16

9 a 33, 27

b

Outcome	Tally	Freq.
27	||	2
28	||||	4
29	ЖЖ |	6
30	ЖЖ ЖЖ ЖЖ ЖЖ	20
31	ЖЖ ЖЖ	10
32	ЖЖ |	6
33	||	2
	Total	50

c 12
d 18

e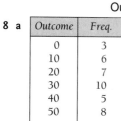

10 a

Responses		Tally	Freq.
Strongly agree	(A)	ЖЖ ЖЖ ЖЖ ЖЖ ЖЖ ЖЖ |||	28
Agree	(B)	ЖЖ ЖЖ ЖЖ ЖЖ ЖЖ ЖЖ ЖЖ ЖЖ ЖЖ ЖЖ |	46
Disagree	(C)	ЖЖ ЖЖ ЖЖ ЖЖ |	21
Strongly disagree	(D)	ЖЖ	5

b 28
c 5%
d 74%
e 26%

f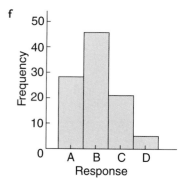

Exercise 14:03

1 a i 3 **ii** 3 **iii** 40 **iv** 5 **v** 3
   vi 5 **vii** 7 **viii** 0.4 **ix** 6 **x** 5
  b i 5 **ii** 7 **iii** 10 **iv** 17, 20
   v 50 **vi** 8 **vii** 4 **viii** 1.1, 1.3
   ix 17 **x** 148, 151
  c i 4 **ii** 7 **iii** 25 **iv** 20 **v** 50
   vi 9 **vii** 4 **viii** 1.2 **ix** 17 **x** 150
  d i 3.8 **ii** 7.6 **iii** 26.7 **iv** 19.4 **v** 49.6
   vi 9.2 **vii** 4.6 **viii** 1.2 **ix** 17 **x** 149.6
2 a 30.3 **b** 74.2 **c i** 40 **ii** 11
  d 2
3 a no **b** the mean

4 a

Outcome	fx
1	2
2	8
3	15
4	24
5	15
Total	64

Mean = 3.2

b

Outcome	fx
5	5
6	30
7	21
8	64
9	45
10	30
Total	195

Mean = 7.8

c

Outcome	fx
18	18
19	57
20	20
21	84
22	110
23	69
24	24
25	50
Total	432

Mean = 21.6

4 a

Outcome	fx
1	2
2	8
3	15
4	24
5	15
Total	64

Mean = 3·2

b

Outcome	fx
5	5
6	30
7	21
8	64
9	45
10	30
Total	195

Mean = 7·8

c

Outcome	fx
18	18
19	57
20	20
21	84
22	110
23	69
24	24
25	50
Total	432

Mean = 21·6

5 a 4   **b** 8   **c** 22

6 a 3   **b** 8   **c** 22

7 a

Outcome	Tally	Freq.	fx
0					3	0
1	卌	5	5
2						4	8
3					3	9
4				2	8
5			1	5
Totals		18	35

d highest column

b i 5   **ii** 1   **iii** 2   **iv** $1·9\dot{4}$ or $1\frac{17}{18}$

c

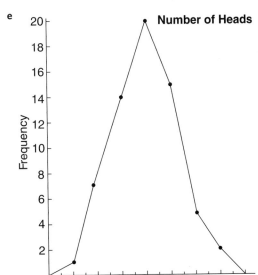

8 a

Outcome	Tally	Freq.	fx
0			1	0
1	卌 ||	7	7
2	卌 卌 ||||	14	28
3	卌 卌 卌 卌	20	60
4	卌 卌 卌	15	60
5	卌	5	25
6				2	12
Totals		64	192

b 3   **c** 14   **d** 14

9 a

Outcome	Freq.	fx
0	3	0
1	4	4
2	6	12
3	5	15
4	3	12
5	1	5
6	2	12
Totals	24	60

b 2
c 2
d 2·5
e 12

10 a Barbara's results

Outcome	Tally	Freq.
3	||	2
4		0
5	||||	4
6	||||	4
7	JHT ||||	9
8	JHT JHT |||	13
9	JHT JHT	10
10	JHT |||	8
	Total	50

Rob's results

Outcome	Tally	Freq
3	|	1
4	||||	4
5	|||	3
6	JHT ||	7
7	JHT |	6
8	JHT |	6
9	JHT |||	8
10	JHT JHT JHT	15
	Total	50

b

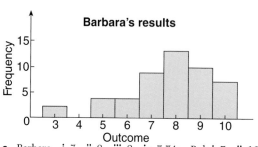

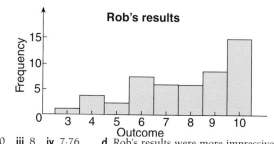

c Barbara **i** 7 **ii** 8 **iii** 8 **iv** 7·74; Rob **i** 7 **ii** 10 **iii** 8 **iv** 7·76 **d** Rob's results were more impressive.

Exercise 14:04

1

Class	Tally	Frequency
31–40	JHT	5
41–50	JHT |	6
51–60	JHT JHT |	11
61–70	|||	3
71–80	JHT |	6
81–90	|||	3
91–100	|	1
	Total	35

2

Class	Tally	Frequency
0–2	JHT	5
3–5	JHT JHT ||	12
6–8	JHT JHT ||	12
9–11	JHT JHT |||	13
12–14	|||	3
15–17	|||	3
	Total	48

3

Class	Class centre	Tally	Freq.
1–5	3	JHT JHT	10
6–10	8	JHT JHT ||	12
11–15	13	JHT ||||	9
16–20	18	||||	4
21–25	23	|||	3
26–30	28	||	2
		Total	40

4

Outcome	Tally	Freq.
0		0
1		0
2	|	1
3		0
4	|||	3
5	JHT	5
6	JHT ||	7
7	JHT |||	8
8	||||	4
9	|	1
10	|	1
	Total	30

Class	Tally	Freq.
2–4	||||	4
5–7	JHT JHT JHT JHT	20
8–10	JHT |	6
	Total	30

In the second table the value of the individual scores is lost.

5

Class	Class centre	Frequency
0–2	1	25
3–5	4	22
6–8	7	13
	Total	60

a Using three classes does not show the spread of scores realistically as it makes the first two classes appear very similar. If the classes 0–1, 2–3, 4–5 etc had been used, it would show how different they are.

b It would be difficult to use more than 5 classes in this case since there are only 9 outcomes. Having groups with the same number of outcomes would not be possible if more than 5 outcomes are used.

6 a

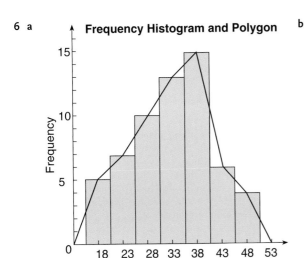

Frequency Histogram and Polygon

b

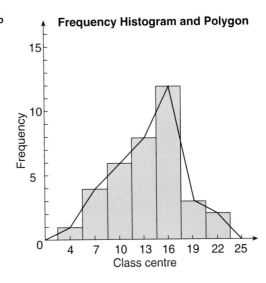

Frequency Histogram and Polygon

7 a

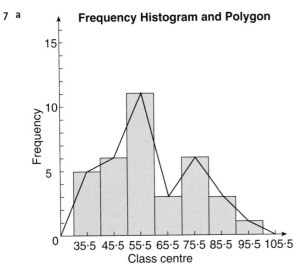

Frequency Histogram and Polygon

b

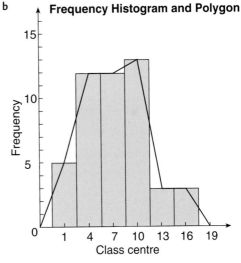

Frequency Histogram and Polygon

c

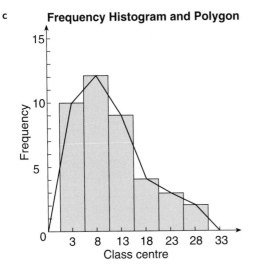

Frequency Histogram and Polygon

8 a The class 51–60 was by far the most popular class. Nobody scored less than 31.

b Most of the scores were between 3 and 11 with nobody scoring over 17.

c Marks were low with most scoring in the range 1 to 15 with nobody scoring more than 30.

Exercise 14:05

1 a 19   **b** $20 - 6 = 14$ **c** 17   **d** 6 is the only outlier.   **e** 3
   f An outlier is any score that lies apart from the main body of scores.

2

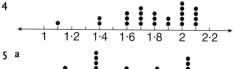

     a 11   **b** 16   **c** 11
     d 19 is an outlier.   **e** 6

3 a

	Mode	Median	Mean	Range
1986	20	12	12·1	19
1996	0	4	7	22

b Overall they are smoking much less and, apart from the three who have died, four have given up smoking. Factors could include:
- an increased awareness of the dangers of smoking
- decreased health that forces a reduction in smoking
- an awareness of reduced fitness because of smoking
- consideration for others
- restrictions on where people can smoke
- the increasing cost of smoking

4

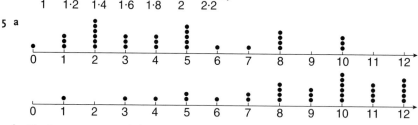

5 a

b The improvement made by particular individuals can no longer be seen.

c

	Mode	Median	Mean	Range
Beginning	2	4	4·5	10
End	10	9·5	8·7	11

6 a no relationship   **b** inverse relationship   **c** direct relationship   **d** inverse relationship
   e direct relationship   **f** no relationship

7 a **i** Maths 5, English 7   **ii** Maths 20, English 19   **iii** Maths 9, English 13   **iv** Maths 18, English 14
   b **i** 20   **ii** 19
   c The scatter diagram suggests that students tend to get similar results in Maths and English.
   d 16   **e** 13   **f** 11   **g** 12

8 a

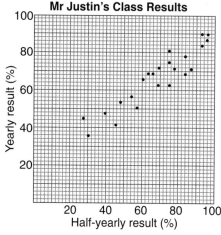

Mr Justin's Class Results

b From the pattern at the left, it is obvious that students tended to perform as well in both tests.
c equal 12th   **d** 16th   **e** 75   **f** 69

9

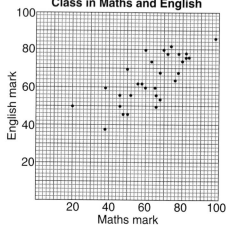

Results of Mrs Everingham's Class in Maths and English

10 Answers will vary, but should say that students tended to perform about the same in both tests. Some, like R Tist, have positions that were not close. Marks tended to be higher in the half-yearly exam than in the yearly exam. No marks were lower than 27% in either test.

Exercise 14:06

1 a Test Marks
(2/6 represents 26.)

Stem	Leaf
1	5 9 7 6 8
2	6 6 9 8 6
3	3 8 5 6 0
4	7 0 7 1 7
5	1 8
6	2 2

b Test Marks
(5/3 represents 53.)

Stem	Leaf
4	5 4 9 2
5	3 7 9
6	7 0 5 3
7	4 2 0 7 3
8	1 0 2 0 1 8
9	1 2

2 a Test Marks
(2/6 represents 26.)

Stem	Leaf
1	5 6 7 8 9
2	6 6 6 8 9
3	0 3 5 6 8
4	0 1 7 7 7
5	1 8
6	2 2

median $= \dfrac{33 + 35}{2}$
$= 34$

b Test Marks
(5/3 represents 53.)

Stem	Leaf
4	2 4 5 9
5	3 7 9
6	0 3 5 7
7	0 2 3 4 7
8	0 0 1 1 2 8
9	1 2

median $= \dfrac{70 + 72}{2}$
$= 71$

3 a Runs Scored at Cricket
(0/8 represents 8 runs.)

Stem	Leaf	Frequency (f)
0	8 6 4 1 9 2	6
1	5 8 9 1	4
2	0 7 6 9	4
3	6 3 2	3
4	6 5 0 3	4
5		0
6	2	1
	Total	22

b

Stem	Leaf	Frequency (f)
0	1 2 4 6 8 9	6
1	1 5 8 9	4
2	0 6 7 9	4
3	2 3 6	3
4	0 3 5 6	4
5		0
6	2	1
	Total	22

c range 61, median $\dfrac{20 + 26}{2} = 23$, mean $= 24 \cdot 18$ (to 2 dec. pl.). The only outlier is 62.
d 45·5%

4 a Year 8, Total Score, Darts

Stem	Leaf
0	1 1 1 2 3 4 5 5 6 7 8 8 8 9 9 9
1	0 1 1 2 2 3 3 4 4 4 4 5 6 7 7 7 8 9
2	0 2 4 5 6 7 8
3	0 0 1 3 5 7 9 9
4	1 2 2 2 3 4 4 4 5 5 6 6 6 7 8 9
5	0 1 1 2 2 2 3 3 4 4 5 5 5
6	0

b range 59; mode 14; median 26·5
c 60 is the only outlier. There are no obvious clusters. The scores tend to be either good or poor. This means the distribution has a bulge at each end of the scale.
d 41 is 12·7 above the mean, is 19 below the highest score and is the 30th highest of the 80 scores.

5 a 3 × tables   **b** mode = 12 s, median = 27 s, range = 47 s
c There are two modes, 32 s and 59 s, median = (39 + 41) ÷ 2 = 40 s, range = 44 s.
d No outlier is present in the data for either table as no score stands alone at one end of the data.

6 a Quiz Scores

Students			Parents
Leaf		Stem	Leaf
		0	6
9 9 8 5		1	1 6 6 8 8
8 8 6 5 4 3 2 1 0 0		2	0 1 2 3 4 5 6 6 7
9 7 5 5 4 3 0 0 0 0		3	0 1 1 2 2 5 7 8
7 5 4 2 2 1 1 0		4	0 1 2 2 2

b Students: mode = 30, median = 30, range = 32
Parents: mode = 42, median = 26·5, range = 36
c the median
d Students' mean $\doteqdot$ 30·72
Parents' mean $\doteqdot$ 27·57

7 a

Pulse Rates

Adults		Children
Leaf	Stem	Leaf
2	1	
	2	
	3	
	4	
98765	5	
888444100	6	27
66222	7	2778
100	8	125556668
2	9	2445899
	10	02

b For the adults' pulse rates, 12 and 92 are outliers. For the children's pulse rates, 62 might be considered an outlier (or might not).

c The outlier 12 can be ignored unless you know that the adult was dying at the time. It is outside the range of human pulse rates and so must be an error in measurement.

d *Adults:* median = (64 + 68) ÷ 2 = 66 (If the score 12 is ignored, the median for adults is 68.) There are three modes: 64, 68 and 72. *Children:* median = 86. There are two modes: 85 and 86.

e The adult pulse rates range from 55 to 92 (a range of 37), have a median of 68, modes of 64, 68 and 72 and a mean of 65·625. (For this description the score 12 has been ignored.) The child pulse rates range from 62 to 102 (a range of 40), have a median of 86 and modes of 85 and 86. Overall, the pulse rates of these children tend to be about 18 beats per minute more than those of these adults.

Diagnostic Test 14: Statistics

1 a

Outcome	Tally	Freq.
1					3
2	JHT ||	7
3						4
4						4
5				2
	Total	20

b

Outcome	Tally	Freq.
0					3
2	JHT	5
4	JHT ||||	9
6	JHT	5
8				3
	Total	25

c

Outcome	Tally	Freq.
3				2
4			1
5					3
6						4
7	JHT		6
8					3
9						4
10				2
	Total	25

2 a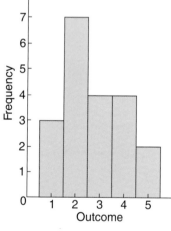

b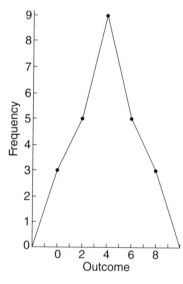

c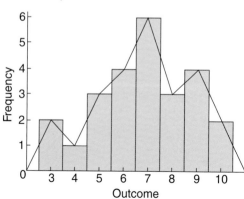

3 a 6	**b** 7	**c** 0·7
4 a 6	**b** 3	**c** 4, 6
5 a 2	**b** 4	**c** 7
6 a 7	**b** 6	**c** 4·5
7 a 2·5	**b** 4	**c** 7
8 a 6	**b** 5·625	**c** 6
9 a 2·75	**b** 4	**c** 6·84

10

Class	Class centre	Tally	Frequency
0–4	2	|||	3
5–9	7	Жll Жll	10
10–14	12	Жll |||	8
15–19	17	Жll		6
20–24	22	|||	3
		Total	30

11 a i 29 cm **ii** 29·5 cm **iii** 13 cm **b** 20 cm

12

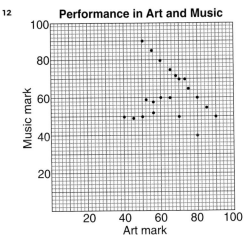

Performance in Art and Music

No. There is not a positive relationship between Art marks and Music marks because many who scored high in one subject scored low in the other subject. Yet some did just as well in each subject.

13 a 35 in the Grade 4 results is an outlier.
b mode = 42, median = 48, range = 41
c mode = 79, median = (65 + 68) ÷ 2 = 66·5, range = 45

14A Revision Assignment

1 a 3375 cm³ **b** 750 cm³ **c** 2625 cm³
2 a $a = 15$ (∠s in a right ∠) **b** $b = 40$ (∠s in a right ∠) **c** $x = 120$ (∠s at a point)
3 5 m; 70 mm **4** 3 min, 12 sec; 62·5 m **5** 30 km/h
6 a 0·3 ha **b** 6 cm **7 a** $y = 2x$ **b** $y = 3x + 1$ **c** $y = x^2$
8 a 0·6% **b** 400% **9 a** −11 **b** −18 **c** 5 **d** −2
10 a

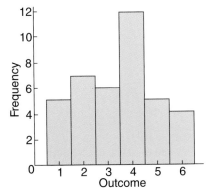

b Range = 5
Mode = 4
Mean = 3·4 (to 1 dec. pl.)

14B Working Mathematically

1

Digit	0	1	2	3	4	5	6	7	8	9
Number needed	13	15	15	61	12	5	5	4	4	4

2 1248 **3** 4 cm² **4** 16 (assuming that all are different people). **5** 9
6 a *hectare* **b** *regular* shapes **c** *net* of a cube **d** *cross-section*
  e *face* **f** *vertex* **g** *edge* **h** *axes of symmetry*
  i *reflection (or flip)* **j** *translation (or slide)* **k** *rotation (or turn)* **l** *tessellation*

Chapter 15:   Probability

Prep Quiz 15:01

1 A: The result 'tails' is just as likely as the result 'heads'.   **2** B: Buses don't often break down.
3 C: Most people on their birthdays are given a present.   **4** B: Not many people score 100 runs when they play cricket.
5 A: A girl being born is just as likely as a boy being born.

Exercise 15:01

1 a For something to be impossible means that it will never happen.
  b For something to be certain means that it will always happen.
2 a Event 1: unlikely; Event 2: even chance; Event 3: even chance; Event 4: impossible; Event 5: certain
  b Event 1: even chance; Event 2: unlikely; Event 3: impossible; Event 4: certain; Event 5: likely
  c Event 1: likely; Event 2: certain; Event 3: impossible; Event 4: unlikely; Event 5: likely
3 a B, A, C   **b** A, C, B   **c** B is the least likely. A and C have the same probability, which is greater than that of B.

Prep Quiz 15:02

1 False. Having failed on the last three attempts, I am not likely to be successful on the fourth attempt. Also, getting tired and/or despondent has a detrimental effect.
2 True. The total shown on two dice can be 2, 3, 4, 5, 6, 7, 8, 9, 10, 11 or 12.
3 True. All numbers between 1 and 10 have 1 digit.
4 True. For each toss, the chance of a head will always be $\frac{1}{2}$, irrespective of the number of heads previously thrown.
5 False. There is one chance in 1000 that the counter chosen will be yellow.

Exercise 15:02

1 a 1, 2, 3, 4, 5, 6   **b** head, tail   **c** A, B, C, D, E   **d** red, blue, green, pink, brown, yellow, orange
2 a 2   **b** 99   **c** 101   **d** 10
3 a $\frac{1}{6}$ **b** 0   **c** $\frac{1}{2}$ **d** $\frac{1}{2}$ **e** $\frac{1}{3}$ **f** $\frac{1}{2}$ **g** 1
4 a i $\frac{1}{2}$ ii $\frac{1}{2}$ **b** i 50%   ii 50%
5 a $\frac{1}{5}$ **b** $\frac{3}{5}$ **c** $\frac{2}{5}$ **d** 0
6 a A $\frac{1}{4}$, B $\frac{1}{5}$, C $\frac{1}{8}$ **b** A $\frac{1}{2}$, B $\frac{4}{5}$, C $\frac{3}{8}$ **c** A $\frac{1}{4}$, B 0, C $\frac{1}{4}$ **d** A $\frac{3}{4}$, B 1, C $\frac{1}{2}$
7 a $\frac{1}{3}$ **b** $\frac{1}{6}$ **c** $\frac{2}{3}$ **d** 0   **e** $\frac{2}{3}$
8 a $\frac{1}{4}$ **b** $\frac{3}{4}$
9 a $\frac{1}{100}$ **b** $\frac{1}{10}$ **c** $\frac{1}{20}$ **d** $\frac{21}{25}$ (ie $\frac{84}{100}$)
  e 0. If I don't buy any tickets, it is impossible for me to win.
  f 100. Only if I buy all the tickets can I be certain of winning.
10 a B   **b** C   **c** A
11 a $\frac{1}{13}$ **b** $\frac{1}{13}$ **c** $\frac{3}{13}$ **d** 1   **e** 0   **f** $\frac{2}{13}$
12 a $\frac{1}{4}$ **b** $\frac{1}{2}$ **c** $\frac{1}{2}$ **d** $\frac{1}{13}$ **e** $\frac{3}{13}$ **f** $\frac{2}{13}$

Prep Quiz 15:03

1 $\frac{1}{10}$ **2** $\frac{9}{10}$ **3** $\frac{3}{10}$ **4** $\frac{7}{10}$ **5** $\frac{2}{10}$ (or $\frac{1}{5}$)   **6** $\frac{8}{10}$ (or $\frac{4}{5}$)   **7** $\frac{4}{10}$ (or $\frac{2}{5}$)   **8** $\frac{6}{10}$ (or $\frac{3}{5}$)   **9** 0   **10** 1   **11** 1

Exercise 15:03

1 a It won't rain tomorrow.   **b** I won't win the race.   **c** A six will not be rolled.
  d I will catch a cold next year.   **e** That team will beat us.   **f** Alice will not be school captain.
2 a The egg will not break.   **b** The plate will break.   **c** We will not score 200 runs.
  d We will toss no heads.   **e** I will not win the raffle.   **f** We will not win the soccer match.
3 a 98%   **b** $\frac{1}{3}$ **c** 60%   **d** 0·01   **e** 0   **f** $\frac{3}{10}$
4 a $\frac{1}{2}$ **b** $\frac{1}{2}$ **c** 1   **d** 0
5 a $\frac{16}{17}$ **b** $\frac{7}{10}$ **c** $\frac{133}{170}$
6 a $\frac{3}{4}$ **b** $\frac{7}{8}$ **c** $\frac{17}{20}$ **d** 98%   **e** 79%   **f** $\frac{797}{800}$
7 a $\frac{37}{200}$ **b** $\frac{163}{200}$ **c** $\frac{43}{200}$ **d** $\frac{157}{200}$ **e** $\frac{3}{5}$ **f** $\frac{2}{5}$ **g** 1
8 a $\frac{1}{5}$ **b** $\frac{4}{5}$ **c** $\frac{2}{5}$ **d** $\frac{3}{5}$
9 a $\frac{43}{100}$ (ie 43%)   **b** $\frac{18}{25}$ (ie 72%)   **c** $\frac{4}{5}$ (ie 80%)   **d** $\frac{51}{100}$ (ie 51%)   **e** $\frac{57}{100}$ (ie 57%)   **f** $\frac{7}{25}$ (ie 28%)

10 a Yes. The probabilities of the given ticket colours combined do not add up to 1.
  b 0·625   **c** 0·875   **d** 0·75   **e** 0·25

11 a $\frac{1}{4}$ **b** $\frac{3}{4}$ **c** $\frac{1}{13}$ **d** $\frac{12}{13}$ **e** $\frac{3}{13}$ **f** $\frac{10}{13}$ **g** $\frac{3}{13}$ **h** $\frac{10}{13}$ **i** 1

12 a $\frac{27}{53}$ **b** $\frac{1}{53}$

13 a $\frac{61}{170}$ **b** $\frac{109}{170}$ **c** $\frac{44}{85}$ **d** $\frac{41}{85}$ **e** 170 or 340 stamps, etc. The total number of stamps in this collection must be some multiple of 170 as there have to be 37 French stamps to choose (or some multiple of 37).

14 a $\frac{223}{800}$ **b** $\frac{577}{800}$ **c** 46% (ie $\frac{23}{50}$)   **d** 54% (ie $\frac{27}{50}$)
  e 800 or 1600. The total number of coins in this collection must be a multiple of 800 since the probability with the largest denominator is P(Chinese) = $\frac{3}{800}$, so there must be at least 3 Chinese coins in the collection (or some multiple of 3).

Fun Spot 15:03

1 a $\frac{1}{6}$ **b** 0   **c** $\frac{1}{6}$ **d** $\frac{1}{3}$ **2 a** $\frac{1}{3}$ **b** $\frac{2}{3}$ **3 a** $\frac{1}{6}$ **b** $\frac{1}{3}$ **c** 0   **d** $\frac{1}{3}$

Prep Quiz 15:04

1 1, 2, 3, 4, 5, 6   **2** tail, head   **3** cleared, not cleared   **4** 52   **5** 4   **6** 13

7 hearts, diamonds, clubs, spades   **8** $\frac{1}{6}$ **9** $\frac{1}{2}$ **10** 0

Exercise 15:04

1 a Manchester United football team is very likely to win this Saturday.
  b Early showers are likely today.
  c The drought has been severe and it is very unlikely it will rain tomorrow.
  d We believe that our company is very likely to fail.
  e This election has Ayun Jun and Danielle with an even chance of victory.
  f Everybody overboard. The ship is certain to sink!

2 a $\frac{4}{11}$ **b** $\frac{7}{11}$ **c** $\frac{4}{11}$ **d** $\frac{7}{11}$ **e** 1

3 a $\frac{1}{5}$ **b** $\frac{4}{5}$ **4** 0·97

5 a $\frac{1}{10}$ **b** $\frac{3}{10}$ **c** 0   **d** $\frac{4}{5}$ **e** $\frac{2}{5}$ **f** 1

6 a 0·35   **b** 0·59   **c** 0·66   **7** 0·32   **8** 95%

9 a $\frac{1}{8}$ **b** $\frac{3}{8}$ **c** $\frac{3}{8}$ **d** $\frac{1}{8}$ **e** $\frac{7}{8}$

10 a 30   **b** 90   **c** 75   **d** 300

Diagnostic Test 15: Probability

1 a B, A, C   **b** A, B, C   **2 a** head, tail   **b** 1, 2, 3, 4, 5, 6

3 a 6   **b** 52   **4 a** $\frac{3}{4}$ **b** $\frac{1}{4}$ **c** $\frac{3}{4}$

5 a $\frac{2}{5}$ **b** 1   **c** 0   **d** $\frac{4}{5}$

6 a $\frac{3}{10}$ **b** $\frac{31}{36}$ **c** Not choosing a picture card, $\frac{10}{13}$ **d** Not winning the game, $\frac{3}{10}$

15A Revision Assignment

1 A and C   **2 a** 11·18   **b** 7·94   **3 a** yes   **b** 10
4 yes, yes   **5** 6·3 cm (to 1 dec. pl.)   **6 a** 37·5%   **b** 87·5%
7 a 0·045   **b** 0·125
8 a 98 g   **b** $\frac{2}{15}$ **c** 6·25%   **d** $13.80   **e** $10.20
9 a $2100   **10**   **11** $y = 10x + 1$

x	0	1	2	15
y	11	15	19	71

12 a 2 m   **b** $7x$ **c** $4ab$ **d** $5x^2$ **e** $9a + b$ **f** $-7a$ **g** $-18y$ **h** $28ab$
  i 8   **j** $3a$ **k** a^2 **l** $6a^2$
13 a 66   **b** 149   **c** -9 **d** -72
14 a m^4 **b** $5a^3$ **c** $12x + 12$ **d** $18m - 13$ **e** $\frac{3x}{10}$ **f** $\frac{5m}{6}$ **g** $\frac{2a^2}{15}$ **h** $\frac{5x}{4}$
15 a $2(x + 7)$ **b** $m(m - 3)$ **c** $11(2 - 3y)$ **d** $3a(3b + 4a)$

15B Working Mathematically

1 a *parallel* lines   b *perpendicular* lines   c *concurrent* lines   d *angle ABC or CBA*
   e *acute* angle   f *right* angle   g *obtuse* angle   h *straight* angle
   i *reflex* angle   j *revolution*   k *adjacent angles*   l *360°*

2 14   3 2 836 000 sheets

4 a 365 Days in a Year   b 9 Lives of a Cat   c 52 Cards in a Standard Pack
   d 26 Letters in the Alphabet   e 66 Books of the Bible   f 12 Months in a Year
   g 1000 Years in a Millennium   h 64 Squares on a Chess Board

5 a The only reasonable answer is 3 sound systems because $5683.89 divided by 3 is equal to $1894.63.
     Dividing $5683.89 by any other reasonable number does not give a whole number of cents.
   b $1894.63

6 a As one wheel turns it forces the other wheels to turn because the wheels are interlocked. If a wheel is turning
     clockwise, it will force the interlocked wheel to turn anticlockwise.
   b There would be about 90 cogs on this wheel. The method used would be to count the number of cogs on a quarter
     of the wheel and multiply by 4.

7 a A greater percentage of young men (40%) are disabled through accident than are young women (25%). 60% of
     young men and 75% of young women are disabled through sickness.
   b Men may be more reckless and would be more likely to be involved in dangerous occupations, while women may
     be more susceptible to illness.

Chapter 16: Graph theory

Exercise 16:01

1 A vertex is a train station and the edges are train lines.
2 There are loops and more connections between lines.
3 There is too much information on the map which makes it confusing and it is not as easy to use as the graph.
4 a Vertices are airports and edges are air routes.
   b None of the branches are linked.
5 a 4   b 3   c 6
6 They all have degree 1.
7 a No, it's only a graphical representation.   b 6, 4   c 15

Exercise 16:02

1 Delhi Metro, Dragonair and the Victoria Line subgraph.

2

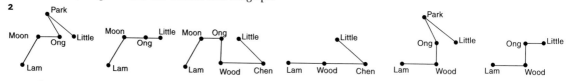

4 $n - 1$.
5 Airlines operate over large distances and subways are for local transport and so need to connect more places.
6 There are many solutions to these questions; examples below.

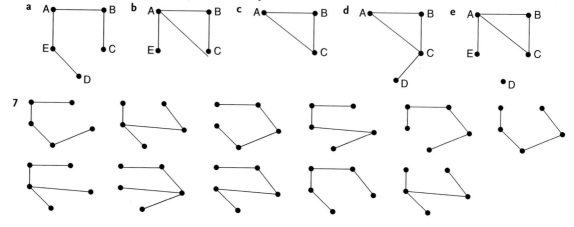

Exercise 16:03

2 A possible answer:

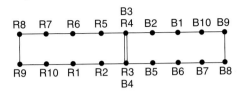

Exercise 16:04

1 a

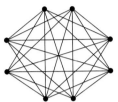

b 20 hellos

3 By starting with the vertices and joining the minimum connectors, this minimum spanning tree is formed. The minimum distance of wire is 86 metres.

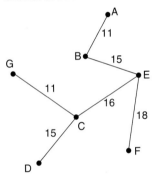

3 A possible answer:

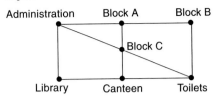

2 a By creating a graph, and making sure vertices that are joined are not the same colour, the result 4 is obtained.

  b Still 4. The same as Bolivia.

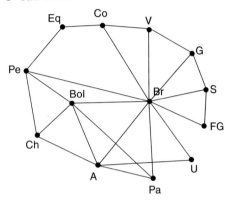

4

Diagnostic Test 16: Graphs and Networks

1

	Graph 1	Graph 2	Graph 3	Graph 4	Graph 5
Degree of vertex A	2	3	2	3	2
Degree of vertex B	1	2	3	3	2
Degree of vertex C	1	2	3	3	1
Degree of vertex D	0	1	2	3	1

2

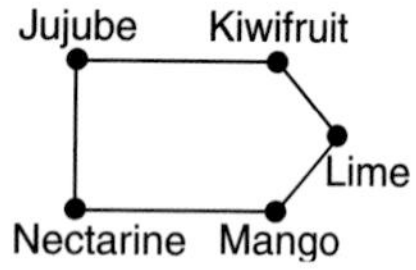

Jujube Kiwifruit

Lime

Nectarine Mango

3 Answers will vary. **4 a** Yes **b** No

16A Revision Assignment

1 a $\dfrac{5}{8}$ **b** $\dfrac{1}{3}$ **2 a** $800   **b** $\dfrac{2}{3}$

3 a $-3a$ **b** $21b + 6d$ **c** $2x^2 - 2y$ **d** $16mn$ **4 a** 90°   **b** 60°   **c** 36°

5 a 16   **b** $\dfrac{1}{2}$ litre   **6 a** 9·66 cm²   **b** 24 m²   **c** 16·2 mm²

7 a 3   **b** 10·75   **c** 52·81   **8 a** 14   **c** $\dfrac{4}{15}$

16B Working Mathematically

1 4   **2** 18 days   **3** 10 chickens and 15 goats

4 a 4   **b** 12   **5 a** 2:00 am   **b** 11 hours 45 minutes

6 12 years old

Answers to ID Cards

ID Card 1 (Metric Units) page xiv

1 metres	2 decimetres	3 centimetres	4 millimetres
5 kilometres	6 square metres	7 square centimetres	8 square kilometres
9 hectares	10 cubic metres	11 cubic centimetres	12 seconds
13 minutes	14 hours	15 metres per second	16 kilometres per hour
17 grams	18 milligrams	19 kilograms	20 tonnes
21 litres	22 millilitres	23 kilolitres	24 degrees Celsius

ID Card 2 (Symbols) page xiv

1 add (or plus)	2 subtract (or minus)	3 multiplied by (or times)	4 divided by
5 is equal to	6 is approximately equal to	7 is not equal to	8 is less than
9 is less than or equal to	10 is not less than	11 is greater than	12 is greater than or equal to
13 is not greater than	14 is not greater than or equal to	15 4 squared	16 4 cubed
17 the square root of 25	18 the cube root of 27	19 per cent	20 therefore
21 for example	22 that is	23 numerator	24 denominator

ID Card 3 (Language) page xv

1 $6 - 2 = 4$	2 $6 + 2 = 8$	3 $6 \div 2 = 3$	4 $6 - 2 = 4$	5 $6 \div 2 = 3$
6 2	7 6	8 $6 \times 2 = 12$	9 $6 - 2 = 4$	10 $6 \times 2 = 12$
11 $2 + 6 = 8$	12 $6 - 2 = 4$	13 $6^2 = 36$	14 $\sqrt{36} = 6$	15 $6 - 2 = 4$
16 $6 \times 2 = 12$	17 $(6 + 2) \div 2 = 4$	18 $6 + 2 = 8$	19 $6^2 = 36$	20 $6 - 2 = 4$
21 $6 - 2 = 4$	22 $6 + 2 = 8$	23 $6 \div 2 = 3$	24 $6 + 2 = 8$	

ID Card 4 (Language) page xvi

1 square	2 rectangle	3 parallelogram	4 rhombus
5 trapezium	6 regular pentagon	7 regular hexagon	8 regular octagon
9 kite	10 scalene triangle	11 isosceles triangle	12 equilateral triangle
13 circle	14 oval (or ellipse)	15 cube	16 rectangular prism
17 triangular prism	18 square pyramid	19 rectangular pyramid	20 triangular pyramid
21 cylinder	22 cone	23 sphere	24 hemisphere

ID Card 5 (Language) page xvii

1 point A	2 interval AB	3 line AB	4 ray AB
5 collinear points	6 midpoint	7 number line	8 diagonals
9 acute-angled triangle	10 right-angled triangle	11 obtuse-angled triangle	12 vertices
13 $\triangle ABC$	14 hypotenuse	15 $180°$	16 $(a + b)°$
17 $360°$	18 $a° = b°$	19 $a° = 60°$	20 $3 \times 180° = 540°$
21 AB is a diameter. OC is a radius.		22 circumference	23 semicircle
24 AB is a tangent. CD is an arc. EF is a chord.			

ID Card 6 (Language) page xviii

1 parallel lines	2 perpendicular lines	3 vertical, horizontal	4 concurrent lines
5 angle ABC or CBA	6 acute angle	7 right angle	8 obtuse angle
9 straight angle	10 reflex angle	11 revolution	12 adjacent angles
13 complementary angles	14 supplementary angles	15 vertically opposite angles	16 $360°$
17 transversal	18 corresponding angles	19 alternate angles	20 cointerior angles
21 bisecting an interval	22 bisecting an angle	23 $\angle CAB = 60°$	24 CD is perpendicular to AB

ID Card 7 (Language) page xix

1 anno Domini	2 before Christ	3 ante meridiem	4 post meridiem
5 hectare	6 regular shapes	7 net of a cube	8 cross-section
9 face	10 vertex	11 edge	12 axes of symmetry
13 reflection (or flip)	14 translation (or slide)	15 rotation (or turn)	16 tessellation
17 coordinates	18 tally	19 picture graph	20 column graph
21 line graph	22 sector (or pie) graph	23 bar graph	24 scatter diagram

Index

Acknowledgments

We would like to thank the following for permission to reproduce photographs, texts and illustrations.

The following abbreviations are used in this list: t = top, b = bottom, c = centre, l = left, r = right,

British Crime Survey: p.212.

Carey, Kevin: pp.10, 18, 32, 145.

Delhi Metro: By courtesy Delhi Metro, p.419t.

Dragonair.com: p.421b.

Getty Images: pp.237, 369.

Land Transport Authority of Singapore: p.419b.

McSeveny, Alan: pp.172, 311, 334, 353, 354, 356, 376, 381.

Microsoft Corporation: pp.109, 111, screenshots reprinted with permission if Microsoft Corporation.

National Statistics Office Library & Information Unit: p.204.

National Australia Bank: p.219.

Photolibrary: p.204.

Piemonte, Lisa: pp.110, 267, 293, 372, 405, 408.

Singapore Department of Statistics: p.224.

Statistics Canada: p.240.

ToSingapore.com: p.421t.

Transport for London: pp.420, 422.

University of Michigan: p.219.

Utrecht University Library: p.238.

Every effort has been made to trace and acknowledge copyright. However, should any infringement have occurred, the publishers tender their apologies and invite the copyright owners to contact them.